BIOZONE

M000250857

CIE BIOLOGY 1

Cambridge International Examination

A Level Year 1/AS | **Student Workbook**

CIE BIOLOGY 1

Cambridge International Examination

A Level Year 1/AS **Student Workbook**

Meet the Writing Team

Tracey
Senior Author

Tracey Greenwood
I have been writing resources for students since 1993. I have a Ph.D in biology, specialising in lake ecology and I have taught both graduate and undergraduate biology.

Lissa
Author

Lissa Bainbridge-Smith
I worked in industry in a research and development capacity for 8 years before joining BIOZONE in 2006. I have an M.Sc from Waikato University.

Kent
Author

Kent Pryor
I have a BSc from Massey University majoring in zoology and ecology and taught secondary school biology and chemistry for 9 years before joining BIOZONE as an author in 2009.

Richard
Founder & CEO

Richard Allan
I have had 11 years experience teaching senior secondary school biology. I have a Masters degree in biology and founded BIOZONE in the 1980s after developing resources for my own students.

First edition 2015

ISBN 978-1-927309-31-5

Copyright © 2015 Richard Allan

Published by BIOZONE International Ltd

Printed by REPLIKA PRESS PVT LTD using paper produced from renewable and waste materials

Purchases of this workbook may be made direct from the publisher:

BIOZONE

BIOZONE Learning Media (UK) Ltd
United Kingdom, Europe, Middle East
Telephone: +44 1283 530 366
Fax: +44 1283 831 900
Email: sales@biozone.co.uk
Web: www.biozone.co.uk

BIOZONE International Ltd
Head office, New Zealand
Telephone: +64 7 856 8104
Fax: +64 7 856 9243
Email: sales@biozone.co.nz
Web: www.biozone.co.nz

BIOZONE Corporation
USA and Canada
FREE phone: 1-855-246-4555
FREE fax: 1-855-935-3555
Email: sales@thebiozone.com
Web: www.thebiozone.com

Cover photograph

Barn owl (*Tyto alba*) is one of the most widely distributed bird species. It is found worldwide, except in polar regions and deserts, and is a successful nocturnal predator of small vertebrates, particularly shrews, voles, mice, and rats. Although not globally threatened, local populations can be at risk through intensification of agricultural land, loss of nesting sites, and use of rodenticides. PHOTO: © curiostiger/bigstockphoto.com

Thanks to:

The staff at BIOZONE, including Julie Fairless, and Nell Travaglia for design and graphics support, Paolo Curray for IT support, Debbie Antoniadis and Tim Lind for office handling and logistics, and the BIOZONE sales team.

All rights reserved. No part of this publication may be reproduced, stored in a retrieval system, or transmitted in any form or by any means, electrical, mechanical, **photocopying**, recording or otherwise, without the permission of BIOZONE International Ltd. This workbook may not be **re-sold**. The conditions of sale specifically prohibit the photocopying of exercises, worksheets, and diagrams from this workbook for any reason.

Contents

Activity is marked: ☐ to be done; ☑ when completed

Contents

Activity is marked: ☐ to be done; ☑ when completed

Using This Workbook

This first edition of CIE Biology 1 has been specifically written to meet the content and skills requirements of AS/A Level CIE Biology. Learning outcomes in the introduction to each chapter provide you with a concise guide to the knowledge and skills requirements for each module. Each learning outcome is matched to the activity or activities addressing it. Practical skills are identified in the chapter introductions by a code (PRAC) and supported by activities designed to provide background and familiarity with apparatus, techniques, experimental design, and interpretation of results. A wide range of activities will help you to build on what you already know, explore new topics, work collaboratively, and practise your skills in data handling and interpretation. We hope that you find the workbook valuable and that you make full use of its features.

▶ The outline of the chapter structure below will help you to navigate through the material in each chapter.

Introduction
- A check list of the knowledge and skills requirements for the chapter.
- A list of key terms.

Activities
- The KEY IDEA provides your focus for the activity.
- Annotated diagrams help you understand the content.
- Questions review the content of the page.

Review
- Create your own summary for review.
- Hints help you to focus on what is important.
- Your summary will consolidate your understanding of the content in the chapter.

Literacy
- Activities are based on, but not restricted to, the introductory key terms list.
- Several types of activities test your understanding of the concepts and biological terms in the chapter.

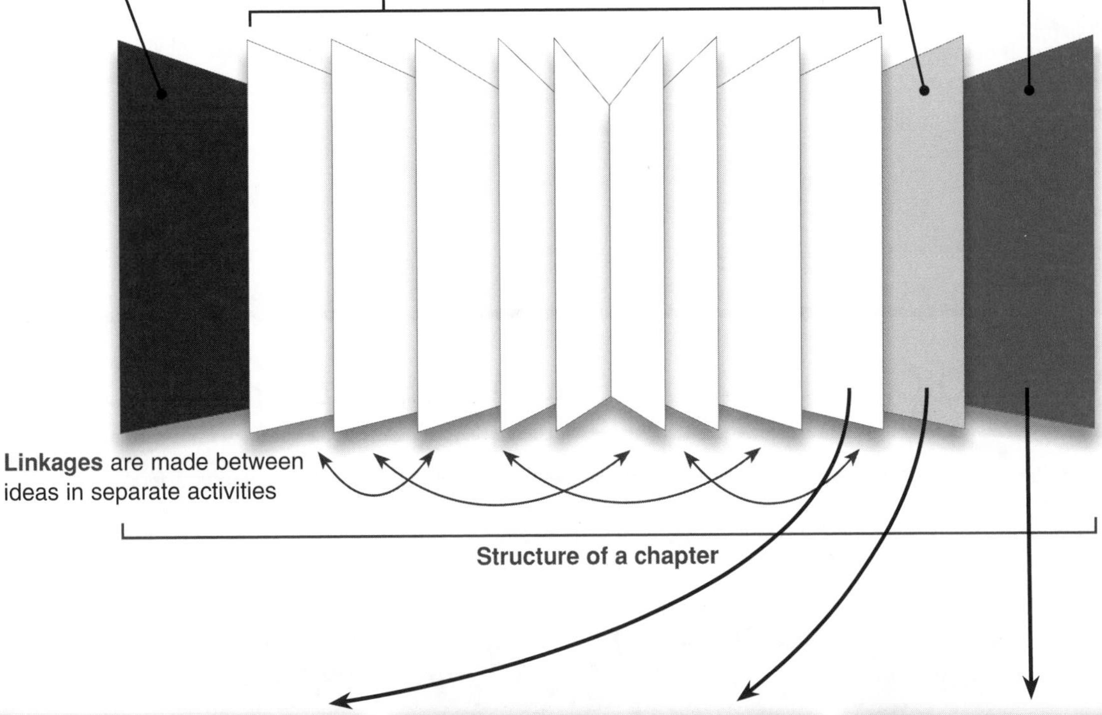
Linkages are made between ideas in separate activities
Structure of a chapter

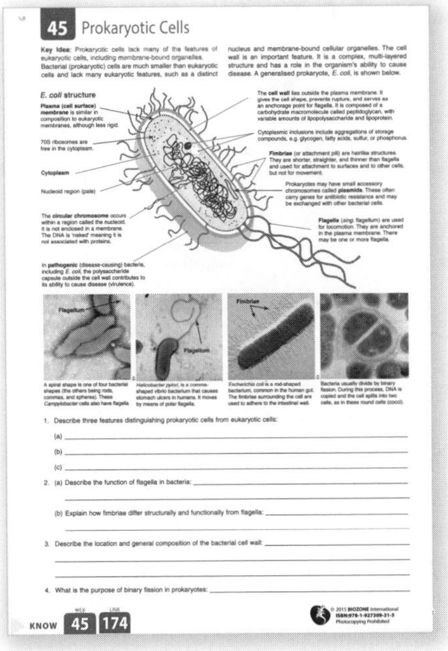
45 Prokaryotic Cells
KNOW

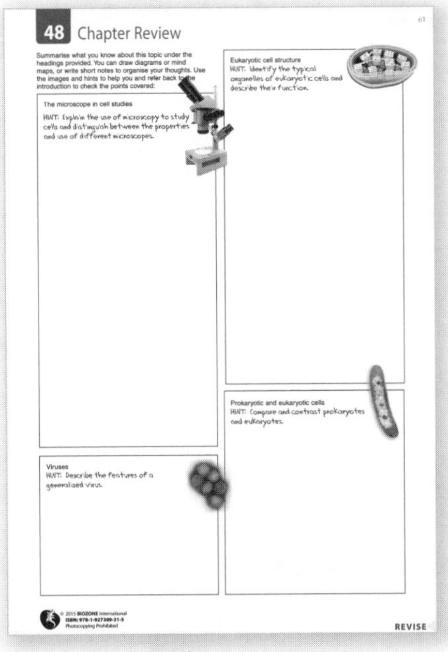
48 Chapter Review
REVISE

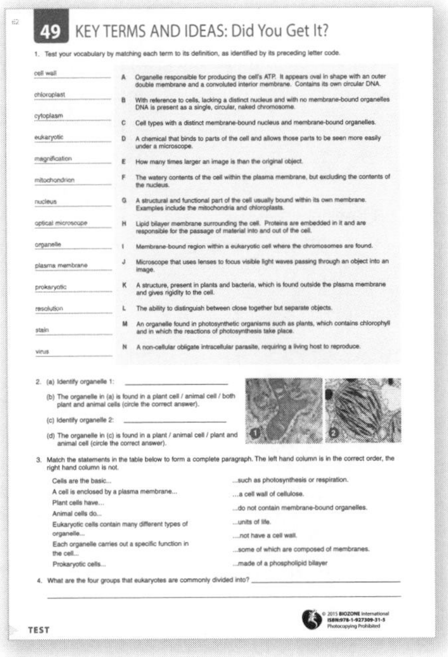
49 KEY TERMS AND IDEAS: Did You Get It?
TEST

Using the Tab System

The tab system is a useful system for quickly identifying related content and online support. Links generally refer to activities that build on the information in the activity in depth or extent. In the example below, the weblink 71 describes the basics of enzyme kinetics. Activity 74 introduces the principles of enzyme kinetics including the Michaelis-Menten equation. Sometimes, a link will reflect on material that has been covered earlier as a reminder for important terms that have already been defined or for a formula that may be required to answer a question. The weblinks code is always the same as the activity number on which it is cited. On visiting the weblink page (below), find the number and it will correspond to one or more external websites providing a video or animation of some aspect of the activity's content. Occasionally, the weblink may provide a bank of photographs where images are provided in colour, e.g. for plant and animal histology.

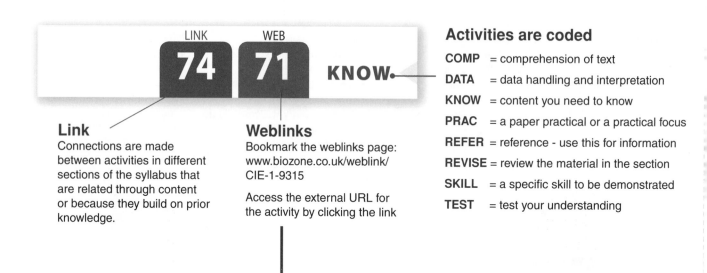

LINK
74
WEB
71
KNOW

Link
Connections are made between activities in different sections of the syllabus that are related through content or because they build on prior knowledge.

Weblinks
Bookmark the weblinks page: www.biozone.co.uk/weblink/CIE-1-9315

Access the external URL for the activity by clicking the link

Activities are coded

COMP = comprehension of text

DATA = data handling and interpretation

KNOW = content you need to know

PRAC = a paper practical or a practical focus

REFER = reference - use this for information

REVISE = review the material in the section

SKILL = a specific skill to be demonstrated

TEST = test your understanding

www.biozone.co.uk/weblink/CIE-1-9315

This WEBLINKS page provides links to **external websites** with supporting information for the activities. These sites are distinct from those provided in the BIOLINKS area of BIOZONE's web site. For the most part, they are narrowly focussed animations and video clips directly relevant to some aspect of the activity on which they are cited. They provide great support to help your understanding of basic concepts.

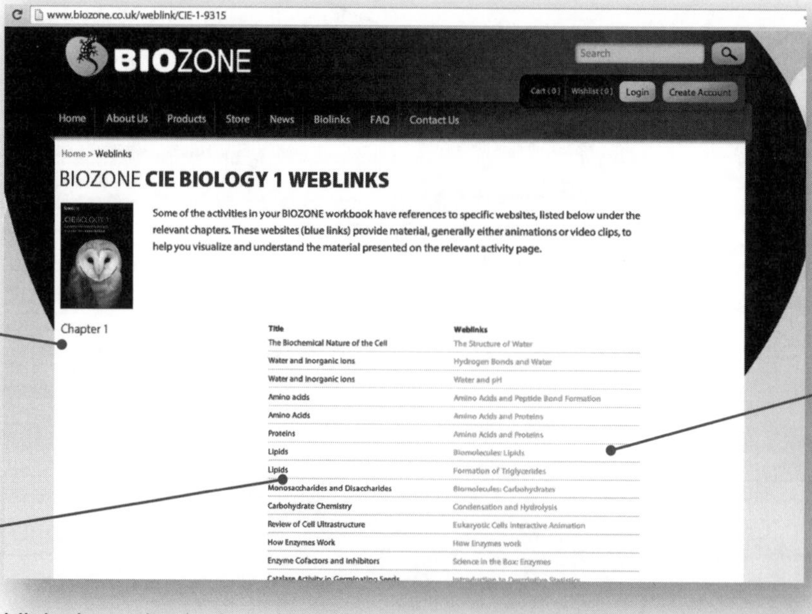

www.biozone.co.uk/weblink/CIE-1-9315
BIOZONE
Search
Login
Create Account
Home
About Us
Products
Store
News
Biolinks
FAQ
Contact Us
Home > Weblinks
BIOZONE CIE BIOLOGY 1 WEBLINKS
Some of the activities in your BIOZONE workbook have references to specific websites, listed below under the relevant chapters. These websites (blue links) provide material, generally either animations or video clips, to help you visualize and understand the material presented on the relevant activity page.
Chapter 1
Title
Weblinks
The Biochemical Nature of the Cell
Water and Inorganic Ions
Amino acids
Proteins
Lipids
Monosaccharides and Disaccharides
Carbohydrate Chemistry
Review of Cell Ultrastructure
How Enzymes Work
Enzyme Cofactors and Inhibitors
Chapter in the workbook
Activity in the workbook
Hyperlink to the external website page.

Bookmark weblinks by typing in the address: it is not accessible directly from BIOZONE's website

Corrections and clarifications to current editions are always posted on the weblinks page

▶ Understanding the activity coding system and making use of the online material identified will enable you to get the most out of this resource. The chapter content is structured to build knowledge and skills but this structure does not necessarily represent a strict order of treatment. Be guided by your teacher, who will assign activities as part of a wider programme of independent and group-based work.

Look out for these features and know how to use them:

The **chapter introduction** provides you with a summary of the knowledge and skills requirements for the topic, phrased as a set of learning outcomes. Use the check boxes to identify and mark off the points as you complete them. The chapter introduction also provides you with a list of key terms for the chapter, from which you can construct your own glossary as you work through the activities.

The **activities** form most of this workbook. They are numbered sequentially and each has a task code identifying the skill emphasised. Each activity has a short introduction with a key idea identifying the main message of the page. Most of the information is associated with pictures and diagrams, and your understanding of the content is reviewed through the questions. Some of the activities involve modelling and group work.

Free response questions allow you to use the information provided to answer questions about the content of the activity, either directly or by applying the same principles to a new situation. In some cases, an activity will assume understanding of prior content.

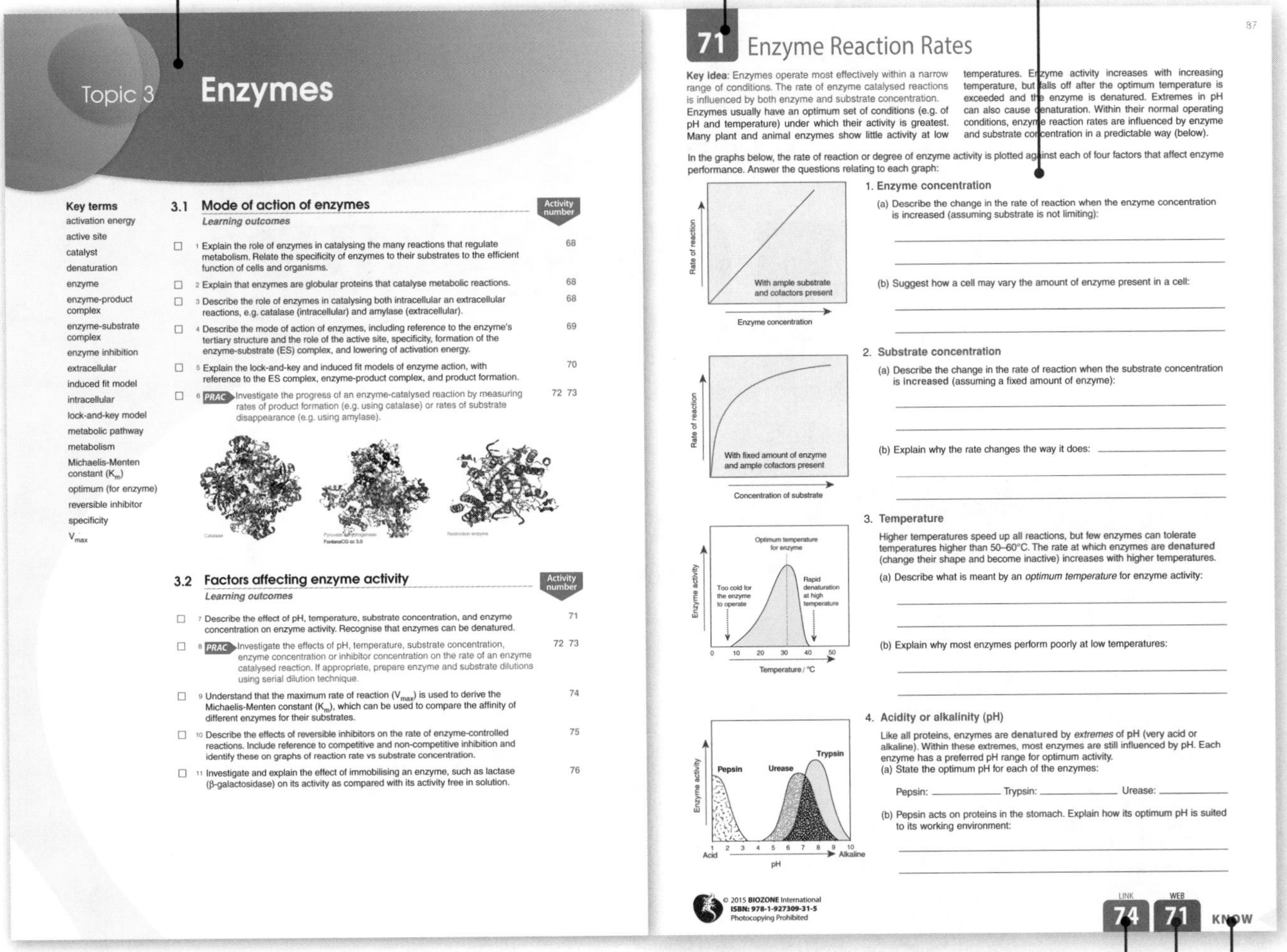

Topic 3 **Enzymes**

Key terms
activation energy
active site
catalyst
denaturation
enzyme
enzyme-product complex
enzyme-substrate complex
enzyme inhibition
extracellular
induced fit model
intracellular
lock-and-key model
metabolic pathway
metabolism
Michaelis-Menten constant (K_m)
optimum (for enzyme)
reversible inhibitor
specificity
V_{max}

3.1 Mode of action of enzymes

Learning outcomes

		Activity number
☐	1 Explain the role of enzymes in catalysing the many reactions that regulate metabolism. Relate the specificity of enzymes to their substrates to the efficient function of cells and organisms.	68
☐	2 Explain that enzymes are globular proteins that catalyse metabolic reactions.	68
☐	3 Describe the role of enzymes in catalysing both intracellular an extracellular reactions, e.g. catalase (intracellular) and amylase (extracellular).	68
☐	4 Describe the mode of action of enzymes, including reference to the enzyme's tertiary structure and the role of the active site, specificity, formation of the enzyme-substrate (ES) complex, and lowering of activation energy.	69
☐	5 Explain the lock-and-key and induced fit models of enzyme action, with reference to the ES complex, enzyme-product complex, and product formation.	70
☐	6 PRAC Investigate the progress of an enzyme-catalysed reaction by measuring rates of product formation (e.g. using catalase) or rates of substrate disappearance (e.g. using amylase).	72 73

FontanaCG cc 3.0

3.2 Factors affecting enzyme activity

Learning outcomes

		Activity number
☐	7 Describe the effect of pH, temperature, substrate concentration, and enzyme concentration on enzyme activity. Recognise that enzymes can be denatured.	71
☐	8 PRAC Investigate the effects of pH, temperature, substrate concentration, enzyme concentration or inhibitor concentration on the rate of an enzyme catalysed reaction. If appropriate, prepare enzyme and substrate dilutions using serial dilution technique.	72 73
☐	9 Understand that the maximum rate of reaction (V_{max}) is used to derive the Michaelis-Menten constant (K_m), which can be used to compare the affinity of different enzymes for their substrates.	74
☐	10 Describe the effects of reversible inhibitors on the rate of enzyme-controlled reactions. Include reference to competitive and non-competitive inhibition and identify these on graphs of reaction rate vs substrate concentration.	75
☐	11 Investigate and explain the effect of immobilising an enzyme, such as lactase (β-galactosidase) on its activity as compared with its activity free in solution.	76

87

71 Enzyme Reaction Rates

Key idea: Enzymes operate most effectively within a narrow range of conditions. The rate of enzyme catalysed reactions is influenced by both enzyme and substrate concentration.

Enzymes usually have an optimum set of conditions (e.g. of pH and temperature) under which their activity is greatest. Many plant and animal enzymes show little activity at low temperatures. Enzyme activity increases with increasing temperature, but falls off after the optimum temperature is exceeded and the enzyme is denatured. Extremes in pH can also cause denaturation. Within their normal operating conditions, enzyme reaction rates are influenced by enzyme and substrate concentration in a predictable way (below).

In the graphs below, the rate of reaction or degree of enzyme activity is plotted against each of four factors that affect enzyme performance. Answer the questions relating to each graph:

Rate of reaction
With ample substrate and cofactors present
Enzyme concentration

1. **Enzyme concentration**
   (a) Describe the change in the rate of reaction when the enzyme concentration is increased (assuming substrate is not limiting):
   (b) Suggest how a cell may vary the amount of enzyme present in a cell:

Rate of reaction
With fixed amount of enzyme and ample cofactors present
Concentration of substrate

2. **Substrate concentration**
   (a) Describe the change in the rate of reaction when the substrate concentration is increased (assuming a fixed amount of enzyme):
   (b) Explain why the rate changes the way it does:

Enzyme activity
Optimum temperature for enzyme
Too cold for the enzyme to operate
Rapid denaturation at high temperature
0 10 20 30 40 50
Temperature / °C

3. **Temperature**
   Higher temperatures speed up all reactions, but few enzymes can tolerate temperatures higher than 50–60°C. The rate at which enzymes are **denatured** (change their shape and become inactive) increases with higher temperatures.
   (a) Describe what is meant by an *optimum temperature* for enzyme activity:
   (b) Explain why most enzymes perform poorly at low temperatures:

Enzyme activity
Pepsin
Urease
Trypsin
1 2 3 4 5 6 7 8 9 10
Acid
Alkaline
pH

4. **Acidity or alkalinity (pH)**
   Like all proteins, enzymes are denatured by *extremes* of pH (very acid or alkaline). Within these extremes, most enzymes are still influenced by pH. Each enzyme has a preferred pH range for optimum activity.
   (a) State the optimum pH for each of the enzymes:
   Pepsin: ______ Trypsin: ______ Urease: ______
   (b) Pepsin acts on proteins in the stomach. Explain how its optimum pH is suited to its working environment:

© 2015 **BIOZONE** International
ISBN: 978-1-927309-31-5
Photocopying Prohibited

LINK 74 WEB 71 KNOW

LINK tabs at the bottom of the activity page identify activities that are related in that they build on content or apply the same principles to a new situation.

WEB tabs at the bottom of the activity page alert the reader to the **Weblinks** resource, which provides external, online support material for the activity, usually in the form of an animation, video clip, photo library, or quiz. Bookmark the Weblinks page (see next page) and visit it frequently as you progress through the workbook.

A **TASK CODE** on the page tab identifies the type of activity. For example, is it primarily information-based (KNOW), or does it involve modelling (PRAC) or data handling (DATA)? A full list of codes is given on the following page but the codes themselves are relatively self explanatory.

Using BIOZONE's Website

Access the **BIOLINKS** database of web sites directly from the homepage of our website.

Contact us with questions, feedback, ideas, and critical commentary. We welcome your input.

Use Google to search for websites of interest. The more precise your search words are, the better the list of results. Be specific, e.g. "biotechnology medicine DNA uses", rather than "biotechnology".

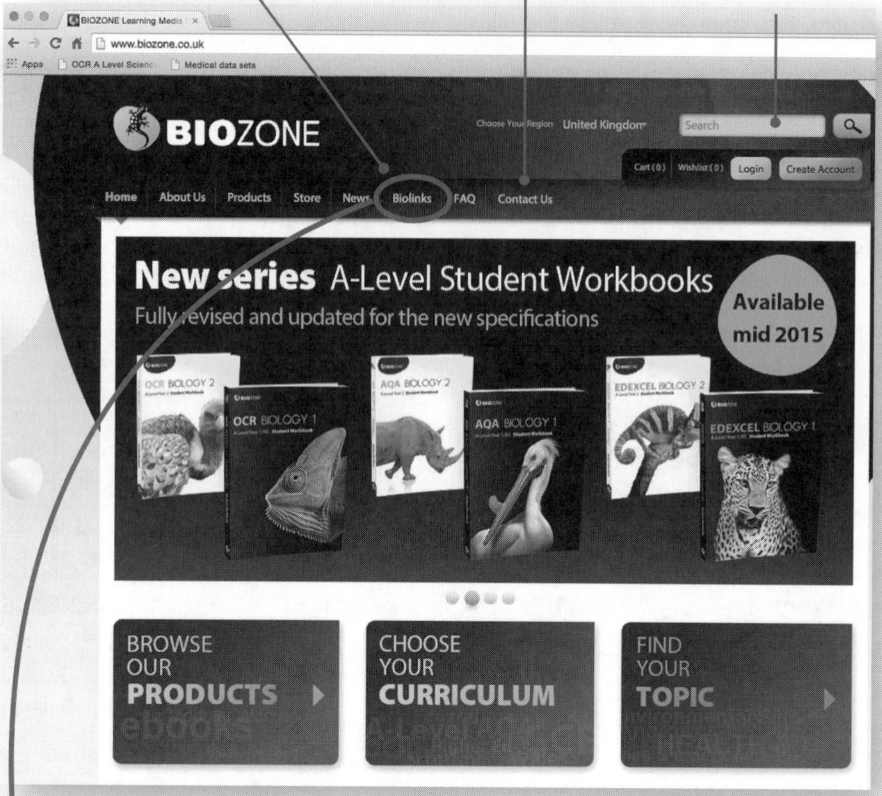
www.biozone.co.uk
BIOZONE
Choose Your Region United Kingdom
Search
Cart (0) Wishlist (0) Login Create Account
Home About Us Products Store News Biolinks FAQ Contact Us
New series A-Level Student Workbooks
Fully revised and updated for the new specifications
Available mid 2015
OCR BIOLOGY 2
OCR BIOLOGY 1
AQA BIOLOGY 2
AQA BIOLOGY 1
EDEXCEL BIOLOGY 2
EDEXCEL BIOLOGY 1
BROWSE OUR PRODUCTS
CHOOSE YOUR CURRICULUM
FIND YOUR TOPIC

Biolinks is organised into easy-to-use sub-sections relating to general areas of interest. It's a great way to quickly find out more on topics of interest.

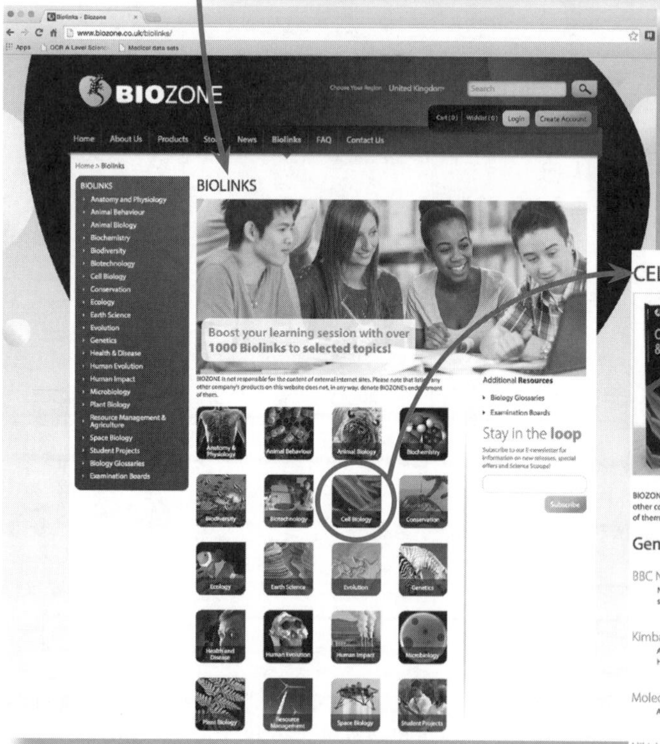
www.biozone.co.uk/biolinks/
BIOZONE
Home About Us Products Store News Biolinks FAQ Contact Us
BIOLINKS
Anatomy and Physiology
Animal Behaviour
Animal Biology
Biochemistry
Biodiversity
Biotechnology
Cell Biology
Conservation
Ecology
Earth Science
Evolution
Genetics
Health & Disease
Human Evolution
Human Impact
Microbiology
Plant Biology
Resource Management & Agriculture
Space Biology
Student Projects
Biology Glossaries
Examination Boards
Boost your learning session with over 1000 Biolinks to selected topics!
Additional Resources
Stay in the loop

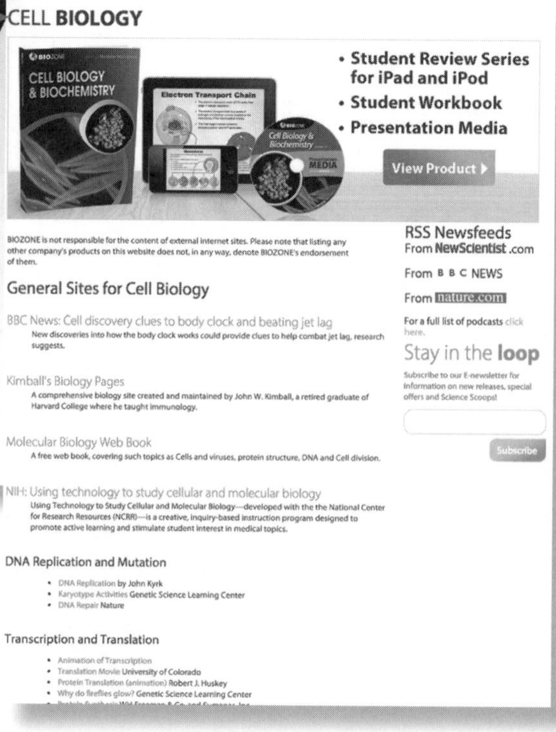
CELL BIOLOGY
CELL BIOLOGY & BIOCHEMISTRY
Electron Transport Chain
• Student Review Series for iPad and iPod
• Student Workbook
• Presentation Media
View Product
BIOZONE is not responsible for the content of external internet sites. Please note that listing any other company's products on this website does not, in any way, denote BIOZONE's endorsement of them.
General Sites for Cell Biology
BBC News: Cell discovery clues to body clock and beating jet lag
New discoveries into how the body clock works could provide clues to help combat jet lag, research suggests.
Kimball's Biology Pages
A comprehensive biology site created and maintained by John W. Kimball, a retired graduate of Harvard College where he taught immunology.
Molecular Biology Web Book
A free web book, covering such topics as Cells and viruses, protein structure, DNA and Cell division.
NIH: Using technology to study cellular and molecular biology
DNA Replication and Mutation
• DNA Replication by John Kyrk
• Karyotype Activities Genetic Science Learning Center
• DNA Repair Nature
Transcription and Translation
• Animation of Transcription
• Translation Movie University of Colorado
• Protein Translation (animation) Robert J. Huskey
• Why do fireflies glow? Genetic Science Learning Center
RSS Newsfeeds
From NewScientist.com
From BBC NEWS
From nature.com
Stay in the loop
Subscribe

Papers 3&5

Experimental and investigative skills

Key terms

accuracy
assumption
bar graph
control
controlled variable
dependent variable
fair test
histogram
hypothesis
independent variable
line graph
mean
median
mode
observation
percentage error
precision
prediction
quantitative data
qualitative data
sample
scatter graph
variable

Practical and investigative skills

Learning outcomes supported as indicated and throughout CIE 1&2

	Learning outcome	Activity number
☐	1 Demonstrate an understanding of science as inquiry.	1 2
☐	2 Demonstrate an understanding of experimental design including identification of dependent, independent, and controlled variables, choice of a control and range of the independent variable, and awareness of assumptions in your design.	2 3 4 5
☐	3 Use laboratory glassware for a range of techniques, including serial dilution.	5 11 90
☐	4 Use a range of apparatus, materials, and techniques correctly, including use of a light microscope with eyepiece graticule and stage micrometer.	11 28 29 30 32 137
☐	5 Demonstrate an ability to use appropriate units for measurement and record your data systematically and accurately, e.g. in tables or spreadsheets.	6 12
☐	6 Use graphs and tables appropriately to present observations and data.	13 15-19
☐	7 Process, analyse, and interpret qualitative and quantitative experimental data.	4 5 24 25
☐	8 Evaluate results and draw valid conclusions based on evidence. Identify and explain anomalies in experimental measurements.	24 25
☐	9 Identify limitations in experimental procedures and suggest how these could be overcome through improvements to design, apparatus, or technique.	5 24 25
☐	10 Recognise and evaluate the precision and accuracy of collected data, including margins of error, percentage errors and uncertainties in apparatus.	6 11

PASCO

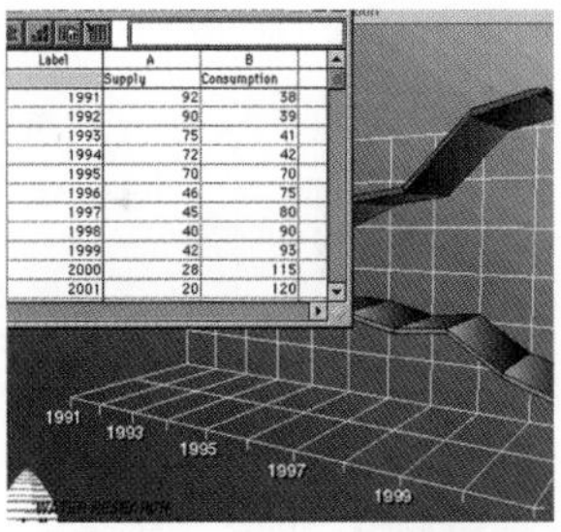

Mathematical skills

Learning outcomes supported as indicated and throughout CIE 1&2

	Learning outcome	Activity number
☐	1 Recognise and use appropriate units in calculations and experimental work.	6 7
☐	2 Use an appropriate number of significant figures in reporting calculations.	6
☐	3 Manipulate equations to calculate size and magnification of objects in drawings and photomicrographs or viewed with a light microscope.	33
☐	4 Carry out calculations involving fractions, percentages, and ratios.	8 10
☐	5 Use a calculator to find and use power, exponential, and logarithmic functions.	9
☐	6 Estimate results to assess if calculated values are appropriate.	7
☐	7 Find arithmetic means for data. Understand use of mean, median, and mode.	21
☐	8 Select an appropriate format to plot two variables from experimental or other data (including histograms, bar graphs, pie graphs, line graphs, and scatter graphs).	14
☐	9 Predict or sketch the shape of a graph with a linear relationship ($y = mx + c$).	20
☐	10 Determine the intercept of a graph.	20
☐	11 Calculate rate of change from a graph showing a linear relationship. Draw and use the slope of a tangent to a curve as a measure of rate of change.	74
☐	12 Make annotated scientific drawings from observations.	22 23

1 How Do We Do Science?

Key Idea: The scientific method is a rigorous, dynamic process of observation, investigation, and analysis that helps us to explain phenomena and predict changes in a system.

Scientific knowledge is gained through a non-linear, dynamic process called the **scientific method**. The scientific method is not a strict set of rules to be followed, but rather a way of approaching problems in a rigorous, but open-minded way. It involves inspiration and creativity, it is dynamic and context dependent, and usually involves collaboration. The model below is one interpretation of the scientific method.

TASK: Before studying the diagram below, write a paragraph about what you think science is and what it involves. Then study the diagram and points below and state if your views differ from this and in what way. Staple your response to this page. At the end of your course, reexamine what you wrote. Have your ideas changed? Be honest in your first response!

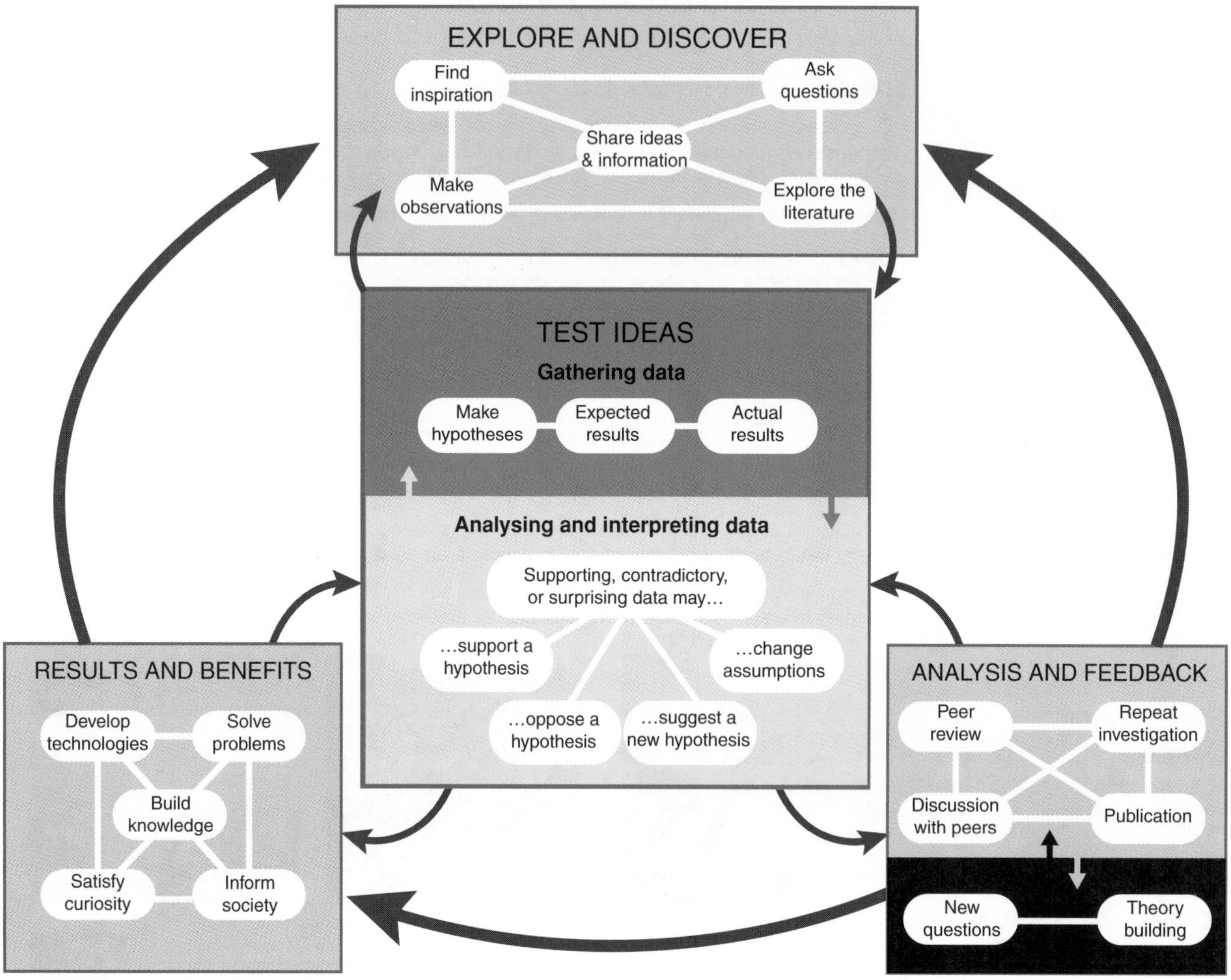

EXPLORE AND DISCOVER
Find inspiration
Ask questions
Share ideas & information
Make observations
Explore the literature
TEST IDEAS
Gathering data
Make hypotheses
Expected results
Actual results
Analysing and interpreting data
Supporting, contradictory, or surprising data may…
…support a hypothesis
…change assumptions
…oppose a hypothesis
…suggest a new hypothesis
RESULTS AND BENEFITS
Develop technologies
Solve problems
Build knowledge
Satisfy curiosity
Inform society
ANALYSIS AND FEEDBACK
Peer review
Repeat investigation
Discussion with peers
Publication
New questions
Theory building

Material adapted from the UC Berkeley's excellent website undsci.berkeley.edu/

Remember what science is and what it is not!

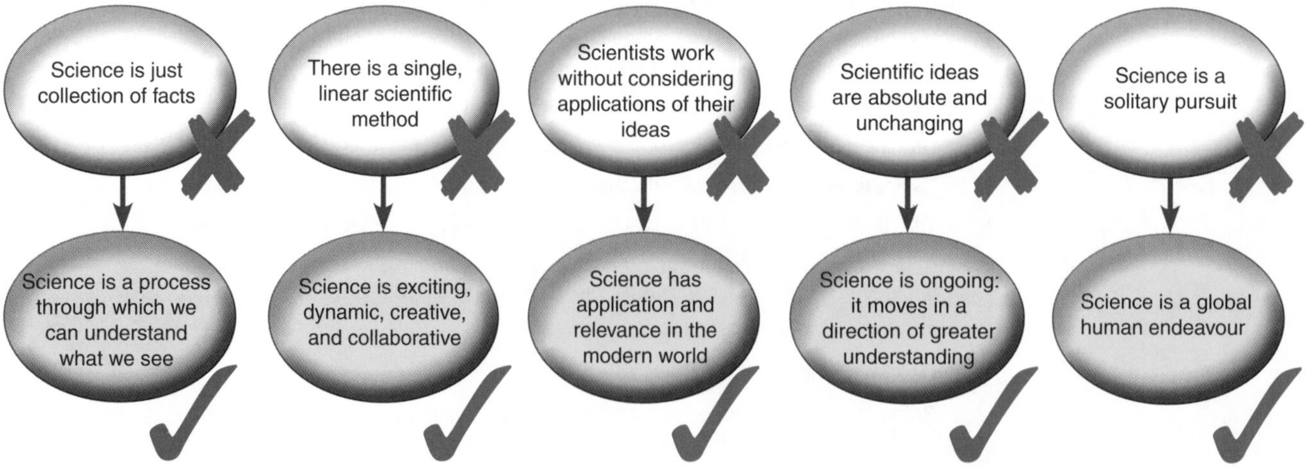

Science is just collection of facts
There is a single, linear scientific method
Scientists work without considering applications of their ideas
Scientific ideas are absolute and unchanging
Science is a solitary pursuit
Science is a process through which we can understand what we see
Science is exciting, dynamic, creative, and collaborative
Science has application and relevance in the modern world
Science is ongoing: it moves in a direction of greater understanding
Science is a global human endeavour

© 2015 **BIOZONE** International
ISBN:978-1-927309-31-5
Photocopying Prohibited

2 Hypotheses and Predictions

Key Idea: A hypothesis is a tentative, testable explanation for an observed phenomenon. An assumption is something that is accepted as true but is not tested.

Scientific hypotheses are tentative testable explanations for observed phenomena. A hypothesis leads to one or more predictions about the way a system will behave so a **research hypothesis** is often written to include a testable prediction, i.e if X is true, then the effect of Y will be Z. For every hypothesis, there is a corresponding **null hypothesis**: a hypothesis of no difference or no effect. A null hypothesis allows a hypothesis to be tested statistically and can be rejected if the experimental results are statistically significant. Hypotheses are not static, but may be modified as more information becomes available.

Observations, hypotheses, and predictions

Observation is the basis for formulating hypotheses and making predictions. An observation may generate a number of plausible hypotheses, and each hypothesis will lead to one or more predictions, which can be tested by further investigation.

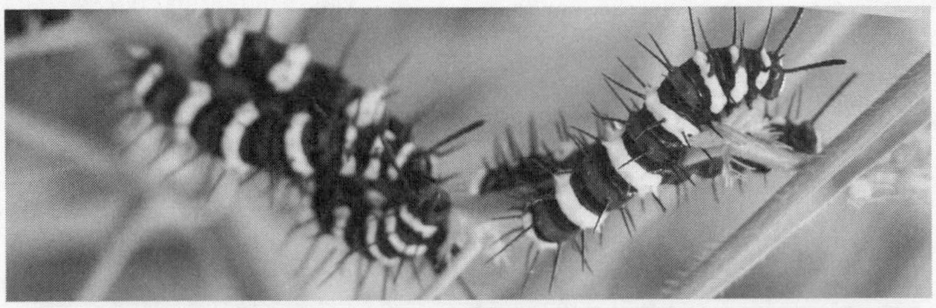

Observation 1: Some caterpillar species are brightly coloured and appear to be conspicuous to predators such as insectivorous (insect-eating) birds.

Predators appear to avoid these species. These caterpillars are often found in groups, rather than as solitary animals.

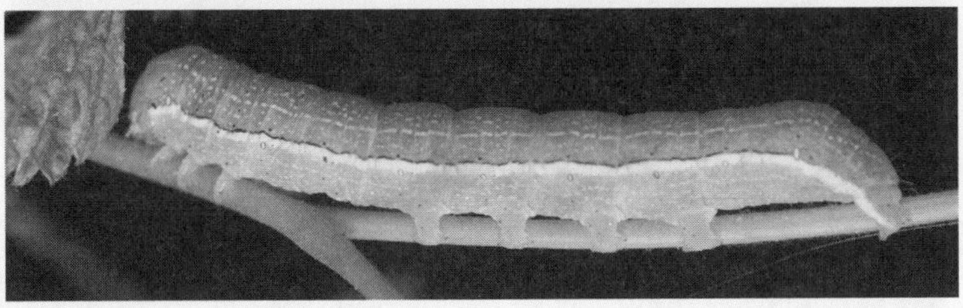

Observation 2: Some caterpillar species are cryptic in their appearance or behaviour.

Their camouflage is so convincing that, when alerted to danger, they are difficult to see against their background. Such caterpillars are often found alone.

Assumptions

Any biological investigation requires you to make assumptions about the system you are working with. Assumptions are features of the system (and investigation) that you assume to be true but do not (or cannot) test. Possible assumptions about the biological system described above include:

- insectivorous birds have colour vision;
- caterpillars that look bright or cryptic to us, also appear that way to insectivorous birds; and
- insectivorous birds can learn about the palatability of prey by tasting them.

1. Study the example above illustrating the features of cryptic and conspicuous caterpillars, then answer the following:

   (a) Generate a hypothesis to explain the observation that some caterpillars are brightly coloured and conspicuous while others are cryptic and blend into their surroundings:

   Hypothesis: ______________________________

   ____

   ____

   (b) State the null form of this hypothesis: ______________________________

   ____

   (c) Describe one of the **assumptions** being made in your hypothesis: ______________________________

   ____

   ____

   (d) Based on your hypothesis, generate a **prediction** about the behaviour of insectivorous birds towards caterpillars:

   ____

   ____

© 2015 **BIOZONE** International
ISBN: 978-1-927309-31-5
Photocopying Prohibited

3 Types of Data

Key Idea: Data is information collected during an investigation. Data may be quantitative, qualitative, or ranked.

Data is information collected during an investigation and it can be quantitative, qualitative, or ranked (below). When planning a biological investigation, it is important to consider the type of data that will be collected. It is best to collect quantitative data, because it is mathematically versatile and easier to analyse it objectively (without bias).

Types of data

Quantitative (interval or ratio)

Characteristics for which measurements or counts can be made, e.g. height, weight, number.
Summary measures: mean, median, standard deviation.

- **Discontinuous (discrete)**
  e.g. Number of children in a family (3, 0, 4)
- **Continuous**
  e.g. Height of children in a family (1.5 m, 0.8 m)

Qualitative (nominal)

Non-numerical and descriptive, e.g. sex, colour, viability (dead/alive), presence or absence of a specific feature.
Summary measures: frequencies and proportions

e.g. Sex of children in a family (male, female)

Ranked (ordinal)

Data are ranked on a scale that represents an order, although the intervals between the orders on the scale may not be equal, e.g. abundance (abundant, common, rare). Summary measures: frequencies and proportions

e.g. Birth order in a family (1, 2, 3)

Discontinuous or discrete data:
The unit of measurement cannot be split up (e.g. can't have half a child).

Continuous data:
The unit of measurement can be a part number (e.g. 5.25 kg).

1. For each of the photographic examples A-C below, classify the data as quantitative, ranked, or qualitative:

A: Skin colour

B: Eggs per nest

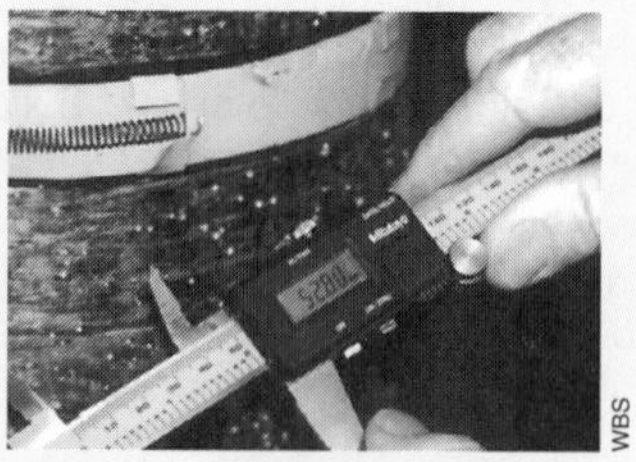
WBS

C: Tree trunk diameter

(a) Skin colour: ______________________

(b) Number of eggs per nest: ______________________

(c) Tree trunk diameter: ______________________

2. Why is it best to collect quantitative data where possible in biological studies? ______________________

3. Give an example of data that could not be collected quantitatively and explain your answer: ______________________

4. Students walked a grid on a football field and ranked plant species present as abundant, common, or rare. How might they have collected and expressed this information more usefully?

© 2015 BIOZONE International
ISBN:978-1-927309-31-5
Photocopying Prohibited

4 Making A Qualitative Investigation

Key Idea: Qualitative data is non-numerical and descriptive. Qualitative data is more difficult to analyse and interpret objectively than quantitative data. It is also more likely to be biased. However, sometimes it is appropriate to collect qualitative data, e.g. when recording colour changes in simple tests for common components of foods. Two common tests for carbohydrates are the iodine/potassium iodide test for starch and the Benedict's test for reducing sugars, such as glucose. These tests indicate the presence of a substance with a colour change. All monosaccharides are reducing sugars as are the disaccharides, lactose and maltose. The monosaccharide fructose is a ketose, but it gives a positive test because it is converted to glucose in the reagent. When a starchy fruit ripens, the starch is converted to reducing sugars.

The aim

To investigate the effect of ripening on the relative content of starch and simple sugars in bananas.

The tests

Iodine-potassium iodide test for starch
The sample is covered with the iodine in potassium iodide solution. The sample turns blue-black if starch is present.

Benedict's test for reducing sugars
The sample is heated with the reagent in a boiling water bath. After 2 minutes, the sample is removed and stirred, and the colour recorded immediately after stirring. A change from a blue to a brick red colour indicates a reducing sugar.

Summary of the method

Two 1 cm thick slices of banana from each of seven stages of ripeness were cut and crushed to a paste. One slice from each stage was tested using the I/KI test for starch, and the other was tested using the Benedict's test.

The colour changes were recorded in a table. Signs (+/–) were used to indicate the intensity of the reaction relative to those in bananas that were either less or more ripe.

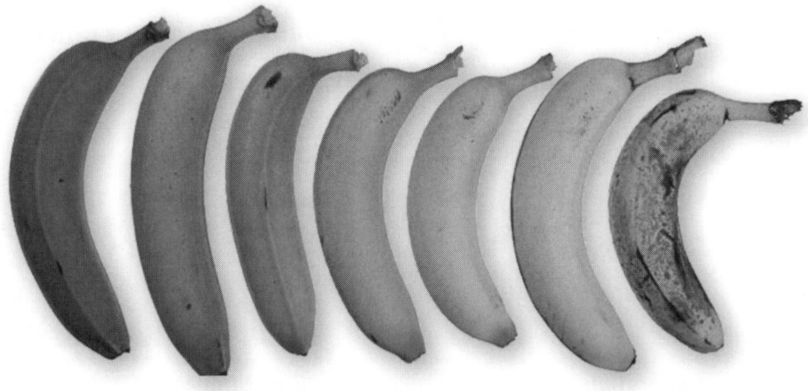

1 2 3 4 5 6 7

Green unripe and hard — Bright yellow ripening but firm with green tip — Mottled yellow/brown ripe and soft

Stage of ripeness	Starch-iodine test		Benedict's test	
1	blue-black	+++++	blue clear	–
2	blue-black	++++	blue clear	–
3	blue-black	+++	green	+
4	blue-black	++	yellow cloudy	++
5	slight darkening	+	orange thick	+++
6	no change	–	orangey-red thick	++++
7	no change	–	brick-red thick	+++++

1. Explain why each of the following protocols was important:

   (a) All samples of banana in the Benedict's reagent were heated for 2 minutes: ______________________

   ____

   (b) The contents of the banana sample and Benedict's reagent were stirred after heating: ______________________

   ____

2. Explain what is happening to the relative levels of starch and glucose as bananas ripen: ______________________

   ____

   ____

3. Fructose is a ketose sugar (not an aldose with an aldehyde functional group like glucose).

   (a) Explain why fructose also gives a positive result in a Benedict's test: ______________________

   ____

   (b) What could this suggest to you about the results of this banana test? ______________________

   ____

© 2015 **BIOZONE** International
ISBN: 978-1-927309-31-5
Photocopying Prohibited

5 Making A Quantitative Investigation

Key Idea: Practical work carried out in a careful and methodical way makes analysis of the results much easier.

The next stage after planning an experiment is to collect the data. Practical work may be laboratory or field based. Typical laboratory based experiments involve investigating how a biological response is affected by manipulating a particular **variable**, e.g. temperature. The data collected for a quantitative practical task should be recorded systematically, with due attention to safe practical techniques, a suitable quantitative method, and accurate measurements to an appropriate degree of precision. If your quantitative practical task is executed well, and you have taken care throughout, your evaluation of the experimental results will be much more straightforward and less problematic.

Carrying out your practical work

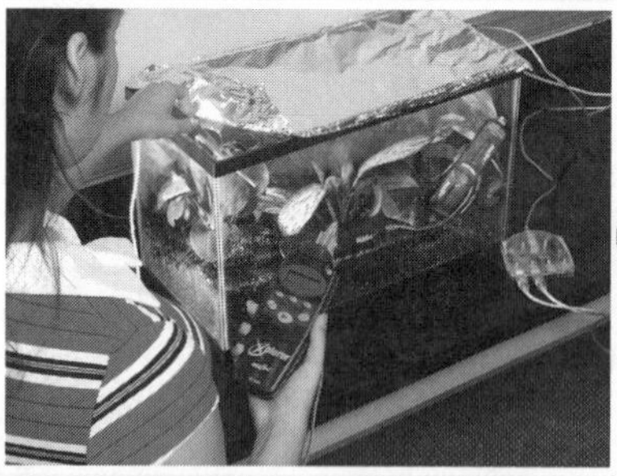

Preparation

Familiarise yourself with the equipment and how to set it up. If necessary, calibrate equipment to give accurate measurements.

Read through the methodology and identify key stages and how long they will take.

Execution

Identify any **assumptions** you make about your set up. Assumptions are features of the system that you assume to be true but do not (or cannot) test. Know how you will take your measurements, how often, and to what degree of precision.

Recording

Record your results systematically, in a hand-written table or on a spreadsheet.

Record your results to the appropriate number of significant figures according to the precision of your measurement.

Identifying variables

A variable is any characteristic or property able to take any one of a range of values. Investigations often look at the effect of changing one variable on another. It is important to identify all variables in an investigation: independent, dependent, and controlled, although there may be nuisance factors of which you are unaware. In all fair tests, only one variable is changed by the investigator.

Dependent variable

- Measured during the investigation.
- Recorded on the y axis of the graph.

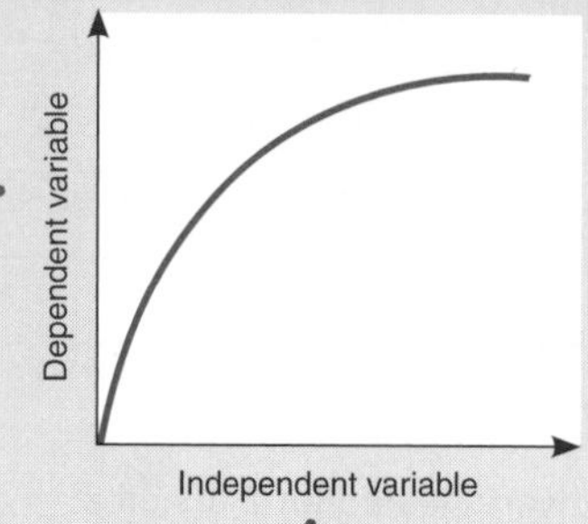

Dependent variable
Independent variable

Controlled variables

- Factors that are kept the same or controlled.
- List these in the method, as appropriate to your own investigation.

Independent variable

- Set by the experimenter.
- Recorded on the graph's x axis.

Experimental controls

A control refers to standard or reference treatment or group in an experiment. It is the same as the experimental (test) group, except that it lacks the one variable being manipulated by the experimenter. Controls are used to demonstrate that the response in the test group is due a specific variable (e.g. temperature). The control undergoes the same preparation, experimental conditions, observations, measurements, and analysis as the test group. This helps to ensure that responses observed in the treatment groups can be reliably interpreted.

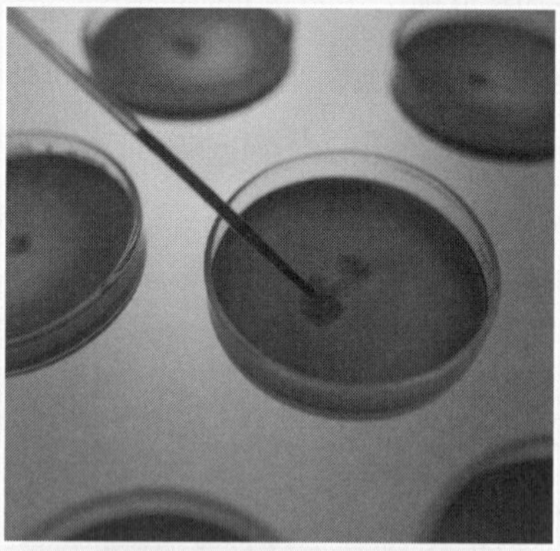

The experiment above tests the effect of a certain nutrient on microbial growth. All the agar plates are prepared in the same way, but the control plate does not have the test nutrient applied. Each plate is inoculated from the same stock solution, incubated under the same conditions, and examined at the same set periods. The control plate sets the baseline; any growth above that seen on the control plate is attributed to the presence of the nutrient.

Examples of investigations

Aim		Variables	
Investigating the effect of varying...	**on the following...**	**Independent variable**	**Dependent variable**
Temperature	Leaf width	Temperature	Leaf width
Light intensity	Activity of woodlice	Light intensity	Woodlice activity
Soil pH	Plant height at age 6 months	pH	Plant height

© 2015 BIOZONE International
ISBN:978-1-927309-31-5
Photocopying Prohibited

Investigation: catalase activity

$$H_2O_{2\,(l)} \xrightarrow{Catalase} H_2O_{(l)} + O_{2\,(g)}$$

Catalase is an enzyme that converts hydrogen peroxide (H_2O_2) to oxygen and water.

An experiment to investigate the effects of temperature on the rate of the catalase reaction is described below.

- 10 cm^3 test tubes were used for the reactions, each tube contained 0.5 cm^3 of catalase enzyme and 4 cm^3 of H_2O_2.
- Reaction rates were measured at four temperatures (10°C, 20°C, 30°C, 60°C).
- For each temperature, there were two reaction tubes (e.g. tubes 1 and 2 were both kept at 10°C).
- The height of oxygen bubbles present after one minute of reaction was used as a measure of the reaction rate. A faster reaction rate produced more bubbles than a slower reaction rate.
- The entire experiment was repeated on two separate days.

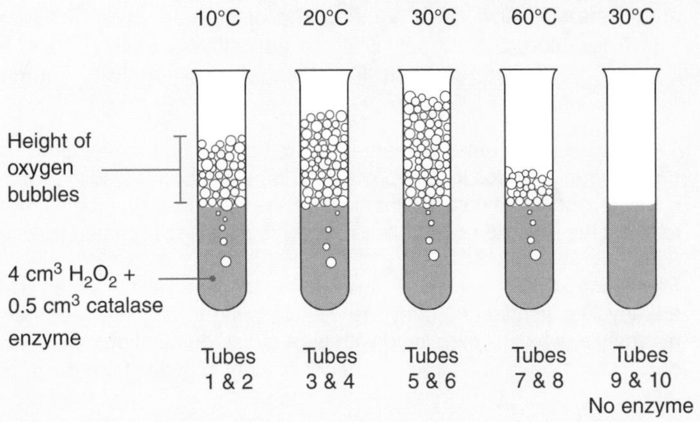
10°C
20°C
30°C
60°C
30°C
Height of oxygen bubbles
4 cm3 H2O2 + 0.5 cm3 catalase enzyme
Tubes 1 & 2
Tubes 3 & 4
Tubes 5 & 6
Tubes 7 & 8
Tubes 9 & 10
No enzyme

1. Write a suitable aim for this experiment: ______________________________

____

2. Write an hypothesis for this experiment: ______________________________

____

3. (a) What is the independent variable in this experiment? ______________________________

   (b) What is the range of values for the independent variable? ______________________________

   (c) Name the unit for the independent variable: ______________________________

   (d) List the equipment needed to set the independent variable, and describe how it was used: ______________________________

   ____

   ____

   ____

4. (a) What is the dependent variable in this experiment? ______________________________

   (b) Name the unit for the dependent variable: ______________________________

   (c) List the equipment needed to measure the dependent variable, and describe how it was used: ______________________________

   ____

5. (a) Each temperature represents a treatment/sample/trial (circle one):

   (b) How many tubes are at each temperature? ______________________________

   (c) What is the sample size for each treatment? ______________________________

   (d) How many times was the whole investigation repeated? ______________________________

6. Which tubes are the control for this experiment? ______________________________

7. Identify three variables that might have been controlled in this experiment, and how they could have been monitored:

   (a) ______________________________

   (b) ______________________________

   (c) ______________________________

© 2015 **BIOZONE** International
ISBN: 978-1-927309-31-5
Photocopying Prohibited

6 Accuracy and Precision

Key Idea: Accuracy refers to the correctness of a measurement (how true it is to the real value). Precision refers to how close the measurements are to each other.

Accuracy refers to how close a measured or derived value is to its true value. Simply put, it is the correctness of the measurement. Precision refers to the closeness of repeated measurements to each other, i.e. the ability to be exact. A balance with a fault in it could give very precise (repeatable) but inaccurate (untrue) results. Data can only be reported as accurately as the measurement of the apparatus allows and is often expressed as significant figures (the digits in a number that express meaning to a degree of accuracy).

The accuracy of a measurement refers to how close the measured (or derived) value is to the true value. The precision of a measurement relates to its repeatability. In most laboratory work, we usually have no reason to suspect a piece of equipment is giving inaccurate measurements (is biased), so making precise measures is usually the most important consideration. We can test the precision of our measurements by taking repeated measurements from individual samples.

Population studies present us with an additional problem. When a researcher makes measurements of some variable in a study (e.g. fish length), they are usually trying to obtain an estimate of the true value for a parameter of interest, e.g. the mean size (which is correlated with age) of fish. Populations are variable, so we can more accurately estimate a population parameter if we take a large number of random samples from the population.

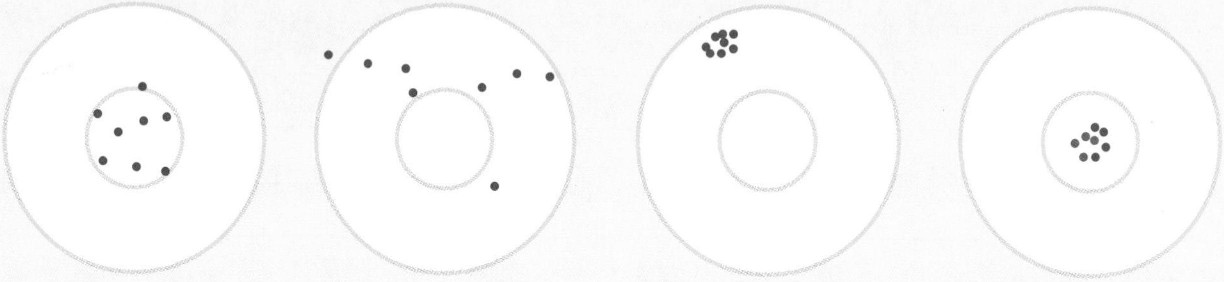

Accurate but imprecise

The measurements are all close to the true value but quite spread apart.

Analogy: The arrows are all close to the bullseye.

Inaccurate and imprecise

The measurements are all far apart and not close to the true value.

Analogy: The arrows are spread around the target.

Precise but inaccurate

The measurements are all clustered close together but not close to the true value.

Analogy: The arrows are all clustered close together but not near the bullseye.

Accurate and precise

The measurements are all close to the true value and also clustered close together.

Analogy: The arrows are clustered close together near the bullseye.

Significant figures

Significant figures (sf) are the digits of a number that carry meaning contributing to its precision. They communicate how well you could actually measure the data.

For example, you might measure the height of 100 people to the nearest cm. When you calculate their mean height, the answer is 175.0215 cm. If you reported this number, it implies that your measurement technique was accurate to 4 decimal places. You would have to round the result to the number of significant figures you had accurately measured. In this instance the answer is 175 cm.

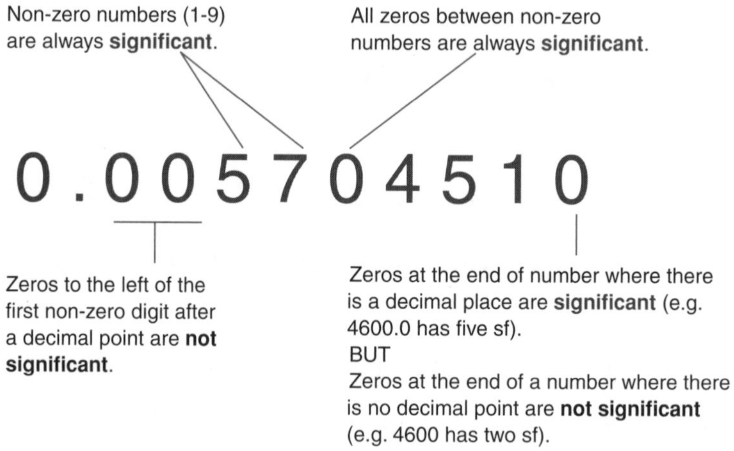
Non-zero numbers (1-9) are always **significant**.
All zeros between non-zero numbers are always **significant**.
0.005704510
Zeros to the left of the first non-zero digit after a decimal point are **not significant**.
Zeros at the end of number where there is a decimal place are **significant** (e.g. 4600.0 has five sf).
BUT
Zeros at the end of a number where there is no decimal point are **not significant** (e.g. 4600 has two sf).

1. Distinguish between accuracy and precision: ______________________________

____

____

2. State the number of significant figures in the following examples:

(a) 3.15985 ______________ (d) 1000.0 ______________

(b) 0.0012 ______________ (e) 42.3006 ______________

(c) 1000 ______________ (f) 120 ______________

© 2015 BIOZONE International
ISBN:978-1-927309-31-5
Photocopying Prohibited

7 Working with Numbers

Key Idea: Using correct mathematical notation and being able to carry out simple calculations and conversions are fundamental skills in biology.

Mathematics is used in biology to analyse, interpret, and compare data. It is important that you are familiar with mathematical notation (the language of mathematics) and can confidently apply some basic mathematical principles and calculations to your data.

Commonly used mathematical symbols

In mathematics, universal symbols are used to represent mathematical concepts. They save time and space when writing. Some commonly used symbols are shown below.

- $=$ Equal to
- $<$ The value on the left is **less than** the value on the right
- $\ll$ The value on the left is **much less than** the value on the right
- $>$ The value on the left is **greater than** the value on the right
- $\gg$ The value on the left is **much greater than** the value on the right
- $\propto$ Proportional to. $A \propto B$ means that A = a constant X B
- $\sim$ Approximately equal to

Conversion factors and expressing units

Measurements can be converted from one set of units to another by the use of a **conversion factor**.

A conversion factor is a numerical factor that multiplies or divides one unit to convert it into another. Conversion factors are commonly used to convert non-SI units to SI units (e.g. converting pounds to kilograms). Note that mL and cm^3 are equivalent, as are L and dm^3.

In the space below, convert 5.6 cm^3 to mm^3 (1 cm^3 = 1000 mm^3):

1. ______________________

The value of a variable must be written with its units where possible. SI units or their derivations should be used in recording measurements: volume in cm^3 or dm^3, mass in kilograms (kg) or grams (g), length in metres (m), time in seconds (s).

For example the rate of oxygen consumption would be expressed:

Oxygen consumption / $cm^3 g^{-1} s^{-1}$

Estimates

When carrying out mathematical calculations, typing the wrong number into your calculator can put your answer out by several orders of magnitude. An **estimate** is a way of roughly calculating what answer you should get, and helps you decide if your final calculation is correct.

Numbers are often rounded to help make estimation easier. The rounding rule is, if the next digit is 5 or more, round up. If the next digit is 4 or less, it stays as it is.

For example, to estimate 6.8 x 704 you would round the numbers to 7 x 700 = 4900. The actual answer is 4787, so the estimate tells us the answer (4787) is probably right.

Use the following examples to practise estimating:

2. 43.2 x 1044: ______________________

3. 3.4 x 72 ÷ 15: ______________________

4. 658 ÷ 22: ______________________

Decimal and standard form

Decimal form (also called ordinary form) is the longhand way of writing a number (e.g. 15 000 000). Very large or very small numbers can take up too much space if written in decimal form and are often expressed in a condensed **standard form**. For example, 15 000 000 is written as 1.5×10^7 in standard form.

In standard form a number is always written as $A \times 10^n$, where A is a number between 1 and 10, and n (the exponent) indicates how many places to move the decimal point. n can be positive or negative.

For the example above, A = 1.5 and n = 7 because the decimal point moved seven places (see below).

$$1\,5\,0\,0\,0\;0\,0\,0 = 1.5 \times 10^7$$

Small numbers can also be written in standard form. The exponent (n) will be negative. For example, 0.00101 is written as 1.01×10^{-3}.

$$0.0\,0\,1\,0\,1 = 1.01 \times 10^{-3}$$

Converting can make calculations easier. Work through the following example to solve $4.5 \times 10^4 + 6.45 \times 10^5$.

5. Convert $4.5 \times 10^4 + 6.45 \times 10^5$ to decimal form:

____

6. Add the two numbers together: ______________________

7. Convert to standard form: ______________________

Rates

Rates are expressed as a measure per unit of time and show how a variable changes over time. Rates are used to provide meaningful comparisons of data that may have been recorded over different time periods.

Often rates are expressed as a mean rate over the duration of the measurement period, but it is also useful to calculate the rate at various times to understand how rate changes over time. The table below shows the reaction rates for a gas produced during a chemical reaction. A worked example for the rate at 4 minutes is provided below the table.

Time / Minute	Cumulative gas produced / cm^3	Rate of reaction / $cm^3 min^{-1}$
0	0	0
2	34	17
4	42	4*
6	48	3
8	50	1
10	50	0

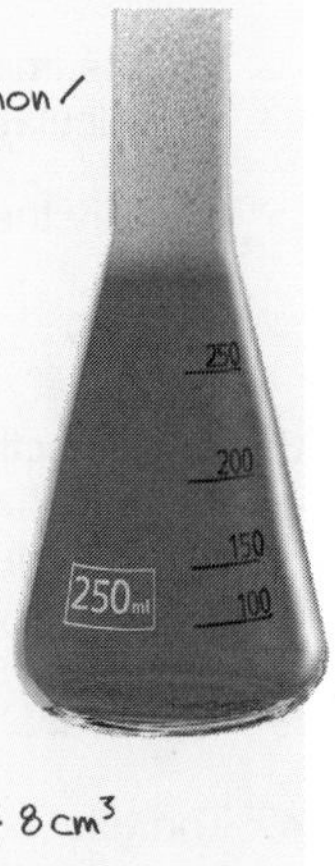
250ml
250
200
150
100

*Gas produced between 2-4 min: 42 cm^3 – 34 cm^3 = 8 cm^3

Rate of reaction between 2-4 mins: 8 ÷ 2 minutes = 4 $cm^3 min^{-1}$

© 2015 BIOZONE International
ISBN: 978-1-927309-31-5
Photocopying Prohibited

8 Fractions, Percentages, and Ratios

Key Idea: Percentages and ratios are alternative ways to express fractions. All forms are commonly used in biology. The data collected in the field or laboratory are called raw data. Data are often expressed in ways that make them easy to understand, visualise, and work with. Fractions, ratios, and percentages are widely used in biology and are often used to provide a meaningful comparison of sample data where the sample sizes are different.

Fractions

- Fractions express how many parts of a whole are present.
- Fractions are expressed as two numbers separated by a solidus (/) (e.g. 1/2).
- The top number is the numerator. The bottom number is the denominator. The denominator can not be zero.
- Fractions are often written in their simplest form (the top and bottom numbers cannot be any smaller, while still being whole numbers). Simplifying makes working with fractions easier.

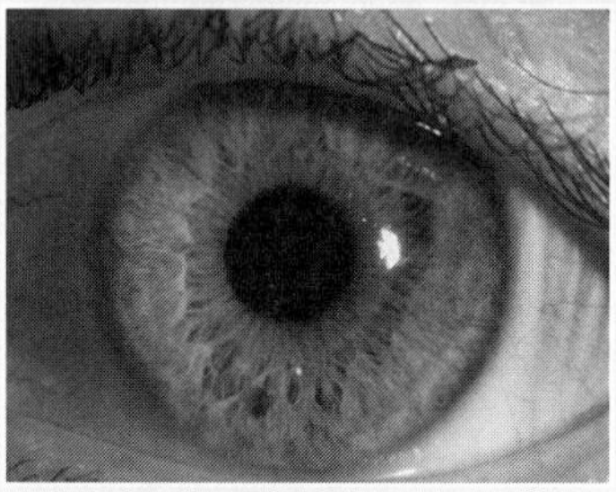

In a class of 20 students, five had blue eyes. This fraction is 5/20. To simplify this fraction, divide the numerator and denominator by a common factor (a number which both are divisible by). In this instance the lowest common factor is five (1/4). To add fractions with different denominators, obtain a common denominator, add numerators, then simplify.

Ratios

- Ratios give the relative amount of two or more quantities, and provide an easy way to identify patterns.
- Ratios do not require units.
- Ratios are usually expressed as a : b.
- Ratios are calculated by dividing all the values by the smallest number.

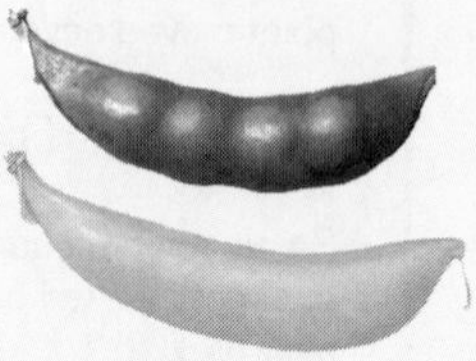

882 inflated

299 constricted

Pea pod shape:
Ratio = 2.95 : 1

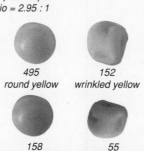

495 round yellow

152 wrinkled yellow

158 round green

55 wrinkled green

Pea seed shape and colour:
Ratio = 9 : 2.8 : 2.9 : 1

Example: Calculating phenotype ratios in Mendelian genetics

Percentages

- Percentages are expressed as a fraction of 100 (e.g. 20/100 = 20%).
- Percentages provide a clear expression of what proportion of data fall into any particular category, e.g. for pie graphs.
- Allows meaningful comparison between different samples.
- Useful to monitor change (e.g. % increase from one year to the next).

Volume of food colouring / cm^3	Volume of water / cm^3	Concentration of solution / %
10	0	100
8	2	80
6	4	60
4	6	40
2	8	20
0	10	0

Example: Producing standards for a calibration curve.

1. (a) A student prepared a slide of the cells of an onion root tip and counted the cells at various stages in the cell cycle. The results are presented in the table (right). Calculate the ratio of cells in each stage (show your working):

____

____

(b) Assuming the same ratio applies in all the slides examined in the class, calculate the number of cells in each phase for a cell total count of 4800.

Cell cycle stage	No. of cells counted	No. of cells calculated
Interphase	140	
Prophase	70	
Telophase	15	
Metaphase	10	
Anaphase	5	
Total	240	4800

2. Simplify the following fractions:

(a) 3/9 : ____________ (b) 84/90: ____________ (c) 11/121: ____________

3. In the fraction example pictured above 5/20 students had blue eyes. In another class, 5/12 students had blue eyes. What fraction of students had blue eyes in both classes combined?

____

4. The total body mass and lean body mass for women with different body types is presented in the table (right). Complete the table by calculating the % lean body mass column.

Women	Body mass / kg	Lean body mass / kg	% lean body mass
Athlete	50	38	
Lean	56	41	
Normal weight	65	46	
Overweight	80	48	
Obese	95	52	

© 2015 BIOZONE International
ISBN:978-1-927309-31-5
Photocopying Prohibited

9 Logs and Exponents

Key Idea: A function relates an input to an output. Functions are often defined through a formula that tells us how to compute the output for a given input. Logarithmic, power, and exponential functions are all common in biology.

A function is a rule that allows us to calculate an output for any given input. In biology, power functions are often observed in biological scaling, for example, heart beat slows with increasing size in mammals. Exponential growth is often seen in bacterial populations and also with the spread of viral diseases if intervention does not occur. The 2014 Ebola outbreak is one such example. The numbers associated with exponential growth can be very large and are often log transformed. Log transformations reduce skew in data and make data easier to analyse and interpret.

Power function

Power functions are a type of scaling function showing the relationship between two variables, one of which is usually size.

- In power functions, the base value is variable and the exponent (power number) is fixed (constant).
- The equation for an exponential function is $y = x^c$.
- Power functions are not linear, one variable changes more quickly relative to the other.
- Examples of power functions include metabolic rate versus body mass (below), or surface area to volume ratio.

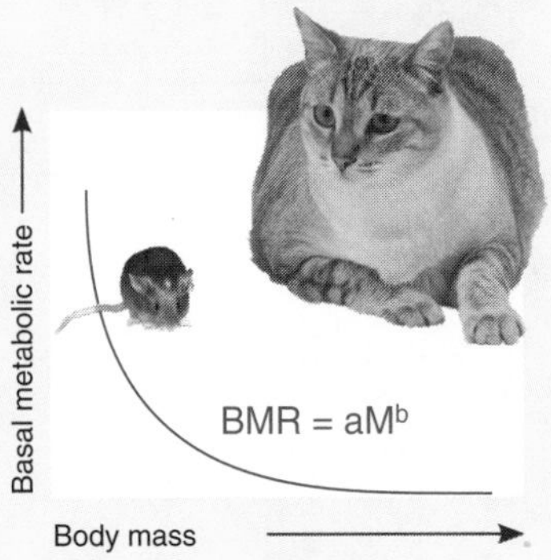
Basal metabolic rate
BMR = aM^b
Body mass

Example: Relationship between body mass and metabolic rate.
M = mass and a and b are constants.

Exponential function

Exponential growth occurs at an increasingly rapid rate in proportion to the growing total number or size.

- In an exponential function, the base number is fixed (constant) and the exponent is variable.
- The equation for an exponential function is $y = c^x$.
- Exponential growth is easy to identify because the curve has a J-shape appearance due to its increasing steepness over time. It grows more rapidly than a power function
- Examples of exponential growth include the growth of microorganisms in an unlimiting growth environment.

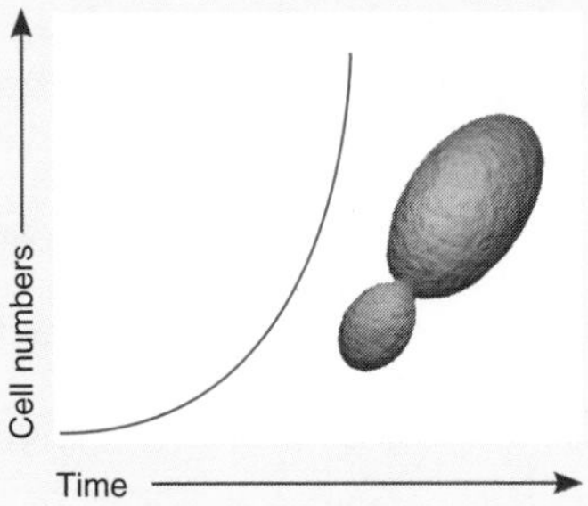
Cell numbers
Time

Example: Cell growth in a yeast culture in optimal growth conditions.

Log transformations

A log transformation has the effect of normalising data and making very large numbers easier to work with. Biological data often have a positive skew so log transformations can be very useful.

- The log of a number is the exponent to which a fixed value (the base) is raised to get that number. So $\log_{10}(1000) = 3$ because $10^3 = 1000$.
- Both $\log_{10}$ and $\log_e$ (natural logs or *ln*) are commonly used.
- Log transformations are useful for data where there is an exponential increase in numbers (e.g. cell growth).
- Log transformed data will plot as a straight line.
- To find the $\log_{10}$ of a number, e.g. 32, using a calculator, key in [log] [32] = . The answer should be 1.51.

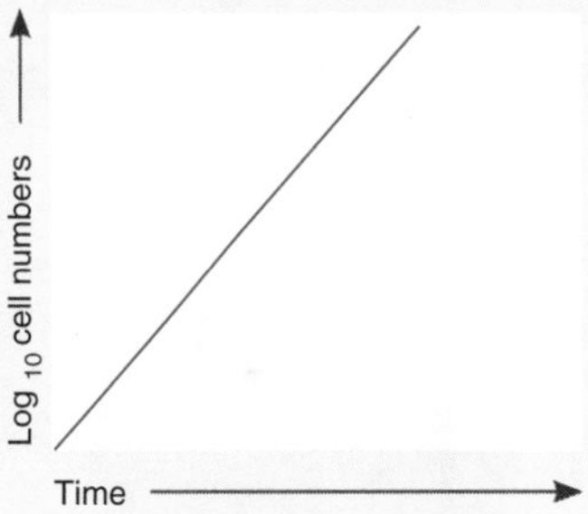
Log 10 cell numbers
Time

Example: Yeast cell growth plotted on logarithmic scale.

1. Describe the relationship between body mass and metabolic rate: ____________________

2. Describe the difference between a power function and exponential growth: ____________________

3. (a) On what type of data would you carry out a log transformation? ____________________

   (b) What is the purpose of a log transformation? ____________________

© 2015 **BIOZONE** International
ISBN: 978-1-927309-31-5
Photocopying Prohibited

10 Practising with Data

Key Idea: This activity allows you to practise working with data and applying the skills you have learned in previous activities.

1. Complete the transformations for each of the tables below. The first value is provided in each case.

(a) Photosynthetic rate at different light intensities

Light intensity / %	Average time for leaf disc to float / min	Reciprocal of time* / min^{-1}
100	15	0.067
50	25	
25	50	
11	93	
6	187	

** Reciprocal of time gives a crude measure of rate.*

(b) Plant water loss using a bubble potometer

Time / min	Pipette arm reading / cm^3	Plant water loss / cm^3 min^{-1}
0	9.0	–
5	8.0	0.2
10	7.2	
15	6.2	
20	4.9	

(c) Incidence of cyanogenic clover in different areas

Clover plant type	Frost free area		Frost prone area		Totals
	Number	%	Number	%	
Cyanogenic	124	78	26		
Acyanogenic	35		115		
Total	159				

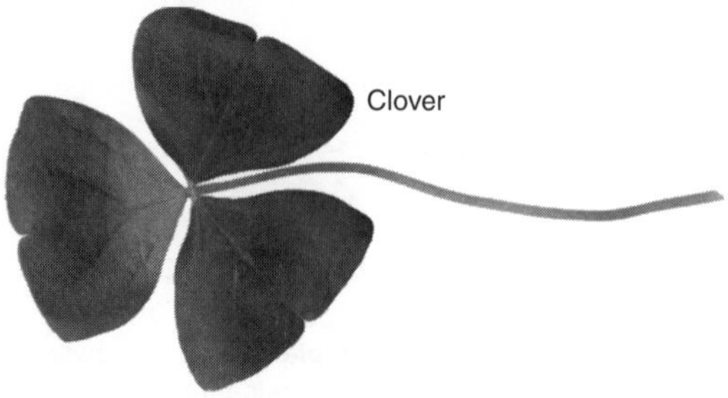
Clover

(d) Frequency of size classes in a sample of eels

Size class / mm	Frequency	Relative frequency / %
0-50	7	2.6
50-99	23	
100-149	59	
150-199	98	
200-249	50	
250-299	30	
300-349	3	
Total	270	

2. Convert the following decimal form numbers to standard form:

(a) 8970 ____________ (b) 0.046 ____________ (c) 1 467 851 ____________

3. Convert the following standard form numbers to decimal form:

(a) 4.3×10^{-1} ____________ (b) 0.0031×10^{-2} ____________ (c) 6.2×10^{4} ____________

4. (a) The table on the right shows the nutritional label found on a can of chilli beans. Use the information provided to complete the table by calculating the percentage composition for each of the nutritional groups listed:

(b) How much of the total carbohydrates is made up of:

Dietary fibre? ____________

Sugars? ____________

(c) Manufacturers do not have to state the volume of water, which makes up the remainder of the serving size. What percentage of the can of beans is water?

____

Chilli beans nutrition facts Serving size 1 cup (253 g)		
Amount per serving		% Composition
Total Fat	8 g	
– Saturated Fat	3 g	
Total Carbohydrate	22 g	
– Dietary Fibre	9 g	
– Sugars	4 g	
Protein	25 g	

© 2015 BIOZONE International
ISBN:978-1-927309-31-5
Photocopying Prohibited

11 Apparatus and Measurement

Key Idea: The apparatus used in experimental work must be appropriate for the experiment or analysis and it must be used correctly to eliminate experimental errors.

Using scientific equipment can generate experimental errors. These can be reduced by selecting the right equipment for what you want to measure and by using it correctly. Some error is inevitable, but evaluating experimental error helps to interpret and assess the validity of the results.

Selecting the correct equipment

When measuring physical properties it is vital that you choose equipment that is appropriate for the type of measurement you want to take. For example, if you wanted to accurately weigh out 5.65 g of sucrose, you need a balance that accurately weighs to two decimal places. A balance that weighs to only one decimal place would not allow you to make an accurate enough measurement.

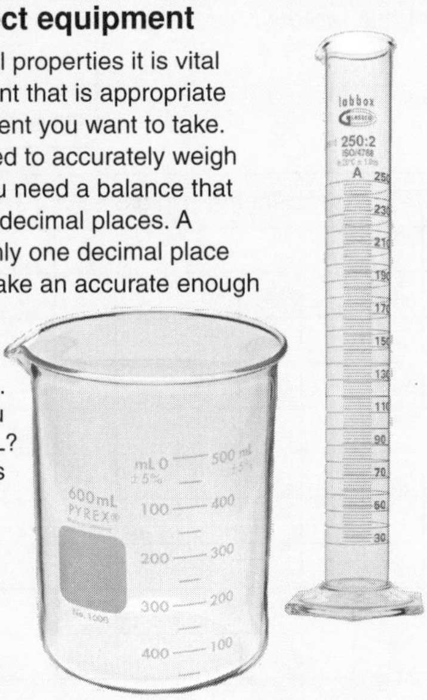

Study the glassware (right). Which would you use if you wanted to measure 225 mL? The graduated cylinder has graduations every 10 mL whereas the beaker has graduations every 50 mL. It would be more accurate to measure 225 mL in a graduated cylinder.

Percentage errors

Percentage error is a way of mathematically expressing how far out your result is from the ideal result. The equation for measuring percentage error is:

$$\frac{\text{experimental value - ideal value}}{\text{ideal value}} \times 100$$

For example, you want to know how accurate a 5 mL pipette is. You dispense 5 mL of water from a pipette and weigh the dispensed volume on a balance. The volume is 4.98 mL.

$$\frac{\text{experimental value } (\mathbf{4.98}) \text{ - ideal value } (\mathbf{5.0})}{\text{ideal value } (\mathbf{5.0})} \times 100$$

The percentage error = –0.4% (the negative sign tells you the pipette is dispensing **less** than it should).

Recognising potential sources of error

It is important to know how to use equipment correctly to reduce errors. A spectrophotometer measures the amount of light absorbed by a solution at a certain wavelength. This information can be used to determine the concentration of the absorbing molecule (e.g. density of bacteria in a culture). The more concentrated the solution, the more light is absorbed. Incorrect use of the spectrophotometer can alter the results. Common mistakes include incorrect calibration, errors in sample preparation, and errors in sample measurement.

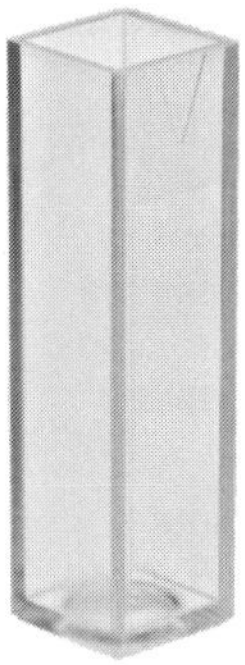

A cuvette (left) is a small clear tube designed to hold spectrophotometer samples. Inaccurate readings occur when:

- The cuvette is dirty or scratched (light is absorbed giving a falsely high reading).
- Some cuvettes have a frosted side to aid alignment. If the cuvette is aligned incorrectly, the frosted side absorbs light, giving a false reading.
- Not enough sample is in the cuvette and the beam passes over, rather than through the sample, giving a lower absorbance reading.

1. Assume that you have the following measuring devices available: 50 mL beaker, 50 mL graduated cylinder, 25 mL graduated cylinder, 10 mL pipette, 10 mL beaker. What would you use to accurately measure:

   (a) 21 mL: ____________ (b) 48 mL: ____________ (c) 9 mL: ____________

2. Calculate the percentage error for the following situations (show your working):

   (a) A 1 mL pipette delivers a measured volume of 0.98 mL: ____________

   ____

   (b) A 10 mL pipette delivers a measured volume of 9.98 mL: ____________

   ____

   (c) The pipettes used in (a) and (b) above both under-delivered 0.02 mL, yet the percentage errors are quite different. Use this data to describe the effect of volume on percentage error:

   ____

   ____

© 2015 **BIOZONE** International
ISBN: 978-1-927309-31-5
Photocopying Prohibited

12 Recording Results

Key Idea: Accurately recording results in a table makes it easier to understand and analyse your data later.

A table is a good way to record your results systematically, both during the course of your experiment and in presenting your results. A table can also be used to show calculated values, such as rates or means. An example of a table for recording results is shown below. It relates to an investigation of the net growth of plants at three pH levels, but it represents a relatively standardised layout. The labels on the columns and rows are chosen to represent the design features of the investigation. The first column shows the entire range of the independent variable. There are spaces for multiple sampling units, repeats (trials), and calculated mean values. A version of this table would be given in the write-up of the experiment.

Dependent variable and its units

Space for repeats of the experimental design (in this case, three trials).

All masses are in grams and to the nearest 0.1 g.

		Trial 1 / plant mass in grams						**Trial 2** / plant mass in grams						**Trial 3** / plant mass in grams					
		Day No.						Day No.						Day No.					
		0	2	4	6	8	10	0	2	4	6	8	10	0	2	4	6	8	10
pH 3	1	0.5	1.1																
	2	0.6	1.2																
	3	0.7	1.3																
	Mean	0.6	1.2																
pH 5	1	0.6	1.4																
	2	0.8	1.7																
	3	0.5	1.9																
	Mean	0.6	1.7																
pH 7	1	0.7	1.3																
	2	0.8	1.3																
	3	0.4	1.7																
	Mean	0.6	1.4																

Space for three plants at each pH

The range of values for the independent variable are in this column

Recordings of the dependent variable

Space for calculated means

1. In the box (below) design a table to collect data from the case study below. Include space for individual results and averages from the three set ups (use the table above as a guide).

CO_2 levels in a respiration chamber

A datalogger was used to monitor the concentrations of carbon dioxide (CO_2) in respiration chambers containing five green leaves from one plant species. The entire study was performed in conditions of full light (quantified) and involved three identical set-ups.

The CO_2 concentrations were measured every minute, over a period of 10 minutes, using a CO_2 sensor. A mean CO_2 concentration (for the three set-ups) was calculated. The study was carried out two more times, two days apart.

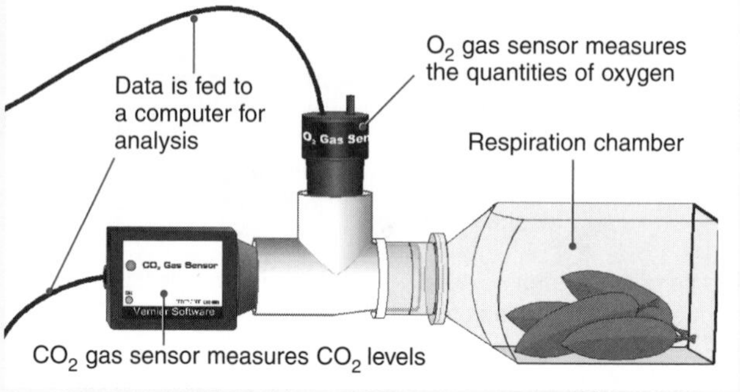

Data is fed to a computer for analysis
O_2 gas sensor measures the quantities of oxygen
Respiration chamber
CO_2 gas sensor measures CO_2 levels

Image courtesy of Vernier

2. Next, the effect of various light intensities (low light, half-light, and full light) on CO_2 concentration was investigated. How would the results table for this investigation differ from the one you have drawn above (for full light only):

© 2015 BIOZONE International
ISBN:978-1-927309-31-5
Photocopying Prohibited

13 Constructing Tables and Graphs

Key Idea: Tables and graphs provide a way to organise and visualise data in a way that helps to identify trends.

Tables and graphs are ways to present data and they have different purposes. **Tables** provide an accurate record of numerical values and allow you to organise your data so that relationships and trends are apparent. **Graphs** provide a visual image of trends in the data in a minimum of space. It is useful to plot your data as soon as possible, even during your experiment, as this will help you to evaluate your results as you proceed and make adjustments as necessary (e.g. to the sampling interval). The choice between graphing or tabulation in the final report depends on the type and complexity of the data and the information that you are wanting to convey. Usually, both are appropriate.

Presenting data in tables

Table 1: Length and growth of the third internode of bean plants receiving three different hormone treatments

Treatment	Sample size	Mean rate of internode growth / mm day^{-1}	Mean internode length / mm
Control	50	0.60	32.3
Hormone 1	46	1.52	41.6
Hormone 2	98	0.82	38.4
Hormone 3	85	2.06	50.2

Tables provide a way to systematically record and condense a large amount of information. They provide an accurate record of numerical data and allow you to organise your data in a way that allows you to identify relationships and trends. This can help to decide the best way to graph the data if graphing is required.

Table titles and row and column headings must be clear and accurate so the reader knows exactly what the table is about. Calculations such as rates and summary statistics (such as mean or standard deviation) may be included on a table.

Summary statistics make it easier to identify trends and compare different treatments. Rates are useful in making multiple data sets comparable, e.g. if recordings were made over different time periods.

Presenting data in graphs

Fig. 1: Yield of two bacterial strains at different antibiotic levels (± 95% confidence intervals, n= 6)

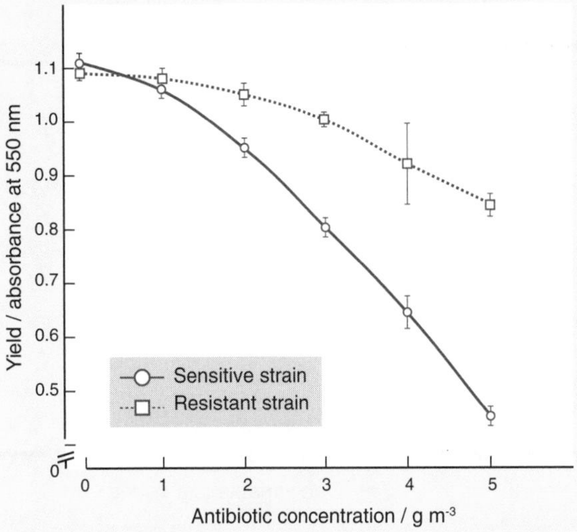

Yield / absorbance at 550 nm
1.1
1.0
0.9
0.8
0.7
0.6
0.5
0
Sensitive strain
Resistant strain
0
1
2
3
4
5
Antibiotic concentration / g m-3

Graphs are a good way of visually showing trends, patterns, and relationships without taking up too much space. Complex data sets tend to be presented as a graph rather than a table.

Presenting graphs properly requires attention to a few basic details, including correct orientation and labelling of the axes, accurate plotting of points, and a descriptive, accurate title.

1. Describe the advantages of using a table to present information: ______________________

____

____

2. (a) What is the benefit of including summary information (e.g. means) on a table? ______________________

____

(b) In an experiment, a student recorded water lost from a plant shoot over one hour. The next day, he repeated the experiment to test the effect of wind on water loss, but he had only 45 minutes to let the experiment run. How could the student best present the data in a table to compare the two trials?

____

3. What are the main advantages of presenting data in a graph? ______________________

____

____

4. Why might you include both graphs and tables in a final report: ______________________

____

____

© 2015 **BIOZONE** International
ISBN: 978-1-927309-31-5
Photocopying Prohibited

14 Which Graph to Use?

Key Idea: The type of graph you choose to display your data depends on the type of data you have collected.

Before you graph your data, it is important to identify what type of data you have. Choosing the correct type of graph can highlight trends or reveal relationships between variables. Choosing the wrong type of graph can obscure information and make the data difficult to interpret. Examples of common types of graphs and when to use them are provided below.

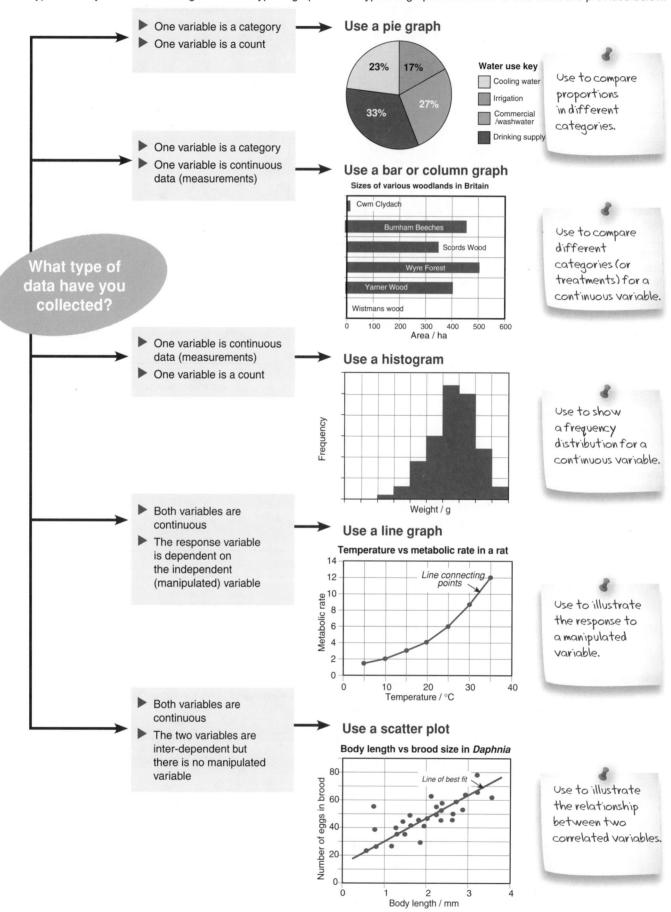

What type of data have you collected?

- One variable is a category
- One variable is a count

→ **Use a pie graph**

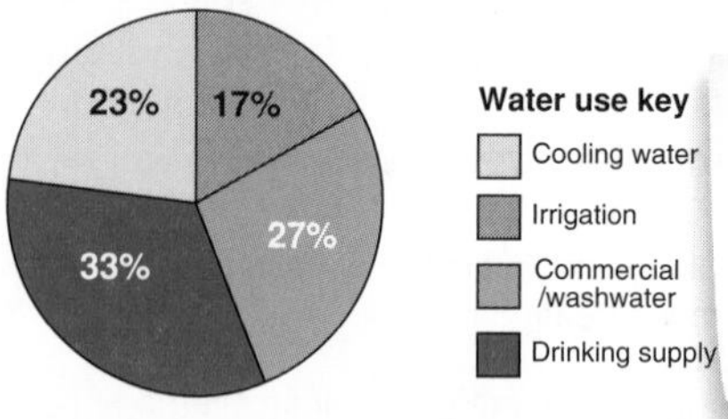
23%
17%
27%
33%
Water use key
Cooling water
Irrigation
Commercial /washwater
Drinking supply

Use to compare proportions in different categories.

- One variable is a category
- One variable is continuous data (measurements)

→ **Use a bar or column graph**

Sizes of various woodlands in Britain

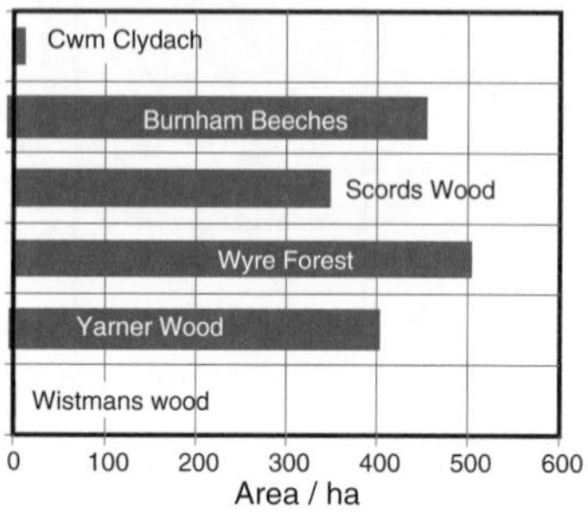
Cwm Clydach
Burnham Beeches
Scords Wood
Wyre Forest
Yarner Wood
Wistmans wood
0
100
200
300
400
500
600
Area / ha

Use to compare different categories (or treatments) for a continuous variable.

- One variable is continuous data (measurements)
- One variable is a count

→ **Use a histogram**

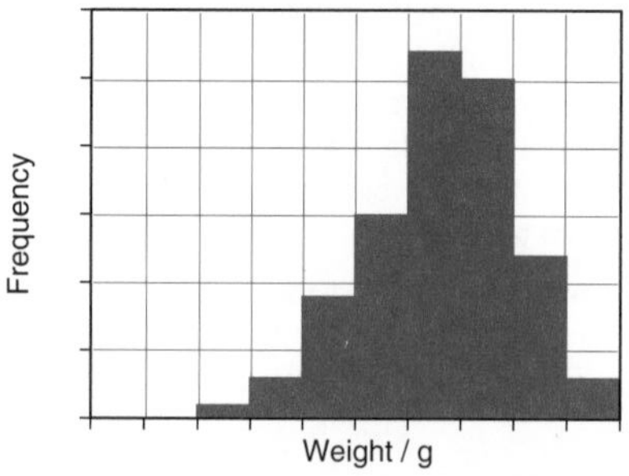
Frequency
Weight / g

Use to show a frequency distribution for a continuous variable.

- Both variables are continuous
- The response variable is dependent on the independent (manipulated) variable

→ **Use a line graph**

Temperature vs metabolic rate in a rat

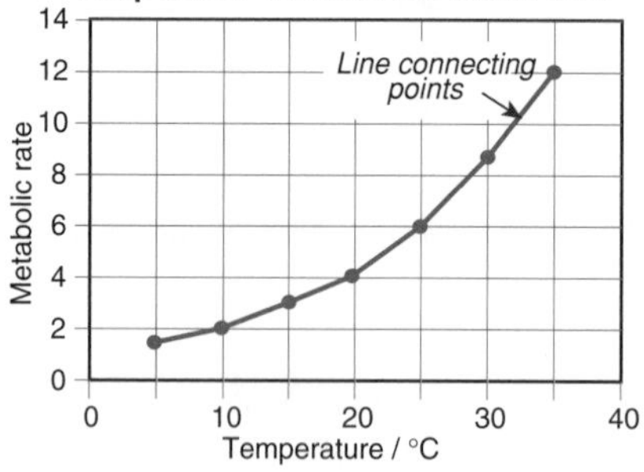
Metabolic rate
14
12
10
8
6
4
2
0
Line connecting points
0
10
20
30
40
Temperature / °C

Use to illustrate the response to a manipulated variable.

- Both variables are continuous
- The two variables are inter-dependent but there is no manipulated variable

→ **Use a scatter plot**

Body length vs brood size in *Daphnia*

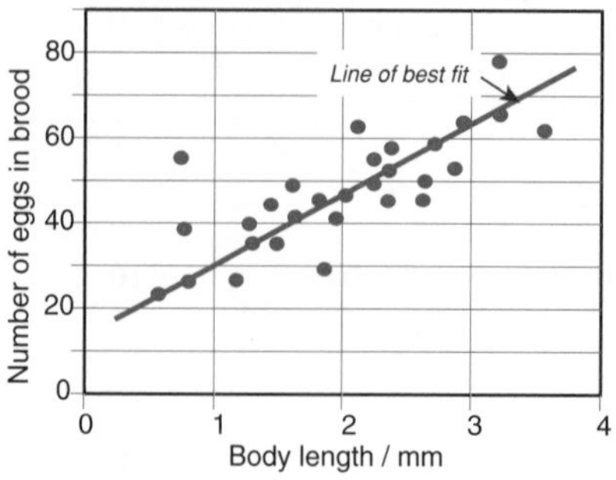
Number of eggs in brood
80
60
40
20
0
Line of best fit
0
1
2
3
4
Body length / mm

Use to illustrate the relationship between two correlated variables.

REFER LINK 15 LINK 16 LINK 17 LINK 18 LINK 19

© 2015 BIOZONE International
ISBN:978-1-927309-31-5
Photocopying Prohibited

15 Drawing Pie Graphs

Key Idea: Pie graphs are used to plot data where one variable is discontinuous (non-numerical or categorical).

Guidelines for pie graphs

Pie graphs can be used instead of bar graphs, generally in cases where there are six or fewer categories involved. A pie graph provides strong visual impact of the relative proportions in each category, particularly where one of the categories is very dominant. Features of pie graphs include:

- The data for one variable are discontinuous (non-numerical or categories).
- The data for the dependent variable are usually in the form of counts, proportions, or percentages.
- Pie graphs are good for visual impact and showing relative proportions.
- They are not suitable for data sets with a large number of categories.

Average residential water use

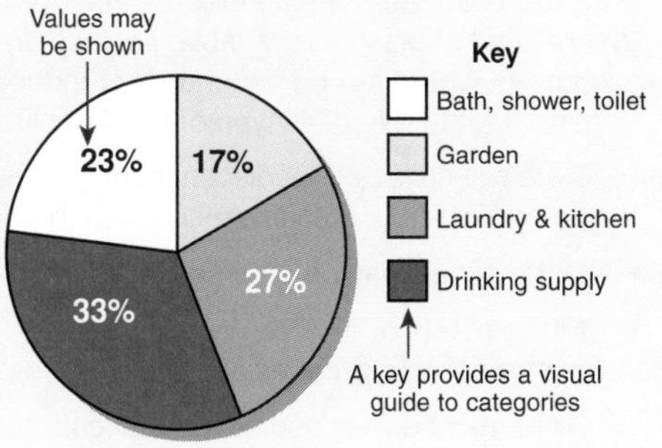
Values may be shown
23%
17%
27%
33%
Key
Bath, shower, toilet
Garden
Laundry & kitchen
Drinking supply
A key provides a visual guide to categories

1. The data provided below are from a study of the diets of three vertebrates.

   (a) Tabulate the data from the notebook shown. Calculate the angle for each percentage, given that each percentage point is equal to 3.6° (the first example is provided: 23.6 x 3.6 = 85).

   (b) Plot a pie graph for each animal in the circles provided. The circles have been marked at 5° intervals to enable you to do this exercise without a protractor. For the purposes of this exercise, begin your pie graphs at the 0° (= 360°) mark and work in a clockwise direction from the largest to the smallest percentage. Use one key for all three pie graphs.

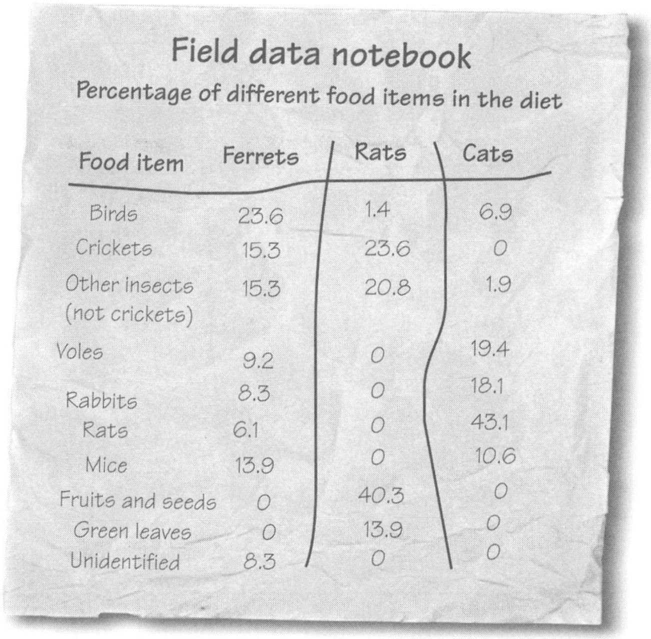

Field data notebook

Percentage of different food items in the diet

Food item	Ferrets	Rats	Cats
Birds	23.6	1.4	6.9
Crickets	15.3	23.6	0
Other insects (not crickets)	15.3	20.8	1.9
Voles	9.2	0	19.4
Rabbits	8.3	0	18.1
Rats	6.1	0	43.1
Mice	13.9	0	10.6
Fruits and seeds	0	40.3	0
Green leaves	0	13.9	0
Unidentified	8.3	0	0

Percentage occurrence of foods in the diet of ferrets, rats, and cats. Graph angle representing the % is shown to help plotting.

Food item in diet	Ferrets		Rats		Cats	
	% in diet	Angle / °	% in diet	Angle / °	% in diet	Angle / °
Birds	23.6	85				

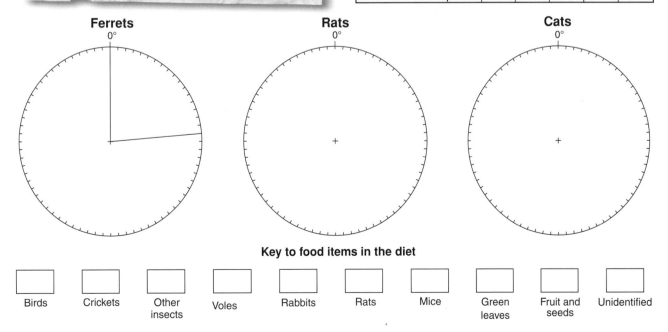

Ferrets

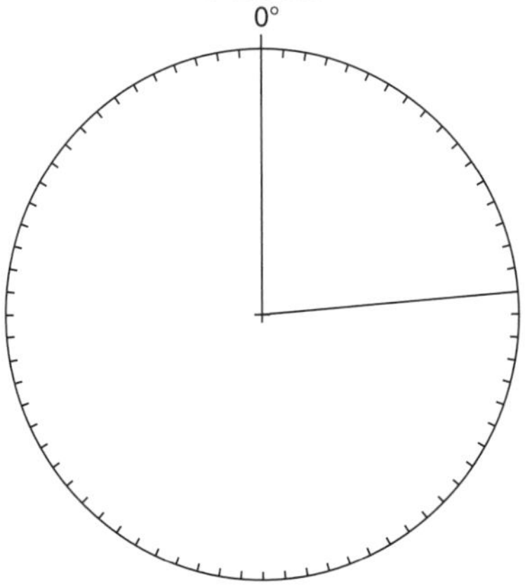
0°

Rats

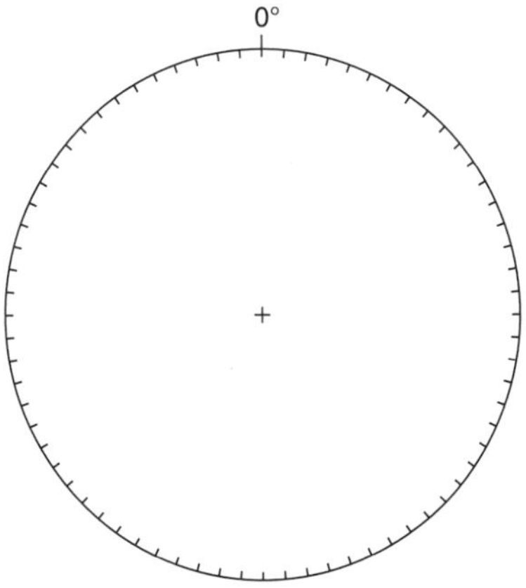
0°

Cats

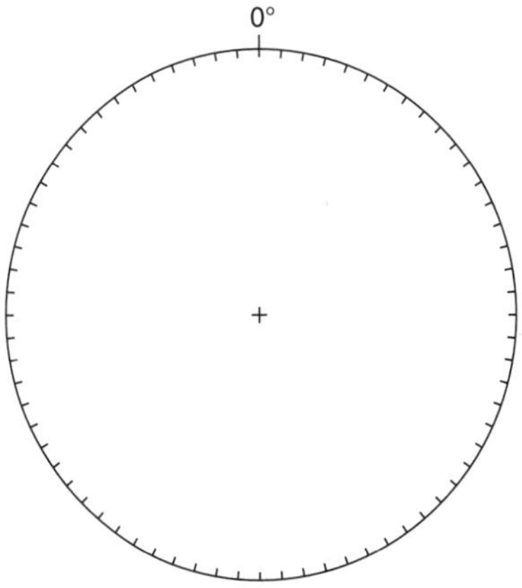
0°

Key to food items in the diet

Birds	Crickets	Other insects	Voles	Rabbits	Rats	Mice	Green leaves	Fruit and seeds	Unidentified

© 2015 BIOZONE International
ISBN: 978-1-927309-31-5
Photocopying Prohibited

16 Drawing Bar Graphs

Key Idea: Bar graphs are used to plot data that is non-numerical or discrete for at least one variable.

Guidelines for bar graphs

Bar graphs are appropriate for data that are non-numerical and **discrete** for at least one variable, i.e. they are grouped into categories. There are no dependent or independent variables. Important features of this type of graph include:

- Data are collected for discontinuous, non-numerical categories (e.g. colour, species), so the bars do not touch.
- Data values may be entered on or above the bars.
- Multiple sets of data can be displayed side by side for comparison (e.g. males and females).
- Axes may be reversed so that the categories are on the x axis, i.e. bars can be vertical or horizontal. When they are vertical, these graphs are called column graphs.

Size of various woodlands in Britain
Cwm Clydach
20
Burnham Beeches
450
Scords Wood
350
Wyre Forest
500
Yarner Wood
400
Wistmans Wood
4
0
100
200
300
400
500
600
Area of woodland / Ha

1. Counts of eight mollusc species were made from a series of quadrat samples at two sites on a rocky shore. The summary data are presented here.
   (a) Tabulate the **mean numbers** per square metre at each site in Table 1 (below left).
   (b) Plot a **bar graph** of the tabulated data on the grid below. For each species, plot the data from both sites side by side using different colours to distinguish the sites.

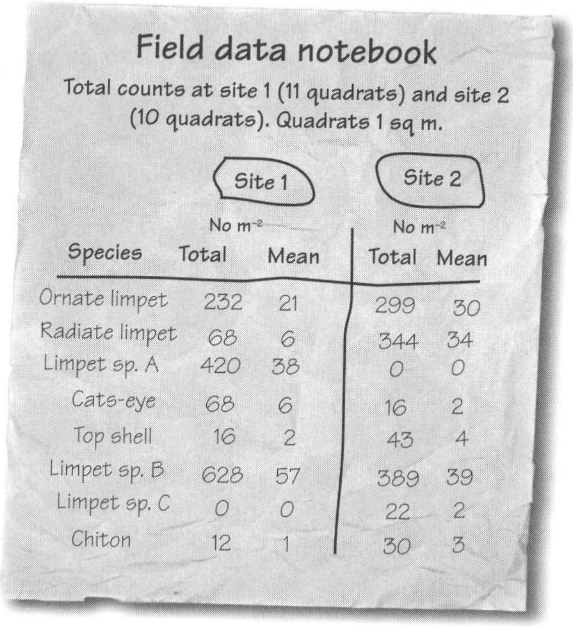

Field data notebook
Total counts at site 1 (11 quadrats) and site 2 (10 quadrats). Quadrats 1 sq m.
Site 1
Site 2

Species	Site 1 Total (No m^{-2})	Site 1 Mean (No m^{-2})	Site 2 Total (No m^{-2})	Site 2 Mean (No m^{-2})
Ornate limpet	232	21	299	30
Radiate limpet	68	6	344	34
Limpet sp. A	420	38	0	0
Cats-eye	68	6	16	2
Top shell	16	2	43	4
Limpet sp. B	628	57	389	39
Limpet sp. C	0	0	22	2
Chiton	12	1	30	3

Mean abundance of 8 molluscan species from two sites along a rocky shore.

Species	Mean / no. m^{-2}	
	Site 1	Site 2

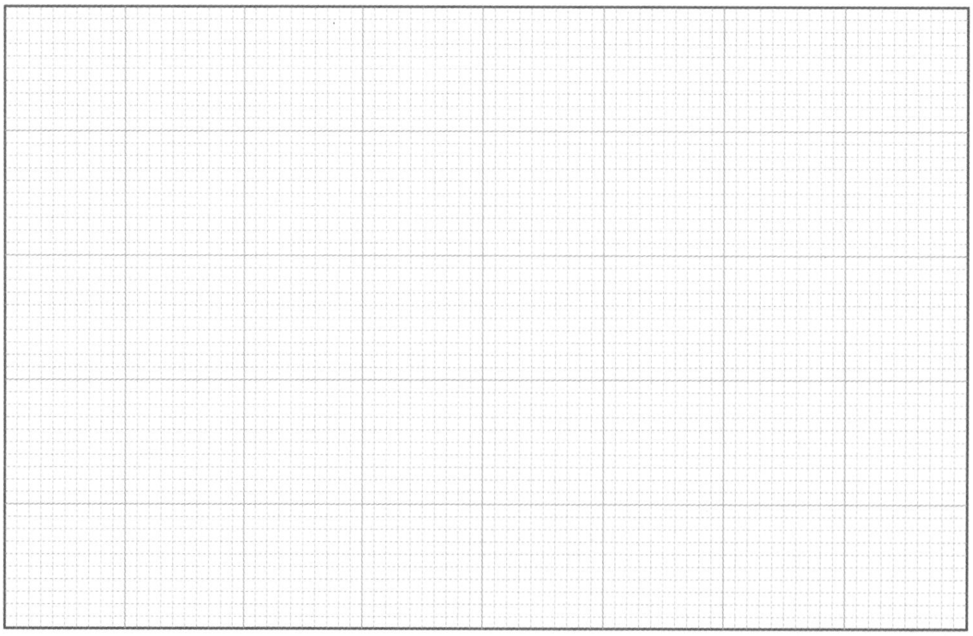

© 2015 BIOZONE International
ISBN:978-1-927309-31-5
Photocopying Prohibited

17 Drawing Histograms

Key Idea: Histograms graphically show the frequency distribution of continuous data.

Guidelines for histograms

Histograms are plots of **continuous** data and are often used to represent frequency distributions, where the y-axis shows the number of times a particular measurement or value was obtained. For this reason, they are often called frequency histograms. Important features of this type of graph include:

- The data are numerical and continuous (e.g. height or weight), so the bars touch.
- The x-axis usually records the class interval. The y-axis usually records the number of individuals in each class interval (frequency).
- A neatly constructed tally chart doubles as a simple histogram.

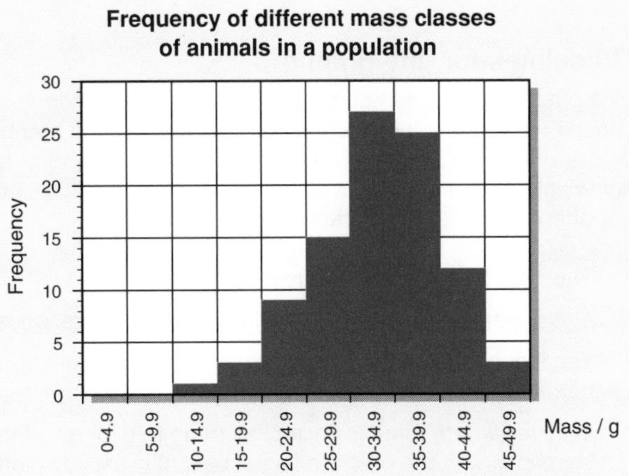
Frequency of different mass classes of animals in a population
Frequency
30
25
20
15
10
5
0
0-4.9
5-9.9
10-14.9
15-19.9
20-24.9
25-29.9
30-34.9
35-39.9
40-44.9
45-49.9
Mass / g

1. The weight data provided below were recorded from 95 individuals (male and female), older than 17 years.

   (a) Create a tally chart (frequency table) in the frame provided, organising the weight data into a form suitable for plotting. An example of the tally for the weight grouping 55-59.9 kg has been completed for you as an example. Note that the raw data values are crossed off the data set in the notebook once they are recorded as counts on the tally chart. It is important to do this in order to prevent data entry errors.

   (b) Plot a **frequency histogram** of the tallied data on the grid provided below.

Weight / Kg	Tally	Total
45-49.9		
50-54.9		
55-59.9	~~||||~~ ||	7
60-64.9		
65-69.9		
70-74.9		
75-79.9		
80-84.9		
85-89.9		
90-94.9		
95-99.9		
100-104.9		
105-109.9		

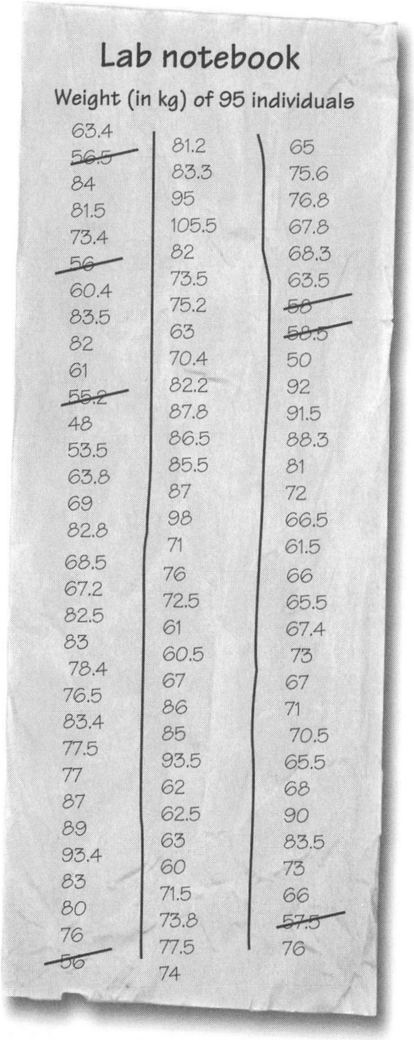
Lab notebook

Weight (in kg) of 95 individuals

63.4	81.2	65
~~56.5~~	83.3	75.6
84	95	76.8
81.5	105.5	67.8
73.4	82	68.3
~~56~~	73.5	63.5
60.4	75.2	~~58~~
83.5	63	~~58.5~~
82	70.4	50
61	82.2	92
~~55.2~~	87.8	91.5
48	86.5	88.3
53.5	85.5	81
63.8	87	72
69	98	66.5
82.8	71	61.5
68.5	76	66
67.2	72.5	65.5
82.5	61	67.4
83	60.5	73
78.4	67	67
76.5	86	71
83.4	85	70.5
77.5	93.5	65.5
77	62	68
87	62.5	90
89	63	83.5
93.4	60	73
83	71.5	66
80	73.8	~~57.5~~
76	77.5	76
~~56~~	74	

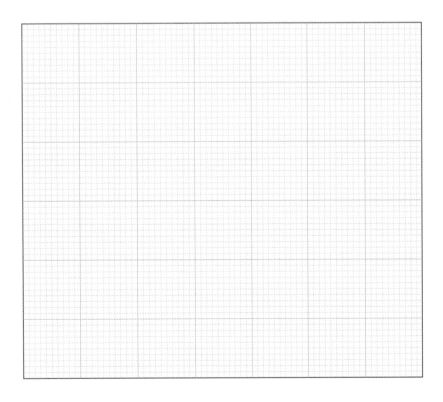

© 2015 BIOZONE International
ISBN: 978-1-927309-31-5
Photocopying Prohibited

18 Drawing Line Graphs

Key Idea: Line graphs are used to plot continuous data in which one variable (the independent variable) directly affects the other (dependent) variable. They are appropriate for data in which the independent variable is manipulated.

Guidelines for line graphs

Line graphs are used when one variable (the independent variable) affects another, the dependent variable. Line graphs can be drawn without a measure of spread (top figure, right) or with some calculated measure of data variability (bottom figure, right). Important features of line graphs include:

- The data must be continuous for both variables.
- The dependent variable is usually the biological response.
- The independent variable is often time or experimental treatment.
- In cases where there is an implied trend (e.g. one variable increases with the other), a line of best fit is usually plotted through the data points to show the relationship.
- If fluctuations in the data are likely to be important (e.g. with climate and other environmental data) the data points are usually connected directly (point to point).
- Line graphs may be drawn with measure of error. The data are presented as points (which are the calculated means), with bars above and below, indicating a measure of variability or spread in the data (e.g. standard error, standard deviation, or 95% confidence intervals).
- Where no error value has been calculated, the scatter can be shown by plotting the individual data points vertically above and below the mean. By convention, bars are not used to indicate the range of raw values in a data set.

Metabolic rate of rats at different temperatures

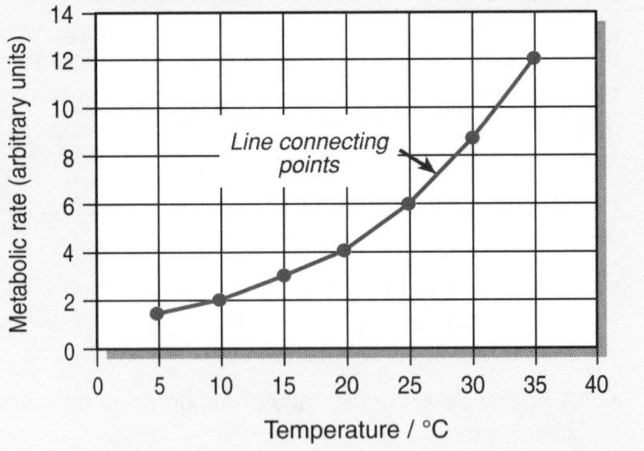
Metabolic rate (arbitrary units)
0
2
4
6
8
10
12
14
Line connecting points
0
5
10
15
20
25
30
35
40
Temperature / °C

Growth rate in peas at different temperatures

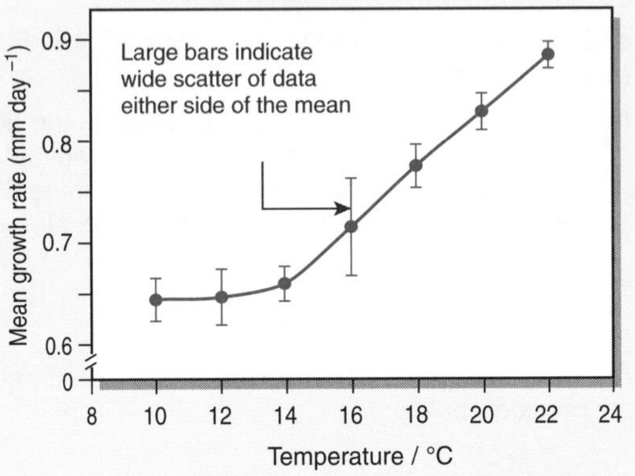
Mean growth rate (mm day^{-1})
0
0.6
0.7
0.8
0.9
Large bars indicate wide scatter of data either side of the mean
8
10
12
14
16
18
20
22
24
Temperature / °C

1. The results (shown right) were collected in a study investigating the effect of temperature on the activity of an enzyme.

   (a) Using the results provided (right), plot a line graph on the grid below:

   (b) Estimate the rate of reaction at 15°C: ______________________

Lab Notebook

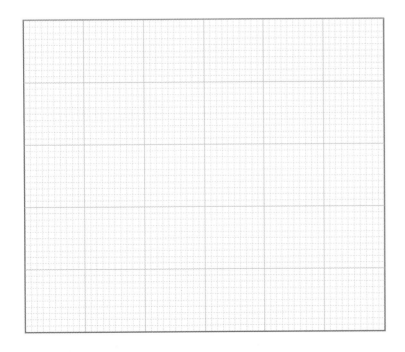

An enzyme's activity at different temperatures

Temperature / °C	Rate of reaction (mg of product formed per minute)
10	1.0
20	2.1
30	3.2
35	3.7
40	4.1
45	3.7
50	2.7
60	0

© 2015 BIOZONE International
ISBN:978-1-927309-31-5
Photocopying Prohibited

Plotting multiple data sets

A single figure can be used to show two or more data sets, i.e. more than one curve can be plotted per set of axes. This type of presentation is useful when comparing the trends for two or more treatments, or the response of one species against the response of another. Important points regarding this format are:

- If the two data sets use the same measurement units and a similar range of values for the independent variable, one scale on the y axis is used.
- If the two data sets use different units and/or have a very different range of values for the independent variable, two scales for the y axis are used (see example right). The scales can be adjusted if necessary to avoid overlapping plots
- The two curves must be distinguished with a key.

Transpiration and root uptake rates in peas at different relative humidity

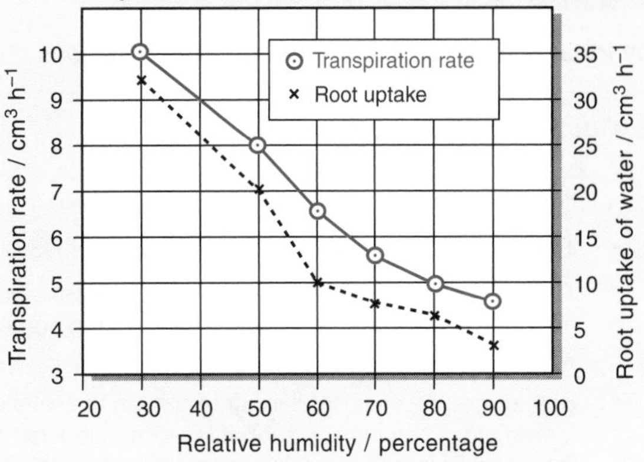
Transpiration rate
Root uptake
Transpiration rate / cm^3 h^{-1}
3 4 5 6 7 8 9 10
Root uptake of water / cm^3 h^{-1}
0 5 10 15 20 25 30 35
20 30 40 50 60 70 80 90 100
Relative humidity / percentage

2. The number of perch and trout in a hydro-electric reservoir were monitored over 19 years. A colony of black shag was also present. Shags feed on perch and (to a lesser extent) trout. In 1960-61, 424 shags were removed from the lake during the nesting season and nest counts were made every spring in subsequent years. In 1971, 60 shags were removed from the lake, and all existing nests dismantled. The results of the population survey are tabulated below.

(a) Plot a line graph (joining the data points) for the survey results. Use one scale (on the left) for numbers of perch and trout and another scale for the number of shag nests. Use different symbols to distinguish the lines and include a key.

(b) Use a vertical arrow to indicate the point at which shags and their nests were removed.

Year	Mean number of fish per haul		Shag nest numbers
	Trout	Perch	
1960	–	–	16
1961	–	–	4
1962	1.5	11	5
1963	0.8	9	10
1964	0	5	22
1965	1	1	25
1966	1	2.9	35
1967	2	5	40
1968	1.5	4.6	26
1969	1.5	6	32

Year (continued)	Mean number of fish per haul		Shag nest numbers
	Trout	Perch	
1970	1.5	6	1.5
1971	0.5	0.7	1.5
1972	1	0.8	0
1973	0.2	4	0
1974	0.5	6.5	0
1975	0.6	7.6	2
1976	1	1.2	10
1977	1.2	1.5	32
1978	0.7	1.2	28

Source: Data adapted from 1987 Bursary Examination

© 2015 **BIOZONE** International
ISBN: 978-1-927309-31-5
Photocopying Prohibited

19 Drawing Scatter Plots

Key Idea: Scatter graphs are used to plot continuous data where there is a relationship between two interdependent variables.

Guidelines for scatter graphs

A scatter graph is used to display continuous data where there is a relationship between two interdependent variables.

- The data must be continuous for both variables.
- There is no independent (manipulated) variable, but the variables are often correlated, i.e. they vary together in some predictable way.
- Scatter graphs are useful for determining the relationship (correlation) between two variables. A relationship does not imply that change in one variable causes change in the other variable.
- The points on the graph need not be connected, but a line of best fit is often drawn through the points to show the relationship between the variables (this may be drawn by eye or computer generated).

Body length vs brood size in *Daphnia*

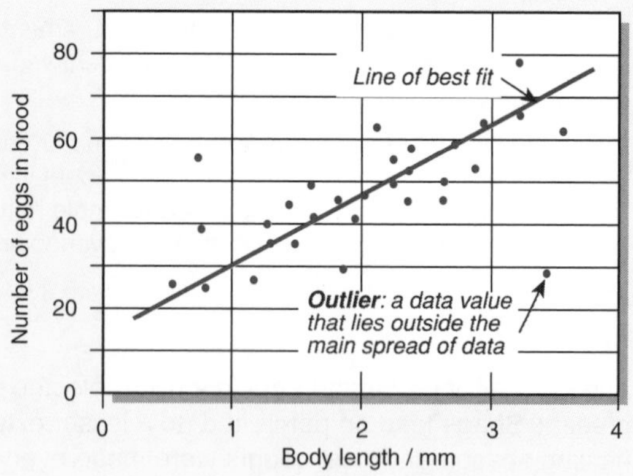
Number of eggs in brood
0
20
40
60
80
Line of best fit
Outlier: *a data value that lies outside the main spread of data*
0
1
2
3
4
Body length / mm

1. In the example below, metabolic measurements were taken from seven Antarctic fish *Pagothenia borchgrevinski*. The fish are affected by a gill disease, which increases the thickness of the gas exchange surfaces and affects oxygen uptake. The results of oxygen consumption of fish with varying amounts of affected gill (at rest and swimming) are tabulated below.

   (a) Using **one** scale only for oxygen consumption, plot the data on the grid below to show the relationship between oxygen consumption and the amount of gill affected by disease. Use different symbols or colours for each set of data (at rest and swimming).

   (b) Draw a line of best fit through each set of points. NOTE: A line of best fit is drawn so that the points are evenly distributed on either side of the line.

Oxygen consumption of fish with affected gills

Fish number	Percentage of gill affected	Oxygen consumption / $cm^3\ g^{-1}\ h^{-1}$	
		At rest	Swimming
1	0	0.05	0.29
2	95	0.04	0.11
3	60	0.04	0.14
4	30	0.05	0.22
5	90	0.05	0.08
6	65	0.04	0.18
7	45	0.04	0.20

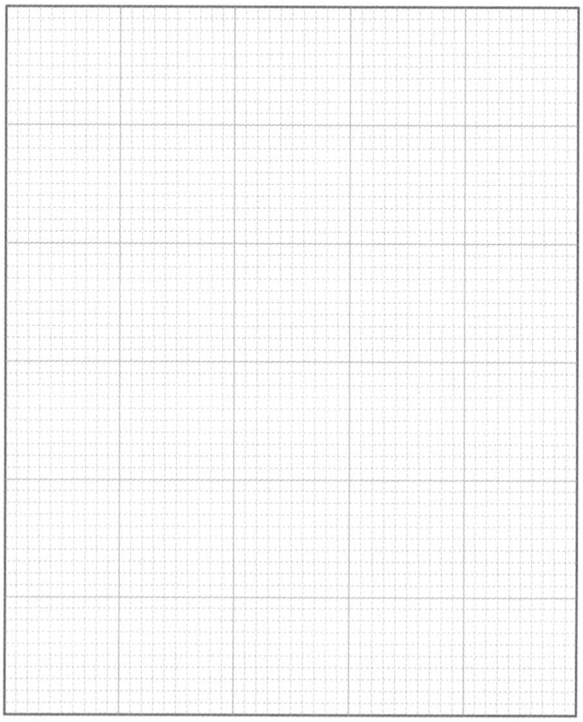

2. Describe the relationship between the amount of gill affected and oxygen consumption in the fish:

   (a) For the **at rest** data set: ______________________

   (b) For the **swimming** data set: ______________________

3. How does the gill disease affect oxygen uptake in resting fish? ______________________

© 2015 **BIOZONE** International
ISBN:978-1-927309-31-5
Photocopying Prohibited

20 Interpreting Line Graphs

Key Idea: The equation for a straight line is y = mx + c. A line may have a positive, negative, or zero slope.
The equation for a linear (straight) line on a graph is y = mx + c. The equation can be used to calculate the gradient (slope) of a straight line and tells us about the relationship between x and y (how fast y is changing relative to x). For a straight line, the rate of change of y relative to x is always constant. A line may have a positive, negative, or zero slope.

Measuring gradients and intercepts

The equation for a straight line is written as:

y = mx + c

Where :

y = the y-axis value

m = the slope (or gradient)

x = the x-axis value

c = the y intercept (where the line cross the y-axis).

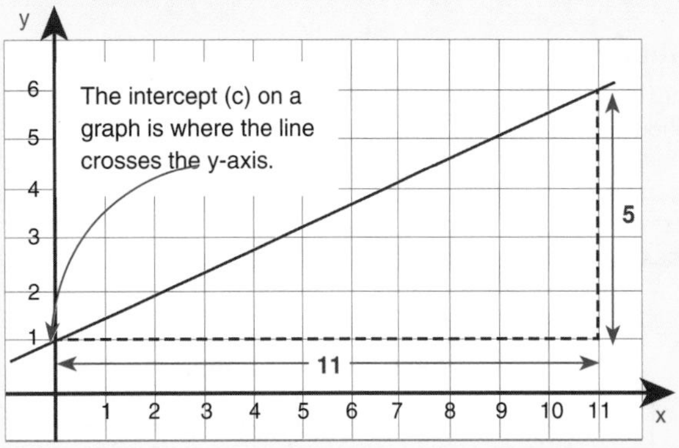

y
The intercept (c) on a graph is where the line crosses the y-axis.
5
11
x

Determining "m" and "c"

To find "c" just find where the line crosses the y-axis.

To find m:

1. Choose any two points on the line.
2. Draw a right-angled triangle between the two points on the line.
3. Use the scale on each axis to find the triangle's vertical length and horizontal length.
4. Calculate the gradient of the line using the following equation:

$$\frac{\text{change in y}}{\text{change in x}}$$

For the example above:

c = 1

m = 0.45 (5 ÷11)

Once c and m have been determined you can choose any value for x and find the corresponding value for y.

For example, when x = 9, the equation would be:

y = 9 x 0.45 + 1

y = 5.05

Interpreting gradients

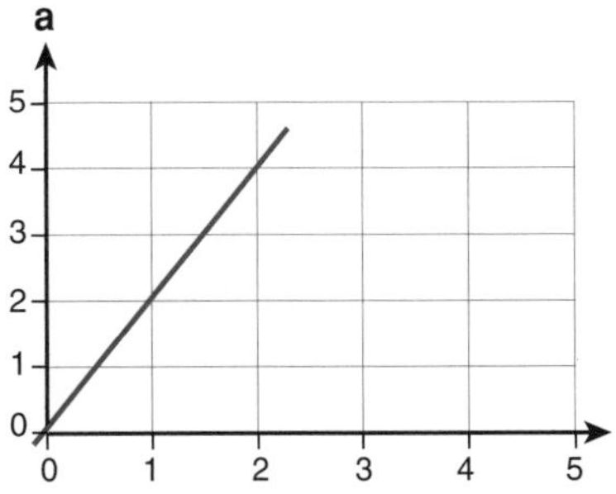

a

Positive gradients: the line slopes upward to the right (y is increasing as x increases).

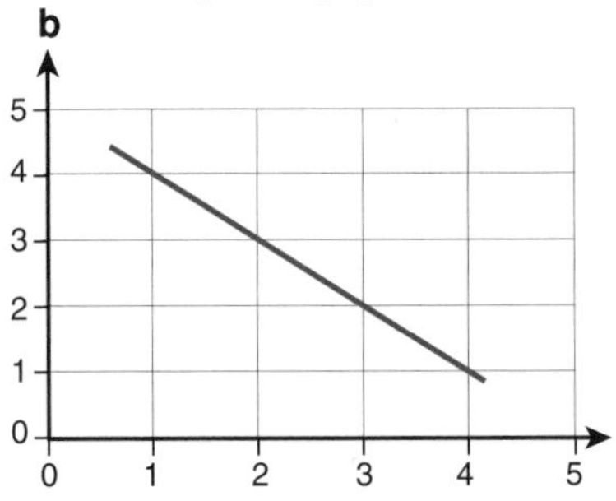

b

Negative gradients: the line slopes downward to the right (y is decreasing as x increases).

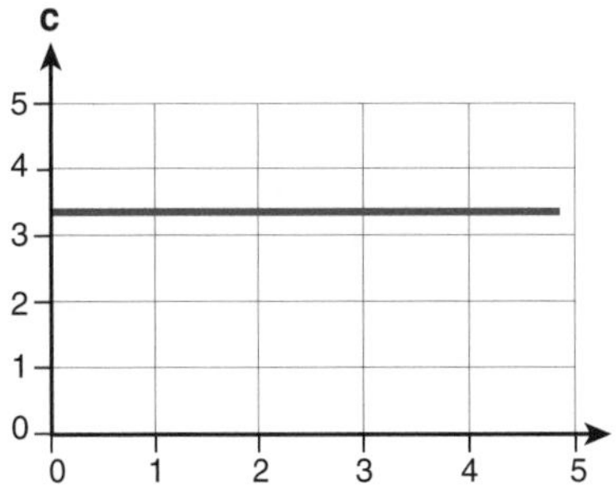

c

Zero gradients: the line is horizontal (y does not change as x increases).

1. State the gradient for graphs a, b, and c (above): (a) ______________ (b) ______________ (c) ______________

2. For a straight line y = 3x + 2,

   (a) Identify the value of c: ______________ (b) Determine y if x = 4: ______________

3. For the graph (right):

   (a) Identify the value of c: ______________

   (b) Calculate the value of m: ______________

   (c) Determine y if x = 2: ______________

   ____

   (d) Describe the slope of the line: ______________

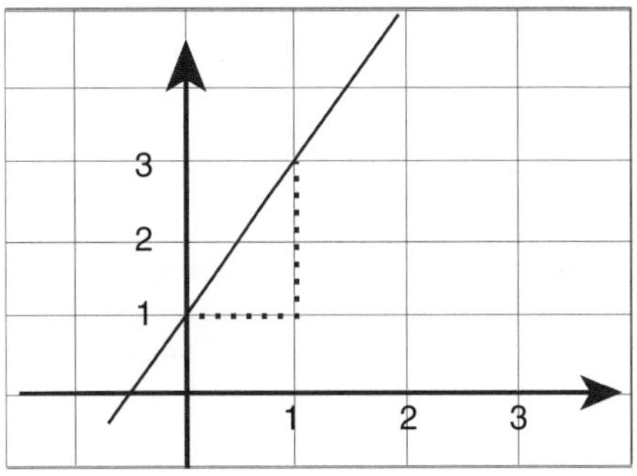

© 2015 BIOZONE International
ISBN: 978-1-927309-31-5
Photocopying Prohibited

21 Mean, Median, and Mode

Key Idea: Mean, median, and mode are measures of the central tendency of data. The distribution of the data will determine which measurement of central tendency you use.

Measures of a biological response are usually made from more than one sampling unit. In lab-based investigations, the sample size (the number of sampling units) may be as small as three or four (e.g. three test-tubes in each of four treatments). In field studies, each individual may be a sampling unit, and the sample size can be very large (e.g. 100 individuals). It is useful to summarise data using **descriptive statistics.** Descriptive statistics, such as mean, median, and mode, can identify the central tendency of a data set. Each of these statistics is appropriate to certain types of data or distribution (as indicated by a frequency distribution).

Variation in data

Whether they are obtained from observation or experiments, most biological data show variability. In a set of data values, it is useful to know the value about which most of the data are grouped, i.e. the centre value. This value can be the mean, median, or mode depending on the type of variable involved (see below). The main purpose of these statistics is to summarise important features of your data and to provide the basis for statistical analyses.

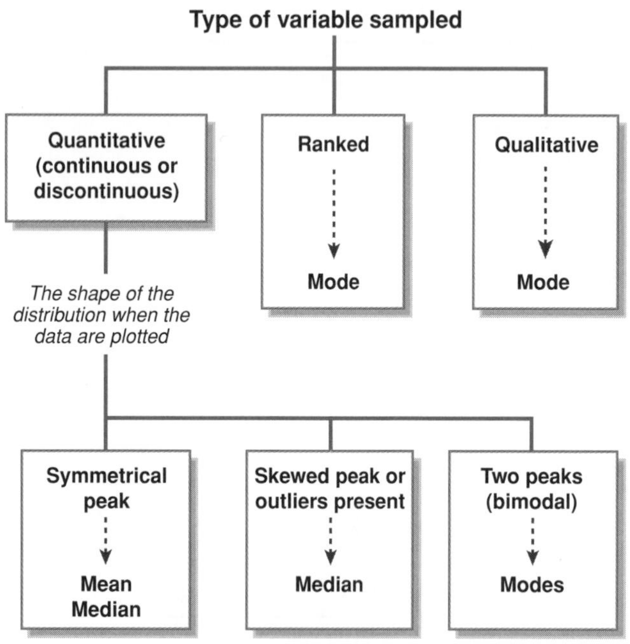
Type of variable sampled
Quantitative (continuous or discontinuous)
Ranked
Qualitative
Mode
Mode
The shape of the distribution when the data are plotted
Symmetrical peak
Mean
Median
Skewed peak or outliers present
Median
Two peaks (bimodal)
Modes

The shape of the distribution will determine which statistic (mean, median, or mode) best describes the central tendency of the sample data.

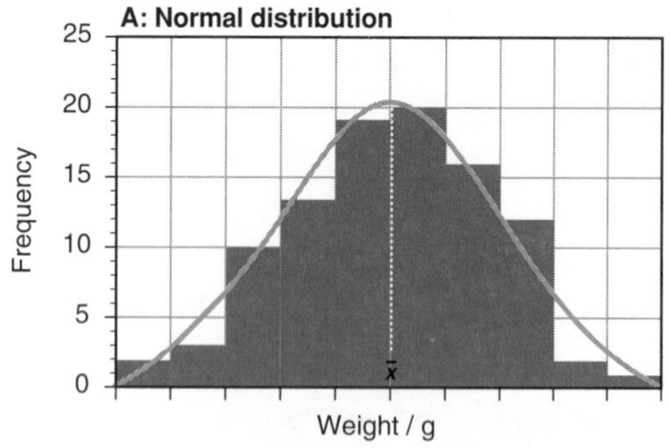
A: Normal distribution
Frequency
25
20
15
10
5
0
$\bar{x}$
Weight / g

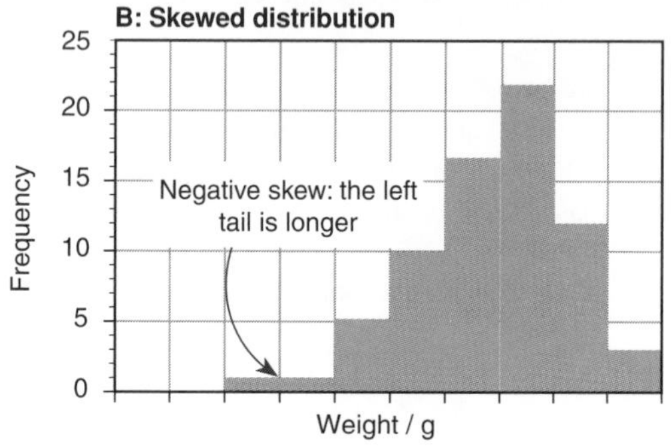
B: Skewed distribution
Frequency
25
20
15
10
5
0
Negative skew: the left tail is longer
Weight / g

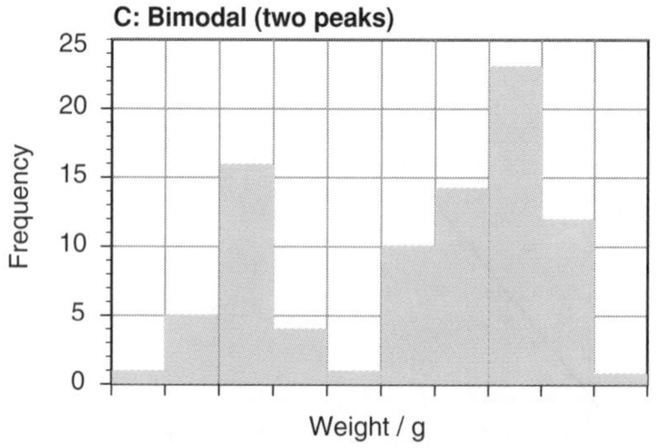
C: Bimodal (two peaks)
Frequency
25
20
15
10
5
0
Weight / g

Statistic	Definition and use	Method of calculation
Mean	• The average of all data entries. • Measure of central tendency for normally distributed data.	• Add up all the data entries. • Divide by the total number of data entries.
Median	• The middle value when data entries are placed in rank order. • A good measure of central tendency for skewed distributions.	• Arrange the data in increasing rank order. • Identify the middle value. • For an even number of entries, find the mid point of the two middle values.
Mode	• The most common data value. • Suitable for bimodal distributions and qualitative data.	• Identify the category with the highest number of data entries using a tally chart or a bar graph.
Range	• The difference between the smallest and largest data values. • Provides a crude indication of data spread.	• Identify the smallest and largest values and find the difference between them.

When NOT to calculate a mean:

In some situations, calculation of a simple arithmetic mean is not appropriate.

Remember:

- *DO NOT* calculate a mean from values that are already means (averages) themselves.
- *DO NOT* calculate a mean of ratios (e.g. percentages) for several groups of different sizes. Go back to the raw values and recalculate.
- *DO NOT* calculate a mean when the measurement scale is not linear, e.g. pH units are not measured on a linear scale.

© 2015 **BIOZONE** International
ISBN:978-1-927309-31-5
Photocopying Prohibited

$$\frac{\text{Total of data entries}}{\text{Number of entries}} = \frac{5221}{29} = 180 \text{ cm}$$

Mean

Height of swimmers (in rank order)		
174	177	185
175	177	185
175	178	185
175	178	186
176	178	186
176	178	186
176	180	188
176	180	188
176	180	189
177	181	

Median: 178

Height (cm)	Tally	Total
174	✓	1
175	✓✓✓	3
176	✓✓✓✓✓	5
177	✓✓✓	3
178	✓✓✓✓	4
179		0
180	✓✓✓	3
181	✓	1
182		0
183		0
184		0
185	✓✓✓	3
186	✓✓✓	3
187		0
188	✓✓	2
189	✓	1

Mode: 176

Case study: height of swimmers

Data (below) and descriptive statistics (left) from a survey of the height of 29 members of a male swim squad.

Raw data: Height / cm					
178	177	188	176	186	175
180	181	178	178	176	175
180	185	185	175	189	174
178	186	176	185	177	176
176	188	180	186	177	

1. Give a reason for the difference between the mean, median, and mode for the swimmers' height data:

Fern spores

Case study: fern reproduction

Raw data (below) and descriptive statistics (right) from a survey of the number of sori found on the fronds of a fern plant.

Raw data: Number of sori per frond							
64	60	64	62	68	66	66	63
69	70	63	70	70	63	63	62
71	69	59	70	66	61	61	70
67	64	63	64				

$$\frac{\text{Total of data entries}}{\text{Number of entries}} = \frac{1641}{25} = 66 \text{ sori}$$

Mean

Number of sori per frond (in rank order)	
59	66
60	66
61	67
62	68
62	69
63	69
63	70
63	70
63	70
64	70
64	70
64	71
64	

Median: 64

Sori per frond	Tally	Total
59	✓	1
60	✓	1
61	✓	1
62	✓✓	2
63	✓✓✓✓	4
64	✓✓✓✓	4
65		0
66	✓✓	2
67	✓	1
68	✓	1
69	✓✓	2
70	✓✓✓✓✓	5
71	✓	1

Mode: 70

2. Give a reason for the difference between the mean, median, and mode for the fern sori data:

3. Calculate the mean, median, and mode for the data on ladybird masses below. Draw up a tally chart and show all calculations:

Ladybird mass / mg		
10.1	8.2	7.7
8.0	8.8	7.8
6.7	7.7	8.8
9.8	8.8	8.9
6.2	8.8	8.4

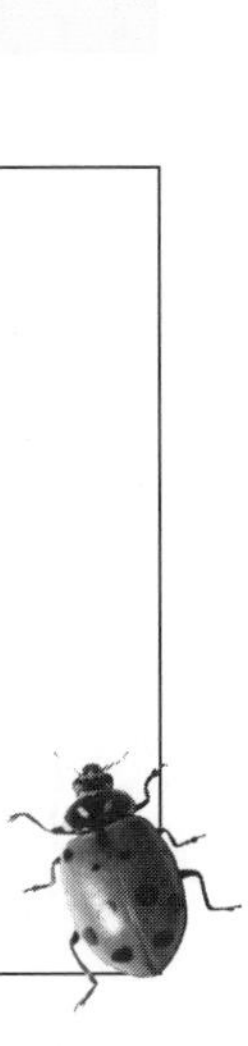

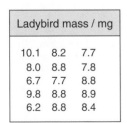

© 2015 **BIOZONE** International
ISBN: 978-1-927309-31-5
Photocopying Prohibited

22 Biological Drawings

Key Idea: Good biological drawings provide an accurate record of the specimen you are studying and enable you to make a record of its important features.

Drawing is a very important skill to have in biology. Drawings record what a specimen looks like and give you an opportunity to record its important features. Often drawing something will help you remember its features at a later date (e.g. in a test). Annotated drawings provide explanatory notes about the labelled structures, while plan diagrams label the main structures observed, but provide no additional detail.

- Biological drawings require you to pay attention to detail. It is very important that you draw what you actually see, and not what you think you should see.
- Biological drawings should include as much detail as you need to distinguish different structures and types of tissue, but avoid unnecessary detail which can make your drawing confusing.
- Attention should be given to the symmetry and proportions of your specimen. Accurate labeling, a statement of magnification or scale, the view (section type), and type of stain used (if applicable) should all be noted on your drawing.
- Some key points for making good biological drawing are described on the example below. The drawing of *Drosophila* (right) is well executed but lacks the information required to make it a good biological drawing.

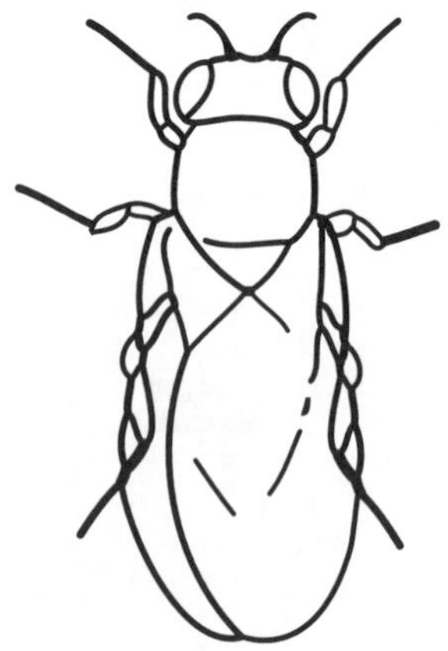

This drawing of *Drosophila* is a fair representation of the animal, but has no labels, title, or scale.

All drawings must include a title. Underline the title if it is a scientific name.

Centre your drawing on the page, not in a corner. This will leave room to place labels around the drawing.

If you need to represent depth, use stippling (dotting). Do not use shading as this can smudge and obscure detail.

Use simple, narrow lines to make your drawings.

Use a sharp pencil to draw with. Make your drawing on plain white paper.

Your drawing must include a scale or magnification to indicate the size of your subject.

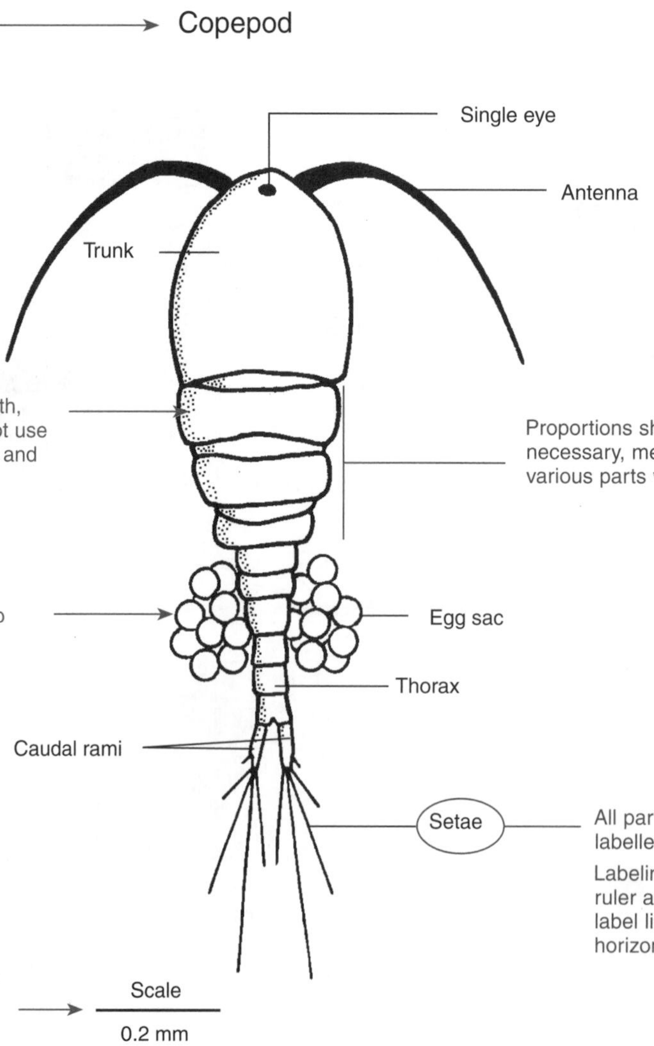
Copepod
Single eye
Antenna
Trunk
Egg sac
Thorax
Caudal rami
Setae
Scale
0.2 mm

Proportions should be accurate. If necessary, measure the lengths of various parts with a ruler.

All parts of your drawing must be labelled accurately.

Labeling lines should be drawn with a ruler and should not cross over other label lines. Try to use only vertical or horizontal lines.

© 2015 BIOZONE International
ISBN:978-1-927309-31-5
Photocopying Prohibited

Annotated diagrams

An annotated diagram is a diagram that includes a series of explanatory notes. These provide important or useful information about your subject.

Transverse section through collenchyma of *Helianthus* stem. Magnification x 450

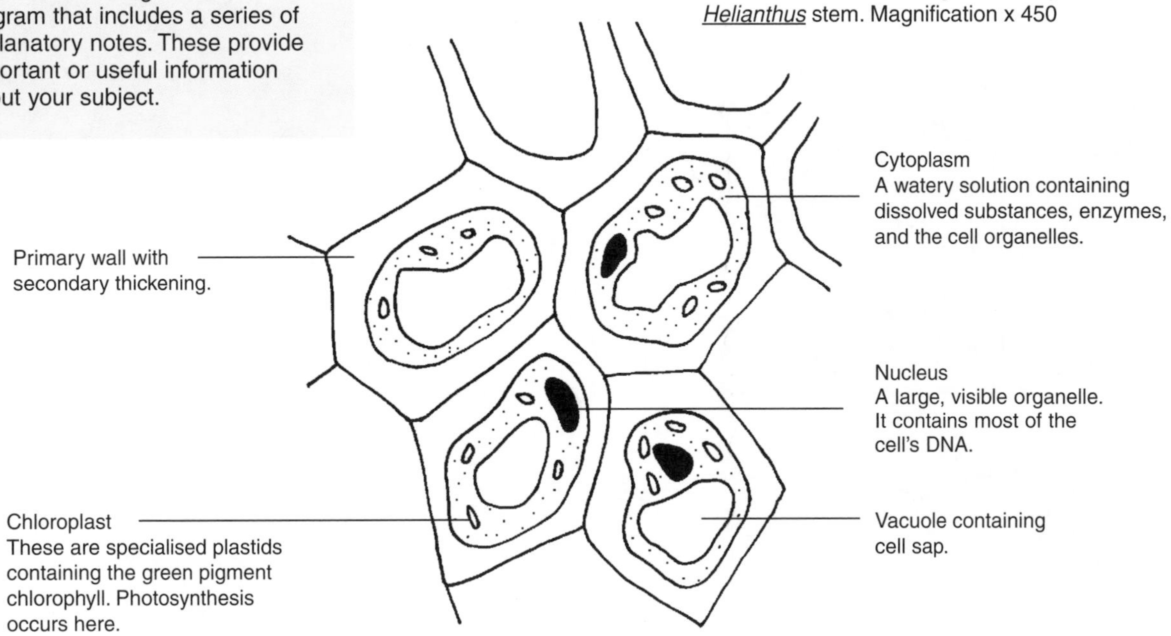
Cytoplasm
A watery solution containing dissolved substances, enzymes, and the cell organelles.
Primary wall with secondary thickening.
Nucleus
A large, visible organelle. It contains most of the cell's DNA.
Chloroplast
These are specialised plastids containing the green pigment chlorophyll. Photosynthesis occurs here.
Vacuole containing cell sap.

Plan diagrams

Plan diagrams are drawings made of samples viewed under a microscope at low or medium power. They are used to show the distribution of the different tissue types in a sample without any cellular detail. The tissues are identified, but no detail about the cells within them is included.

The example here shows a plan diagram produced after viewing a light micrograph of a transverse section through a dicot stem.

Light micrograph of a transverse section through a sunflower stem

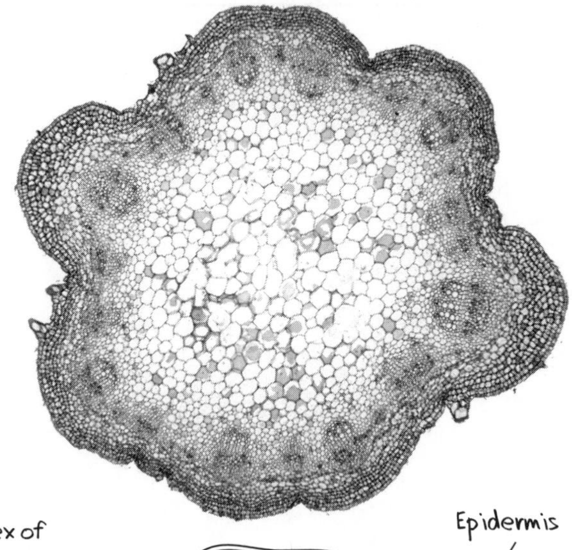

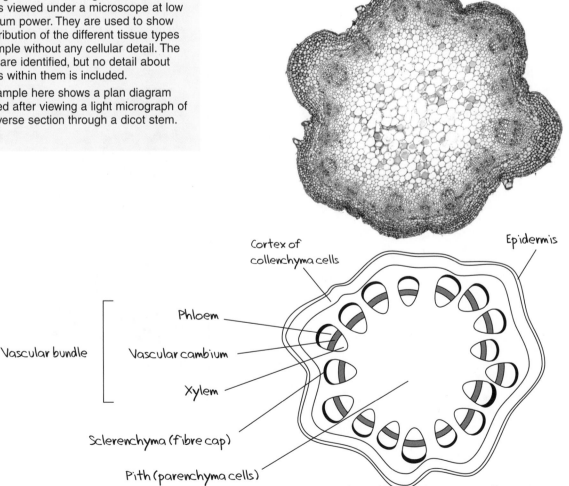

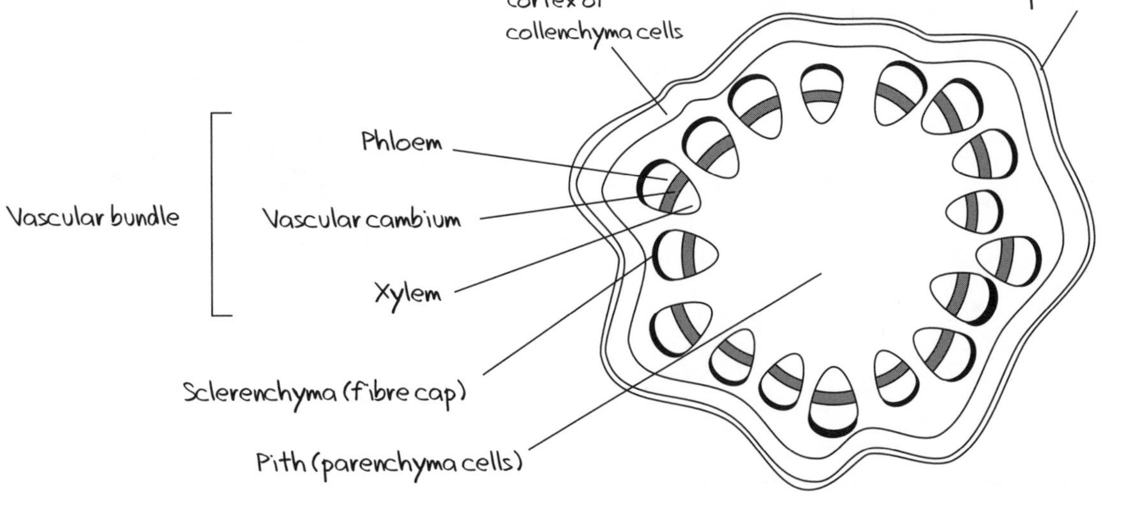
Cortex of collenchyma cells
Epidermis
Phloem
Vascular bundle
Vascular cambium
Xylem
Sclerenchyma (fibre cap)
Pith (parenchyma cells)

© 2015 BIOZONE International
ISBN: 978-1-927309-31-5
Photocopying Prohibited

23 Practising Biological Drawings

Key Idea: Attention to detail is vital when making accurate and useful biological drawings.

In this activity, you will practise the skills required to translate what is viewed into a good biological drawing.

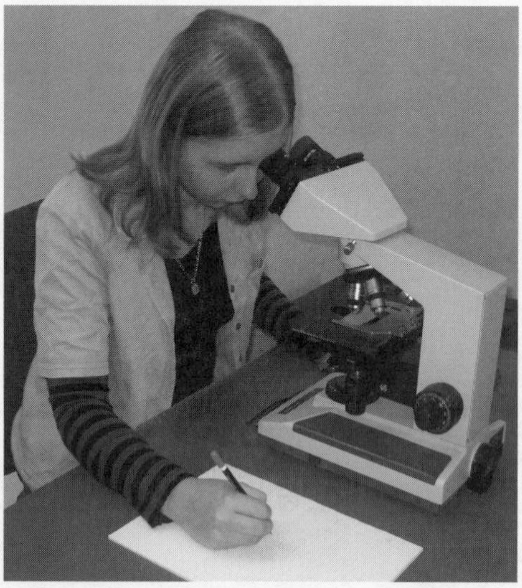

Above: Use relaxed viewing when drawing at the microscope. Use one eye (the left for right handers) to view and the right eye to look at your drawing.

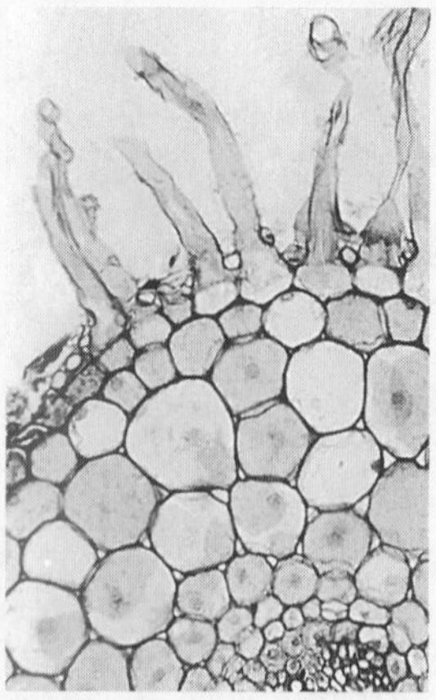

Above: Light micrograph Transverse section (TS) through a *Ranunculus* root.

Right: A biological drawing of the same section.

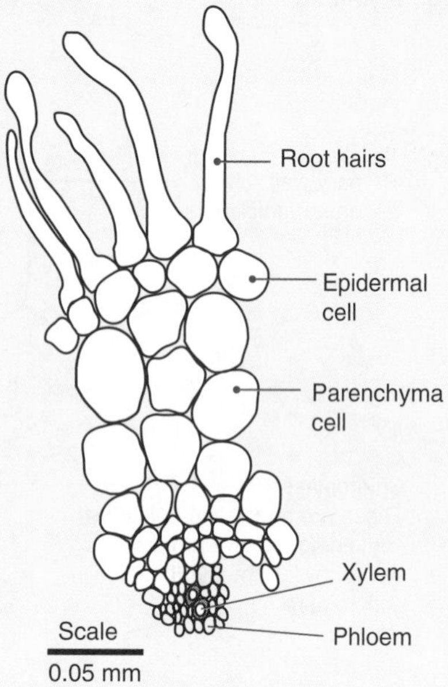
Root hairs
Epidermal cell
Parenchyma cell
Xylem
Phloem
Scale
0.05 mm

TASK

Complete the biological drawing of a cross section through a dicot leaf (below). Use the example above of the *Ranunculus* root as a guide to the detail required in your drawing.

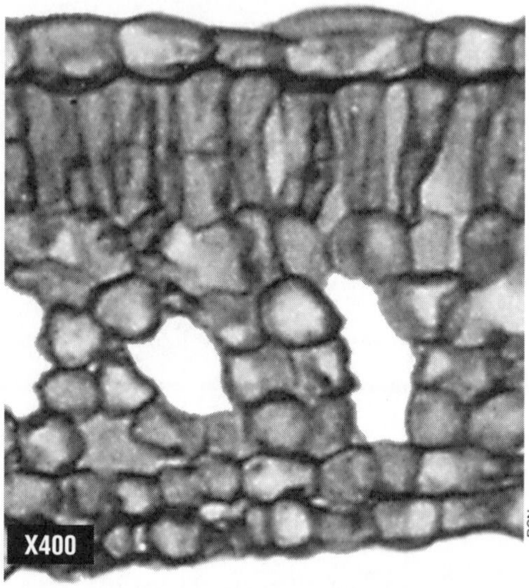
X400
RCN

Light micrograph of a cross section through a leaf.

© 2015 BIOZONE International
ISBN:978-1-927309-31-5
Photocopying Prohibited

24 Investigating Factors Affecting Plant Growth

Key Idea: A fair test is when only one variable is changed and all other variables are kept constant. Conclusions based on results are more likely to be valid when the test is fair.

The experiment below describes a fair test for analysing the effect of urea on duckweed growth. Use this activity to test your knowledge about how to analyse and interpret results.

The aim

To investigate the effect of urea concentration on the growth of duckweed (*Lemna minor*).

Hypothesis

If plants need nitrogen to grow, growth rate of *Lemna* will increase with increasing nitrogen concentration.

Background

Lemna minor (duckweed) is is a small plant commonly found floating in the water of drains and pond edges. It is a small (1-3 mm), free-floating plant with 2-4 leaves held flat against the water's surface and a single root. *Lemna minor* grows very rapidly. In ideal conditions doubling time is as little as 3 days.

Experimental method

Solutions of urea were made up to concentrations of 3×10^{-2}, 3×10^{-3}, 3×10^{-4}, and 3×10^{-5} mol L^{-1}. For each urea concentration, 80 mL of the appropriate solution was pipetted into three separate beakers. Ten duckweed plants, each with one leaf, were placed in each beaker. The beakers were arranged randomly and placed together in direct sunlight. The number of plants in each beaker was counted and recorded eight times over the next three weeks.

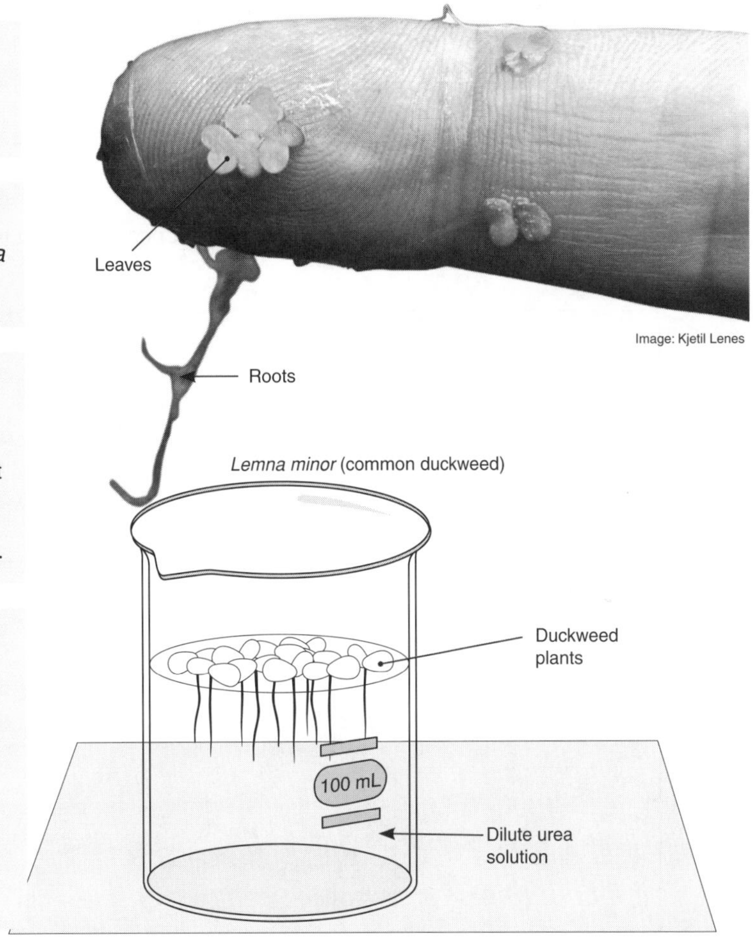
Leaves
Roots
Image: Kjetil Lenes
Lemna minor (common duckweed)
Duckweed plants
100 mL
Dilute urea solution

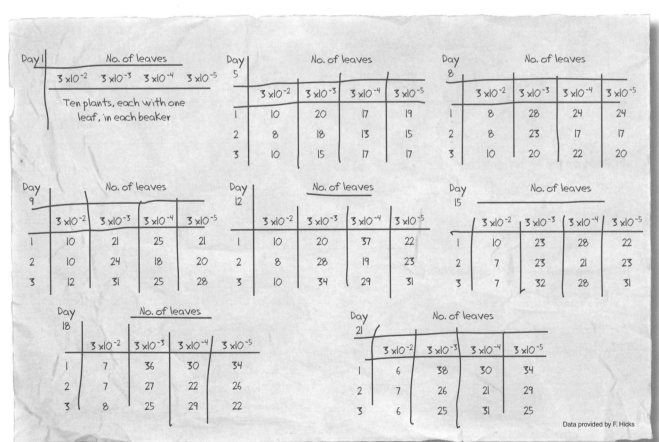

Day 1 — No. of leaves

3×10^{-2}	3×10^{-3}	3×10^{-4}	3×10^{-5}
Ten plants, each with one leaf, in each beaker			

Day 5 — No. of leaves

	3×10^{-2}	3×10^{-3}	3×10^{-4}	3×10^{-5}
1	10	20	17	19
2	8	18	13	15
3	10	15	17	17

Day 8 — No. of leaves

	3×10^{-2}	3×10^{-3}	3×10^{-4}	3×10^{-5}
1	8	28	24	24
2	8	23	17	17
3	10	20	22	20

Day 9 — No. of leaves

	3×10^{-2}	3×10^{-3}	3×10^{-4}	3×10^{-5}
1	10	21	25	21
2	10	24	18	20
3	12	31	25	28

Day 12 — No. of leaves

	3×10^{-2}	3×10^{-3}	3×10^{-4}	3×10^{-5}
1	10	20	37	22
2	8	28	19	23
3	10	34	29	31

Day 15 — No. of leaves

	3×10^{-2}	3×10^{-3}	3×10^{-4}	3×10^{-5}
1	10	23	28	22
2	7	23	21	23
3	7	32	28	31

Day 18 — No. of leaves

	3×10^{-2}	3×10^{-3}	3×10^{-4}	3×10^{-5}
1	7	36	30	34
2	7	27	22	26
3	8	25	29	22

Day 21 — No. of leaves

	3×10^{-2}	3×10^{-3}	3×10^{-4}	3×10^{-5}
1	6	38	30	34
2	7	26	21	29
3	6	25	31	25

Data provided by F. Hicks

© 2015 **BIOZONE** International
ISBN: 978-1-927309-31-5
Photocopying Prohibited

1. Use the raw data on the previous page to complete the table below:

	Mean number of leaves							
Concentration of urea / mol L^{-1}	Day 1	Day 5	Day 8	Day 9	Day 12	Day 15	Day 18	Day 21
3×10^{-2}								
3×10^{-3}								
3×10^{-4}								
3×10^{-5}								

2. Plot the mean number of leaves per day for each concentration on the grid below:

3. (a) What is the sample size for each treatment in this experiment? ______________________

(b) Describe the results: ______________________

(c) Do the results support the hypothesis? ______________________

(d) What relevance might the result have to survival of *Lemna* in different environments? ______________________

© 1988-2013 **BIOZONE** International
ISBN: 978-1-927173-89-3
Photocopying Prohibited

25 Test Your Understanding

Key Idea: Systematic recording and analysis of results can help identify trends and draw conclusions about a biological response in an experiment.

Using the information below, analyse results and draw conclusions about the effect of a nitrogen fertiliser on the growth of radish plants.

Radishes

The aim

To investigate the effect of a nitrogen fertiliser on the growth of radish plants.

Hypothesis

If plants need nitrogen to grow, radish growth will increase with increasing nitrogen concentration.

Background

Inorganic fertilisers revolutionised crop farming when they were introduced during the late 19th and early 20th century. Crop yields soared and today it is estimated around 50% of crop yield is attributable to the use of fertiliser. Nitrogen is a very important element for plant growth and several types of purely nitrogen fertiliser are manufactured to supply it, e.g. urea.

To investigate the effect of nitrogen on plant growth, a group of students set up an experiment using different concentrations of nitrogen fertiliser. Radish seeds were planted into a standard soil mixture and divided into six groups, each with five sample plants (30 plants in total).

Experimental method

This experiment was designed to test the effect of nitrogen fertiliser on plant growth. Radish seeds were planted in separate identical pots (5 cm x 5 cm wide x 10 cm deep) and grown together in normal room temperature (22°C) conditions.

The radishes were watered every day at 10 am and 3 pm with 1.25 L per treatment. Water soluble fertiliser was mixed and added with the first watering on the 1st, 11th and 21st days. The fertiliser concentrations used were: 0.00, 0.06, 0.12, 0.18, 0.24, and 0.30 g dm^{-3} with each treatment receiving a different concentration. The plants were grown for 30 days before being removed, washed, and the root (radish) weighed. Results were tabulated below:

Table 1: Mass (g) of radish plant roots under six different fertiliser concentrations (data given to 1 dp).

Fertiliser concentration / g dm^{-3}	Mass of radish root / g† Sample / n: 1	2	3	4	5	Total mass	Mean mass
0	80.1	83.2	82.0	79.1	84.1	408.5	81.7
0.06	109.2	110.3	108.2	107.9	110.7		
0.12	117.9	118.9	118.3	119.1	117.2		
0.18	128.3	127.3	127.7	126.8	DNG*		
0.24	23.6	140.3	139.6	137.9	141.1		
0.30	122.3	121.1	122.6	121.3	123.1		

† Based on data from M S Jilani, *et al* Journal Agricultural Research

* DNG: Did not germinate

1. Identify the independent variable for the experiment and its range: ______________________________

____

2. What is the sample size for each concentration of fertiliser? ______________________________

© 2015 BIOZONE International
ISBN: 978-1-927309-31-5
Photocopying Prohibited

3. (a) Identify the control fertiliser concentration: ______________________

(b) What is the purpose of the control? ______________________

____

____

4. One of the radishes recorded in Table 1 did not grow as expected and produced an extreme value. Record the **outlying value** here and decide whether or not you should include it in future calculations:

____

____

____

5. Complete the table on the previous page by calculating the **total mass** and **mean mass** of the radish roots:

6. Use the grid below to draw a **line graph** of the experimental results. Use your calculated means and remember to include a title and correctly labelled axes.

7. The students recorded the wet mass of the root (the root still containing water) in their table. What mass should they have actually recorded to get a better representation of the effect of the fertiliser on root mass?

____

____

____

8. Why would measuring just root mass not be a totally accurate way of measuring the effect of fertiliser on radish growth?

____

____

© 2015 **BIOZONE** International
ISBN:978-1-927309-31-5
Photocopying Prohibited

9. Describe some other measurements the students could have taken to make their experiment more complete:

____

____

10. Complete Table 2 by calculating the mean, median and mode for each concentration of fertiliser:

The students decided to further their experiment by recording the number of leaves on each radish plant:

Table 2: Number of leaves on radish plant under six different fertiliser concentrations.

	Number of leaves							
Fertiliser concentration / g dm^{-3}	**Sample / *n***					**Mean**	**Median**	**Mode**
	1	**2**	**3**	**4**	**5**			
0	9	9	10	8	7			
0.06	15	16	15	16	16			
0.12	16	17	17	17	16			
0.18	18	18	19	18	DNG*			
0.24	6	19	19	18	18			
0.30	18	17	18	19	19			

* DNG: Did not germinate

11. (a) Identify the outlier in the table above: ______________________

(b) Recalculate the mean if the outlier was included: ______________________

12. Which concentration of fertiliser appeared to produce the best growth results? ______________________

13. Describe some sources of error for the experiment: ______________________

____

____

____

14. Write a conclusion for the experiment with reference to the aim, hypothesis, and results: ______________________

____

____

____

____

15. The students decided to replicate the experiment (carry it out again). How might this improve the experiment's results?

____

____

____

© 2015 **BIOZONE** International
ISBN: 978-1-927309-31-5
Photocopying Prohibited

26 KEY TERMS AND IDEAS: Did You Get It?

1. For the graph (right) use the equation $y = mx + c$ to answer the following questions:

   (a) What is the value of c?: ______________________

   (b) Using the two reference points marked on the graph, calculate m: ______________

   (c) Describe the slope and the relationship between the variables: ______________

   ____

   (d) What is the value of y when x=5? ______________________

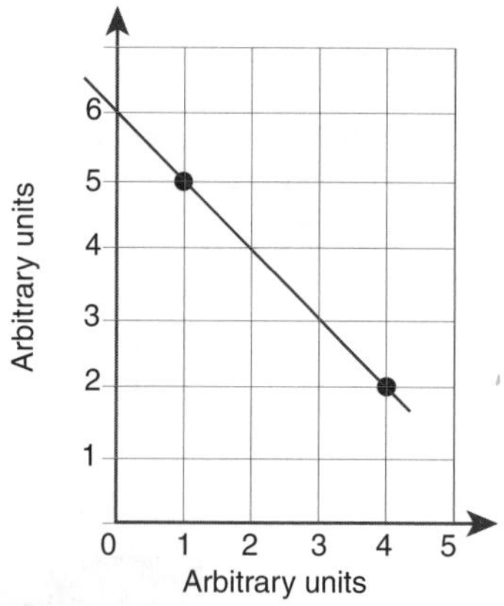

6
5
4
3
2
1
0
1
2
3
4
5
Arbitrary units
Arbitrary units

2. A balance has a calibration error of +0.04 g. A student weighs out 11.71 g of sodium hydroxide. Calculate the percentage error (show your working):

   ____

   ____

3. The table (below right) shows the rate of sweat production in an athlete on a stationary cycle. Complete the table to:

   (a) Convert the cumulative sweat loss to cm^3:

   (b) Determine the rate of sweat loss ($cm^3 min^{-1}$):

   (c) Plot a double axis graph on the grid below to show cumulative sweat loss in cm^3 and rate of sweat loss against time.

   (d) Describe how the rate of sweat loss changes over time:

   ____

   ____

   ____

Time / minutes	Cumulative sweat loss / mm^3	Cumulative sweat loss / cm^3	Rate of sweat loss / $cm^3 min^{-1}$
0	0		
10	50 000		
20	130 000		
30	220 000		
60	560 000		

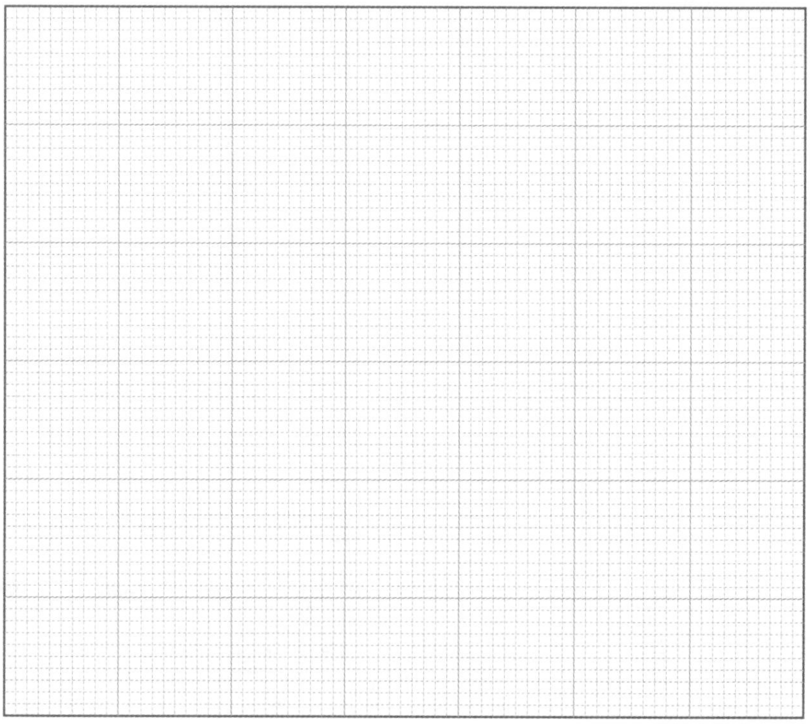

TEST

© 2015 BIOZONE International
ISBN:978-1-927309-31-5
Photocopying Prohibited

Topic 1 Cell structure

Key terms

ATP
cell wall
centrioles
chloroplast
cilia
cytoplasm
cytoskeleton
electron micrograph
endoplasmic reticulum (ER)
eukaryotic cell
eyepiece graticule
flagella
Golgi apparatus
laser scanning confocal microscope
light (=optical) microscope
lysosome
magnification
mitochondrion
nuclear envelope
nucleolus
nucleus
organelle
plasma membrane
prokaryotic cell
resolution
ribosome
rough ER (rER)
scanning electron microscope
smooth ER (sER)
stage micrometer
stain
tonoplast
transmission electron microscope
vacuole

1.1 The microscope in cell studies

Learning outcomes

	Learning outcome	Activity number
☐	1 Appreciate that microscopy has a long history and was fundamental to our understanding of cells and the development of the cell theory.	27 34
☐	2 Outline the principles of light and electron microscopy. Recognise and account for differences between the images produced by light microscopes, transmission electron microscopes, and scanning electron microscopes.	27 28 31
☐	3 Compare the structure of typical animal and plant cells using temporary preparations of live material as well as light and electron photomicrographs.	36-39
☐	4 Calculate the linear magnification of drawings, photomicrographs, and electron micrographs by using the formula: magnification = image size ÷ object size.	33
☐	5 **PRAC** Prepare and examine microscope slides for viewing with a light microscope at high and low power. Demonstrate use of an eyepiece graticule and stage micrometer to calculate the size of specimens.	29 30 32
☐	6 Demonstrate familiarity with the use of different units (mm, μm, nm) used in cell studies and be able to convert between them.	35
☐	7 Distinguish between magnification and resolution. Compare the magnification and resolution achieved using light and electron microscopes.	28 31
☐	8 Calculate actual sizes of specimens from drawings, photomicrographs, and electron micrographs.	33

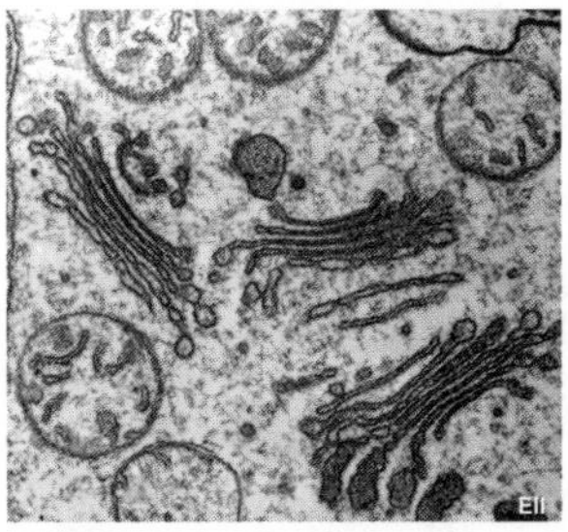

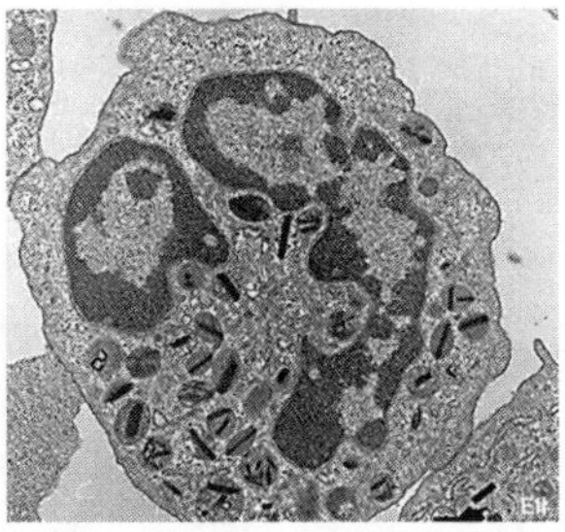

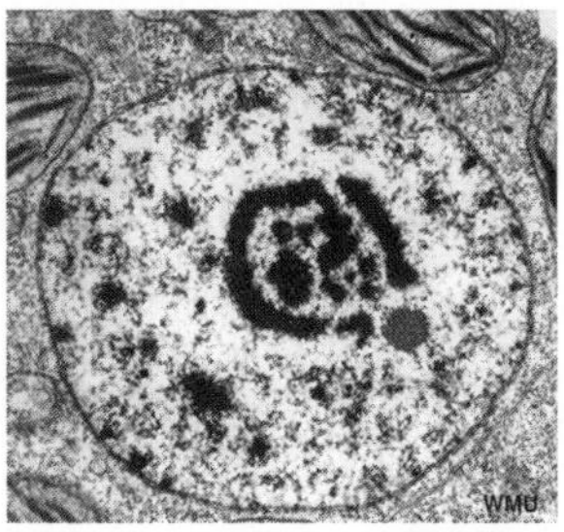

1.2 Cells as the basic units of living organisms

Learning outcomes

	Learning outcome	Activity number
☐	9 Understand that the cell is the basic unit of life and that the structures within cells interact to enable them to function in their environments.	34
☐	10 Describe and interpret electron micrographs and drawings of typical plant and animal cells as seen with an electron microscope.	37 39 42
☐	11 Recognise the following cell structures and outline their functions: cell surface (plasma) membrane, nucleus, nucleolus, nuclear envelope, rough and smooth endoplasmic reticulum, Golgi apparatus, ribosomes (80S and 70S), mitochondria, lysosomes, chloroplasts, centrioles and microtubules, plasmodesmata, cell wall, vacuole and tonoplast of plant cells.	36-41
☐	12 Recognise the relationships between organelles as related to their functions, e.g. the rough ER and Golgi in the production and secretion of proteins.	43
☐	13 Outline the role ATP in cells and state where it is produced in the cell.	44
☐	14 Describe the structure of a typical prokaryotic cell, including size, lack of membrane-bound organelles, cell wall, naked circular DNA, and 70S ribosomes.	45
☐	15 Compare and contrast the structure of prokaryotic and eukaryotic cells.	46
☐	16 Outline the key features of viruses as non-cellular structures to include the nature of the protein coat and the genetic material.	47

27 History of Microscopy

Key Idea: Microscopes are used to view objects that cannot be viewed in detail with the naked eye. Microscopes have become increasingly sophisticated over time with improvements in both magnification and resolution.

Lenses of various descriptions have been used for around 4000 years to view objects, but it is only in the last few hundred years that techniques have developed to build sophisticated devices for viewing microscopic objects. Early microscopes suffered from image distortion such as chromatic aberration (the production of images with the light split into the different colours). The development of more sophisticated techniques in lens and microscope production reduced this problem. The development of electron microscopes has made it possible to image objects to the atomic level.

Milestones in microscopy

1500 Convex lenses with a magnification greater than x5 became available.

1595 **Zacharias Janssen** of Holland has been credited with the first compound microscope (more than one lens).

1662 **Robert Hooke** of England used the term 'cell' in describing the microscopic structure of cork.

1675 **Antoni van Leeuwenhoek** of Holland produced over 500 single lens microscopes that had a magnification of 270 times.

1800s The discovery that lenses combining two types of glass reduced chromatic aberration (the production of images with the light split into the different colours) allows clear images to be viewed.

1830 **Joseph Jackson Lister** demonstrated that spherical aberration (the focussing of light rays at different points due to the curve of the lens) could be reduced by using different lenses at precise distances from each other.

1878 **Ernst Abbe** produced a formula for correlating resolution to the wavelength of light, and so describes the maximum resolution of a light microscope.

1903 **Richard Zsigmondy** developed the ultramicroscope allowing objects smaller than the wavelength of light to be viewed.

1932 **Frits Zernike** invented the phase-contrast microscope making transparent or colourless objects easier to view.

1938 **Ernst Ruska** developed the transmission electron microscope (TEM). Electrons pass through an object and are focused by magnets. The short wavelength of electrons allows study of incredibly small objects. **Manfred von Ardenne** developed the scanning electron microscope (SEM) around the same time allowing the surface of objects to be imaged.

1957-80 **Marvin Minsky** patented the principle of the confocal laser scanning microscope (CLSM) but it takes 30 years for development.

1981 **Gerd Binning** and **Heinrich Rohrer** invented the scanning tunneling electron microscope (STM), producing three dimensional images at the atomic level.

1595

The first compound microscope (the Janssen microscope, right) consisted of three draw tubes with lenses inserted into the tubes. The microscope was focussed by sliding the draw tube in or out.

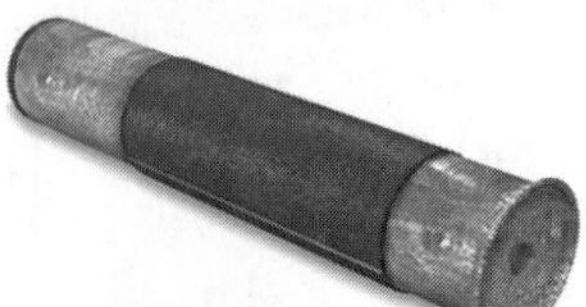

1675

A Leeuwenhoek microscope c. 1673 (right) was only a glorified magnifying glass by today's standards.

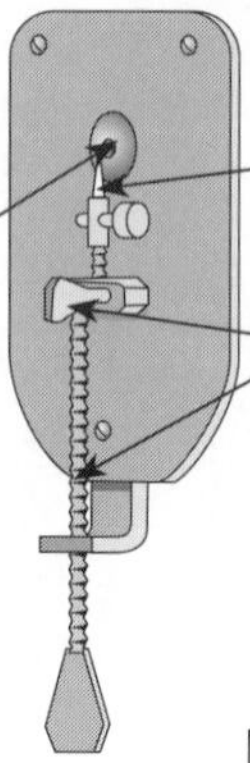
Single lens.
Pointed spike which is the specimen holder.
Screw threads adjusted the position of the specimen (up, down, and focus)

1800s

Chromatic aberration. Blue light refracts more than red light producing different focal points.

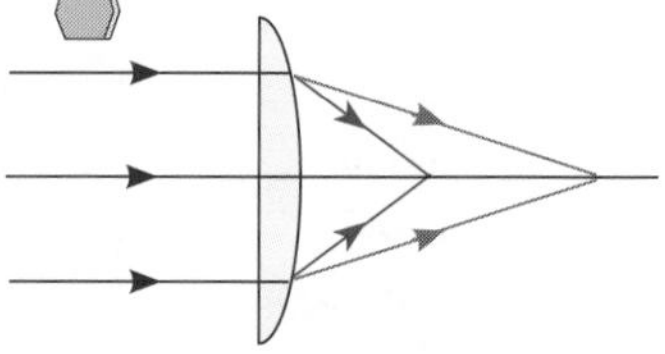

1830

Spherical aberration. Light entering at the edge of the lens focuses closer to the lens than light entering near the centre of the lens.

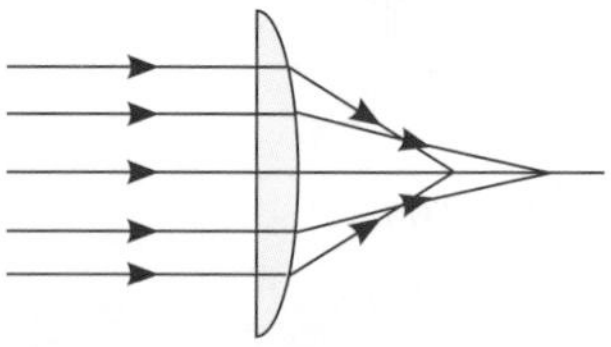

1932

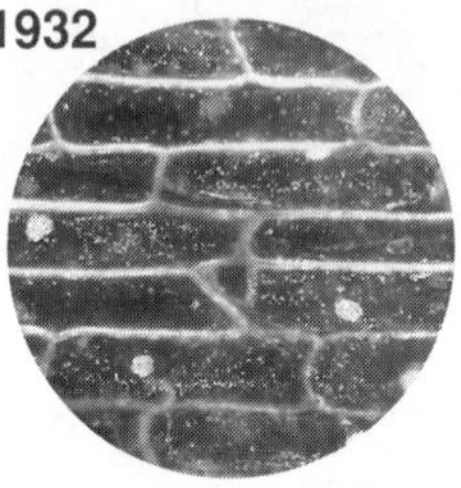

Onion cells viewed by phase contrast.

1938

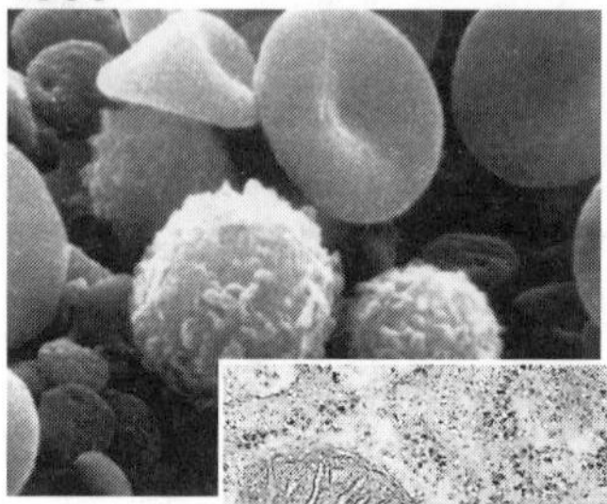

SEM of blood cells

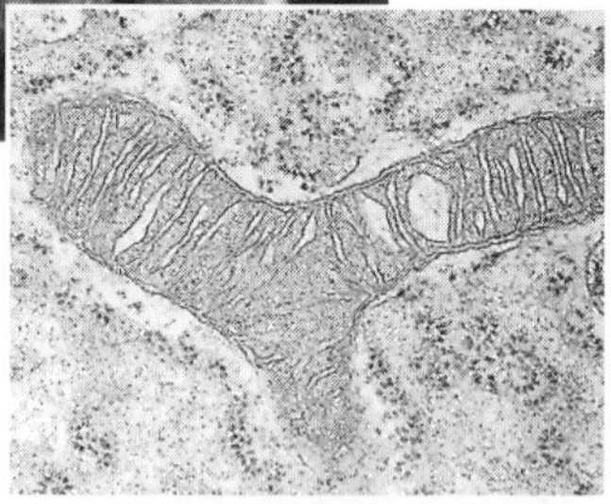

TEM of mitochondrion

1957- 80

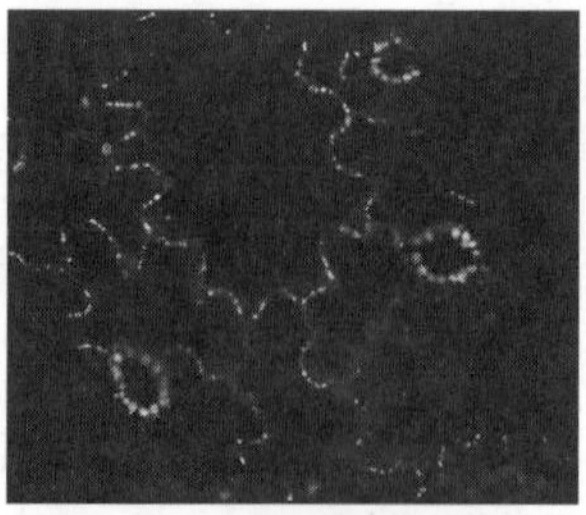

Image: Synapomorphy

CLSM image of proteins in the tobacco mosaic virus. Specimens for viewing with a CLSM are often treated with fluorescent dyes and it is possible to produce optical sections through thick samples of living tissue.

1981

Image: Erwinossen public domain

Gold atoms imaged with an STM

REFER WEB 27 LINK 28 LINK 31

© 2015 BIOZONE International
ISBN:978-1-927309-31-5
Photocopying Prohibited

28 Optical Microscopes

Key Idea: Optical microscopes use light focussed through a series of lenses to magnify objects up to several 100 times.

The light (or optical) microscope is an important tool in biology and using it correctly is an essential skill. High power compound light microscopes use visible light and a combination of lenses to magnify objects up to several 100 times. The resolution of light microscopes is limited by the wavelength of light and specimens must be thin and mostly transparent so that light can pass through. No detail will be seen in specimens that are thick or opaque.

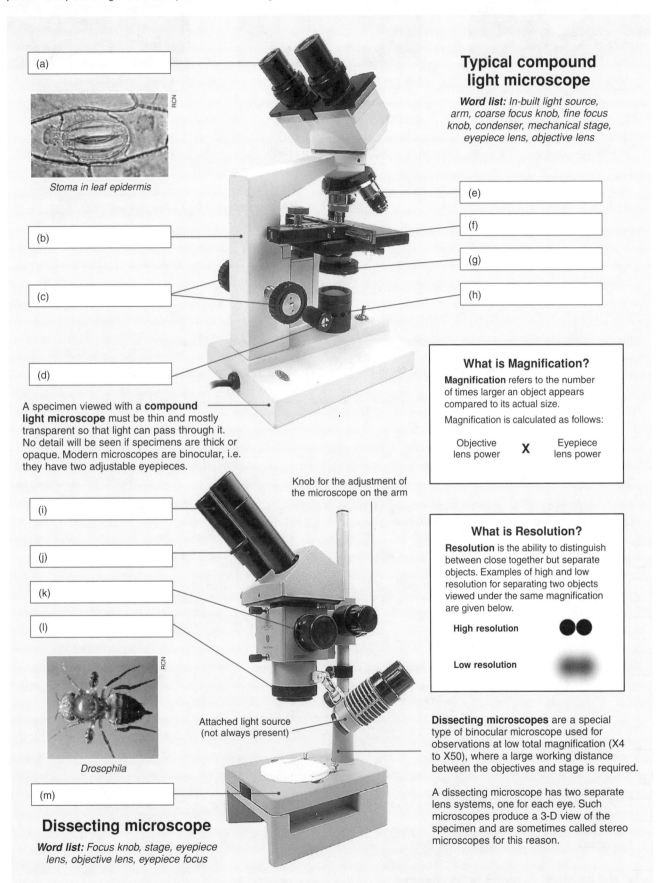

Typical compound light microscope

Word list: *In-built light source, arm, coarse focus knob, fine focus knob, condenser, mechanical stage, eyepiece lens, objective lens*

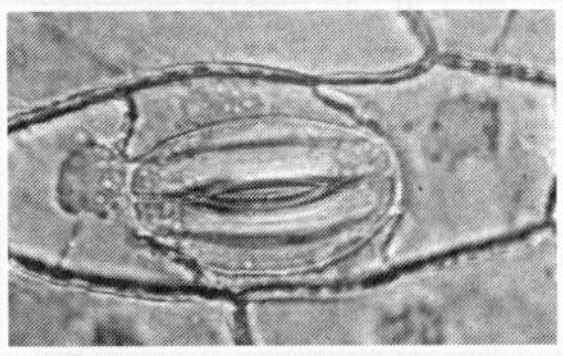
RCN

Stoma in leaf epidermis

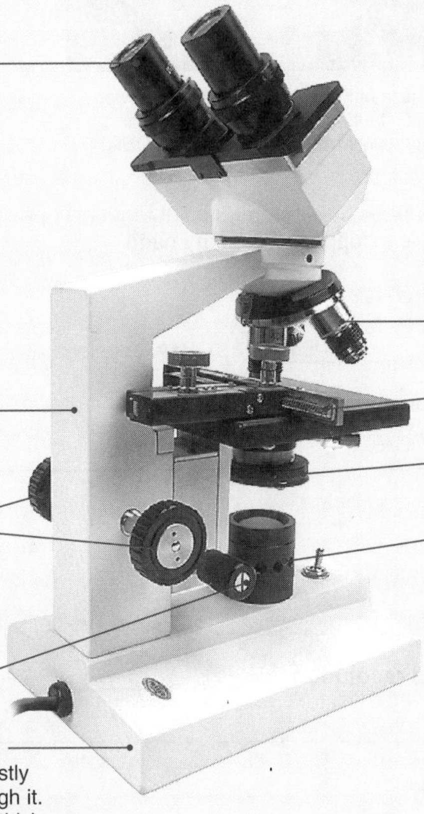
(a)
(b)
(c)
(d)
(e)
(f)
(g)
(h)

A specimen viewed with a **compound light microscope** must be thin and mostly transparent so that light can pass through it. No detail will be seen if specimens are thick or opaque. Modern microscopes are binocular, i.e. they have two adjustable eyepieces.

What is Magnification?

Magnification refers to the number of times larger an object appears compared to its actual size.

Magnification is calculated as follows:

Objective lens power **X** Eyepiece lens power

What is Resolution?

Resolution is the ability to distinguish between close together but separate objects. Examples of high and low resolution for separating two objects viewed under the same magnification are given below.

High resolution

Low resolution

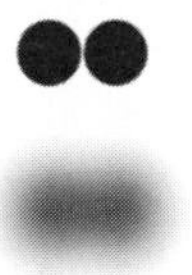

Dissecting microscope

Word list: *Focus knob, stage, eyepiece lens, objective lens, eyepiece focus*

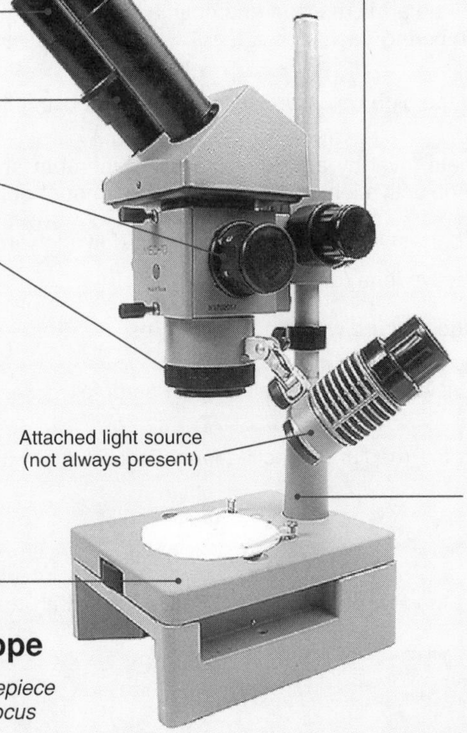
(i)
(j)
(k)
(l)
(m)
Knob for the adjustment of the microscope on the arm
Attached light source (not always present)

RCN

Drosophila

Dissecting microscopes are a special type of binocular microscope used for observations at low total magnification (X4 to X50), where a large working distance between the objectives and stage is required.

A dissecting microscope has two separate lens systems, one for each eye. Such microscopes produce a 3-D view of the specimen and are sometimes called stereo microscopes for this reason.

© 2015 **BIOZONE** International
ISBN: 978-1-927309-31-5
Photocopying Prohibited

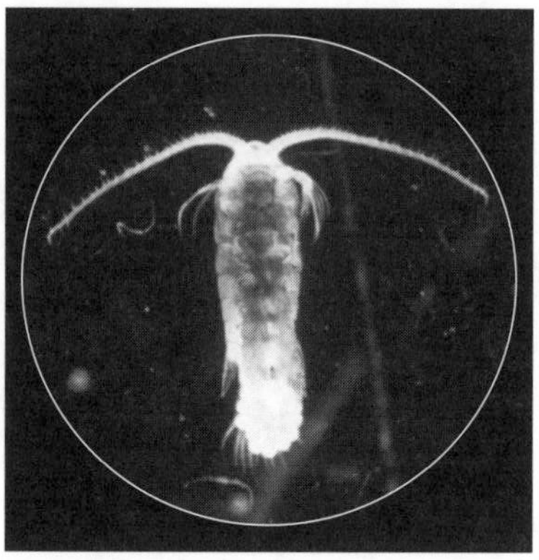
JDG

Dissecting microscopes are used for identifying and sorting organisms, observing microbial cultures, and dissections.

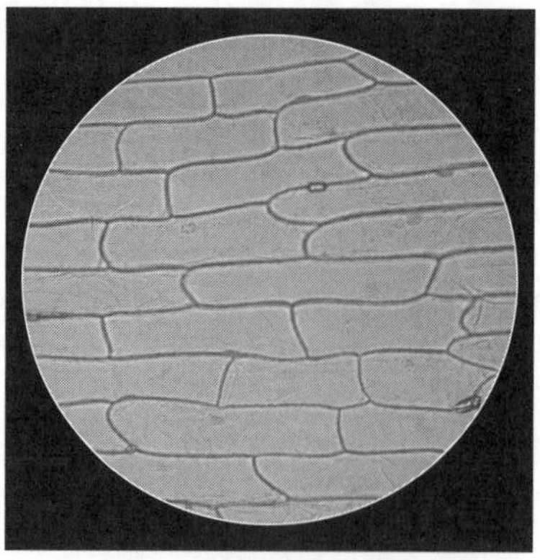

These onion epidermal cells are viewed with standard **bright field** lighting. Very little detail can be seen (only cell walls) and the cell nuclei are barely visible.

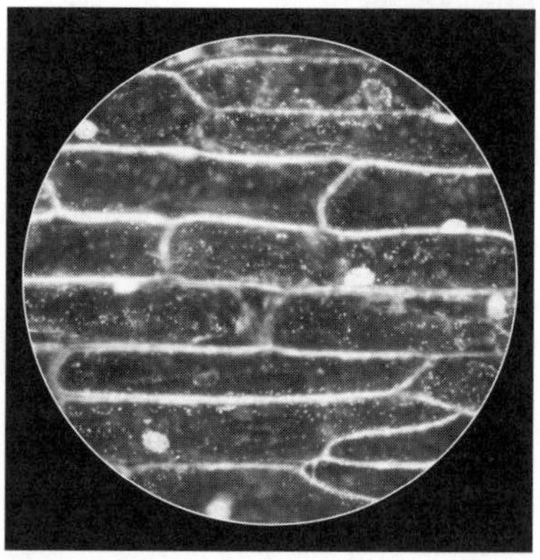
Photos: Ell

Dark field illumination is excellent for viewing specimens that are almost transparent. The nuclei of these onion epidermal cells are clearly visible.

1. Label the two photographs on the previous page, the compound light microscope (a) to (h) and the dissecting microscope (i) to (m). Use words from the lists supplied for each image.

2. Determine the magnification of a microscope using:

   (a) 15 X eyepiece and 40 X objective lens: __________ (b) 10 X eyepiece and 60 X objective lens: __________

3. Describe the main difference between a compound light microscope and a dissecting microscope: __________

4. What type of microscope would you use to:

   (a) Count stream invertebrates in a sample: __________ (b) Observe cells in mitosis: __________

5. (a) Distinguish between **magnification** and **resolution**: __________

   (b) Explain the benefits of a higher resolution: __________

6. Below is a list of ten key steps taken to set up a microscope and optimally view a sample. The steps have been mixed up. Put them in their **correct order** by numbering each step:

☐ Focus and centre the specimen using the high objective lens. Adjust focus using the fine focus knob only.

☐ Adjust the illumination to an appropriate level by adjusting the iris diaphragm and the condenser. The light should appear on the slide directly below the objective lens, and give an even amount of illumination.

☐ Rotate the objective lenses until the shortest lens is in place (pointing down towards the stage).
This is the lowest / highest power objective lens (delete one).

☐ Place the slide on the microscope stage. Secure with the sample clips.

☐ Fine tune the illumination so you can view maximum detail on your sample.

☐ Focus and centre the specimen using the medium objective lens. Focus firstly with the coarse focus knob, then with the fine focus knob (if needed).

☐ Turn on the light source.

☐ Focus and centre the specimen using the low objective lens. Focus firstly with the coarse focus knob, then with the fine focus knob.

☐ Focus the eyepieces to adjust your view.

☐ Adjust the distance between the eyepieces so that they are comfortable for your eyes.

© 2015 **BIOZONE** International
ISBN:978-1-927309-31-5
Photocopying Prohibited

29 Preparing a Slide

Key Idea: Correctly preparing and mounting a specimen on a slide is important if structures are to be seen clearly under a microscope. A wet mount is suitable for most slides.

Specimens are often prepared in some way before viewing in order to highlight features and reveal details. A wet mount is a temporary preparation in which a specimen and a drop of fluid are trapped under a thin coverslip. Wet mounts are used to view thin tissue sections, live microscopic organisms, and suspensions such as blood. A wet mount improves a sample's appearance and enhances visible detail. Sections must be made very thin for two main reasons. A thick section stops light shining through making it appear dark when viewed. It also ends up with too many layers of cells, making it difficult to make out detail.

Preparing a specimen

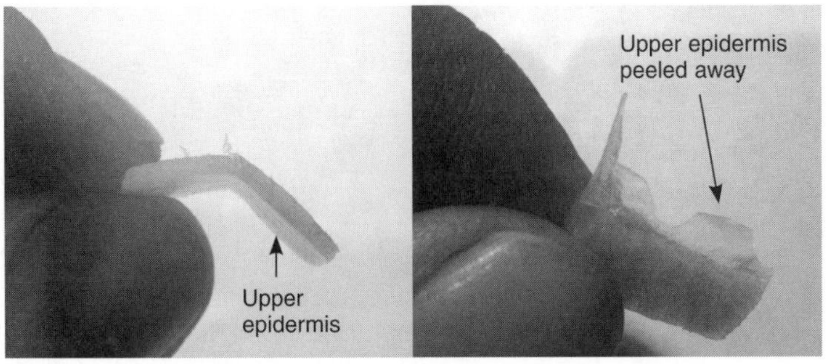
Upper epidermis
Upper epidermis peeled away
KP

Onions make good subjects for preparing a simple wet mount. A square segment is cut from a thick leaf from the bulb. The segment is then bent towards the upper epidermis and snapped so that just the epidermis is left attached. The epidermis can then be peeled off to provide a thin layer of cells for viewing.

KP

Sections through stems or other soft objects need to be made with a razor blade or scalpel, and must be very thin. Cutting at a slight angle to produce a wedge shape creates a thin edge. Ideally specimens should be set in wax first, to prevent crushing and make it easier to cut the specimen accurately.

Mounting a specimen

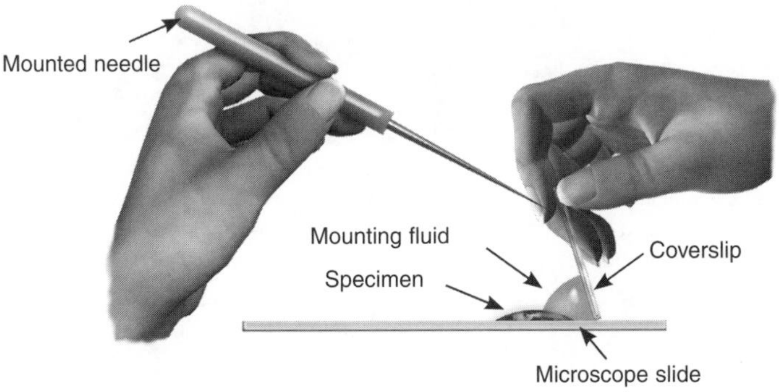
Mounted needle
Mounting fluid
Specimen
Coverslip
Microscope slide

Mounting: The thin layer is placed in the centre of a clean glass microscope slide and covered with a drop of mounting liquid (e.g. water, glycerol, or stain). A coverslip is placed on top using a mounted needle to support and lower it gently over the specimen. This avoids including air in the mount.

Viewing

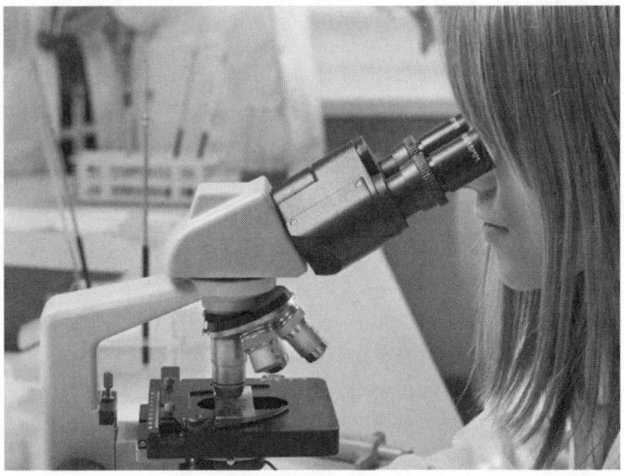

Locate the specimen or region of interest at the lowest magnification. Focus using the lowest magnification first, before switching to the higher magnifications.

1. Why must sections viewed under a microscope be very thin? ______________________

2. What is the purpose of the coverslip? ______________________

3. Why would no chloroplasts be visible in an onion epidermis cell slide? ______________________

4. Why is it necessary to focus on the lowest magnification first, before switching to higher magnifications? ______________________

© 2015 **BIOZONE** International
ISBN: 978-1-927309-31-5
Photocopying Prohibited

30 Staining a Slide

Key Idea: Staining material to be viewed under a microscope can make it easier to distinguish particular cell structures.

Stains and dyes can be used to highlight specific components or structures. Most stains are **non-viable**, and are used on dead specimens, but harmless viable stains can be applied to living material. Stains contain chemicals that interact with molecules in the cell. Some stains bind to a particular molecule making it easier to see where those molecules are. Others cause a change in a target molecule, which changes their colour, making them more visible.

Some commonly used stains

Stain	Final colour	Used for
Iodine solution	blue-black	Starch
Crystal violet	purple	Gram staining
Aniline sulfate	yellow	lignin
Methylene blue	blue	Nuclei
Hematoxylin and eosin (H&E)	H=dark blue/violet E=red/pink	H=Nuclei E=Proteins

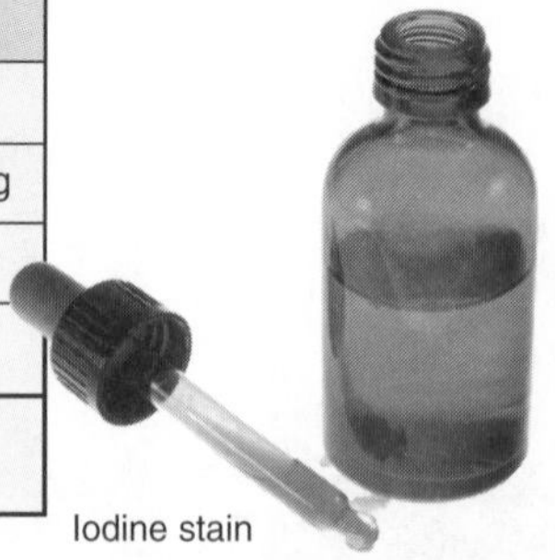
Iodine stain

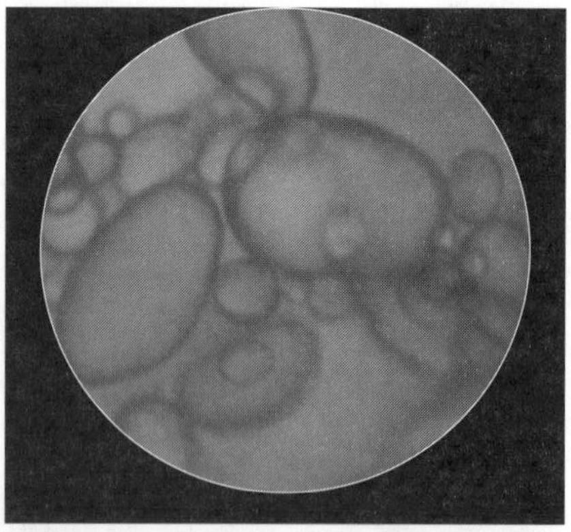
Iodine stains starch-containing organelles, such as **potato amyloplasts**, blue-black.

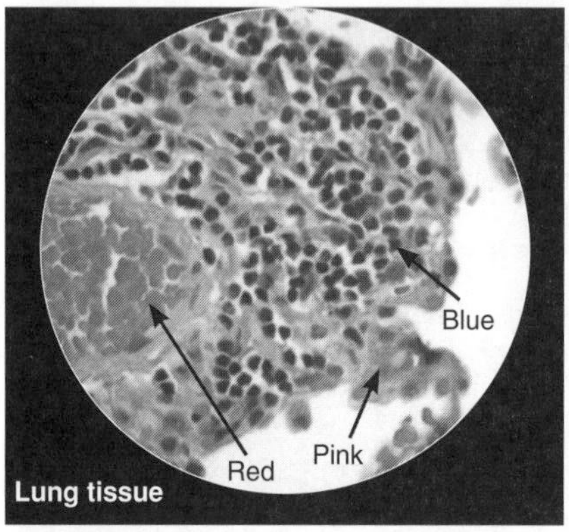
Blue
Red
Pink
Lung tissue
PloS
H&E stain is one of the most common histological stains. Nuclei stain dark blue, whereas proteins, extracellular material, and red blood cells stain pink or red.

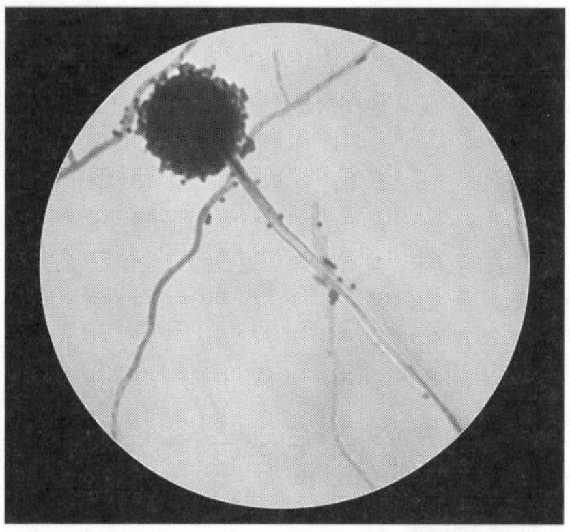
CDC: Dr Lucille K. Georg
Viable (or vital) **stains** do not immediately harm living cells. **Trypan blue** is a vital stain that stains dead cells blue but is excluded by live cells. It is also used to study fungal hyphae.

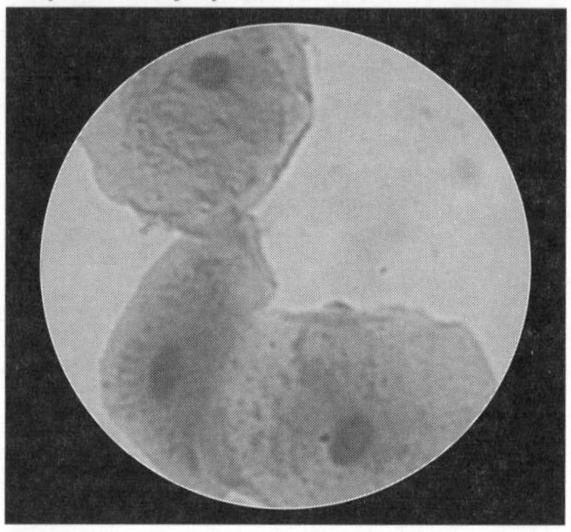
Methylene blue is a common temporary stain for animal cells, such as these **cheek cells**. It stains DNA and so makes the **nuclei** more visible. It is distinct from methyl blue, a histological stain.

How to apply a simple stain

If a specimen is already mounted, a drop of stain can be placed at one end of the coverslip and drawn through using filter paper (below). Water can be drawn through in the same way to remove excess stain.

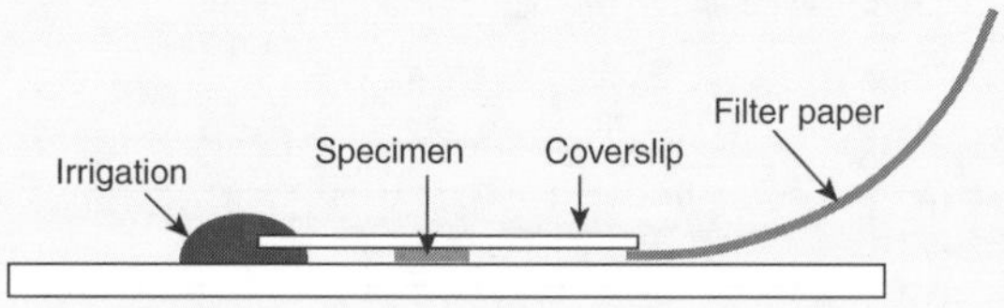
Irrigation
Specimen
Coverslip
Filter paper

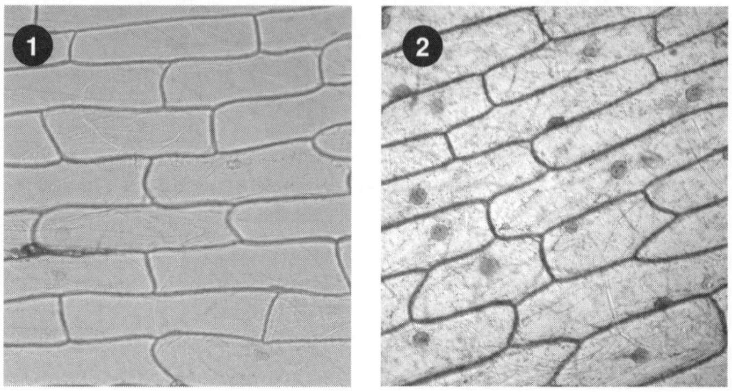
1
2
The light micrographs 1 and 2 (above) illustrate how the use of a stain can enhance certain structures. The left image (1) is unstained and only the cell wall is easily visible. Adding iodine (2) makes the cell wall and nuclei stand out.

1. What is the main purpose of using a stain? ______________________________

____

2. What is the difference between a viable and non-viable stain? ______________________________

____

3. Identify a stain that would be appropriate for distinguishing each of the following:

(a) Live vs dead cells: ____________ (c) Lignin in a plant root section: ____________

(b) Red blood cells in a tissue preparation: ____________ (d) Nuclei in cheek cells: ____________

© 2015 BIOZONE International
ISBN:978-1-927309-31-5
Photocopying Prohibited

31 Electron Microscopes

Key Idea: Electron microscopes use the short wavelengths of electrons to produce high resolution images of extremely small objects.

Electron microscopes (EMs) use a beam of electrons, instead of light, to produce an image. The higher resolution of EMs is due to the shorter wavelengths of electrons. There are two basic types of electron microscope: **scanning electron microscopes** (SEM) and **transmission electron microscopes** (TEM). In SEMs, the electrons are bounced off the surface of an object to produce detailed images of the external appearance. TEMs produce very clear images of specially prepared thin sections.

Transmission electron microscope (TEM)

CDC

The transmission electron microscope is used to view extremely thin sections of material. Electrons pass through the specimen and are scattered. Magnetic lenses focus the image onto a fluorescent screen or photographic plate. The sections are so thin that they have to be prepared with a special machine, called an ultramicrotome, which can cut wafers to just 30 thousandths of a millimetre thick. It can magnify several hundred thousand times.

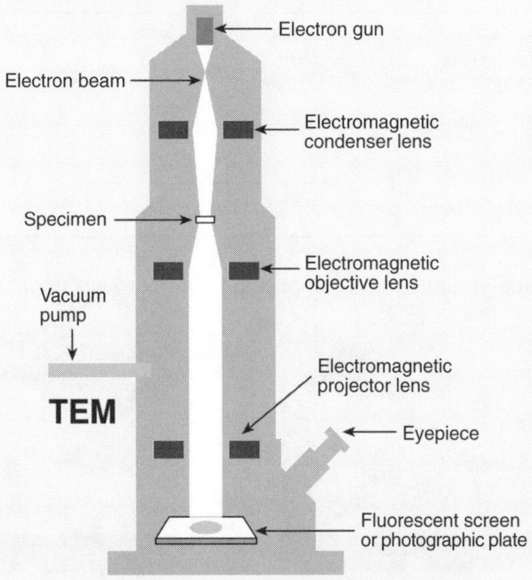
Electron gun
Electron beam
Electromagnetic condenser lens
Specimen
Electromagnetic objective lens
Vacuum pump
Electromagnetic projector lens
TEM
Eyepiece
Fluorescent screen or photographic plate

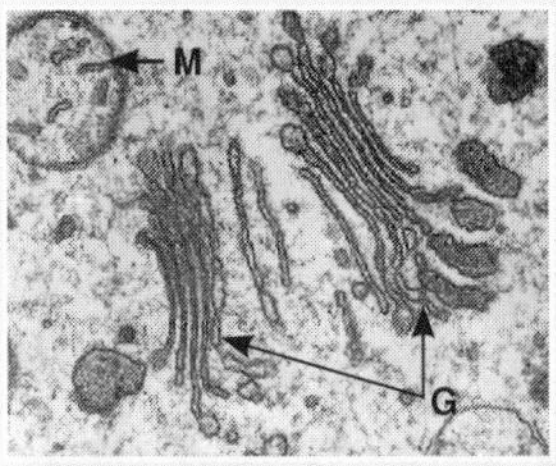
M
G
WMU

TEM photo showing the Golgi (**G**) and a mitochondrion (**M**).

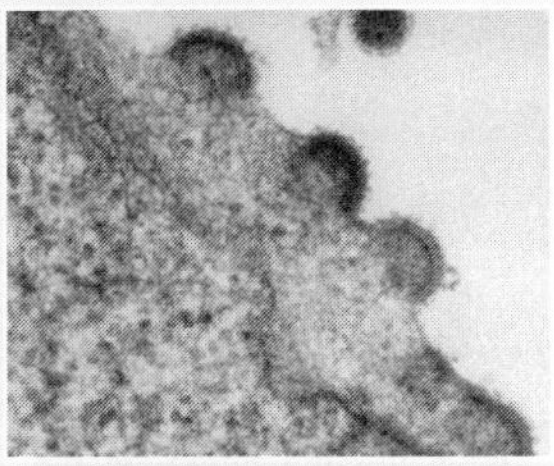
EII

Three HIV viruses budding out of a human lymphocyte (TEM).

Scanning electron microscope (SEM)

Olaboy

The scanning electron microscope scans a sample with a beam of primary electrons, which knocks electrons from the sample's surface. These secondary electrons are picked up by a collector, amplified, and transmitted onto a viewing screen or photographic plate, producing a 3-D image. A microscope of this power easily obtains clear images of very small organisms such as bacteria, and small particles such as viruses. The image produced is of the outside surface only.

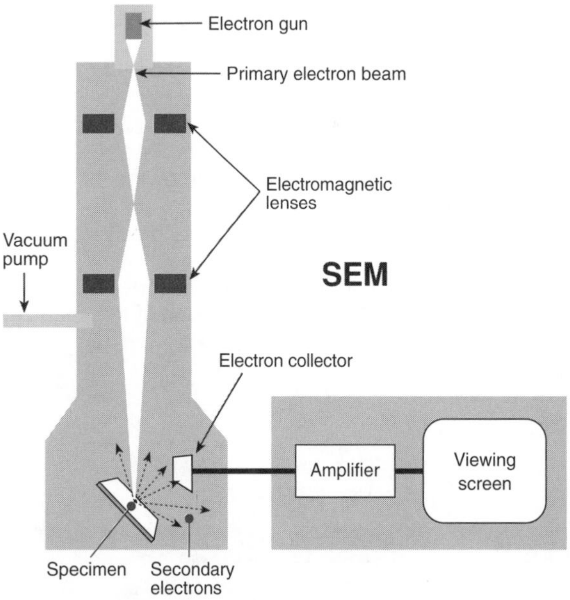
Electron gun
Primary electron beam
Electromagnetic lenses
Vacuum pump
SEM
Electron collector
Amplifier
Viewing screen
Specimen
Secondary electrons

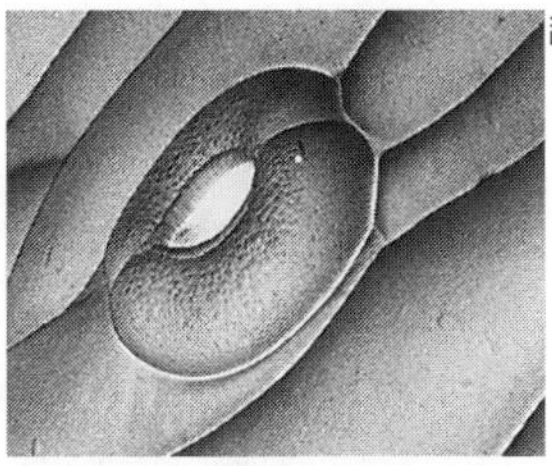
EII

SEM photo of stoma and epidermal cells on the upper surface of a leaf.

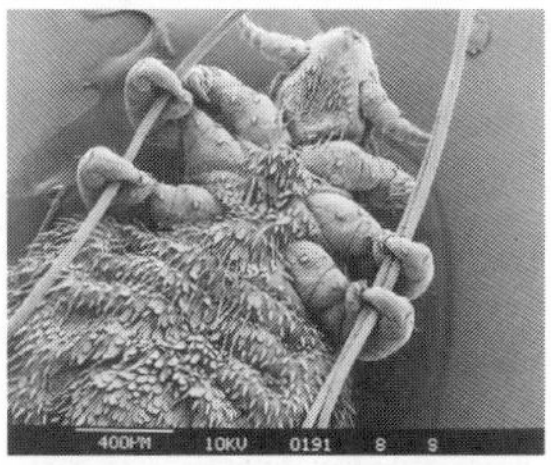
GW

Image of hair louse clinging to two hairs on a Hooker's sealion (SEM).

© 2015 BIOZONE International
ISBN: 978-1-927309-31-5
Photocopying Prohibited

	Light microscope	Transmission electron microscope (TEM)	Scanning electron microscope (SEM)
Radiation source:	light	electrons	electrons
Wavelength:	400-700 nm	0.005 nm	0.005 nm
Lenses:	glass	electromagnetic	electromagnetic
Specimen:	living or non-living supported on glass slide	non-living supported on a small copper grid in a vacuum	non-living supported on a metal disc in a vacuum
Maximum resolution:	200 nm	1 nm	10 nm
Maximum magnification:	1500 x	250 000 x	100 000 x
Stains:	coloured dyes	impregnated with heavy metals	coated with carbon or gold
Type of image:	coloured, surface or section	monochrome, section	monochrome, surface only

1. Explain why electron microscopes are able to resolve much greater detail than a light microscope:

2. Which type of microscope [TEM, SEM, compound light microscope, or dissecting microscope] would you use for each of the following scenarios. Explain your choice in each case:

   (a) Distinguishing extinct plant species on the basis of pollen surface features:

   (b) Resolving the ultrastructure of a chloroplast:

   (c) Performing a count of white blood cells from the blood of a person with an infection:

   (d) Counting the heart rate and rate of limb beating in a water flea (*Daphnia*):

3. Identify which type of electron microscope (SEM or TEM) or optical microscope (compound light microscope or dissecting) was used to produce each of the images in the photos below (A-H):

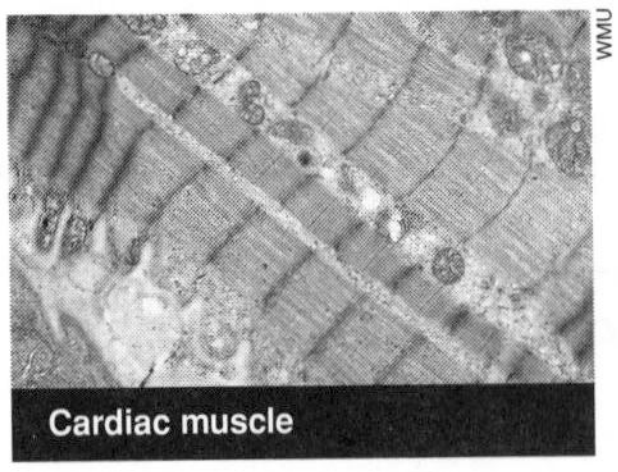
Cardiac muscle

A

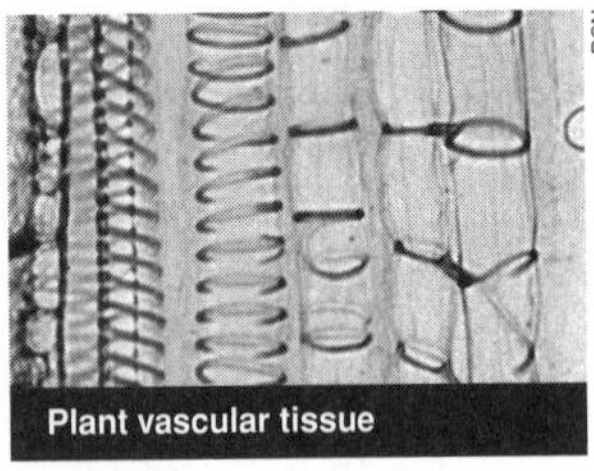
Plant vascular tissue

B

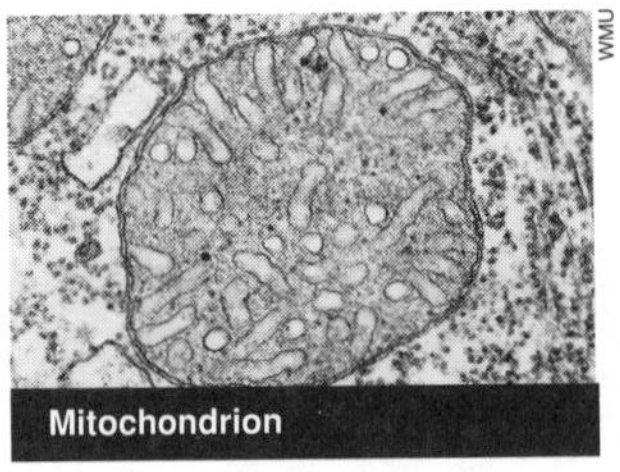
Mitochondrion

C

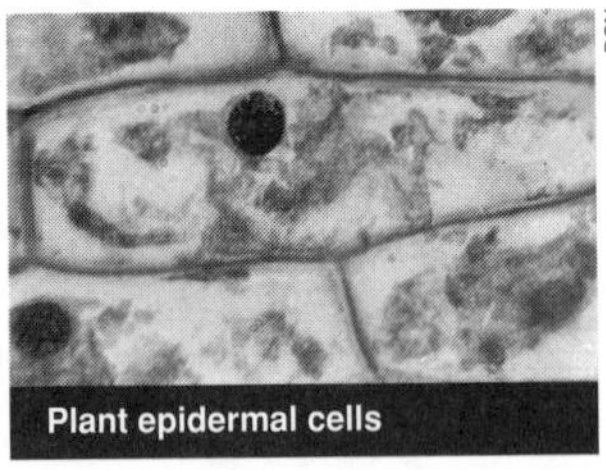
Plant epidermal cells

D

Head louse

E

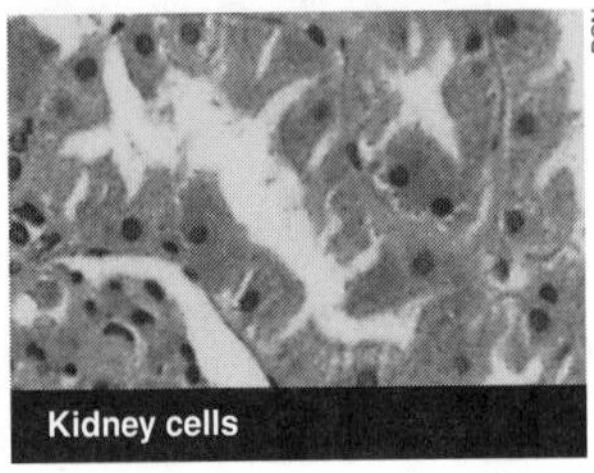
Kidney cells

F

Alderfly larva

G

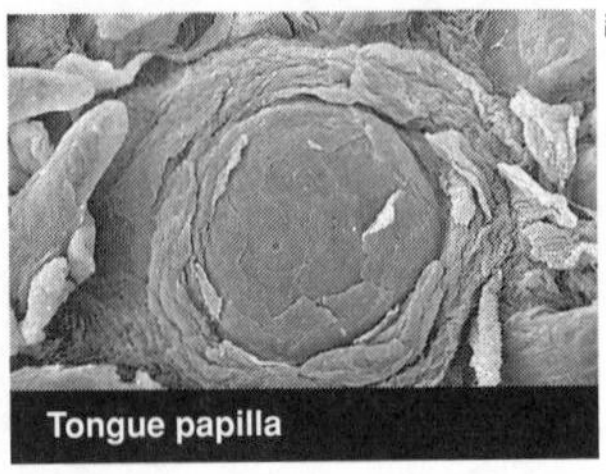
Tongue papilla

H

© 2015 **BIOZONE** International
ISBN:978-1-927309-31-5
Photocopying Prohibited

32 Measuring and Counting Using a Microscope

Key Idea: Graticules make it possible to measure cell size. Haemocytometers are used to count the number of cells.

Measuring and counting objects to be viewed under a microscope requires precisely marked measuring equipment. Two common pieces of equipment are the graticule and the haemocytometer. A graticule can be used to measure the size of an object whereas a haemocytometer is used to count the number of cells in a set area or volume.

Measuring cell size

A graticule is a scale placed in the eyepiece of a microscope. It is usually about 1 mm long and divided into 100 equal units. A graticule is used in combination with a stage micrometer to work out the size of an object being viewed. The stage micrometer is a slide with a scale that is exactly 1 mm long and also divided into 100 divisions (so that each division is 0.01 mm) and is placed on the microscope stage. The stage micrometer allows the graticule to be calibrated so that a precise scale can be calculated at each magnification.

The scale on the graticule is lined up with the stage micrometer. The number of graticule divisions between the divisions of the stage micrometer can then be read off. In the example right, each division of the stage micrometer is equal to four large divisions of the graticule. Each large division of the graticule is therefore 2.5 x 10^{-3} mm at 400x magnification.

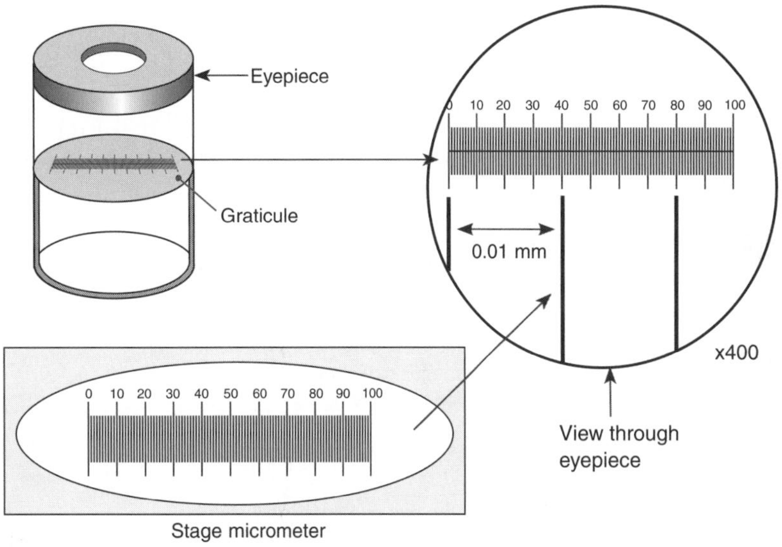
Eyepiece
Graticule
0 10 20 30 40 50 60 70 80 90 100
0.01 mm
x400
View through eyepiece
0 10 20 30 40 50 60 70 80 90 100
Stage micrometer

Counting cells

Microscopes can be used as a tool to count cells or other small objects (e.g pollen grains). By counting the number of cells in a known area, the total number of cells in a larger area can be calculated. A haemocytometer is commonly used to count cells viewed with a light microscope. It is a simple slide with precisely etched lines forming a grid and was developed for counting blood cells. There are a number of types of haemocytometer, including the Improved Neubauer, shown below. The slide holds a coverslip 0.1 mm above the surface of the grid, allowing volume to be calculated. The central counting grid is divided into 25 large squares, each of which is further divided into 16 squares.

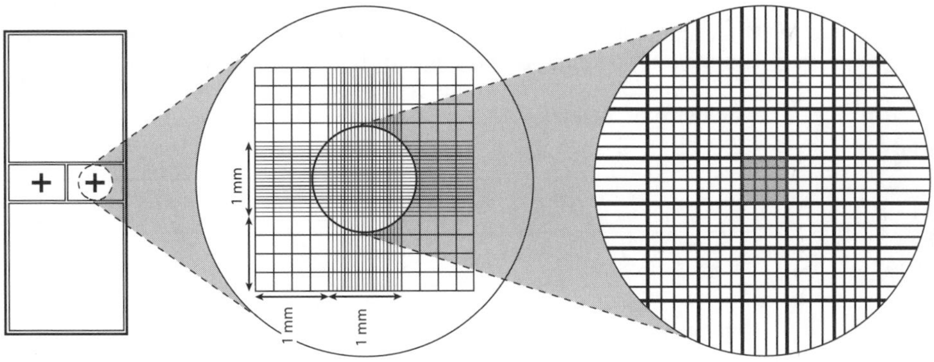
1 mm
1 mm
1 mm

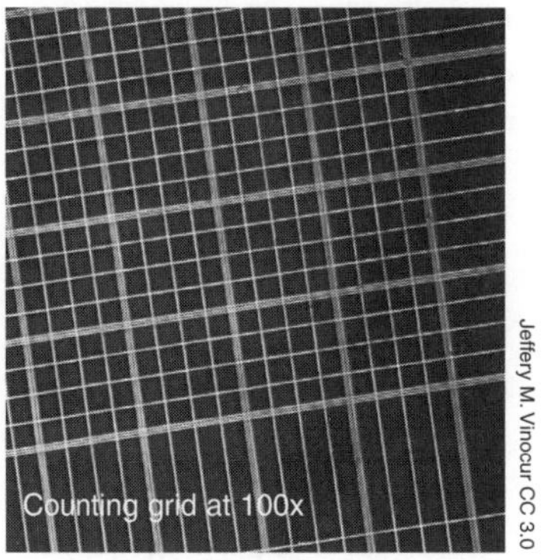
Counting grid at 100x
Jeffery M. Vinocur CC 3.0

1. A student using the graticule scale shown at the top of this page found a cell to be 56 divisions wide. Calculate the width of the cell in mm and in µm:

____

2. A second student grew yeast cells in 5 cm^3 of nutrient solution. The student used the haemocytometer shown above to count the number of yeast cells each day for 3 days.

   (a) Calculate the area and volume of the grid shown in blue: Area: ___________ Volume: ___________

   (b) The student counted yeast cells in the central blue grid. Complete the table below based on the counts obtained:

	Day 1	Day 2	Day 3
Number of cells counted	4	9	17
Cells in 5 cm^3			

3. A botanist wished to know the number of pollen grains produced per anther by a flower with eight anthers. She cut the anthers and placed them in 3 cm^3 of distilled water, shaking the mix vigorously. Using a haemocytometer she counted 6 grains in the large central counting grid (1 x 1 mm). Calculate the total number of pollen grains produced **per anther**:

____

____

© 2015 **BIOZONE** International
ISBN: 978-1-927309-31-5
Photocopying Prohibited

33 Calculating Linear Magnification

Key Idea: Magnification is how much larger an object appears compared to its actual size. Magnification can be calculated from the ratio of image size to object size.

Microscopes produce an enlarged (magnified) image of an object allowing it to be observed in greater detail than is possible with the naked eye. **Magnification** refers to the number of times larger an object appears compared to its actual size. Linear magnification is calculated by taking a ratio of the image height to the object's actual height. If this ratio is greater than one, the image is enlarged. If it is less than one, it is reduced. To calculate magnification, all measurements are converted to the same units. Often, you will be asked to calculate an object's actual size, in which case you will be told the size of the object and the magnification.

Calculating linear magnification: a worked example

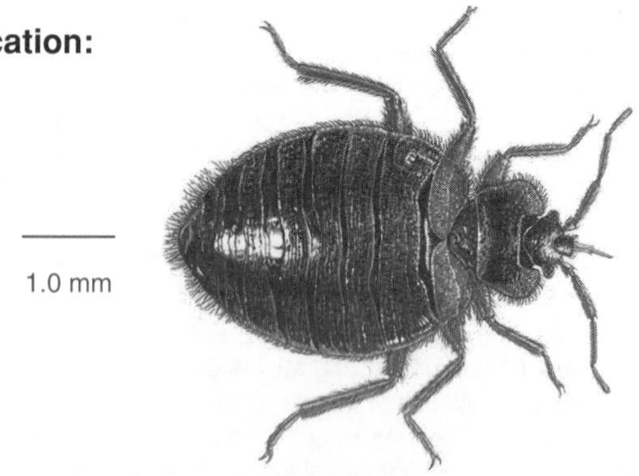
1.0 mm

1. Measure the body length of the bed bug image (right). Your measurement should be 40 mm (***not*** including the body hairs and antennae).

2. Measure the length of the scale line marked 1.0 mm. You will find it is 10 mm long. The magnification of the scale line can be calculated using equation 1 (below right).

   The magnification of the scale line is **10** (10 mm / 1 mm)

   **NB: The magnification of the bed bug image will also be 10x because the scale line and image are magnified to the same degree.*

3. Calculate the actual (real) size of the bed bug using equation 2 (right):

   The actual size of the bed bug is **4 mm** (40 mm / 10 x magnification)

Microscopy equations

$$1.\quad \text{Magnification} = \frac{\text{measured size of the object}}{\text{actual size of the object}}$$

$$2.\quad \text{Actual object size} = \frac{\text{size of the image}}{\text{magnification}}$$

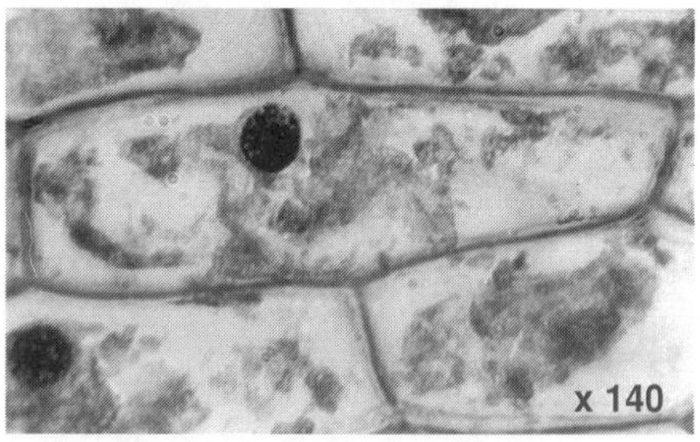
x 140

1. The bright field microscopy image on the left is of onion epidermal cells. The measured length of the onion cell in the centre of the photograph is 52 000 µm (52 mm). The image has been magnified 140 x. Calculate the actual size of the cell:

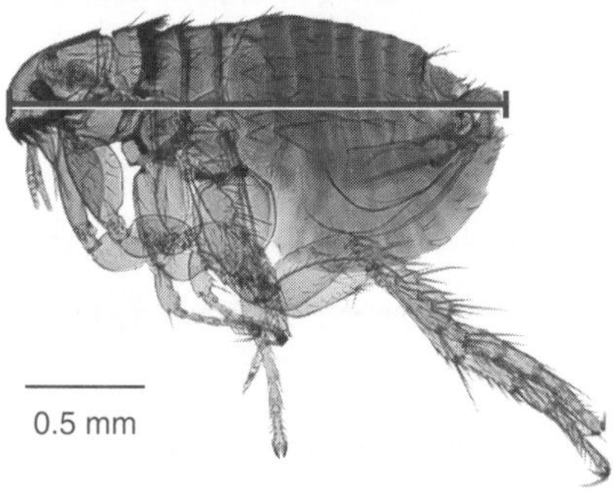
0.5 mm

2. The image of the flea (left) has been captured using light microscopy.

   (a) Calculate the magnification using the scale line on the image:

   (b) The body length of the flea is indicated by a line. Measure along the line and calculate the actual length of the flea:

3. The image size of the *E.coli* cell (left) is 43 mm, and its actual size is 2 µm. Using this information, calculate the magnification of the image:

© 2015 BIOZONE International
ISBN:978-1-927309-31-5
Photocopying Prohibited

34 The Cell is the Unit of Life

Key Idea: All living organisms are composed of cells. Cells are broadly classified as prokaryotic or eukaryotic.

The cell theory is a fundamental idea of biology. This idea, that all living things are composed of cells, developed over many years and is strongly linked to the invention and refinement of the microscope in the 1600s.

The cell theory

The idea that cells are fundamental units of life is part of the cell theory. The basic principles of the theory are:

- ► All living things are composed of cells and cell products.
- ► New cells are formed only by the division of pre-existing cells.
- ► The cell contains inherited information (genes) that are used as instructions for growth, functioning, and development.
- ► The cell is the functioning unit of life; all chemical reactions of life take place within cells.

All cells show the functions of life

Cells use food (e.g. glucose) to maintain a stable internal environment, grow, reproduce, and produce wastes. The sum total of all the chemical reactions that sustain life is called metabolism.

Movement
Respiration
Sensitivity
Growth
Reproduction
Excretion
Nutrition

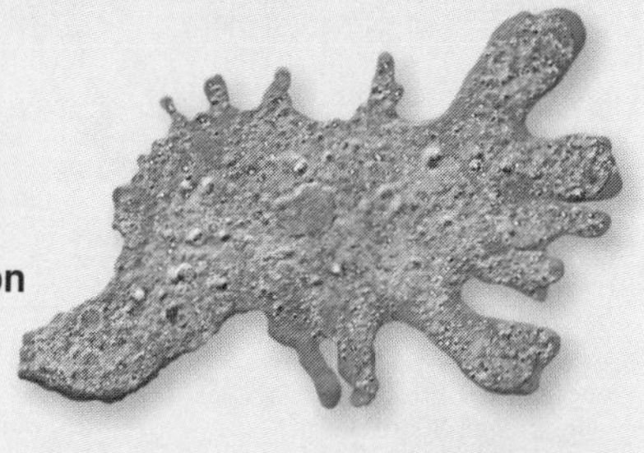

Living things

Cells

Prokaryotic (bacterial) cells

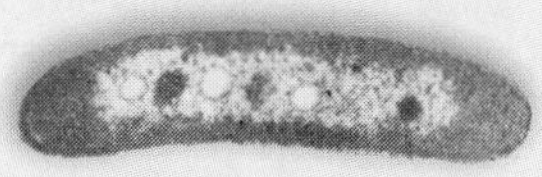

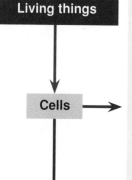

- Autotrophic or heterotrophic
- Single celled
- Lack a membrane-bound nucleus and membrane-bound organelles
- Cells 0.5-10 μm
- DNA a single, circular chromosome. There may be small accessory chromosomes called plasmids.
- Cell walls containing peptidoglycan.

Viruses are non-cellular

- Non-cellular.
- Typical size range: 20-300 nm.
- Contain no cytoplasm or organelles.
- No chromosome, just RNA or DNA strands.
- Enclosed in a protein coat.
- Depend on cells for metabolism and reproduction (replication).

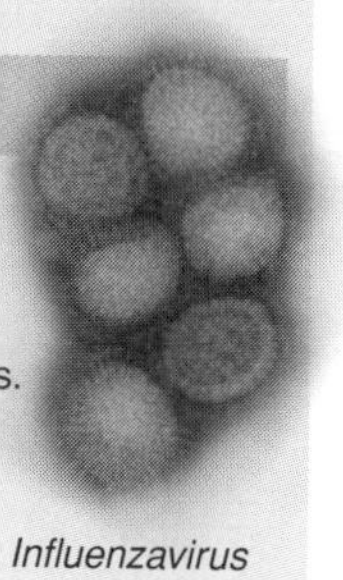

Influenzavirus

Eukaryotic cells

• Cells 30-150 μm • Membrane-bound nucleus and membrane-bound organelles • Linear chromosomes

Plant cells

- Exist as part of multicellular organism with specialisation of cells into many types.
- Autotrophic (make their own food): photosynthetic cells with chloroplasts.
- Cell walls of cellulose.

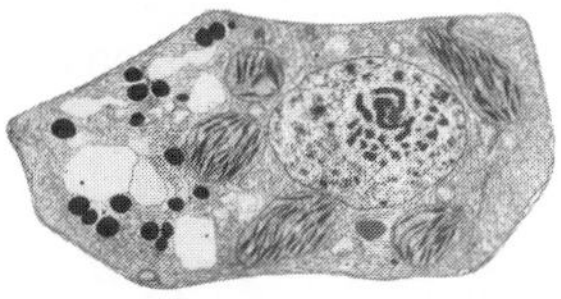

Generalised plant cell

Animal cells

- Exist as part of multicellular organism with specialisation of cells into many types.
- Lack cell walls.
- Heterotrophic (rely on other organisms for food).

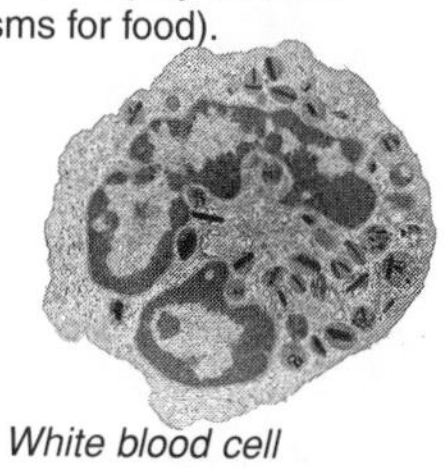

White blood cell

Protoctist cells

- Mainly single-celled or exist as cell colonies.
- Some are autotrophic and carry out photosynthesis.
- Some are heterotrophic.

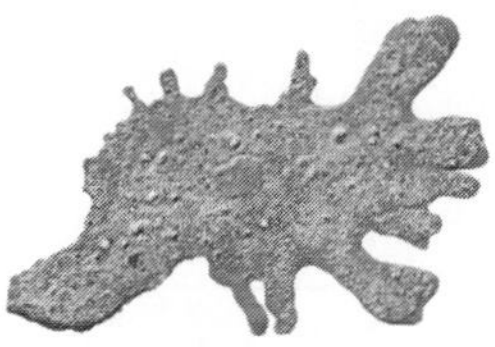

Amoeba cell

Fungal cells

- Rarely exist as discrete cells, except for some unicellular forms (e.g. yeasts)
- Plant-like, but lack chlorophyll.
- Rigid cell walls containing chitin.
- Heterotrophic.

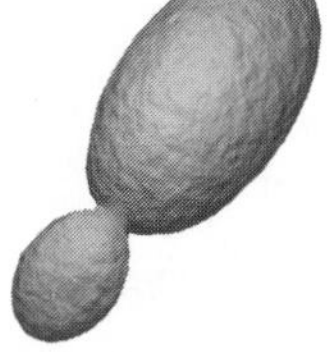

Yeast cell

1. What are the characteristic features of a prokaryotic cell? ______________________

____

2. What are the characteristic features of a eukaryotic cell? ______________________

____

3. Why are viruses considered to be non-cellular (non-living)? ______________________

____

© 2015 **BIOZONE** International
ISBN: 978-1-927309-31-5
Photocopying Prohibited

LINK 45 LINK 38 LINK 36 WEB 34 KNOW

35 Cell Sizes

Key Idea: Cells vary in size (2-100 µm), with prokaryotic cells being approximately 10 times smaller than eukaryotic cells. Cells can only be seen properly when viewed through the magnifying lenses of a microscope. The images below show a variety of cell types, including a multicellular microscopic animal and a virus (non-cellular) for comparison. For each of these images, note the scale and relate this to the type of microscopy used.

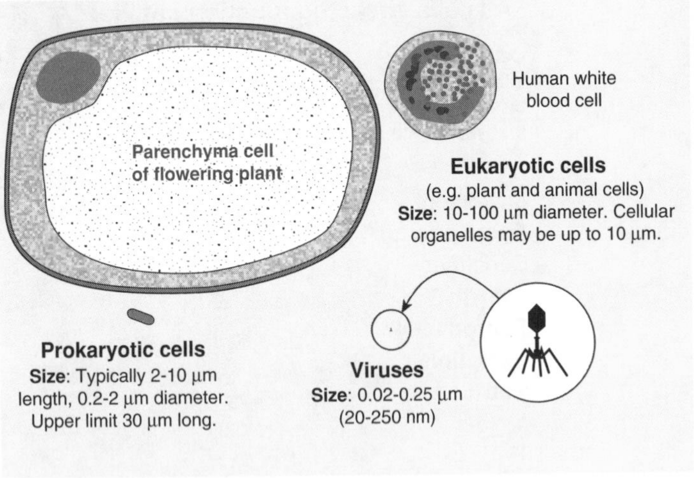
Parenchyma cell of flowering plant
Human white blood cell
Eukaryotic cells
(e.g. plant and animal cells)
Size: 10-100 µm diameter. Cellular organelles may be up to 10 µm.
Prokaryotic cells
Size: Typically 2-10 µm length, 0.2-2 µm diameter. Upper limit 30 µm long.
Viruses
Size: 0.02-0.25 µm (20-250 nm)

Unit of length (international system)

Unit	Metres	Equivalent
1 metre (m)	1 m	= 1000 millimetres
1 millimetre (mm)	10^{-3} m	= 1000 micrometres
1 micrometre (µm)	10^{-6} m	= 1000 nanometres
1 nanometre (nm)	10^{-9} m	= 1000 picometres

Micrometres are sometime referred to as microns. Smaller structures are usually measured in nanometres (nm) e.g. molecules (1 nm) and plasma membrane thickness (10 nm).

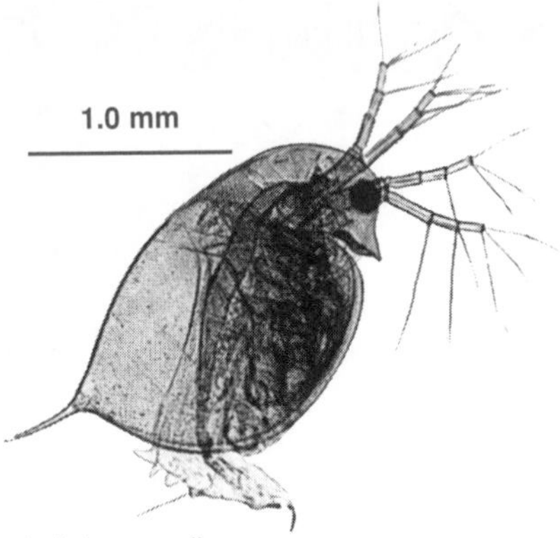
1.0 mm

Daphnia is a small crustacean found as part of the zooplankton of lakes and ponds.

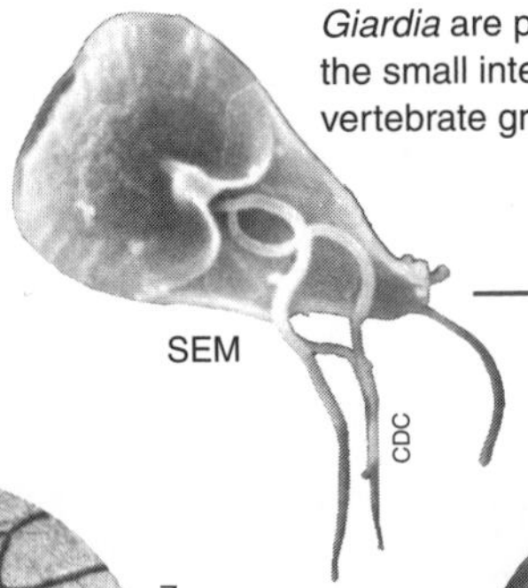
10 µm
SEM
CDC

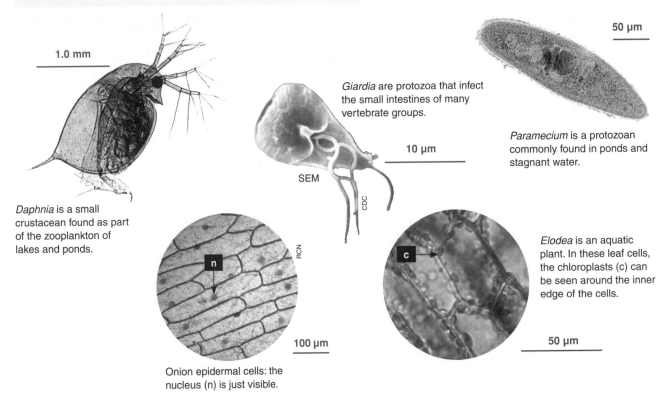

Giardia are protozoa that infect the small intestines of many vertebrate groups.

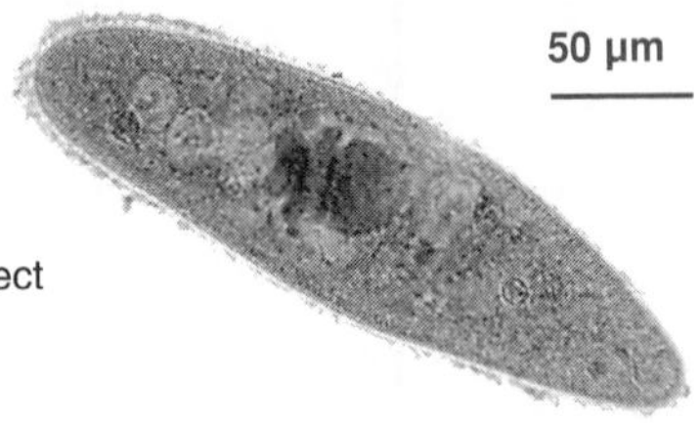
50 µm

Paramecium is a protozoan commonly found in ponds and stagnant water.

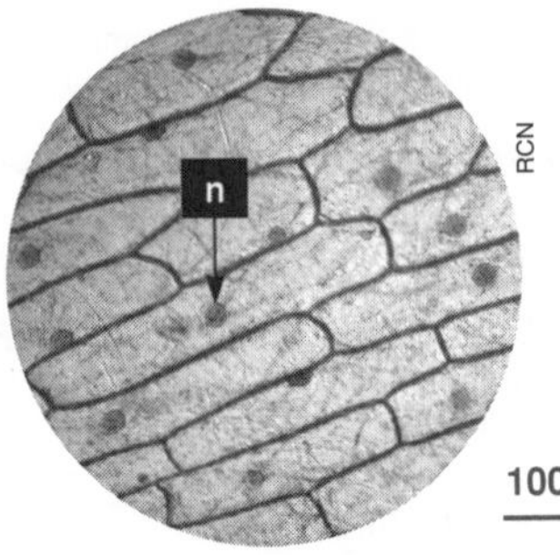
n
RCN
100 µm

Onion epidermal cells: the nucleus (n) is just visible.

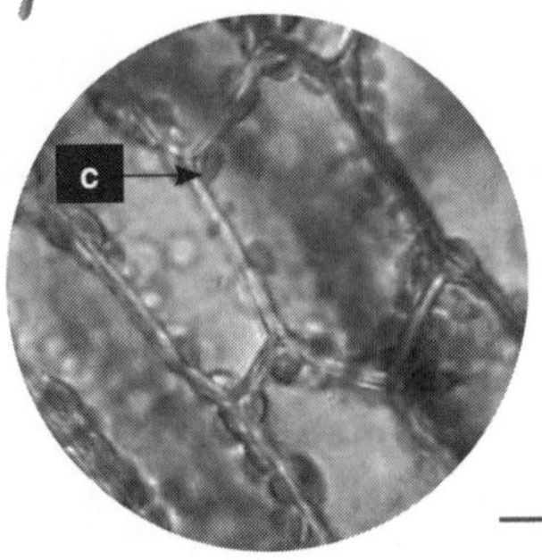
c
50 µm

Elodea is an aquatic plant. In these leaf cells, the chloroplasts (c) can be seen around the inner edge of the cells.

1. Using the measurement scales provided on each of the photographs above, determine the longest dimension (length or diameter) of the cell/animal/organelle indicated in µm and mm. Attach your working:

(a) *Daphnia*: ____________ µm ____________ mm

(b) *Giardia*: ____________ µm ____________ mm

(c) Nucleus ____________ µm ____________ mm

(d) *Elodea* leaf cell: ____________ µm ____________ mm

(e) Chloroplast: ____________ µm ____________ mm

(f) *Paramecium*: ____________ µm ____________ mm

2. (a) List a-f in question 1 in order of size, from the smallest to the largest:

____

(b) Study your ruler. Which one of the above could you see with your unaided eye?____________

3. Calculate the equivalent length in millimetres (mm) of the following measurements:

(a) 0.25 µm: ____________ (b) 450 µm: ____________ (c) 200 nm: ____________

© 2015 **BIOZONE** International
ISBN:978-1-927309-31-5
Photocopying Prohibited

36 Plant Cells

Key Idea: Plant cells are eukaryotic cells. They have features in common with animal cells, but also several unique features. Eukaryotic cells have a similar basic structure, although they may vary tremendously in size, shape, and function. Certain features are common to almost all eukaryotic cells, including their three main regions: a **nucleus**, surrounded by a watery **cytoplasm**, which is itself enclosed by the **plasma membrane**. Plant cells are enclosed in a cellulose cell wall, which gives them a regular, uniform appearance. The cell wall protects the cell, maintains its shape, and prevents excessive water uptake. It provides rigidity to plant structures but permits the free passage of materials into and out of the cell.

Generalised plant cell

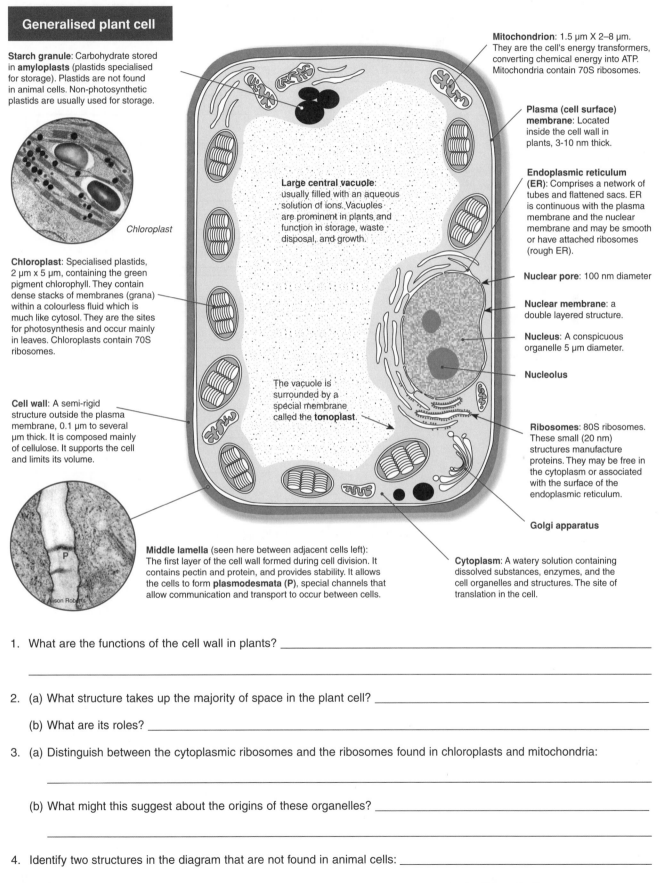

Starch granule: Carbohydrate stored in **amyloplasts** (plastids specialised for storage). Plastids are not found in animal cells. Non-photosynthetic plastids are usually used for storage.

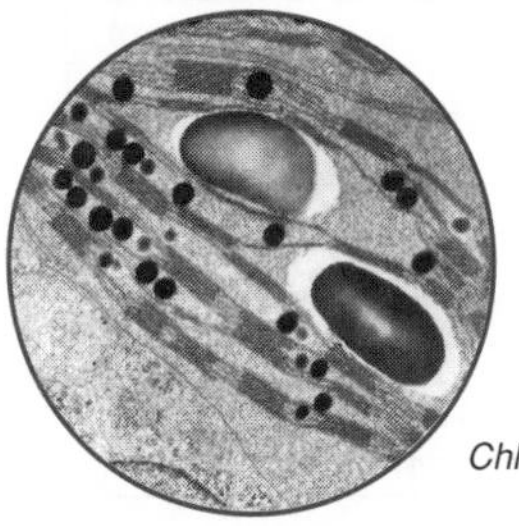

Chloroplast

Chloroplast: Specialised plastids, 2 µm x 5 µm, containing the green pigment chlorophyll. They contain dense stacks of membranes (grana) within a colourless fluid which is much like cytosol. They are the sites for photosynthesis and occur mainly in leaves. Chloroplasts contain 70S ribosomes.

Cell wall: A semi-rigid structure outside the plasma membrane, 0.1 µm to several µm thick. It is composed mainly of cellulose. It supports the cell and limits its volume.

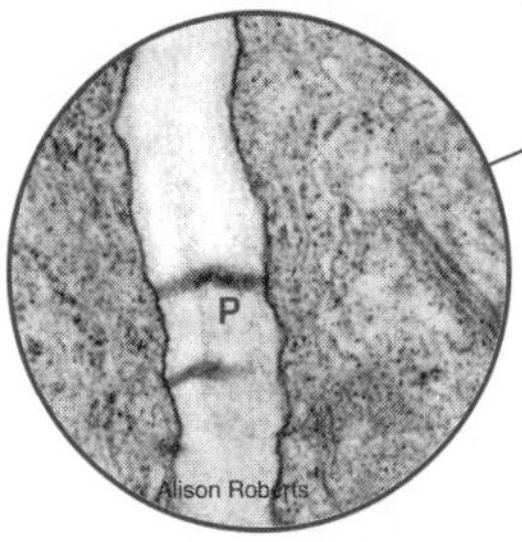
P
Alison Roberts

Middle lamella (seen here between adjacent cells left): The first layer of the cell wall formed during cell division. It contains pectin and protein, and provides stability. It allows the cells to form **plasmodesmata (P)**, special channels that allow communication and transport to occur between cells.

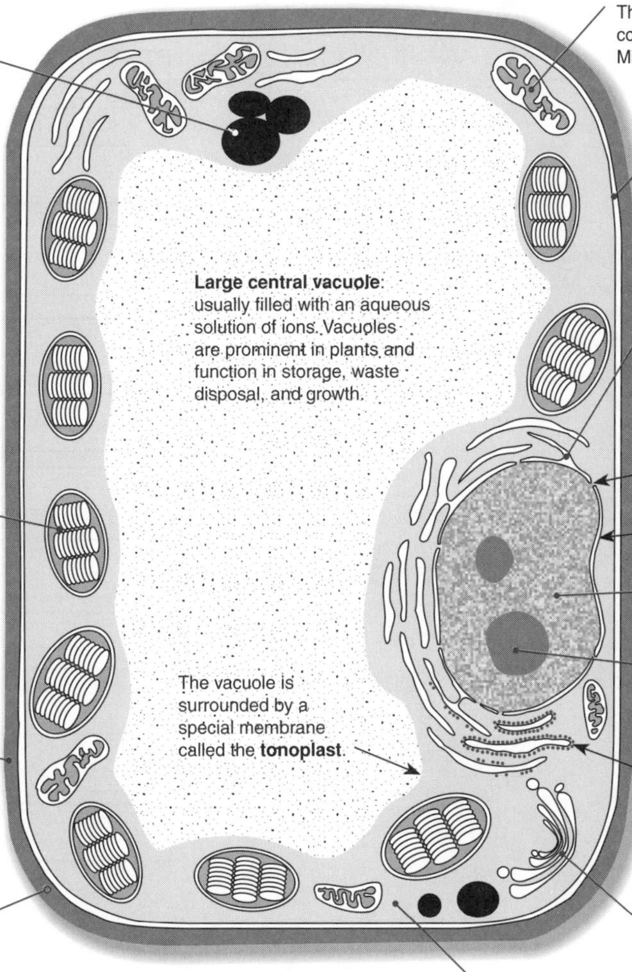
Large central vacuole: usually filled with an aqueous solution of ions. Vacuoles are prominent in plants and function in storage, waste disposal, and growth.
The vacuole is surrounded by a special membrane called the tonoplast.

Mitochondrion: 1.5 µm X 2–8 µm. They are the cell's energy transformers, converting chemical energy into ATP. Mitochondria contain 70S ribosomes.

Plasma (cell surface) membrane: Located inside the cell wall in plants, 3-10 nm thick.

Endoplasmic reticulum (ER): Comprises a network of tubes and flattened sacs. ER is continuous with the plasma membrane and the nuclear membrane and may be smooth or have attached ribosomes (rough ER).

Nuclear pore: 100 nm diameter

Nuclear membrane: a double layered structure.

Nucleus: A conspicuous organelle 5 µm diameter.

Nucleolus

Ribosomes: 80S ribosomes. These small (20 nm) structures manufacture proteins. They may be free in the cytoplasm or associated with the surface of the endoplasmic reticulum.

Golgi apparatus

Cytoplasm: A watery solution containing dissolved substances, enzymes, and the cell organelles and structures. The site of translation in the cell.

1. What are the functions of the cell wall in plants? ______________________

____

2. (a) What structure takes up the majority of space in the plant cell? ______________________

   (b) What are its roles? ______________________

3. (a) Distinguish between the cytoplasmic ribosomes and the ribosomes found in chloroplasts and mitochondria:

   ____

   (b) What might this suggest about the origins of these organelles? ______________________

   ____

4. Identify two structures in the diagram that are not found in animal cells: ______________________

© 2015 **BIOZONE** International
ISBN: 978-1-927309-31-5
Photocopying Prohibited

37 Identifying Structures in a Plant Cell

Key Idea: The position and appearance of the organelles in an electron micrograph can be used to identify them.

1. Study the diagrams on the other pages in this chapter to familiarise yourself with the structures found in eukaryotic cells. Identify the 11 structures in the cell below using the following word list: *cytoplasm, smooth endoplasmic reticulum, mitochondrion, starch granule, chromosome, nucleus, vacuole, plasma membrane, cell wall, chloroplast, nuclear membrane*

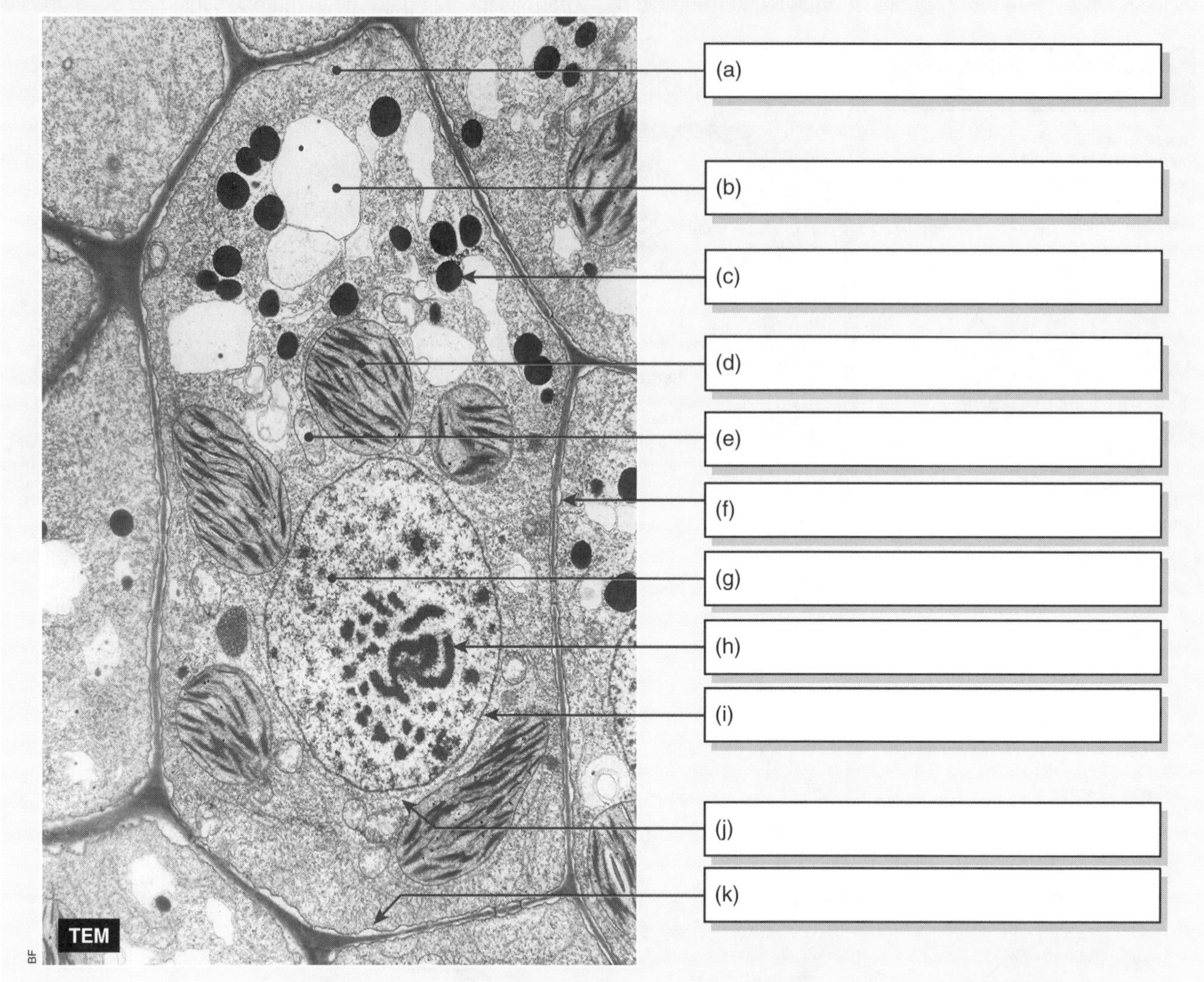

TEM
BF
(a)
(b)
(c)
(d)
(e)
(f)
(g)
(h)
(i)
(j)
(k)

2. State how many cells, or parts of cells, are visible in the electron micrograph above: ______

3. Describe the features that identify this cell as a plant cell: ______

______

______

4. (a) Explain where cytoplasm is found in the cell: ______

______

(b) Describe what cytoplasm is made up of: ______

______

5. Describe two structures, pictured in the cell above, that are associated with storage:

(a) ______

______

(b) ______

______

© 2015 **BIOZONE** International
ISBN:978-1-927309-31-5
Photocopying Prohibited

38 Animal Cells

Key Idea: Animal cells are eukaryotic cells. They have many features in common with plant cells, but also have a number of unique features.

Animal cells, unlike plant cells, do not have a regular shape. In fact, some animal cells (such as phagocytes) are able to alter their shape for various purposes (e.g. engulfing foreign material). The diagram below shows the structure and organelles of a liver cell. It contains organelles common to most relatively unspecialised human cells. Note the differences between this cell and the generalised plant cell. The plant cells activity provides further information on the organelles listed here but not described.

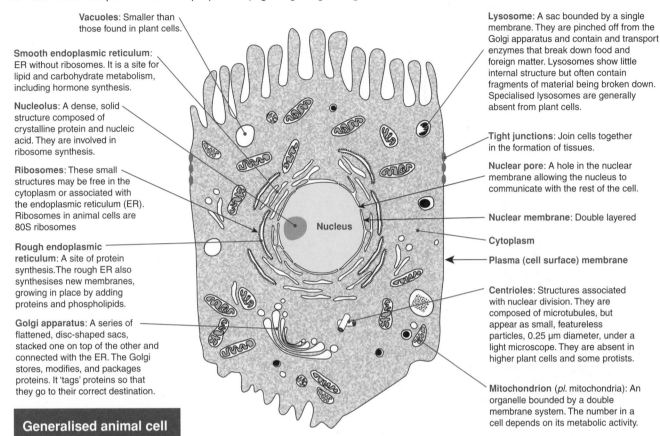

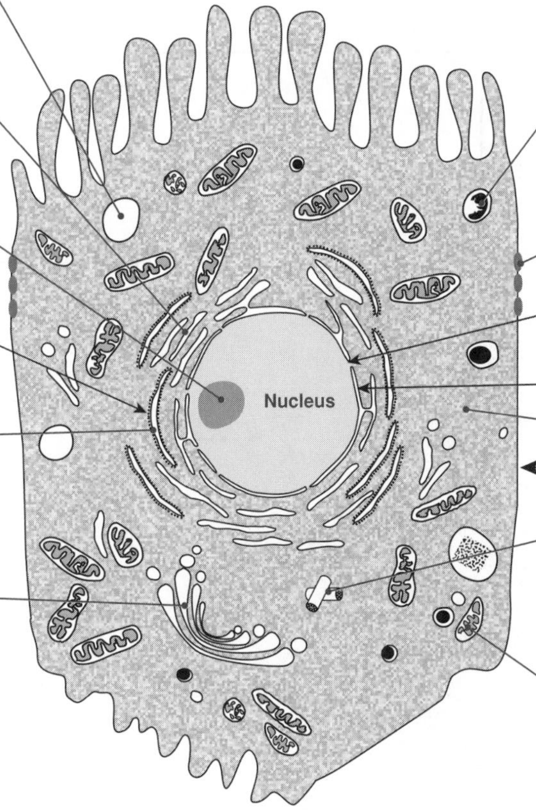
Nucleus
Vacuoles: Smaller than those found in plant cells.
Smooth endoplasmic reticulum: ER without ribosomes. It is a site for lipid and carbohydrate metabolism, including hormone synthesis.
Nucleolus: A dense, solid structure composed of crystalline protein and nucleic acid. They are involved in ribosome synthesis.
Ribosomes: These small structures may be free in the cytoplasm or associated with the endoplasmic reticulum (ER). Ribosomes in animal cells are 80S ribosomes
Rough endoplasmic reticulum: A site of protein synthesis. The rough ER also synthesises new membranes, growing in place by adding proteins and phospholipids.
Golgi apparatus: A series of flattened, disc-shaped sacs, stacked one on top of the other and connected with the ER. The Golgi stores, modifies, and packages proteins. It 'tags' proteins so that they go to their correct destination.
Lysosome: A sac bounded by a single membrane. They are pinched off from the Golgi apparatus and contain and transport enzymes that break down food and foreign matter. Lysosomes show little internal structure but often contain fragments of material being broken down. Specialised lysosomes are generally absent from plant cells.
Tight junctions: Join cells together in the formation of tissues.
Nuclear pore: A hole in the nuclear membrane allowing the nucleus to communicate with the rest of the cell.
Nuclear membrane: Double layered
Cytoplasm
Plasma (cell surface) membrane
Centrioles: Structures associated with nuclear division. They are composed of microtubules, but appear as small, featureless particles, 0.25 µm diameter, under a light microscope. They are absent in higher plant cells and some protists.
Mitochondrion (*pl.* mitochondria): An organelle bounded by a double membrane system. The number in a cell depends on its metabolic activity.

Generalised animal cell

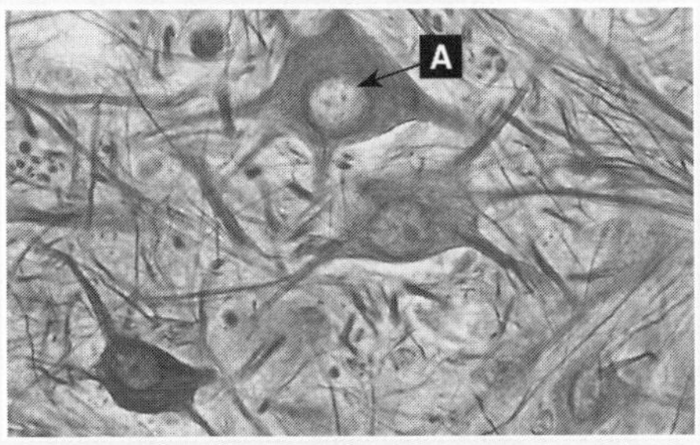
A

Neurones (nerve cells) in the spinal cord

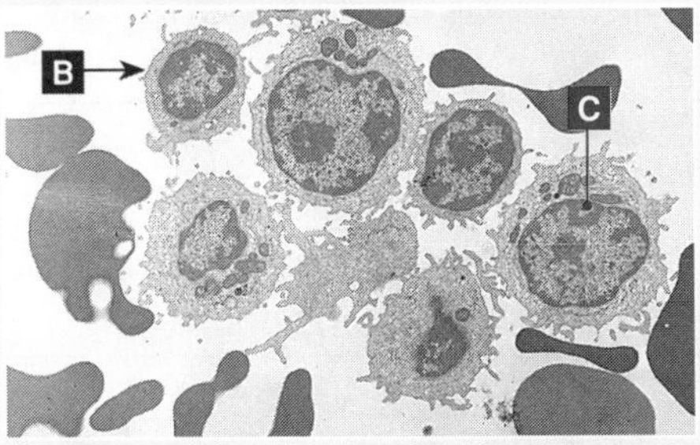
B
C

White blood cells and red blood cells (blood smear)

Photos: EII

1. The two photomicrographs (left) show several types of animal cells. Identify the features indicated by the letters **A-C**:

   A: ______________________

   B: ______________________

   C: ______________________

2. White blood cells are mobile, phagocytic cells, whereas red blood cells are smaller than white blood cells and, in humans, lack a nucleus.

   (a) In the photomicrograph (lower, left), circle a white blood cell and a red blood cell:

   (b) With respect to the features that you can see, explain how you made your decision.

   ____

   ____

   ____

   ____

3. Name one structure or organelle present in generalised animal cells but absent from plant cells and describe its function:

____

____

© 2015 BIOZONE International
ISBN: 978-1-927309-31-5
Photocopying Prohibited

LINK 39 LINK 36 WEB 38 KNOW

39 Identifying Structures in an Animal Cell

Key Idea: The position of the organelles in an electron micrograph can result in variations in their appearance.

Transmission electron microscopy (TEM) is the most frequently used technique for viewing cellular organelles. When viewing TEMs, the cellular organelles may have quite different appearances depending on whether they are in transverse or longitudinal section.

1. Identify and label the structures in the animal cell below using the following list of terms: *cytoplasm, plasma membrane, rough endoplasmic reticulum, mitochondrion, nucleus, centriole, Golgi apparatus, lysosome*

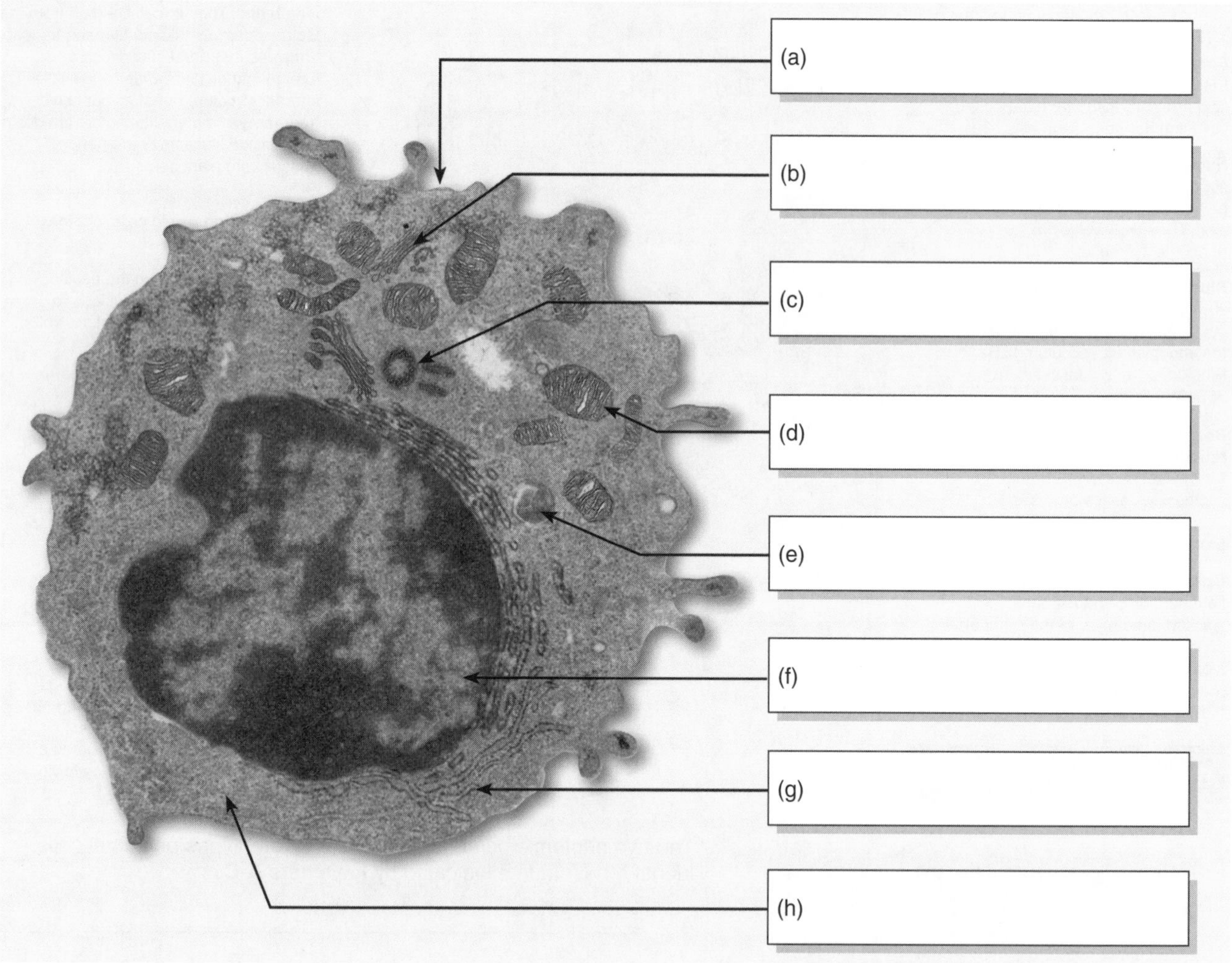

(a)
(b)
(c)
(d)
(e)
(f)
(g)
(h)

2. Which of the organelles in the EM above are obviously shown in both transverse and longitudinal section?

3. Why do plants lack any of the mobile phagocytic cells typical of animal cells?

4. The animal cell pictured above is a lymphocyte. Describe the features that suggest to you that:

   (a) It has a role in producing and secreting proteins:

   (b) It is metabolically very active:

5. What features of the lymphocyte cell above identify it as eukaryotic?

© 2015 BIOZONE International
ISBN:978-1-927309-31-5
Photocopying Prohibited

40 The Cell's Cytoskeleton

Key Idea: The cytoskeleton is a complex structure of tubules and fibres. It resists tension and so provides structural support to maintain the cell's shape.

The cell's cytoplasm is not a fluid filled space; it contains a complex network of fibres called the **cytoskeleton**. The cytoskeleton is made up of three proteinaceous elements: microfilaments, intermediate filaments, and microtubules. Each has a distinct size, structure, and protein composition, and a specific role in cytoskeletal function. Cilia and flagella are made up of microtubules and for this reason they are considered to be part of the cytoskeleton. The elements of the cytoskeleton are dynamic; they move and change to alter the cell's shape, move materials within the cell, and move the cell itself. This movement is achieved through the action of motor proteins, which transport material by 'walking' along cytoskeletal 'tracks', hydrolysing ATP at each step.

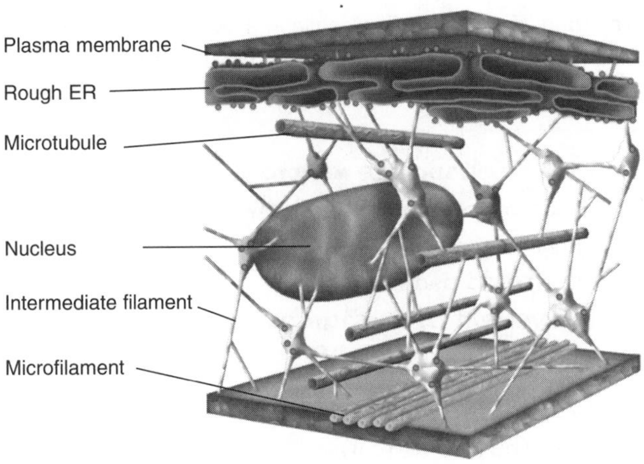
Plasma membrane
Rough ER
Microtubule
Nucleus
Intermediate filament
Microfilament

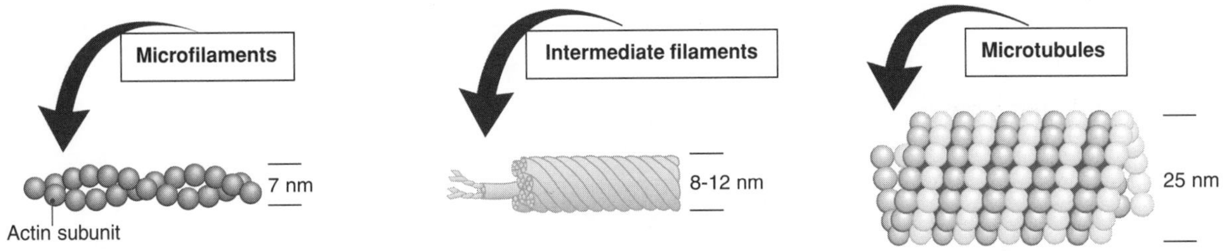
Microfilaments
7 nm
Actin subunit
Intermediate filaments
8-12 nm
Microtubules
25 nm

	Microfilaments	Intermediate filaments	Microtubules
Protein subunits	Actin	Fibrous proteins, e.g. keratin	α and β tubulin dimers
Structure	Two intertwined strands	Fibres wound into thicker cables	Hollow tubes
Functions	• Maintain cell shape • Motility (pseudopodia) • Contraction (muscle) • Cytokinesis of cell division	• Maintain cell shape • Anchor nucleus and organelles	• Maintain cell shape • Motility (cilia and flagella) • Move chromosomes (spindle) • Move organelles

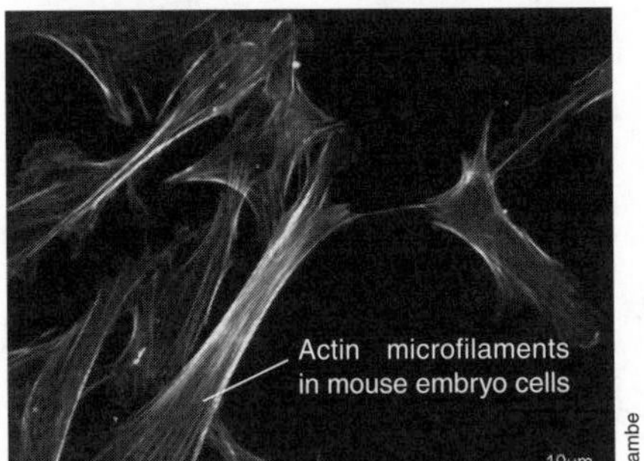
Actin microfilaments in mouse embryo cells
10μm
Y tambe

Microfilaments are long polymers of the protein actin. Microfilaments can grow and shrink as actin subunits are added or taken away from either end. Networks of microfilaments form a matrix that helps to define the cell's shape. Actin microfilaments are also involved in cell division (during cytokinesis) and in muscle contraction.

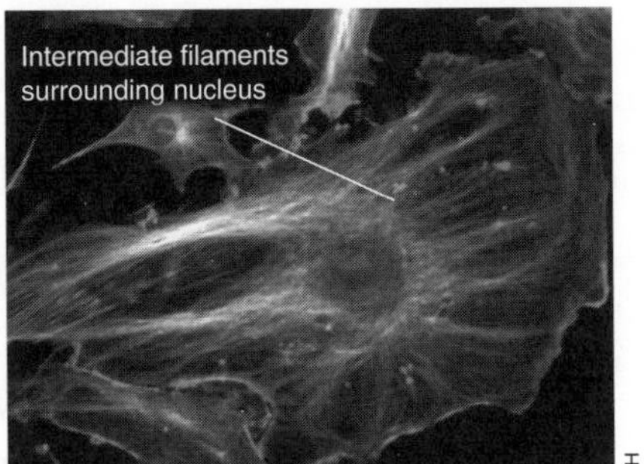
Intermediate filaments surrounding nucleus
NIH

Intermediate filaments can be composed of a number of different fibrous proteins and are defined by their size rather than composition. The protein subunits are wound into cables around 10 nm in diameter. Intermediate filaments form a dense network within and projecting from the nucleus, helping to anchor it in place.

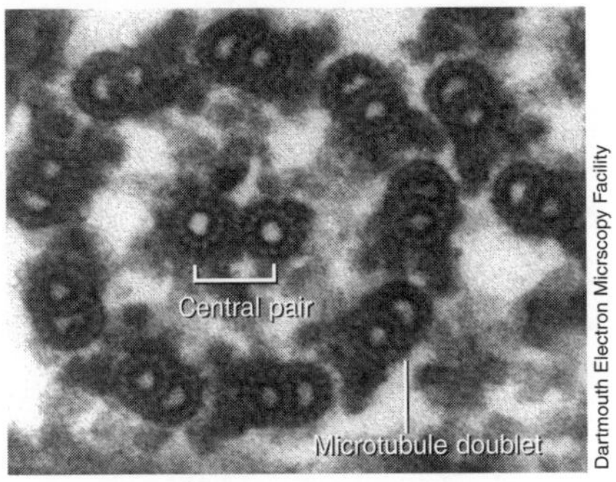
Central pair
Microtubule doublet
Dartmouth Electron Micrscopy Facility

Microtubules are the largest cytoskeletal components and grow or shrink in length as tubulin subunits are added or subtracted from one end. The are involved in movement of material within the cell and in moving the cell itself. This EM shows a cilia from *Chlamydomonas*, with the 9+2 arrangement of microtubular doublets.

1. Describe what all components of the cytoskeleton have in common: ________________

2. Explain the importance of the cytoskeleton being a dynamic structure: ________________

3. Explain how the presence of a cytoskeleton could aid in directing the movement of materials within the cell:

© 2015 BIOZONE International
ISBN: 978-1-927309-31-5
Photocopying Prohibited

41 Cell Structures and Organelles

Key Idea: Each type of organelle in a cell has a specific role. Not all cell types contain every type of organelle.
The diagram below provides spaces for you to summarise information about the organelles found in eukaryotic cells. The log scale of measurements (top of next page) illustrates the relative sizes of some cellular structures.

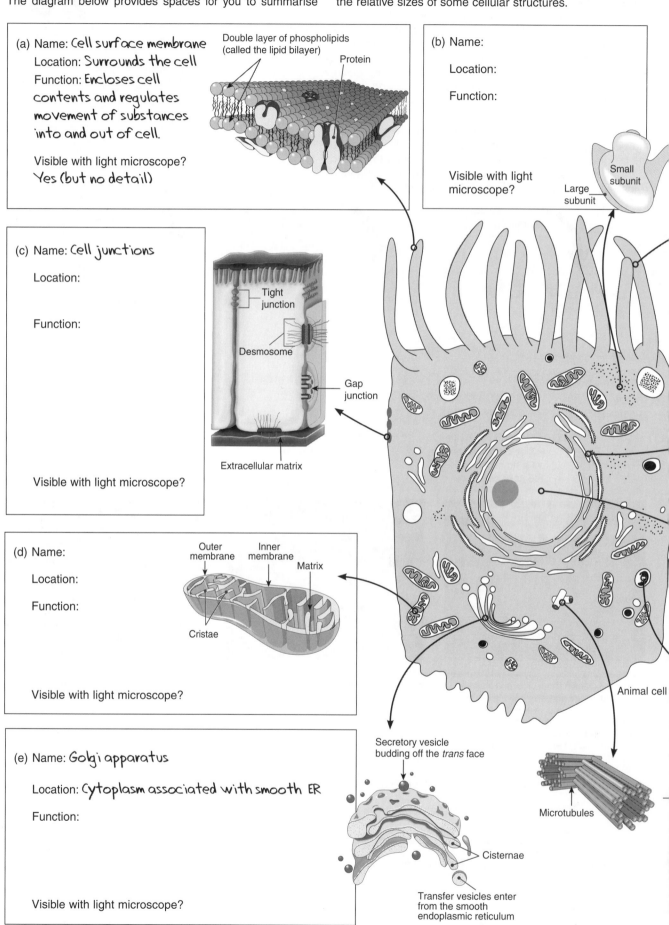

(a) Name: Cell surface membrane
Location: Surrounds the cell
Function: Encloses cell contents and regulates movement of substances into and out of cell.
Visible with light microscope?
Yes (but no detail)

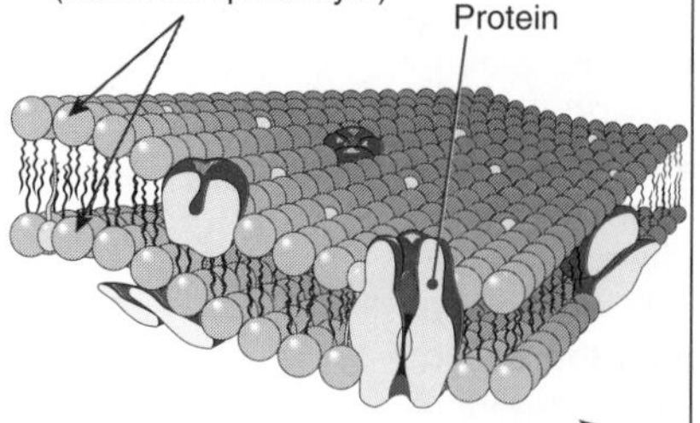

Double layer of phospholipids (called the lipid bilayer)
Protein

(b) Name:
Location:
Function:
Visible with light microscope?

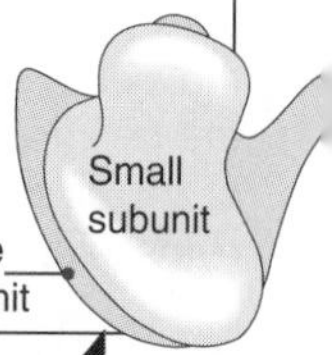

Small subunit
Large subunit

(c) Name: Cell junctions
Location:
Function:
Visible with light microscope?

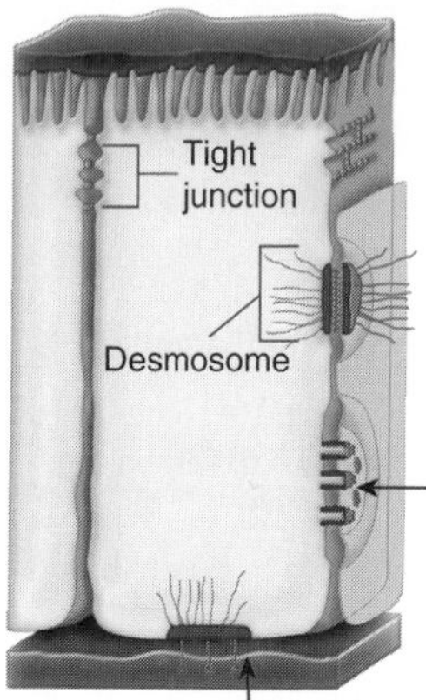

Tight junction
Desmosome
Gap junction
Extracellular matrix

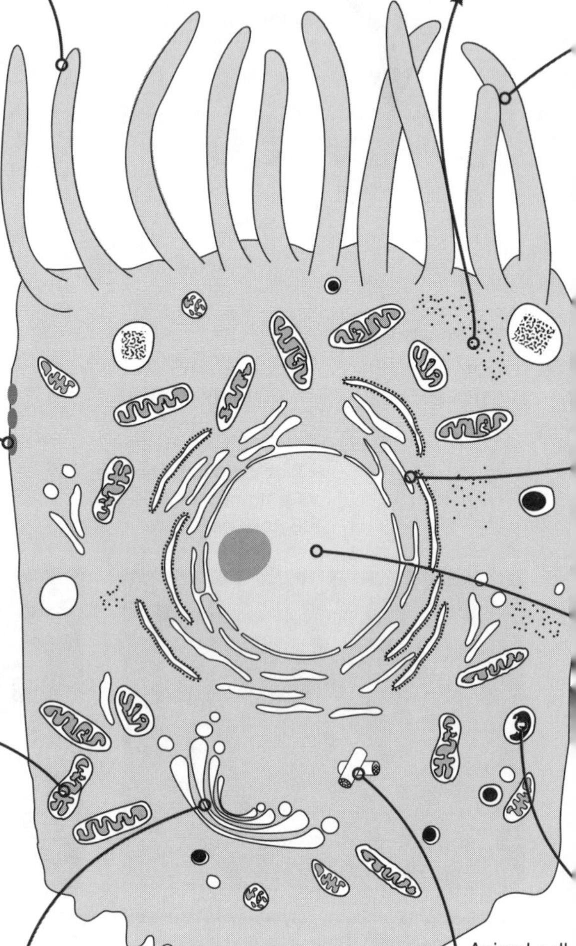

Animal cell

(d) Name:
Location:
Function:
Visible with light microscope?

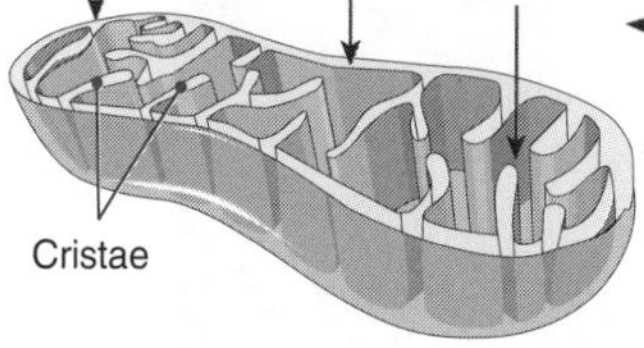

Outer membrane
Inner membrane
Matrix
Cristae

(e) Name: Golgi apparatus
Location: Cytoplasm associated with smooth ER
Function:
Visible with light microscope?

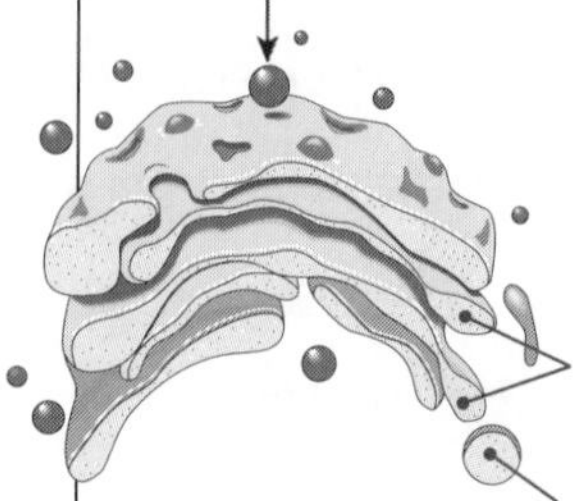

Secretory vesicle budding off the trans face
Cisternae
Transfer vesicles enter from the smooth endoplasmic reticulum

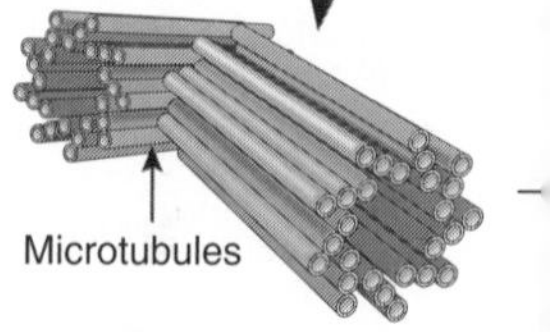

Microtubules

© 2015 BIOZONE International
ISBN:978-1-927309-31-5
Photocopying Prohibited

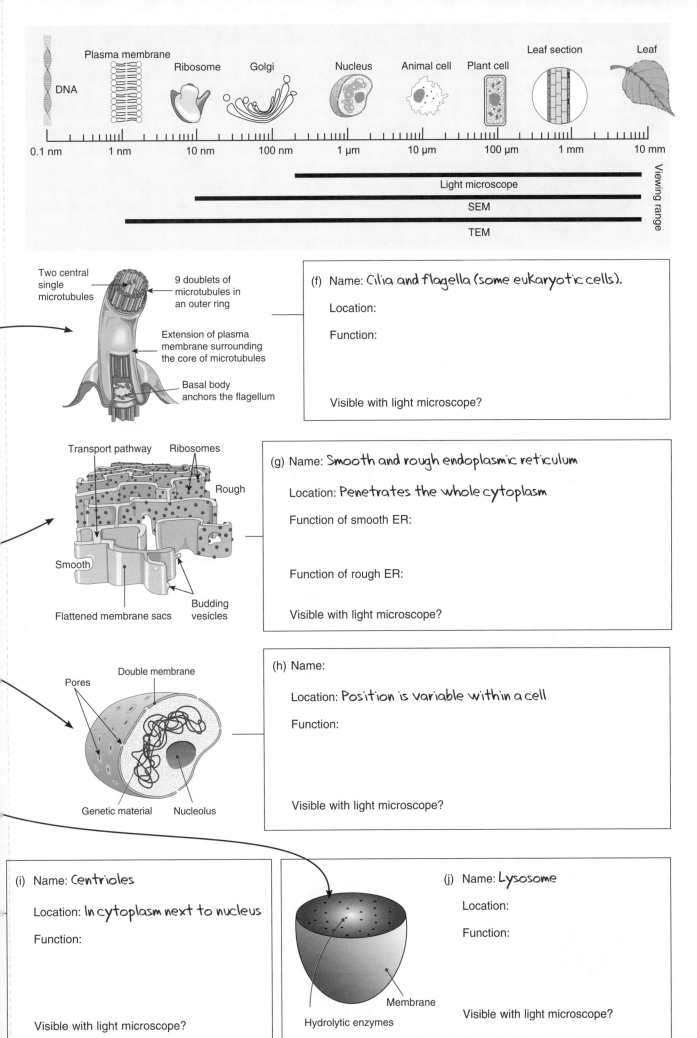

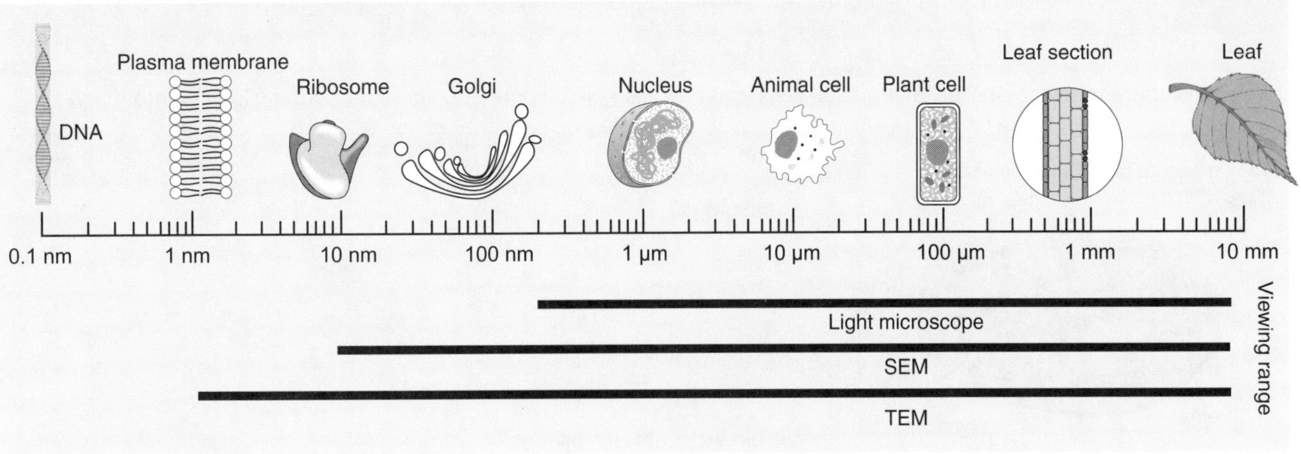
DNA
Plasma membrane
Ribosome
Golgi
Nucleus
Animal cell
Plant cell
Leaf section
Leaf
0.1 nm
1 nm
10 nm
100 nm
1 µm
10 µm
100 µm
1 mm
10 mm
Light microscope
SEM
TEM
Viewing range

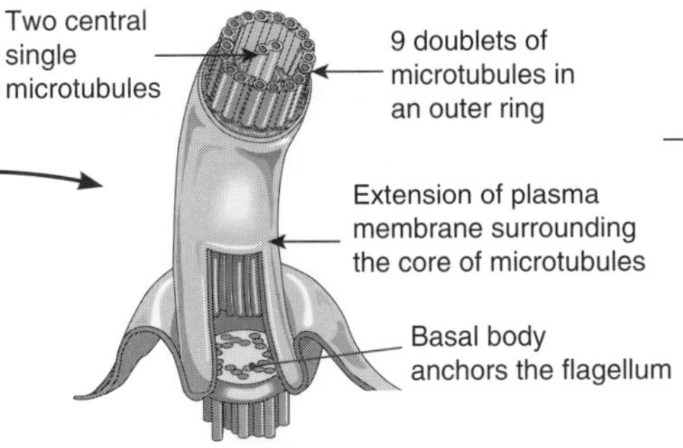
Two central single microtubules
9 doublets of microtubules in an outer ring
Extension of plasma membrane surrounding the core of microtubules
Basal body anchors the flagellum

(f) Name: Cilia and flagella (some eukaryotic cells).

Location:

Function:

Visible with light microscope?

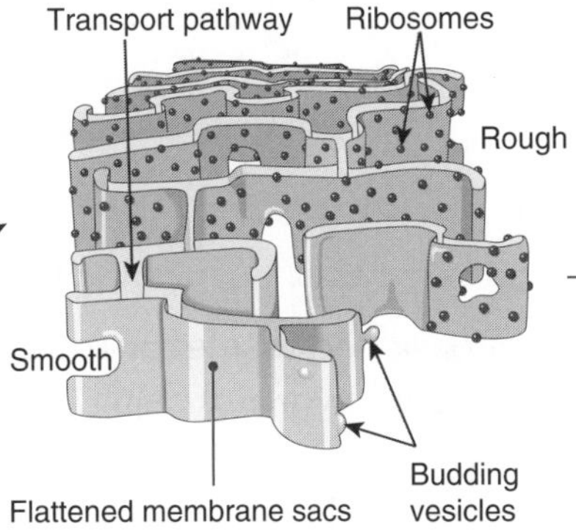
Transport pathway
Ribosomes
Rough
Smooth
Flattened membrane sacs
Budding vesicles

(g) Name: Smooth and rough endoplasmic reticulum

Location: Penetrates the whole cytoplasm

Function of smooth ER:

Function of rough ER:

Visible with light microscope?

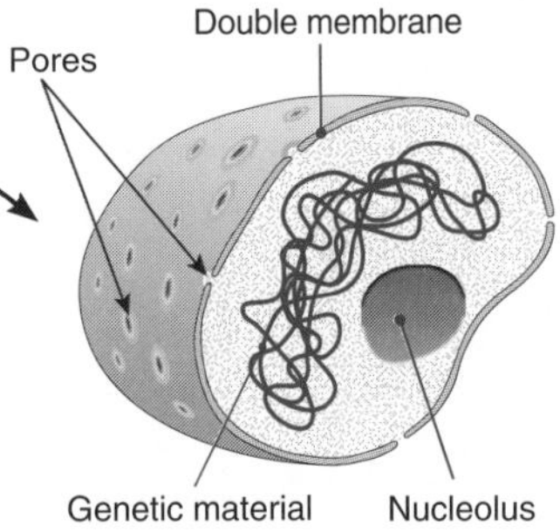
Double membrane
Pores
Genetic material
Nucleolus

(h) Name:

Location: Position is variable within a cell

Function:

Visible with light microscope?

(i) Name: Centrioles

Location: In cytoplasm next to nucleus

Function:

Visible with light microscope?

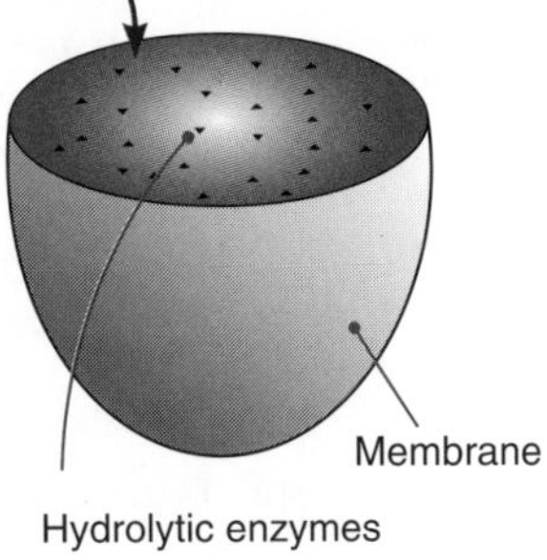
Membrane
Hydrolytic enzymes

(j) Name: Lysosome

Location:

Function:

Visible with light microscope?

© 2015 **BIOZONE** International
ISBN: 978-1-927309-31-5
Photocopying Prohibited

Plant cells share many organelles with animal cells, but they also have some structures and organelles that are unique.

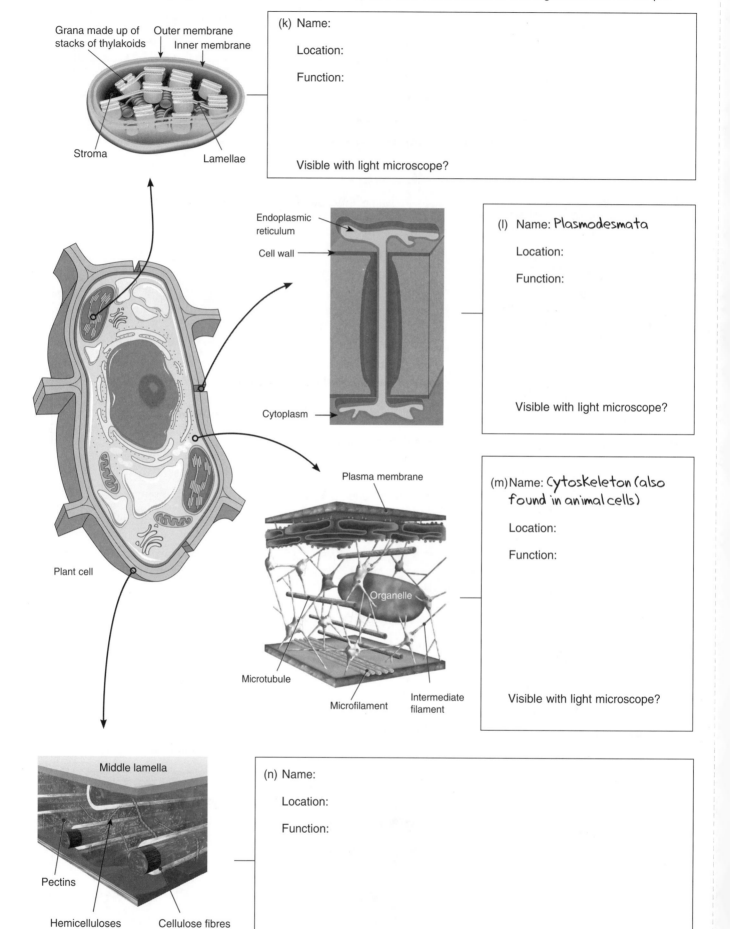

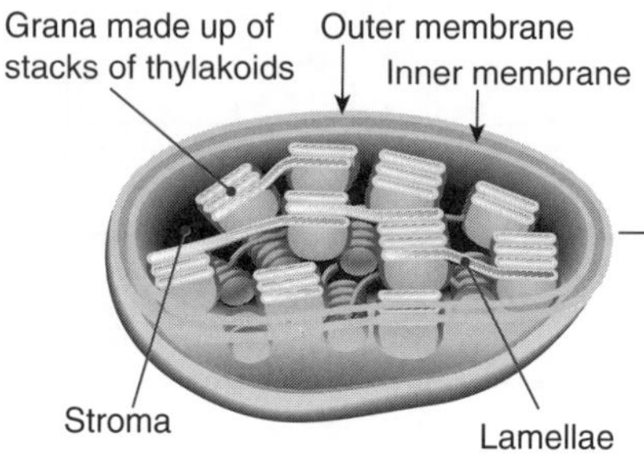
Grana made up of stacks of thylakoids
Outer membrane
Inner membrane
Stroma
Lamellae

(k) Name:

Location:

Function:

Visible with light microscope?

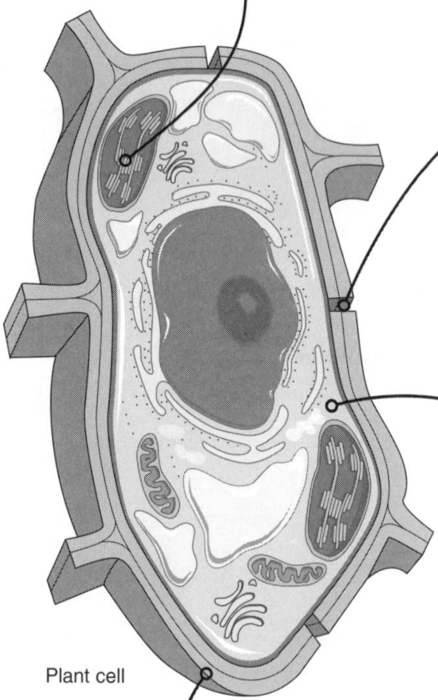
Plant cell

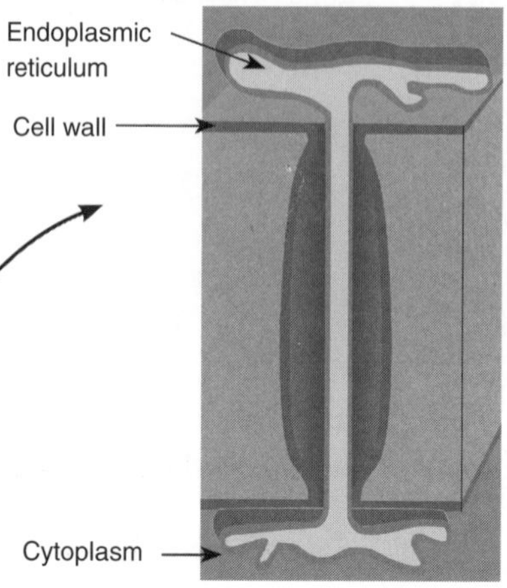
Endoplasmic reticulum
Cell wall
Cytoplasm

(l) Name: Plasmodesmata

Location:

Function:

Visible with light microscope?

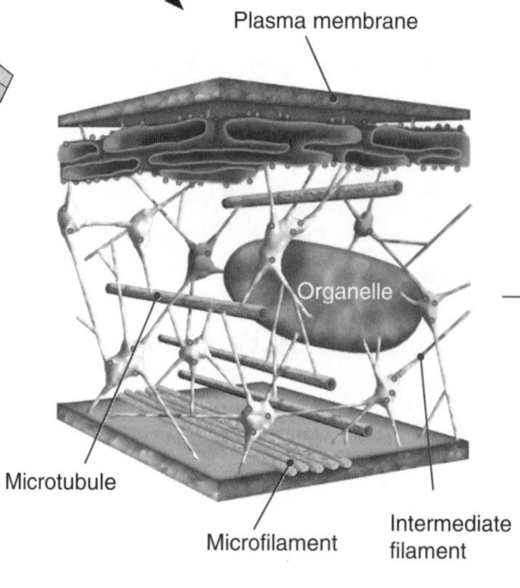
Plasma membrane
Organelle
Microtubule
Microfilament
Intermediate filament

(m) Name: Cytoskeleton (also found in animal cells)

Location:

Function:

Visible with light microscope?

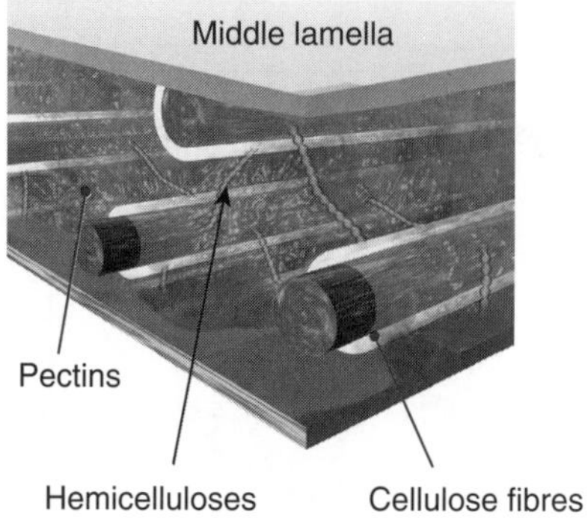
Middle lamella
Pectins
Hemicelluloses
Cellulose fibres

(n) Name:

Location:

Function:

Visible with light microscope?

© 2015 **BIOZONE** International
ISBN:978-1-927309-31-5
Photocopying Prohibited

42 Identifying Organelles

Key Idea: Cellular organelles can be identified in electron micrographs by their specific features.

Electron microscopes produce a magnified image at high resolution (distinguish between close together but separate objects). The transmission electron microscope (TEM) images below show the ultrastructure of some organelles.

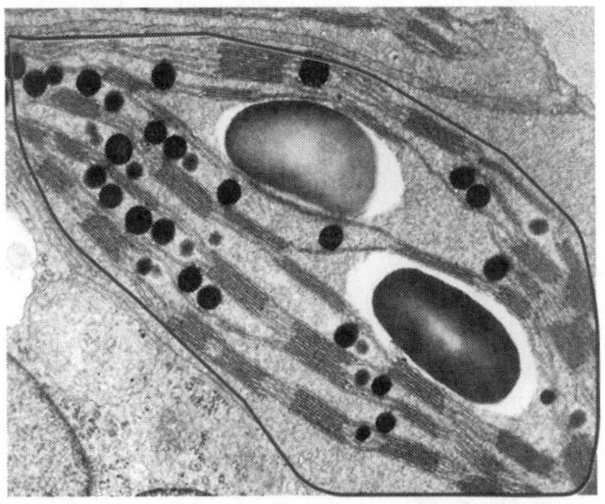

WMU

1. (a) Name the circled organelle:

   (b) Which kind of cell(s) would this organelle be found in?

   (c) Describe the function of this organelle:

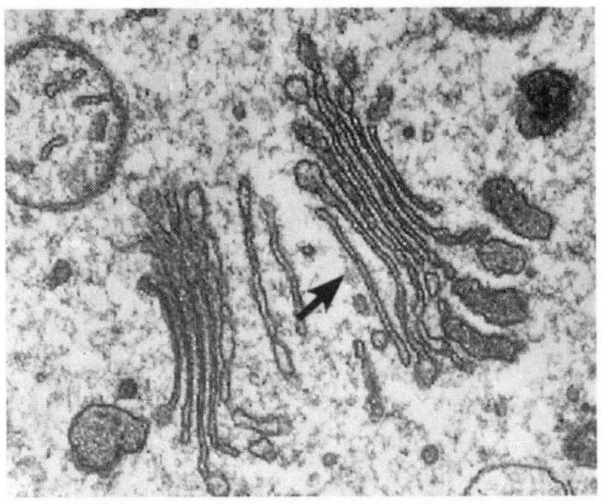

WMU

2. (a) Name this organelle (arrowed):

   (b) State which kind of cell(s) this organelle would be found in:

   (c) Describe the function of this organelle:

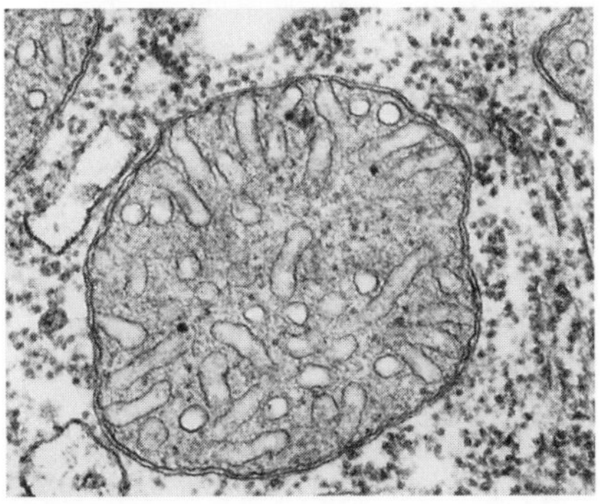

WMU

3. (a) Name the large, circular organelle:

   (b) State which kind of cell(s) this organelle would be found in:

   (c) Describe the function of this organelle:

   (d) Label **two** regions that can be seen **inside** this organelle.

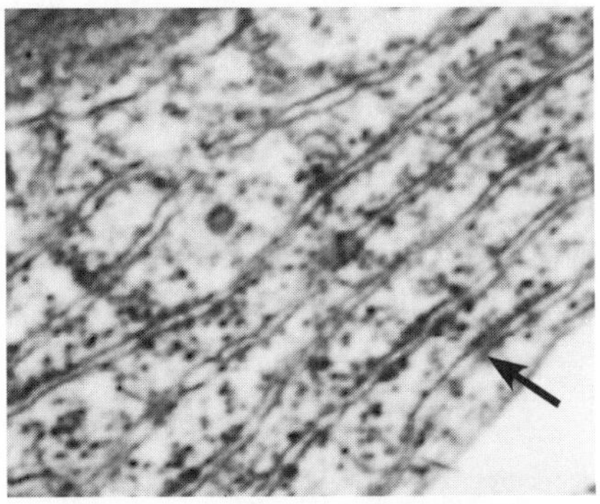

WMU

4. (a) Name and label the ribbon-like organelle in this photograph (arrowed):

   (b) State which kind of cell(s) this organelle is found in:

   (c) Describe the function of this organelle:

   (d) Name the dark 'blobs' attached to the organelle you have labelled:

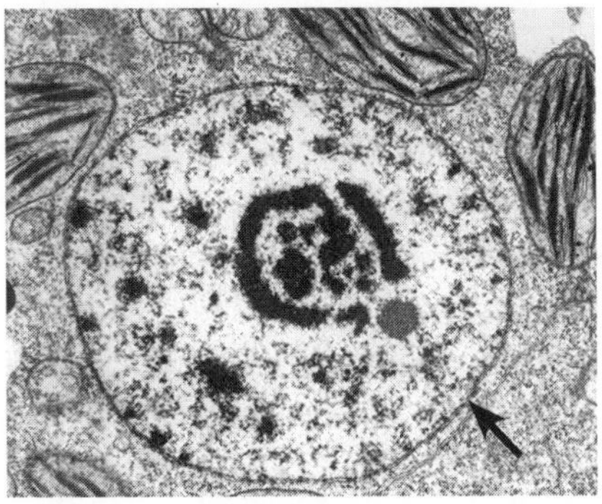

BF

5. (a) Name this large circular organelle (arrowed):

   (b) State which kind of cell(s) this organelle would be found in:

   (c) Describe the function of this organelle:

   (d) Label three features relating to this organelle in the photograph.

© 2015 **BIOZONE** International
ISBN: 978-1-927309-31-5
Photocopying Prohibited

43 Packaging Proteins

Key Idea: Proteins destined for secretion are produced in the rough endoplasmic reticulum and transported in transport vesicles to the Golgi for processing. Vesicles containing mature proteins bud from the Golgi and may fuse with the plasma membrane to secrete the proteins or form lysosomes which help breakdown cells products.

The **Golgi** is made up of stacks of flattened membranes in the shape of curved sacs. At its *cis*- face, the Golgi receives transport vesicles from the ER. Transported substances are modified, stored and shipped from the *trans*- face to the surface of the cell or other destinations.

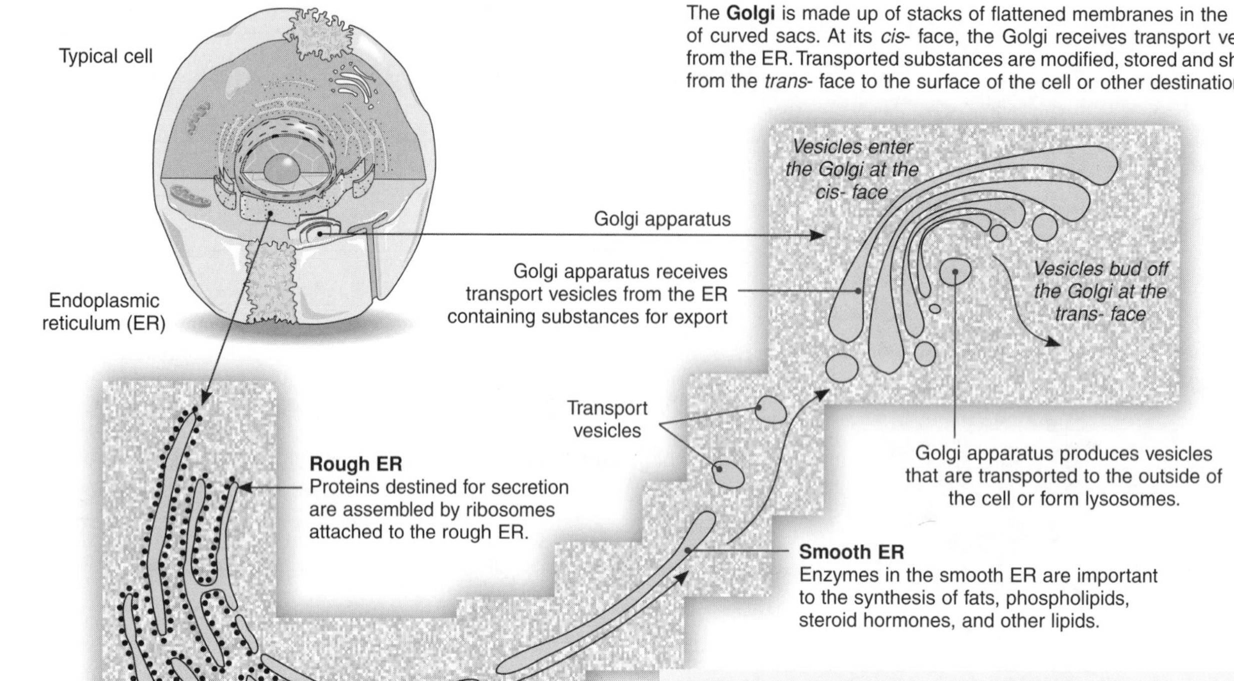

Typical cell
Endoplasmic reticulum (ER)
Golgi apparatus
Vesicles enter the Golgi at the cis- face
Golgi apparatus receives transport vesicles from the ER containing substances for export
Vesicles bud off the Golgi at the trans- face
Transport vesicles
Golgi apparatus produces vesicles that are transported to the outside of the cell or form lysosomes.
Rough ER
Proteins destined for secretion are assembled by ribosomes attached to the rough ER.
Smooth ER
Enzymes in the smooth ER are important to the synthesis of fats, phospholipids, steroid hormones, and other lipids.

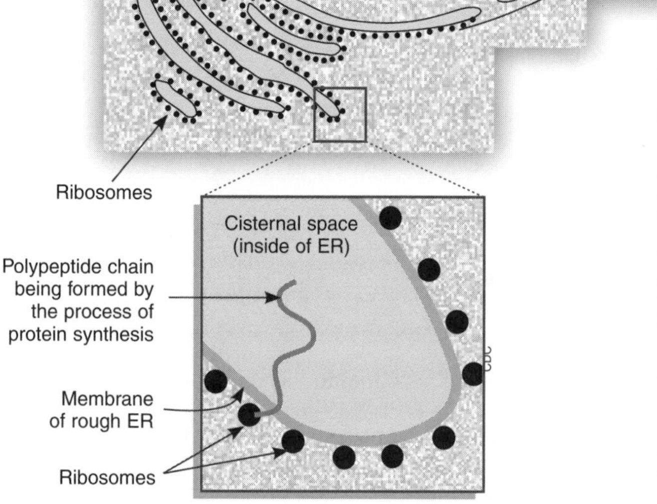

Ribosomes
Cisternal space (inside of ER)
Polypeptide chain being formed by the process of protein synthesis
Membrane of rough ER
Ribosomes

Creating proteins for secretion

1. A polypeptide chain grows from a bound ribosome.
2. The chain is threaded through the ER membrane into the cisternal space, possibly through a pore.
3. As it enters the cisternal space inside the ER, it folds up into its correct 3-dimensional shape.
4. Most proteins destined for secretion are glycoproteins (i.e. they are proteins with carbohydrates added to them). The carbohydrate is attached to the protein by enzymes.
5. The ER membrane keeps proteins for secretion separate from proteins made by free ribosomes in the cytosol.
6. Proteins destined for secretion leave the ER wrapped in transport vesicles which bud off from the end of the ER.
7. These vesicles are received by the Golgi apparatus, modified, stored and eventually shipped to the cell's surface, where they can be exported from the cell by exocytosis.

1. Using examples, explain what is meant by a macromolecule: ______________________

____

2. Why are polypeptides requiring transport synthesised by membrane-bound (rather than free) ribosomes?

____

____

3. Why are most proteins destined for secretion from the cell glycoproteins? ______________________

____

4. Briefly describe the roles of the following organelles in the production of macromolecules:

(a) Rough ER: ______________________

(b) Smooth ER: ______________________

(c) Golgi apparatus: ______________________

(d) Transport vesicles: ______________________

© 2015 **BIOZONE** International
ISBN:978-1-927309-31-5
Photocopying Prohibited

44 The Role of ATP in Cells

Key Idea: Cells need energy to perform the functions essential to life. This energy is provided by cellular respiration and stored in the molecule ATP.

All organisms require energy to be able to perform many of the metabolic processes required for them to function, grow, and reproduce. This energy is obtained through cellular respiration, a set of metabolic reactions which ultimately convert biochemical energy from 'food' into the energy-carrying molecule **ATP** (adenosine triphosphate). ATP is a phosphorylated nucleotide and is regarded as a universal energy carrier, transferring chemical energy within the cell for use in metabolic processes such as biosynthesis, cell division, cell signalling, thermoregulation, cell mobility, and active transport of substances across membranes.

The mitochondrion

Most of an organism's ATP is produced in the mitochondria by a process called cellular respiration. ATP is used to carry out chemical reactions required to sustain life.

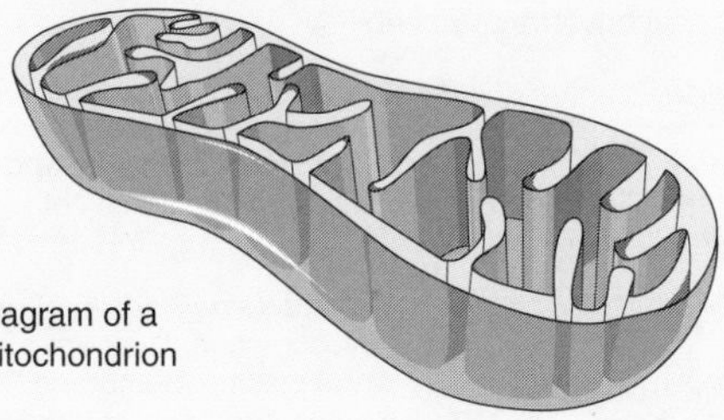

Diagram of a mitochondrion

The chloroplast

The chloroplast is the site of photosynthesis in plant cells. During the first phase of photosynthesis, ATP is produced. The ATP is ultimately used to produce a carbohydrate called glucose during the second phase of photosynthesis. The glucose has many different uses in the cell, including making more ATP via cellular respiration.

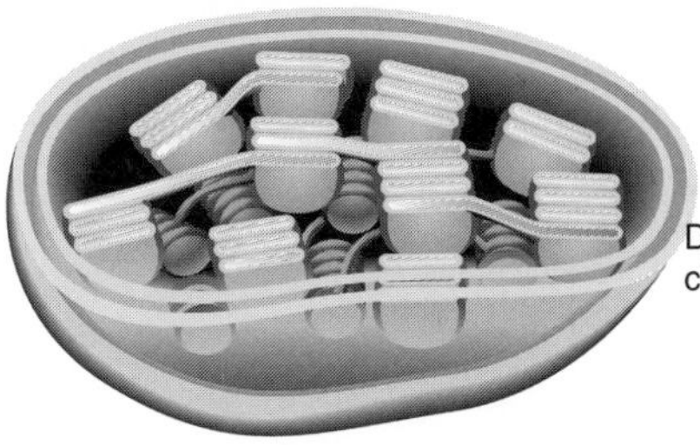

Diagram of a chloroplast

What is ATP used for?

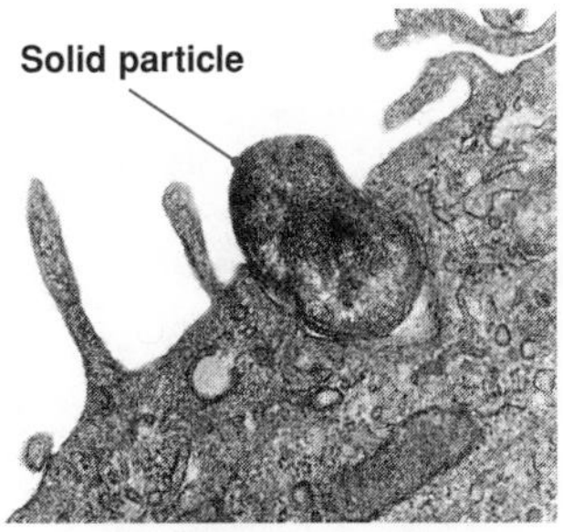
Solid particle

The energy released from the hydrolysis of ATP is used to actively transport molecules and substances across the cellular membrane. Phagocytosis (above), (the engulfment of solid particles) is one such example.

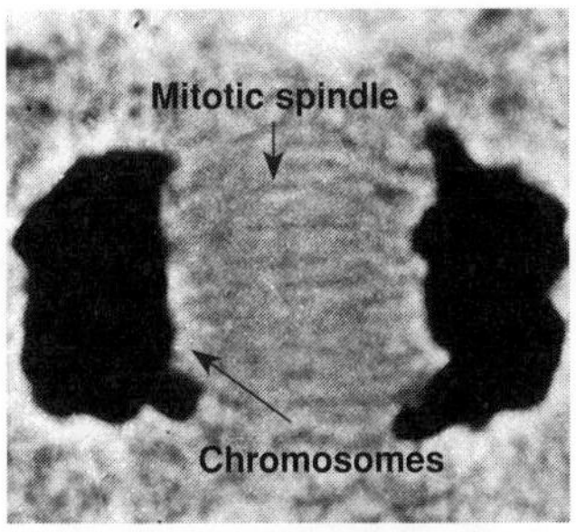
Mitotic spindle
Chromosomes

Cell division (mitosis), as observed in this onion cell, requires ATP to proceed. Formation of the mitotic spindle and chromosome separation are two aspects of cell division which require energy from ATP hydrolysis to occur.

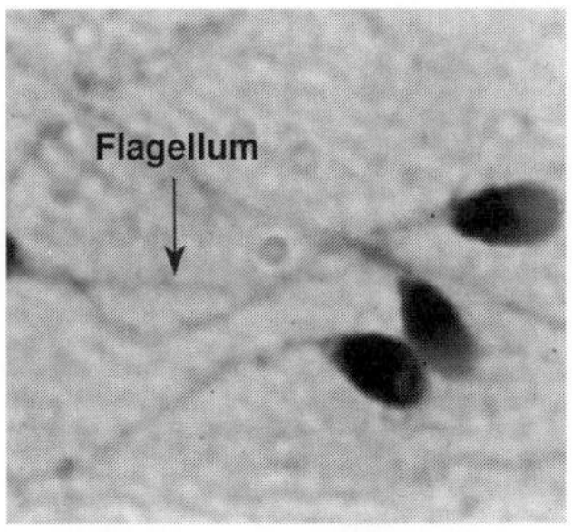
Flagellum

The hydrolysis of ATP provides the energy for motile cells to achieve movement via a tail-like structure called a flagellum. For example, mammalian sperm must be able to move to the ovum to fertilise it.

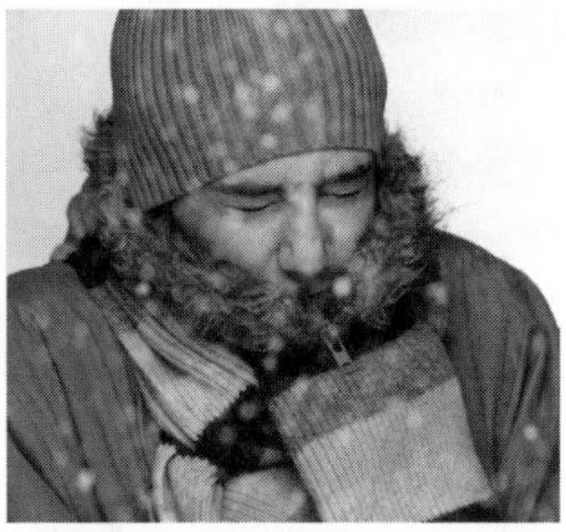

Maintaining body temperature requires energy. To maintain body heat, muscular activity increases (e.g. shivering). Cooling by sweating also requires expenditure of energy. It involves secretion from glands in the skin.

1. What is ATP? ______________________________

____

2. Where is ATP produced in cells? ______________________________

____

____

3. Describe some of the ways in which ATP is used by cells: ______________________________

____

____

____

____

____

© 2015 BIOZONE International
ISBN: 978-1-927309-31-5
Photocopying Prohibited

45 Prokaryotic Cells

Key Idea: Prokaryotic cells lack many of the features of eukaryotic cells, including membrane-bound organelles.

Bacterial (prokaryotic) cells are much smaller than eukaryotic cells and lack many eukaryotic features, such as a distinct nucleus and membrane-bound cellular organelles. The cell wall is an important feature. It is a complex, multi-layered structure and has a role in the organism's ability to cause disease. A generalised prokaryote, *E. coli*, is shown below.

E. coli structure

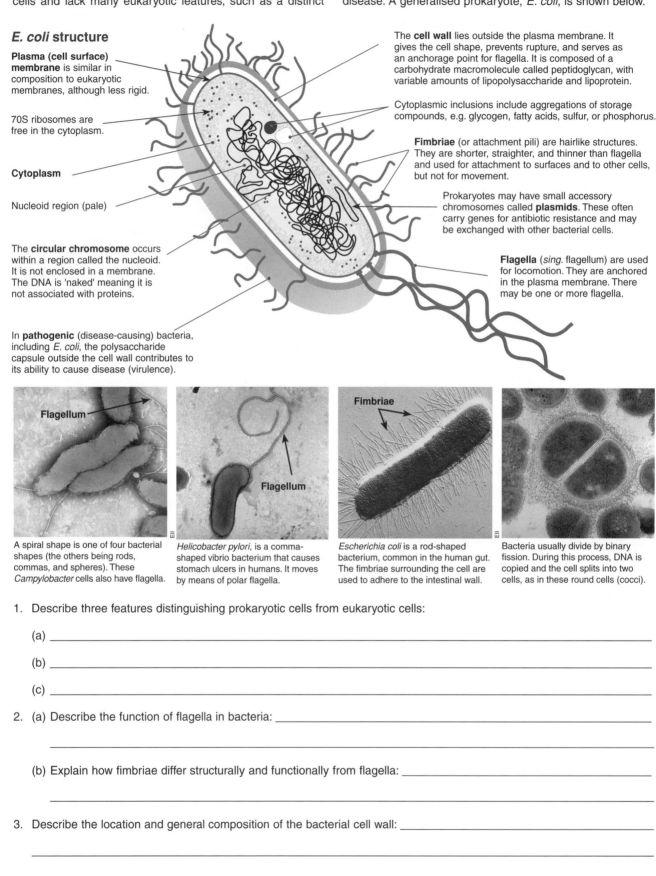

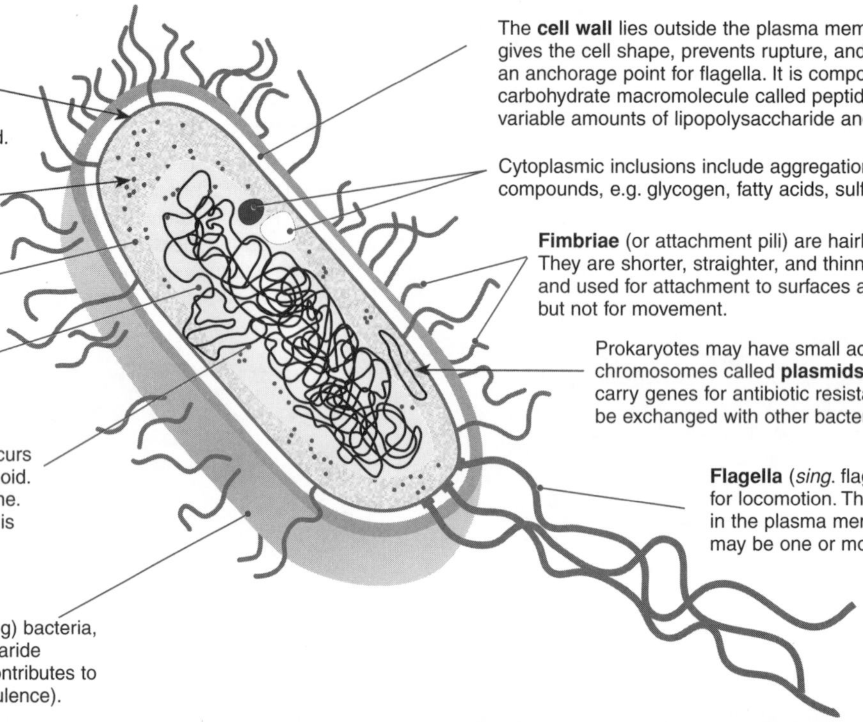
Plasma (cell surface) membrane is similar in composition to eukaryotic membranes, although less rigid.
70S ribosomes are free in the cytoplasm.
Cytoplasm
Nucleoid region (pale)
The **circular chromosome** occurs within a region called the nucleoid. It is not enclosed in a membrane. The DNA is 'naked' meaning it is not associated with proteins.
In **pathogenic** (disease-causing) bacteria, including *E. coli*, the polysaccharide capsule outside the cell wall contributes to its ability to cause disease (virulence).
The **cell wall** lies outside the plasma membrane. It gives the cell shape, prevents rupture, and serves as an anchorage point for flagella. It is composed of a carbohydrate macromolecule called peptidoglycan, with variable amounts of lipopolysaccharide and lipoprotein.
Cytoplasmic inclusions include aggregations of storage compounds, e.g. glycogen, fatty acids, sulfur, or phosphorus.
Fimbriae (or attachment pili) are hairlike structures. They are shorter, straighter, and thinner than flagella and used for attachment to surfaces and to other cells, but not for movement.
Prokaryotes may have small accessory chromosomes called **plasmids**. These often carry genes for antibiotic resistance and may be exchanged with other bacterial cells.
Flagella (*sing.* flagellum) are used for locomotion. They are anchored in the plasma membrane. There may be one or more flagella.

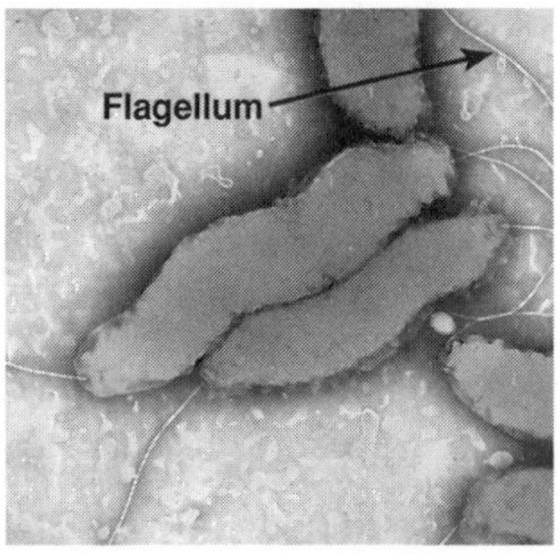
Flagellum
A spiral shape is one of four bacterial shapes (the others being rods, commas, and spheres). These *Campylobacter* cells also have flagella.

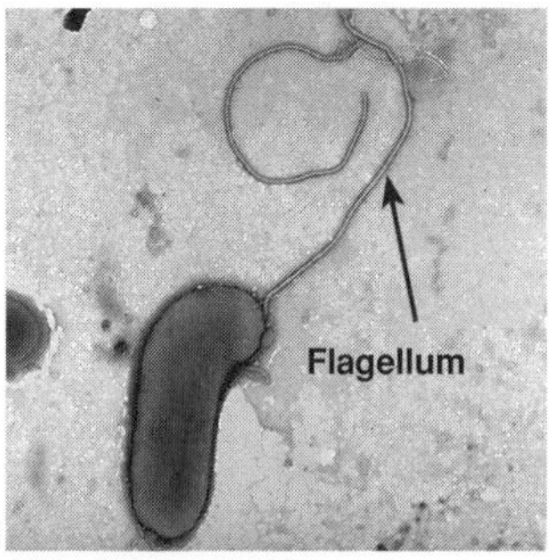
Flagellum
Helicobacter pylori, is a comma-shaped vibrio bacterium that causes stomach ulcers in humans. It moves by means of polar flagella.

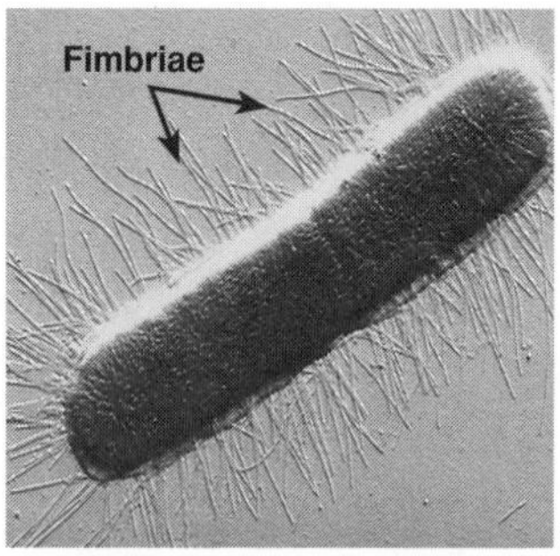
Fimbriae
Escherichia coli is a rod-shaped bacterium, common in the human gut. The fimbriae surrounding the cell are used to adhere to the intestinal wall.

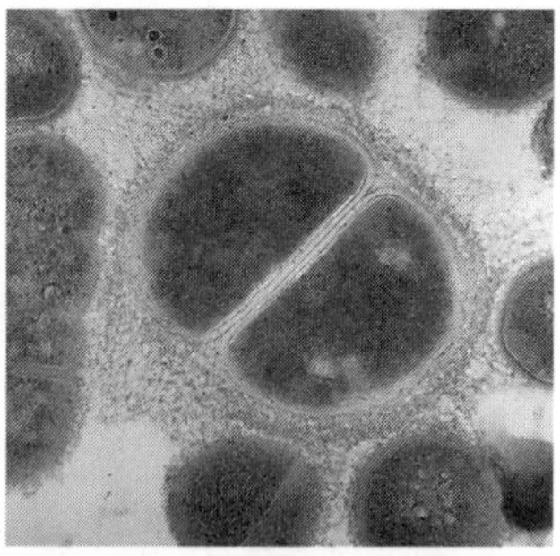
Bacteria usually divide by binary fission. During this process, DNA is copied and the cell splits into two cells, as in these round cells (cocci).

1. Describe three features distinguishing prokaryotic cells from eukaryotic cells:

   (a) ______

   (b) ______

   (c) ______

2. (a) Describe the function of flagella in bacteria: ______

   (b) Explain how fimbriae differ structurally and functionally from flagella: ______

3. Describe the location and general composition of the bacterial cell wall: ______

4. What is the purpose of binary fission in prokaryotes: ______

© 2015 BIOZONE International
ISBN:978-1-927309-31-5
Photocopying Prohibited

46 Prokaryotic and Eukaryotic Cell Summary

Key Idea: Cells are classified as either prokaryotic or eukaryotic and are distinguished on the basis of their size, internal organisation, and complexity.

Cells are divided into two broad groups based on their size and organisation. Prokaryotic cells are small, single cells with a simple internal structure. Eukaryotic cells are larger, more complex cells. All multicellular and some unicellular organisms are eukaryotic.

1. (a) Use your knowledge to list the unique features of prokaryotic and eukaryotic cells in the space below.

   (b) Under common features, list the features that both prokaryotic and eukaryotic cells have in common.

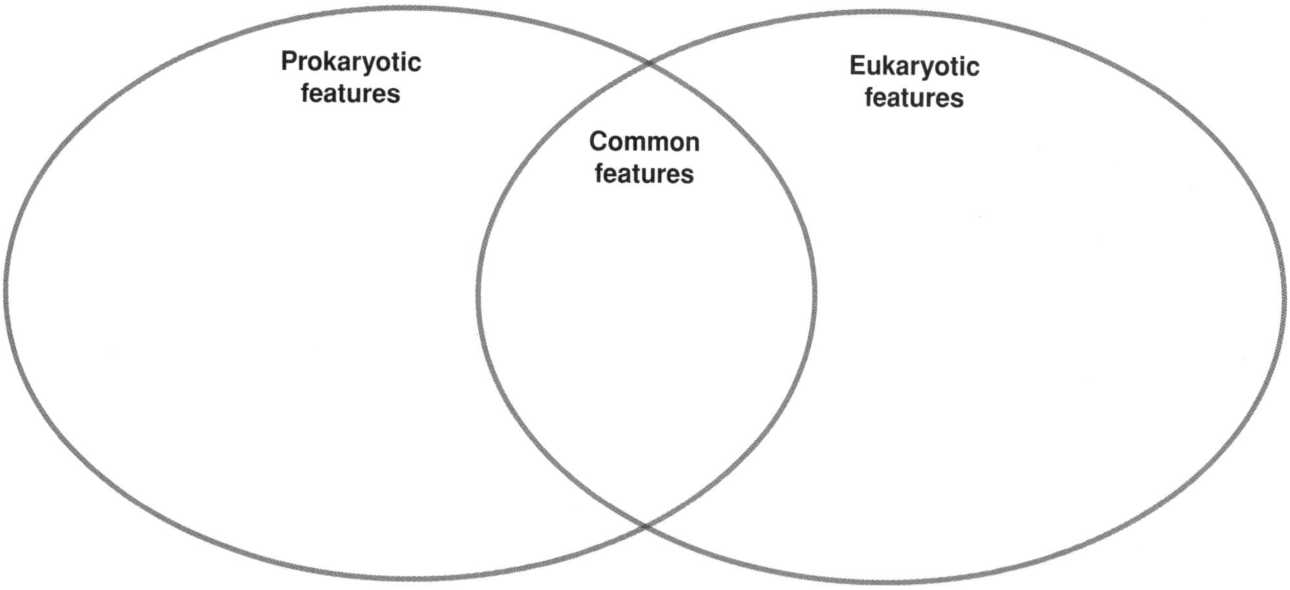
Prokaryotic features
Common features
Eukaryotic features

2. Study the photos below and determine if they are prokaryotic or eukaryotic cells:

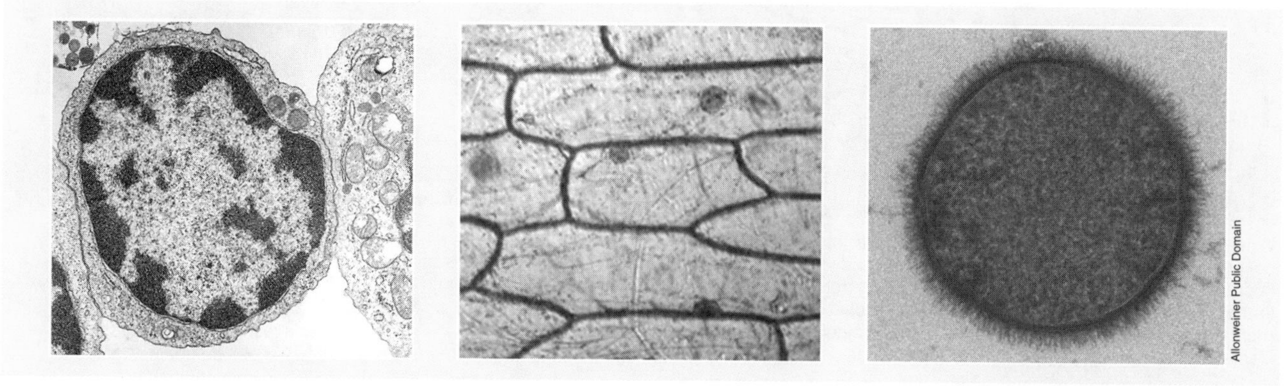
Allonweiner Public Domain

(a) ______________ (b) ______________ (c) ______________

3. (a) Identify the regions indicated by A and B on the diagrams (right):

   A: ______________________________

   B: ______________________________

   (b) Compare and contrast the structure and location of genetic material in a prokaryote and eukaryote cell:

   ____

   ____

   ____

   ____

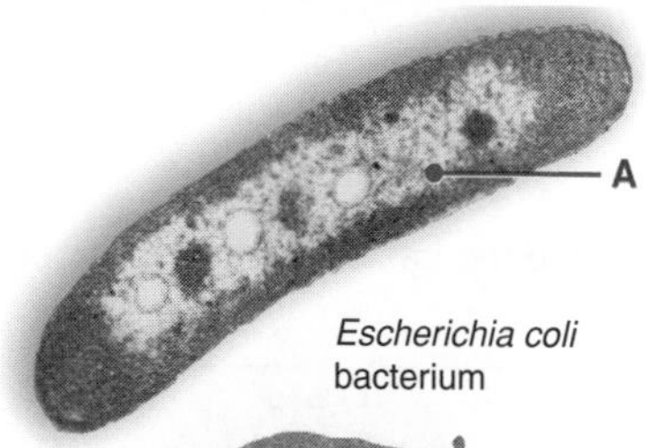
A

Escherichia coli bacterium

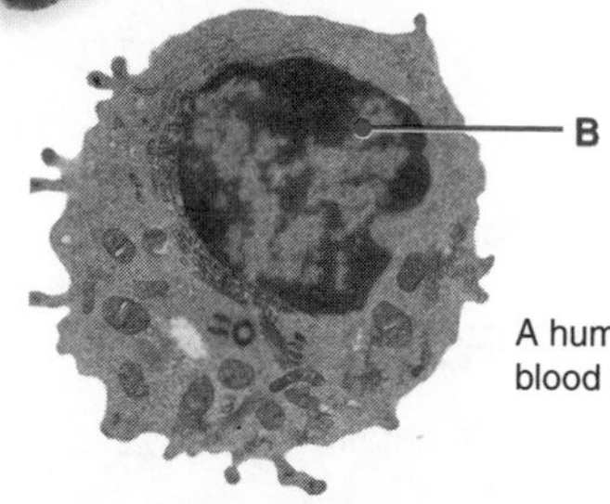
B

A human white blood cell

© 2015 BIOZONE International
ISBN: 978-1-927309-31-5
Photocopying Prohibited

47 Viruses

Key Idea: A virus is an infectious, highly specialised intracellular parasite. They are acellular and non-living.

Viruses are disease-causing agents (**pathogens**), which replicate (reproduce themselves) only inside the living cells of other organisms. Viruses are acellular, meaning they are not made up of cells, so they do not conform to the existing criteria upon which a five or six kingdom classification system is based. A typical virus contains genetic material (DNA or RNA) encased in a protein coat (capsid). Some viruses have an additional membrane, called an envelope, surrounding the capsid. Many viruses have glycoprotein receptor spikes on their envelopes that help them to attach to surface of the host cell they are infecting. Viruses vary greatly in their appearance and the type of host they infect (below).

Viruses are not organisms! Viruses are metabolically inert until they are inside the host cell and hijacking its metabolic machinery to make new viral particles. However, they are often called microorganisms.

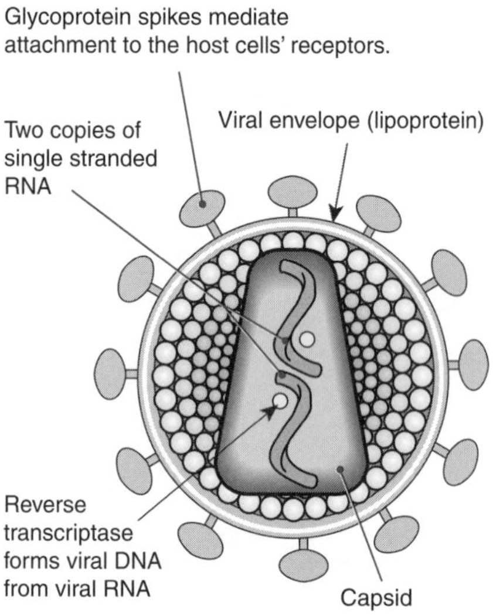
Glycoprotein spikes mediate attachment to the host cells' receptors.
Viral envelope (lipoprotein)
Two copies of single stranded RNA
Reverse transcriptase forms viral DNA from viral RNA
Capsid

Structure of HIV, an enveloped retrovirus.

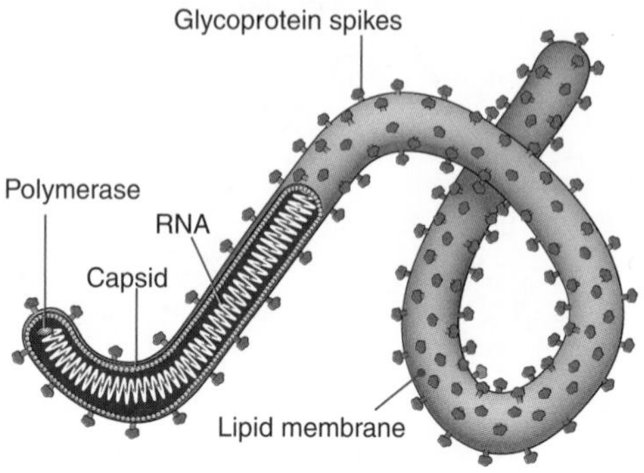
Glycoprotein spikes
Polymerase
RNA
Capsid
Lipid membrane

Structure of Ebola virus, an RNA filovirus that causes Ebola haemorrhagic fever.

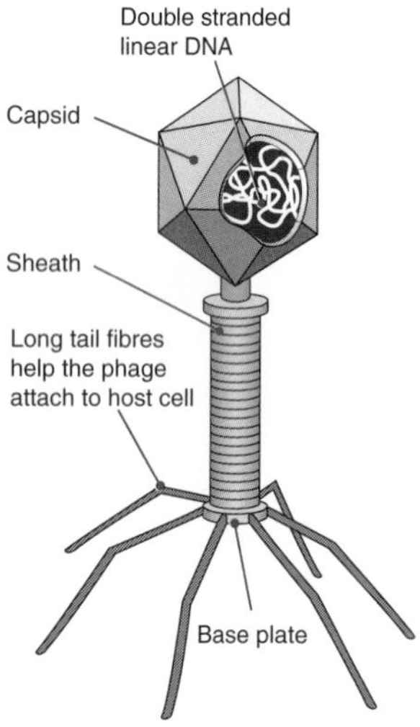
Double stranded linear DNA
Capsid
Sheath
Long tail fibres help the phage attach to host cell
Base plate

Structure of Lambda phage, a bacteriophage that infects E.coli.

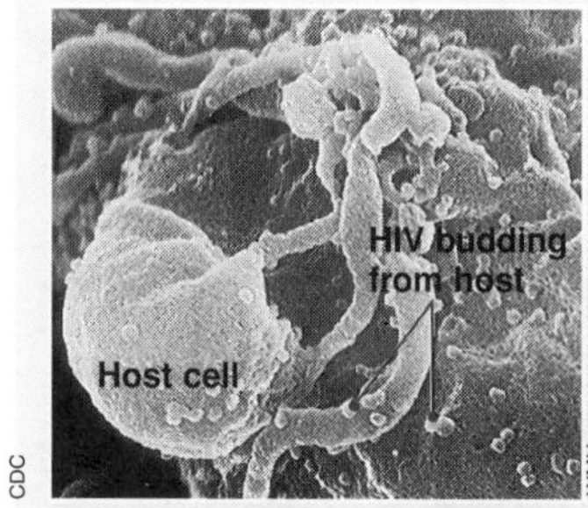
HIV budding from host
Host cell
CDC

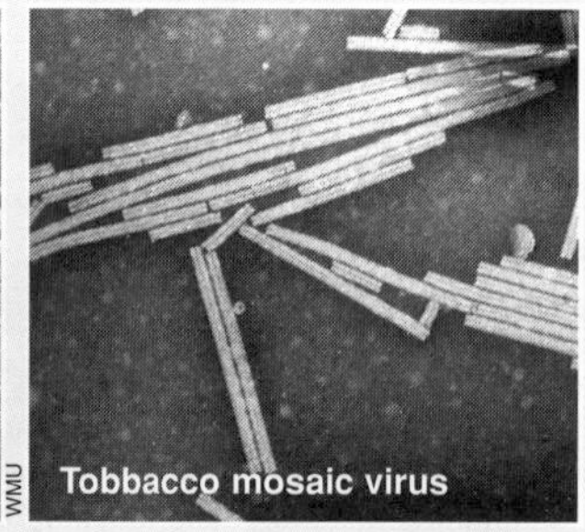
Tobbacco mosaic virus
WMU

When viral replication is complete, new viral particles (**virons**) leave the host cell to infect more cells. In animals, enveloped viruses bud from the host cell, e.g. HIV (left). Plant viruses cannot bud from the host cell due to the rigid cell wall. Instead, plant viruses, e.g. tobacco mosaic virus (right), move through the plasmodesmata that connect neighbouring plant cells.

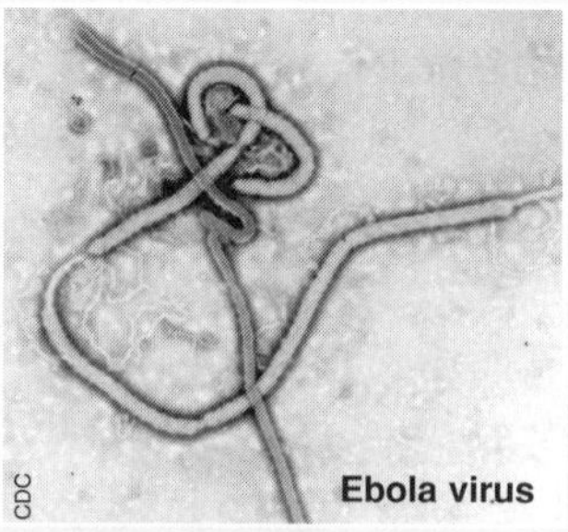
Ebola virus
CDC

Viruses cause a wide variety of common human diseases, e.g. colds, influenza, and life-threatening diseases such as AIDS and Ebola (above).

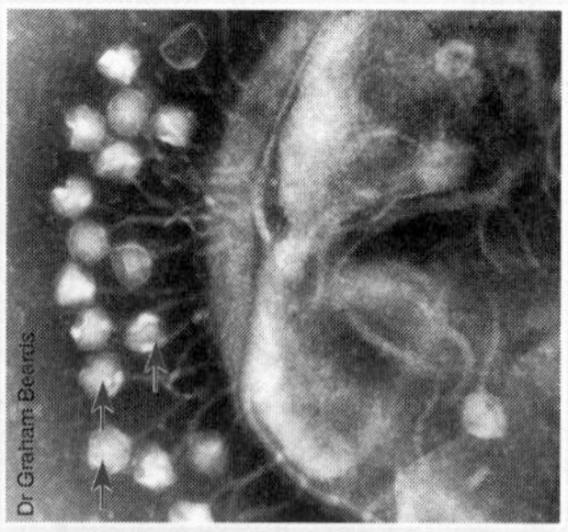
Dr Graham Beards

Bacteriophages (arrowed) infect bacterial cells. They use tail fibres to attach to the host and a contractile region below the capsid to inject their DNA into the cell.

1. Why are viruses considered to be non-living? ___

___

___

2. Describe the basic structure of a generalised virus: ___

___

___

3. Describe the purpose of the following:

(a) Glycoprotein spikes: ___

(b) A bacteriophage's tail fibres: ___

(c) Protein capsid: ___

© 2015 BIOZONE International
ISBN:978-1-927309-31-5
Photocopying Prohibited

48 Chapter Review

Summarise what you know about this topic under the headings provided. You can draw diagrams or mind maps, or write short notes to organise your thoughts. Use the images and hints to help you and refer back to the introduction to check the points covered:

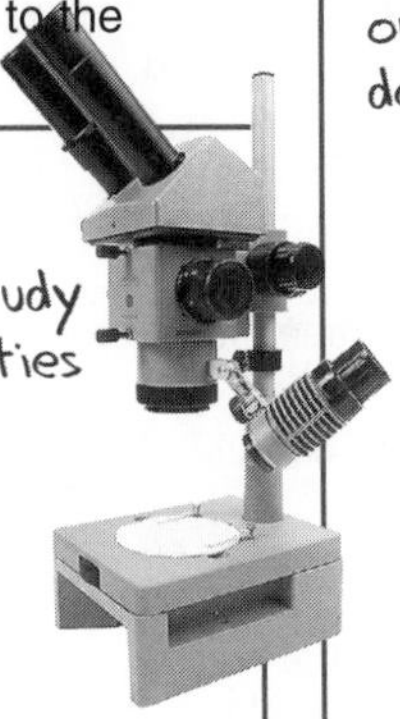

The microscope in cell studies

HINT: Explain the use of microscopy to study cells and distinguish between the properties and use of different microscopes.

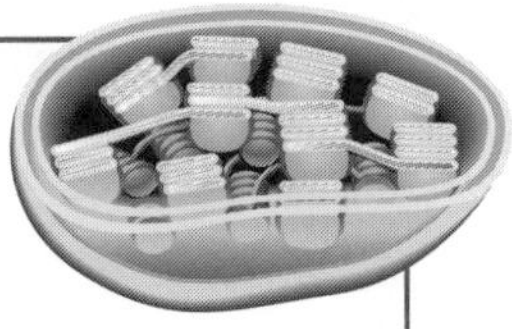

Eukaryotic cell structure

HINT: Identify the typical organelles of eukaryotic cells and describe their function.

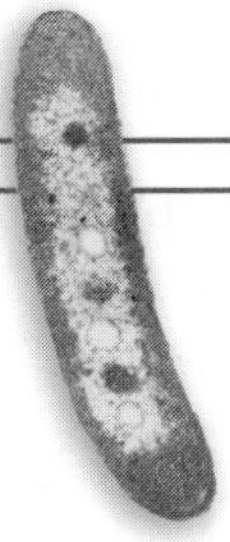

Prokaryotic and eukaryotic cells

HINT: Compare and contrast prokaryotes and eukaryotes.

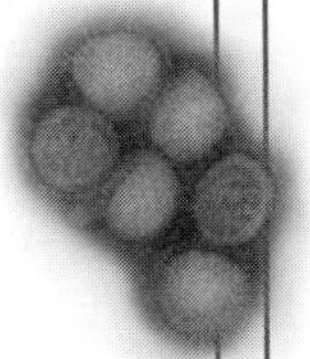

Viruses

HINT: Describe the features of a generalised virus.

© 2015 BIOZONE International
ISBN: 978-1-927309-31-5
Photocopying Prohibited

49 KEY TERMS AND IDEAS: Did You Get It?

1. Test your vocabulary by matching each term to its definition, as identified by its preceding letter code.

cell wall ....

chloroplast ....

cytoplasm ....

eukaryotic ....

magnification ....

mitochondrion ....

nucleus ....

optical microscope ....

organelle ....

plasma membrane ....

prokaryotic ....

resolution ....

stain ....

virus ....

A Organelle responsible for producing the cell's ATP. It appears oval in shape with an outer double membrane and a convoluted interior membrane. Contains its own circular DNA.

B With reference to cells, lacking a distinct nucleus and with no membrane-bound organelles DNA is present as a single, circular, naked chromosome.

C Cell types with a distinct membrane-bound nucleus and membrane-bound organelles.

D A chemical that binds to parts of the cell and allows those parts to be seen more easily under a microscope.

E How many times larger an image is than the original object.

F The watery contents of the cell within the plasma membrane, but excluding the contents of the nucleus.

G A structural and functional part of the cell usually bound within its own membrane. Examples include the mitochondria and chloroplasts.

H Lipid bilayer membrane surrounding the cell. Proteins are embedded in it and are responsible for the passage of material into and out of the cell.

I Membrane-bound region within a eukaryotic cell where the chromosomes are found.

J Microscope that uses lenses to focus visible light waves passing through an object into an image.

K A structure, present in plants and bacteria, which is found outside the plasma membrane and gives rigidity to the cell.

L The ability to distinguish between close together but separate objects.

M An organelle found in photosynthetic organisms such as plants, which contains chlorophyll and in which the reactions of photosynthesis take place.

N A non-cellular obligate intracellular parasite, requiring a living host to reproduce.

2. (a) Identify organelle 1: ______________________

(b) The organelle in (a) is found in a plant cell / animal cell / both plant and animal cells (circle the correct answer).

(c) Identify organelle 2: ______________________

(d) The organelle in (c) is found in a plant / animal cell / plant and animal cell (circle the correct answer).

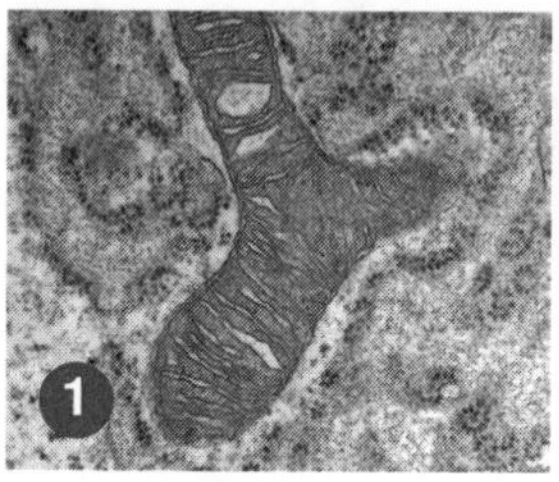
1

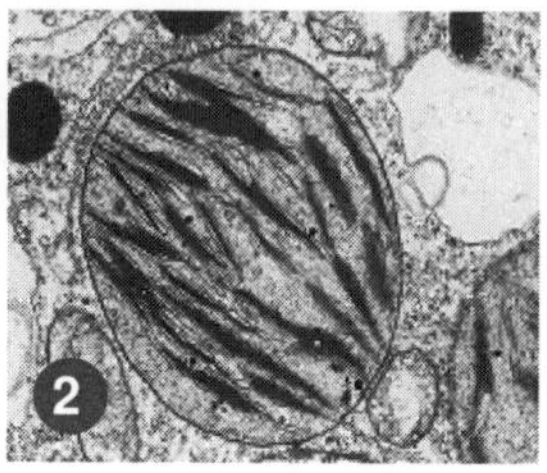
2

3. Match the statements in the table below to form a complete paragraph. The left hand column is in the correct order, the right hand column is not.

Cells are the basic...	...such as photosynthesis or respiration.
A cell is enclosed by a plasma membrane...	...a cell wall of cellulose.
Plant cells have…	...do not contain membrane-bound organelles.
Animal cells do...	...units of life.
Eukaryotic cells contain many different types of organelle...	....not have a cell wall.
Each organelle carries out a specific function in the cell...	...some of which are composed of membranes.
Prokaryotic cells...	...made of a phospholipid bilayer

4. What are the four groups that eukaryotes are commonly divided into? ____

____

TEST

© 2015 **BIOZONE** International
ISBN:978-1-927309-31-5
Photocopying Prohibited

Topic 2 Biological molecules

Key terms

amino acid
Benedict's test
biuret test
carbohydrate
colorimetry
condensation
denaturation
dipeptide
disaccharide
emulsion test
fatty acid
fibrous protein
hydrolysis
globular protein
glycerol
hydrogen bond
iodine test
lipid
macromolecule
monomer
monosaccharide
phospholipid
polymer
polypeptide
polysaccharide
primary structure
protein
quaternary structure
secondary structure
tertiary structure
triglyceride
water

2.1 Testing for biological molecules

Learning outcomes

		Activity number
☐	1 Describe how tests for biological molecules are used, including to identify the contents of mixtures of molecules and to follow the activity of digestive enzymes.	51
☐	2 **PRAC** Use simple tests for reducing and non-reducing sugars, starch, proteins, and lipids to identify the contents of solutions.	51
☐	3 **PRAC** Use a semi-quantitative Benedict's test on a reducing sugar (e.g. glucose) using dilution to produce a standard for estimating concentration.	52

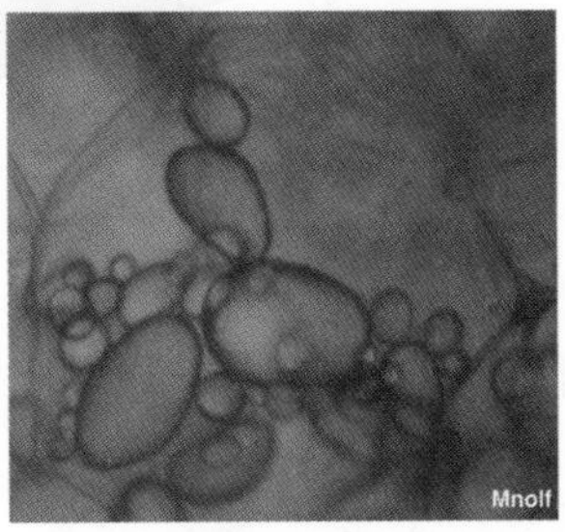
Mnolf

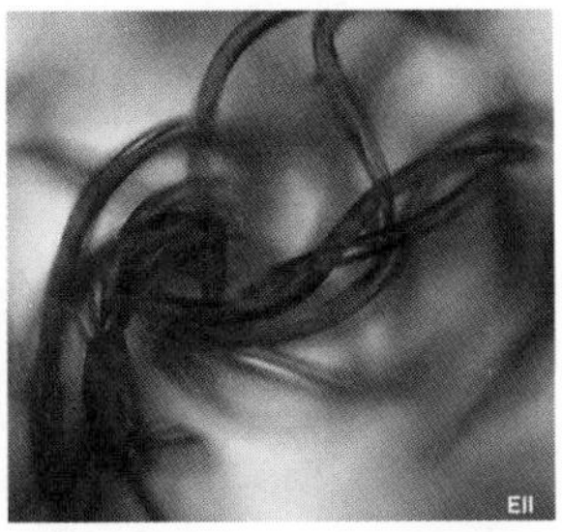
Ell

2.2 Carbohydrates and lipids

Learning outcomes

		Activity number
☐	4 Outline the roles of carbohydrates and lipids in providing and storing energy and in providing barriers around cells (as cell walls and membranes).	50
☐	5 Describe the ring structure and properties of α- and β-glucose.	53 54
☐	6 Distinguish between monomer, polymer, macromolecule, monosaccharide, disaccharide, and polysaccharide.	53
☐	7 Describe how glycosidic bonds are formed in the synthesis (by condensation) of a disaccharide (e.g. sucrose, lactose, maltose) and a polysaccharide.	55 56
☐	8 Describe how glycosidic bonds broken in the hydrolysis of polysaccharides and disaccharides, including reference to the non-reducing sugar test.	55 56
☐	9 Compare and contrast the structure of glucose polymers: starch, cellulose, and glycogen. Relate the structure to their biological function in each case.	56 57
☐	10 Describe the structure of a triglyceride (fat or oil) with reference to the formation of ester bonds. Relate the structure of triglycerides to their biological roles.	58
☐	11 Describe the structure of a phospholipid, including reference to their amphipathic nature. Relate the structure to the biological role of lipids	59

2.3 Proteins and water

Learning outcomes

		Activity number
☐	12 Understand how protein structure is related to function.	61
☐	13 Describe the general structure of an amino acid. Explain how dipeptides and polypeptides are formed and broken apart by condensation and hydrolysis.	60
☐	14 Describe the levels of protein structure to include primary (1°), secondary (2°), tertiary (3°), and quaternary structure (4°), including reference to the types of bonding responsible for holding protein molecules in shape.	62
☐	15 Describe the structure of the globular protein haemoglobin and the fibrous protein collagen. For each, relate its structure to its functional role in the body.	63
☐	16 Describe the structure of water,including reference to the hydrogen bonding between water molecules. Relate the properties of water to its biological roles.	64 65

50 The Biochemical Nature of Cells

Key Idea: The main components of a cell are water and compounds of carbon, hydrogen, nitrogen, and oxygen.

Water is the main component of cells and organisms, providing an aqueous environment in which metabolic reactions can occur. Apart from water, most other substances in cells are compounds of carbon, hydrogen, oxygen, and nitrogen. Carbon can combine with many other elements to form a large number of carbon-based (or organic) molecules. The organic molecules that make up living things can be grouped into four broad classes: carbohydrates, lipids, proteins, and nucleic acids. In addition, a small number of inorganic ions are also components of larger molecules.

Centrioles

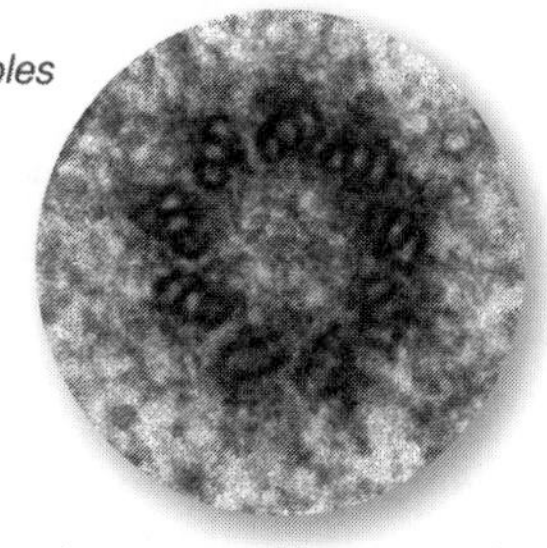

Proteins have an enormous number of structural and functional roles in plants and animals, e.g. as enzymes, structural materials (such as collagen), in transport, and movement (e.g. cytoskeleton and centrioles).

Chloroplasts in plant cells

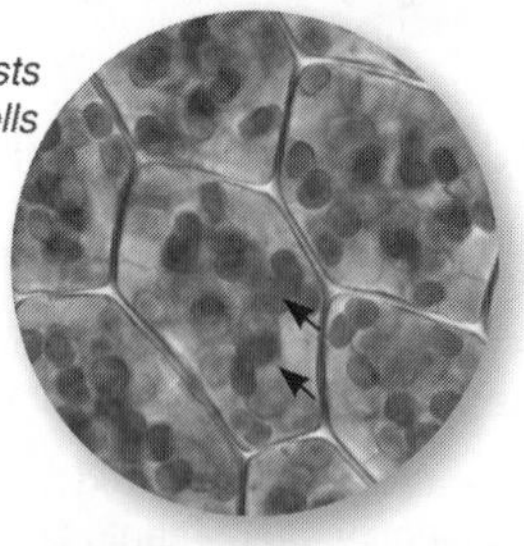

Inorganic ions: Dissolved ions participate in metabolic reactions and are components of larger organic molecules, e.g. Mg^{2+} is a component of the green chlorophyll pigment in the chloroplasts of green plants.

Plant epidermis

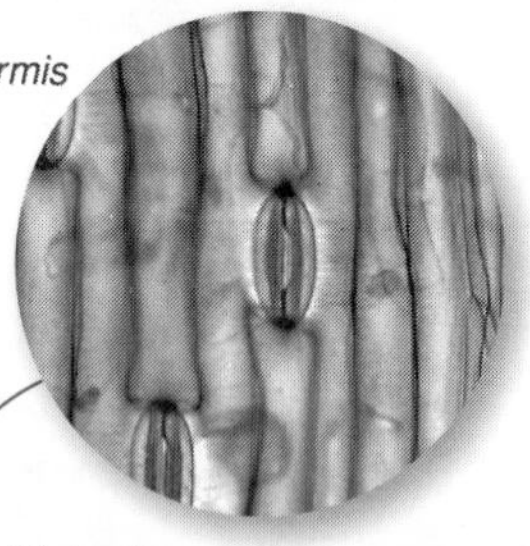

Water is a major component of cells: many substances dissolve in it and metabolic reactions occur in it. In plant cells, fluid pressure against the cell wall provides turgor, which supports the cell.

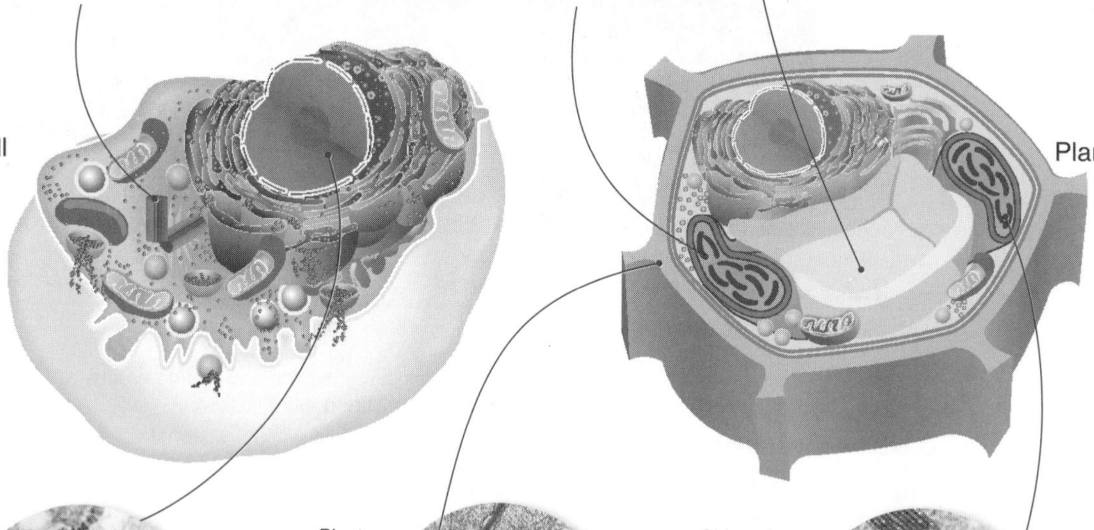
Animal cell
Plant cell

Chromosome

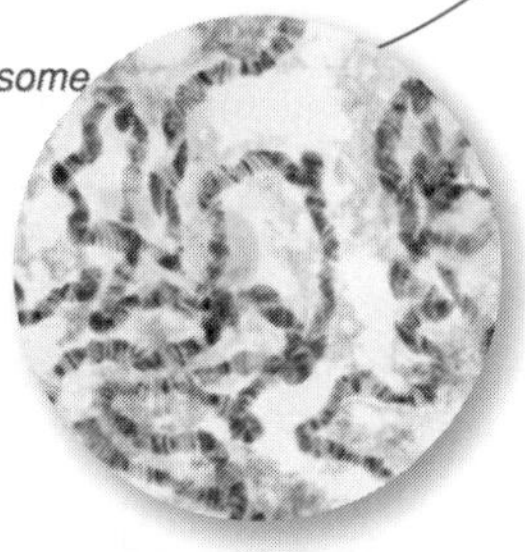

Nucleotides and nucleic acids
Nucleic acids encode information for the construction and functioning of an organism. ATP, a nucleotide derivative, is the energy carrier of the cell.

Plant cell wall

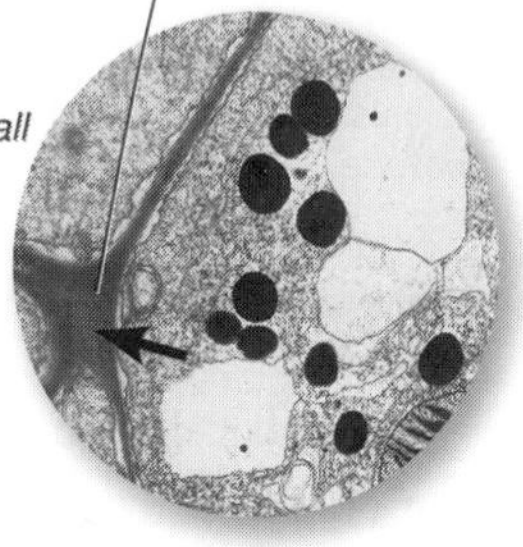

Carbohydrates form the structural components of cells, e.g. cellulose cell walls (arrowed). They are important in energy storage and they are involved in cellular recognition.

Chloroplast membranes

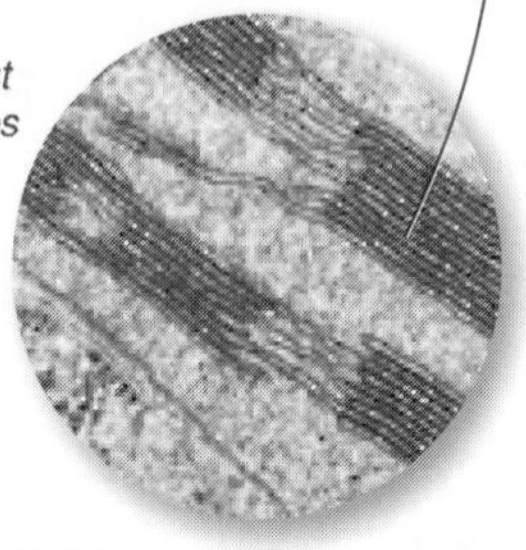

Lipids provide a concentrated source of energy. Phospholipids are a major component of cellular membranes, including the membranes of organelles such as chloroplasts and mitochondria.

1. Summarise the role of each of the following cell components:

(a) Carbohydrates: ____________________

(b) Lipids: ____________________

(c) Proteins: ____________________

(d) Nucleic acids: ____________________

(e) Inorganic ions: ____________________

(f) Water: ____________________

© 2015 BIOZONE International
ISBN:978-1-927309-31-5
Photocopying Prohibited

51 Testing for Biological Molecules

Key Idea: Qualitative biochemical tests detect the presence of a specific molecule in food.

Qualitative biochemical tests can be used to detect the presence of molecules such as lipids, proteins, or carbohydrates (sugars and starch). However, they cannot be used directly to determine absolute concentrations or distinguish between different molecules of the same type (e.g. different sugars in a mixed solution).

Simple food tests

Proteins: The Biuret test

Reagent:	Biuret solution.
Procedure:	A sample is added to biuret solution and gently heated.
Positive result:	Solution turns from blue to lilac.

Starch: The iodine test

Reagent:	Iodine-potassium iodide solution (Lugol's).
Procedure:	Iodine solution is added to the sample.
Positive result:	Blue-black staining occurs.

Lipids: The emulsion test

Reagent:	Ethanol.
Procedure:	The sample is shaken with ethanol. After settling, the liquid portion is distilled and mixed with water.
Positive result:	The solution turns into a cloudy-white emulsion of suspended lipid molecules.

Sugars: The Benedict's test

Reagent:	Benedict's solution.
Procedure:	Non reducing sugars: The sample is boiled with dilute hydrochloric acid (acid hydrolysis), then cooled and neutralised. A test for reducing sugars is then performed. Reducing sugar: Benedict's solution is added, and the sample is placed in a water bath.
Positive result:	Solution turns from blue to orange to red-brown.

A qualitative test for reducing sugar

To determine whether this muffin contains any reducing sugars (e.g. glucose), the **Benedict's test** for reducing sugar is carried out.

The muffin is placed in a blender with some water and mixed until it forms an homogenous (uniform) mixture.

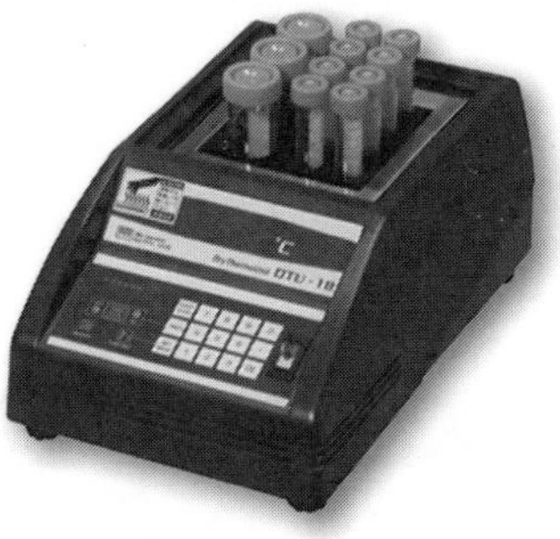

2 -3 mL of the muffin mixture is placed into a test tube with 1 mL of Benedict's solution. The tubes are heated for 4 -10 minutes.

The intensity of the colour depends on the concentration of glucose present in the sample. The darker the colour, the more glucose is present. A **colorimetric analysis** enables the amount of glucose present to be quantified (see the following activity).

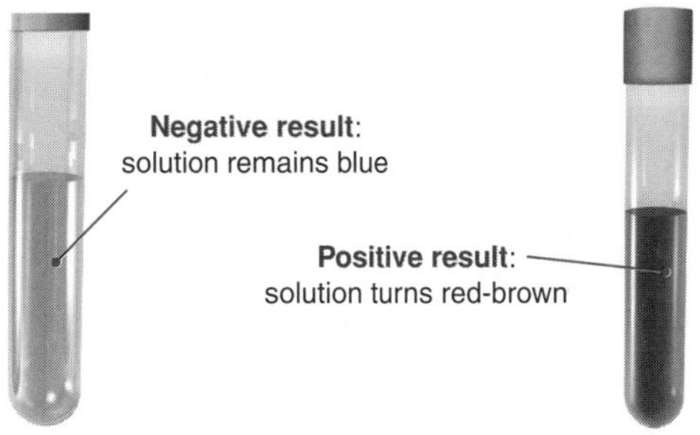
Negative result:
solution remains blue
Positive result:
solution turns red-brown

1. Explain why lipids must be mixed in ethanol before they will form an emulsion in water: ______

2. Explain why the emulsion of lipids, ethanol, and water appears cloudy: ______

3. What is the purpose of the acid hydrolysis step when testing for non-reducing sugars with Benedict's reagent?

4. What are the limitations of qualitative tests such as those described above? ______

© 2015 **BIOZONE** International
ISBN: 978-1-927309-31-5
Photocopying Prohibited

52 Colorimetry

Key Idea: Colorimetric analysis can be used to determine the concentration of a substance in a solution.

Colorimetric analysis is a simple quantitative technique used to determine the concentration of a specific substance in a solution. A specific reagent is added to the test solution where it reacts with the substance of interest to produce a colour. The samples are placed in a colorimeter, which measures the solution's absorbance at a specific wavelength. A dilution series can be used to produce a calibration curve, which can then be used to quantify that substance in samples of unknown concentration. This is illustrated for glucose in the example below.

1 Prepare glucose standards

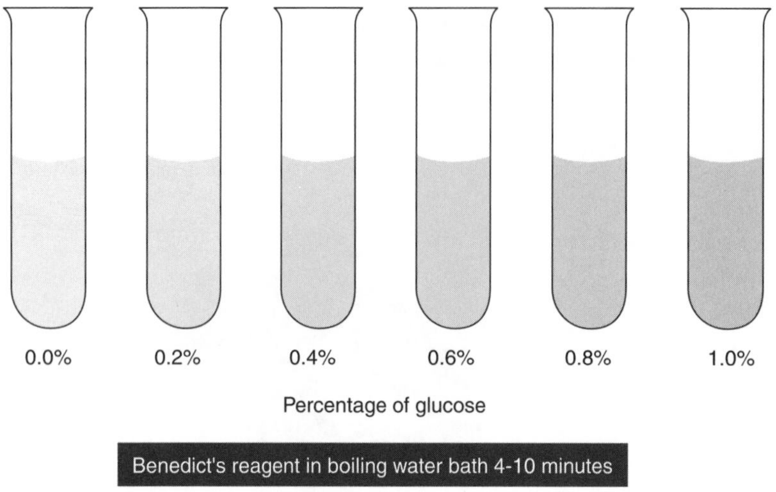
0.0%
0.2%
0.4%
0.6%
0.8%
1.0%
Percentage of glucose
Benedict's reagent in boiling water bath 4-10 minutes

Solutions containing a range of known glucose concentrations are prepared in test tubes. Benedict's reagent (used to detect the presence of a reducing sugar) is added and the test tubes are heated in a boiling waterbath for 4-10 minutes.

At the end of the reaction time, samples containing glucose will have undergone a colour change. The samples are cooled, then filtered or centrifuged to remove suspended particles.

2 Produce a calibration curve

The absorbance of each standard is measured in a colorimeter (or sometimes a spectrophotometer) at 735 nm. These values are used to produce a calibration curve for glucose. The calibration curve can then be used to determine the glucose concentration of any 'unknown' based on its absorbance. For the best results, a new calibration curve should be generated for each new analysis. This accounts for any possible changes in the conditions of the reactants.

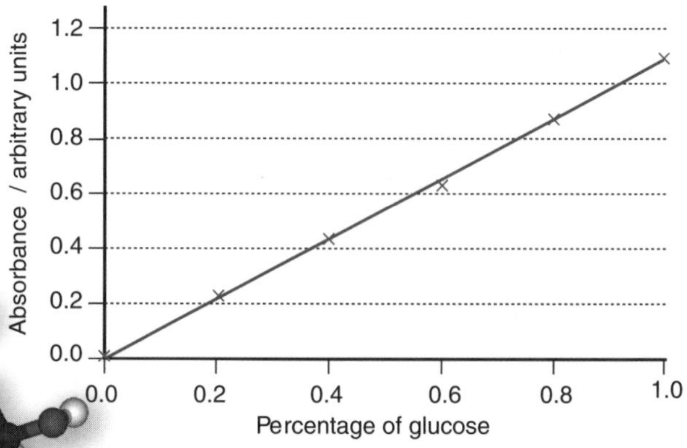
Absorbance / arbitrary units
1.2
1.0
0.8
0.6
0.4
0.2
0.0
0.0
0.2
0.4
0.6
0.8
1.0
Percentage of glucose

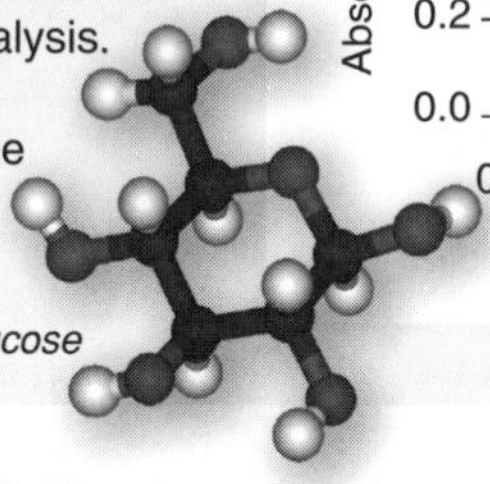

Glucose

1. (a) A sample has an absorbance of 0.5. Use the calibration curve above to estimate how much glucose it contains.

   (b) What would you do if the absorbance values you obtained for most of your 'unknowns' were outside the range of your calibration curve?

2. How could you quantify the amount of glucose in a range of commercially available glucose drinks?

3. Why is it important to remove suspended solids from a sample before measuring its absorbance?

© 2015 **BIOZONE** International
ISBN:978-1-927309-31-5
Photocopying Prohibited

53 Organic Molecules

Key Idea: Organic molecules are those with carbon-hydrogen bonds. They make up most of the chemicals found in living organisms and can be portrayed as formulae or models.

Molecular biology is a branch of science that studies the molecular basis of biological activity. All life is based around carbon, which is able to combine with many other elements to form a large number of carbon-based (or organic) molecules. Specific groups of atoms, called functional groups, attach to a C-H core and determine the specific chemical properties of the molecule. The organic macromolecules that make up living things can be grouped into four classes: carbohydrates, lipids, proteins, and nucleic acids. The diagram (bottom) illustrates some of the common ways in which organic molecules are portrayed.

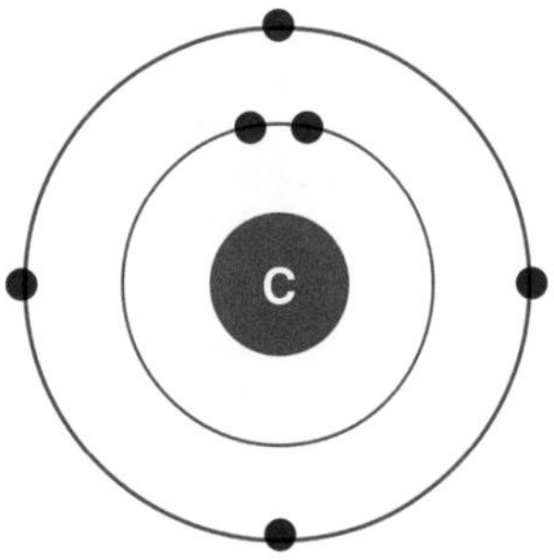
C

A carbon atom (above) has four electrons that are available to form up to four **covalent bonds** with other atoms. A covalent bond forms when two atoms share a pair of electrons. The number of covalent bonds formed between atoms in a molecule determines the shape and chemical properties of the molecule.

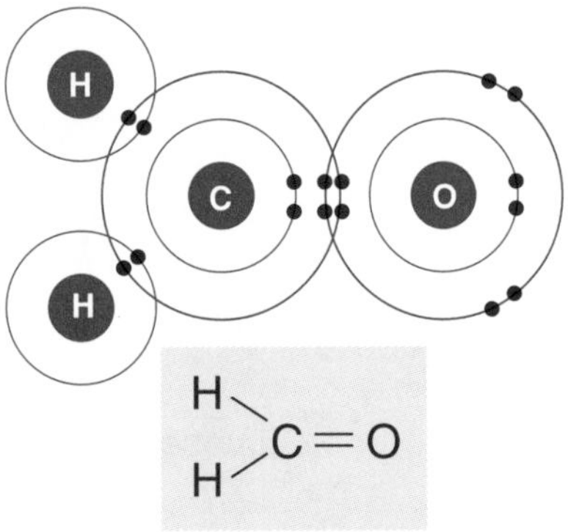
H
C
O
H
H
C=O
H

Methanal (molecular formula CH_2O) is a simple organic molecule. A carbon (C) atom bonds with two hydrogen (H) atoms and an oxygen (O) atom. In the structural formula (blue box), the bonds between atoms are represented by lines. Covalent bonds are very strong, so the molecules formed are very stable.

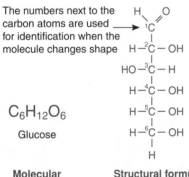

Organic macromolecule	Structural unit	Elements
Carbohydrates	Sugar monomer	C, H, O
Proteins	Amino acid	C, H, O, N, S
Lipids	Not applicable	C, H, O
Nucleic acids	Nucleotide	C, H, O, N, P

The most common elements found in organic molecules are carbon, hydrogen, and oxygen, but organic molecules may also contain other elements, such as nitrogen, phosphorus, and sulfur. Most organic macromolecules are built up of one type of repeating unit or 'building block', except lipids, which are quite diverse in structure.

Portraying organic molecules

The numbers next to the carbon atoms are used for identification when the molecule changes shape

$C_6H_{12}O_6$

Glucose

Molecular formula

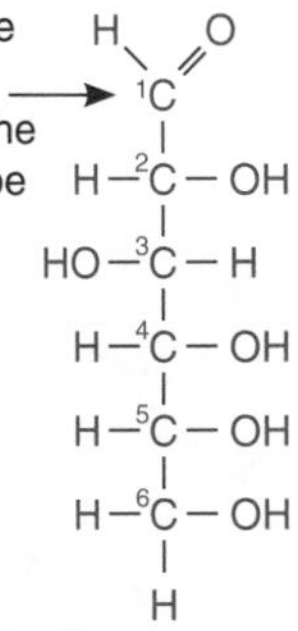

Structural formula
Glucose (straight form)

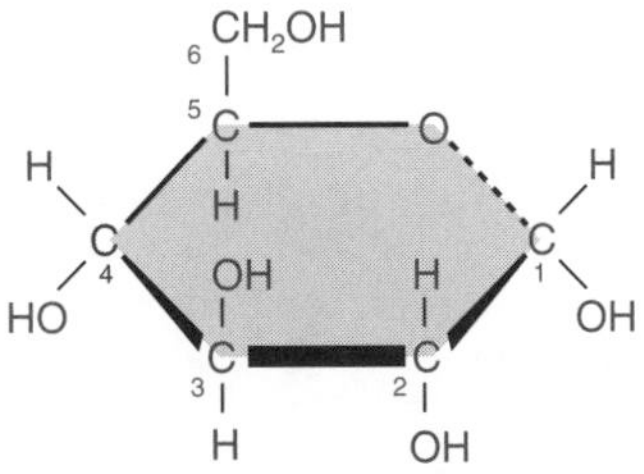

Structural formula
α-glucose (ring form)

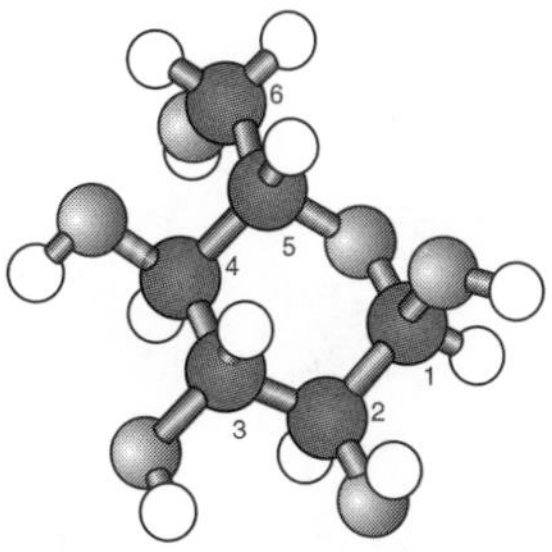

Ball and stick model
Glucose

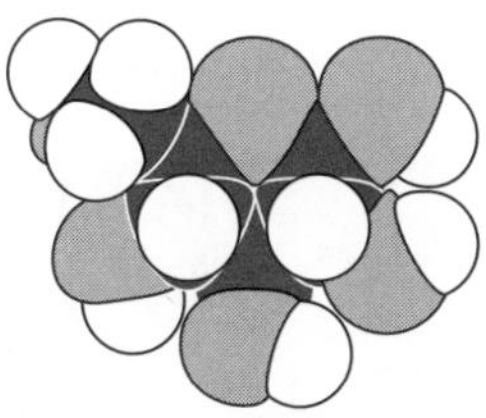

Space filling model
β-D-glucose

The molecular formula expresses the number of atoms in a molecule, but does not convey its structure. This is indicated by the structural formula.

A ball and stick model shows the arrangement of bonds while a space filling model gives a more realistic appearance of a molecule.

1. Study the table above and state the three main elements that make up the structure of organic molecules: ___________

____

2. Name two other elements that are also frequently part of organic molecules: ___________

3. (a) On the diagram of the carbon atom top left, mark with arrows the electrons that are available to form covalent bonds with other atoms.

   (b) State how many covalent bonds a carbon atom can form with neighbouring atoms: ___________

4. Distinguish between molecular and structural formulae for a given molecule: ___________

____

____

© 2015 **BIOZONE** International
ISBN: 978-1-927309-31-5
Photocopying Prohibited

54 Sugars

Key Idea: Monosaccharides are the building blocks for larger carbohydrates. They can exist as isomers.

Sugars (monosaccharides and disaccharides) play a central role in cells, providing energy and joining together to form carbohydrate macromolecules, such as starch and glycogen. Monosaccharide polymers form the major component of most plants (as cellulose). Monosaccharides are important as a primary energy source for cellular metabolism. Carbohydrates have the general formula $C_x(H_2O)_y$, where x and y are variable numbers (often but not always the same).

Monosaccharides

Monosaccharides are single-sugar molecules and include glucose (grape sugar and blood sugar) and fructose (honey and fruit juices). They are used as a primary energy source for fuelling cell metabolism. They can be joined together to form disaccharides (two monomers) and polysaccharides (many monomers).

Monosaccharides can be classified by the number of carbon atoms they contain. Some important monosaccharides are the hexoses (6 carbons) and the pentoses (5 carbons). The most common arrangements found in sugars are hexose (6 sided) or pentose (5 sided) rings (below).

The commonly occurring monosaccharides contain between three and seven carbon atoms in their carbon chains and, of these, the 6C hexose sugars occur most frequently. All monosaccharides are reducing sugars (they can participate in reduction reactions).

Examples of monosaccharide structures

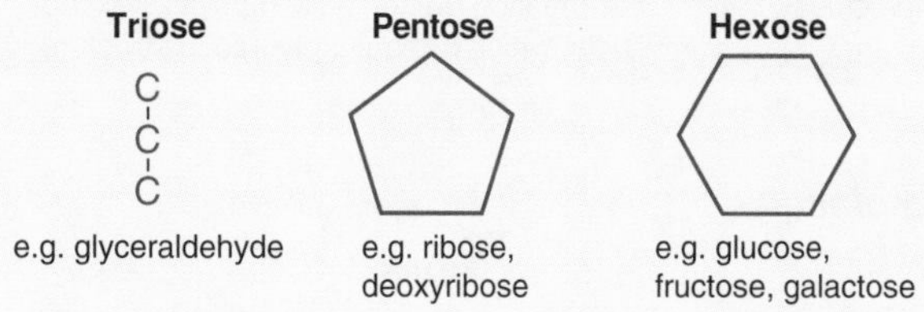
Triose
Pentose
Hexose
C
C
C
e.g. glyceraldehyde
e.g. ribose, deoxyribose
e.g. glucose, fructose, galactose

Ribose: a pentose monosaccharide

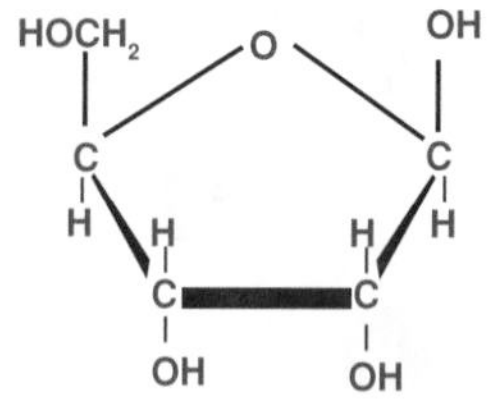
HOCH2
O
OH
C
C
H
H
H
H
C
C
OH
OH

Ribose is a pentose (5 carbon) monosaccharide which can form a ring structure (left). Ribose is a component of the nucleic acid ribonucleic acid (RNA).

Glucose isomers

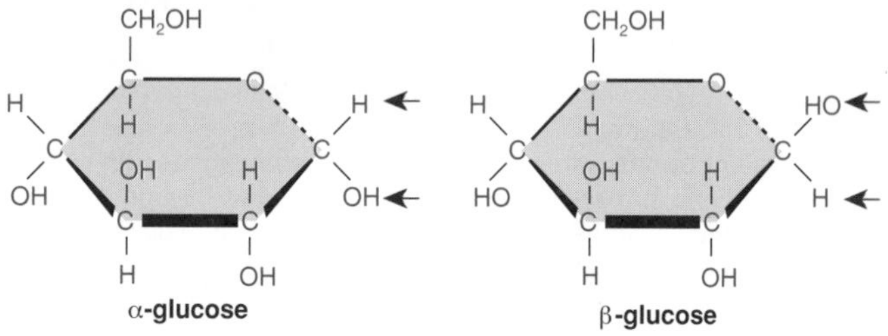
CH2OH
H
OH
H
OH
OH
H
H
OH
α-glucose
CH2OH
H
HO
HO
H
OH
H
H
OH
β-glucose

Isomers are compounds with the same chemical formula (same types and numbers of atoms) but different arrangements of atoms. The different arrangement of the atoms means that each isomer has different properties.

Molecules such as glucose can have many different isomers (e.g. α and β glucose, above) including straight and ring forms.

Glucose is a versatile molecule. It provides energy to power cellular reactions, can form energy storage molecules such as glycogen, or it can be used to build structural molecules.

Plants make their glucose via the process of photosynthesis. Animals and other heterotrophic organisms obtain their glucose by consuming plants or other organisms.

Rufino Uribe

Fructose, often called fruit sugar, is a simple monosaccharide. It is often derived from sugar cane (above). Both fructose and glucose can be directly absorbed into the bloodstream.

1. Describe the two major functions of monosaccharides:

   (a) ______________________________

   (b) ______________________________

2. Describe the structural differences between the ring forms of glucose and ribose: ______________________________

3. Using glucose as an example, define the term **isomer** and state its importance: ______________________________

© 2015 BIOZONE International
ISBN:978-1-927309-31-5
Photocopying Prohibited

55 Condensation and Hydrolysis of Sugars

Key Idea: Condensation reactions join monosaccharides together to form disaccharides and polysaccharides. Hydrolysis reactions split disaccharides and polysaccharides into smaller molecules.

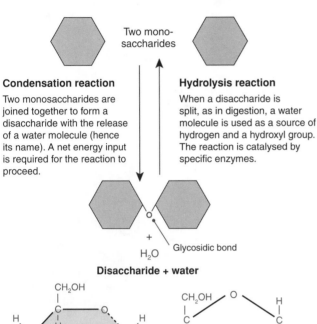

Monosaccharide monomers can be linked together by **condensation reactions** to produce larger molecules (disaccharides and polysaccharides). The reverse reaction, **hydrolysis**, breaks compound sugars down into their constituent monosaccharides. Disaccharides (double-sugars) are produced when two monosaccharides are joined together. Different disaccharides are formed by joining together different combinations of monosaccharides (below).

Condensation and hydrolysis reactions

Monosaccharides can combine to form compound sugars in what is called a condensation reaction. Compound sugars can be broken down by hydrolysis to simple monosaccharides.

Two mono-
saccharides

Condensation reaction

Two monosaccharides are joined together to form a disaccharide with the release of a water molecule (hence its name). A net energy input is required for the reaction to proceed.

Hydrolysis reaction

When a disaccharide is split, as in digestion, a water molecule is used as a source of hydrogen and a hydroxyl group. The reaction is catalysed by specific enzymes.

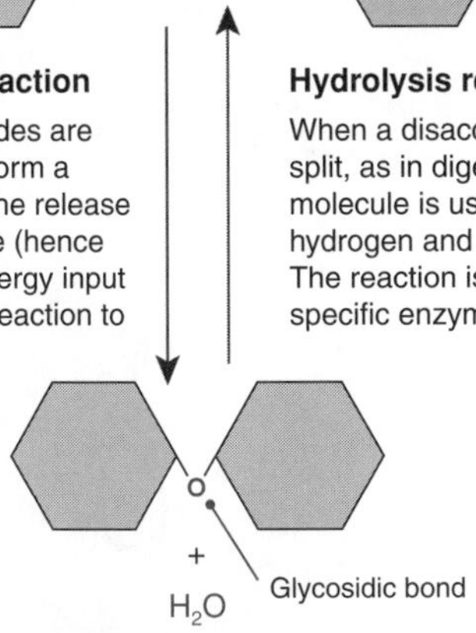
O
+
H_2O
Glycosidic bond

Disaccharide + water

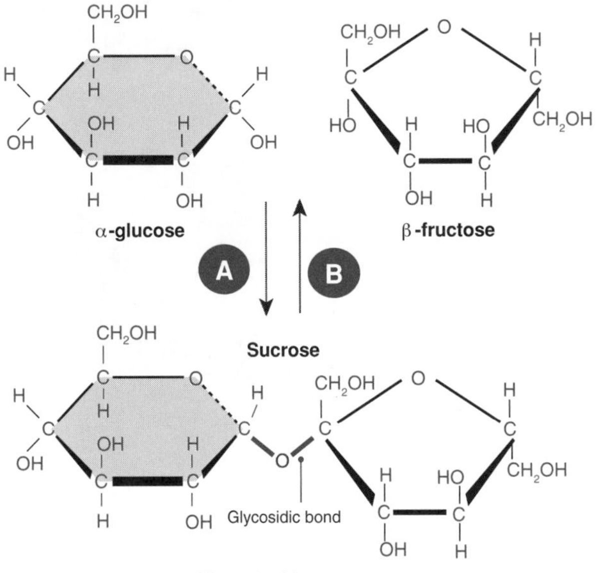
CH_2OH
α-glucose
β-fructose
A
B
Sucrose
Glycosidic bond

Disaccharide + water

Disaccharides

Disaccharides (below) are double-sugar molecules and are used as energy sources and as building blocks for larger molecules. They are important in human nutrition and are found in milk (lactose), table sugar (sucrose), and malt (maltose).

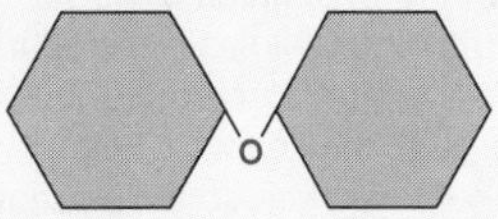
O

The type of disaccharide formed depends on the monomers involved and whether they are in their α- or β- form. Only a few disaccharides (e.g. lactose) are classified as reducing sugars. Some common disaccharides are described below.

Lactose, a milk sugar, is made up of β-glucose + β-galactose. Milk contains 2-8% lactose by weight. It is the primary carbohydrate source for suckling mammalian infants.

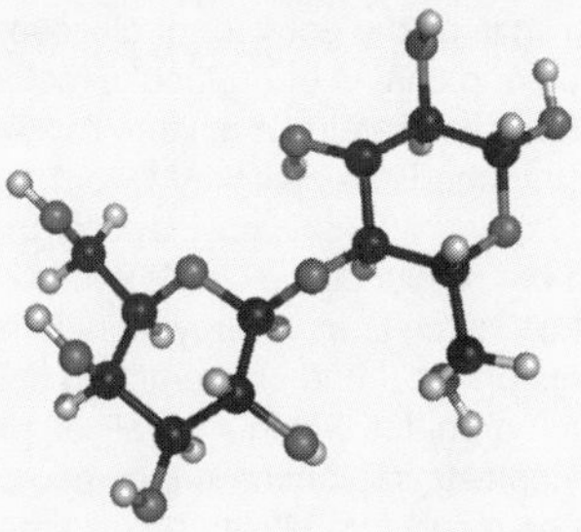

Maltose is composed of two α-glucose molecules. Germinating seeds contain maltose because the plant breaks down their starch stores to use it for food.

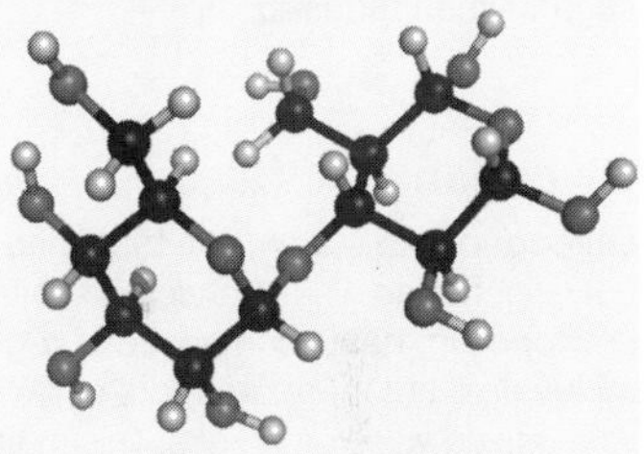

Sucrose (table sugar) is a simple sugar derived from plants such as sugar cane, sugar beet, or maple sap. It is composed of an α-glucose molecule and a β-fructose molecule. Sucrose is a non-reducing sugar, so the non-reducing Benedict's test is used to detect its presence.

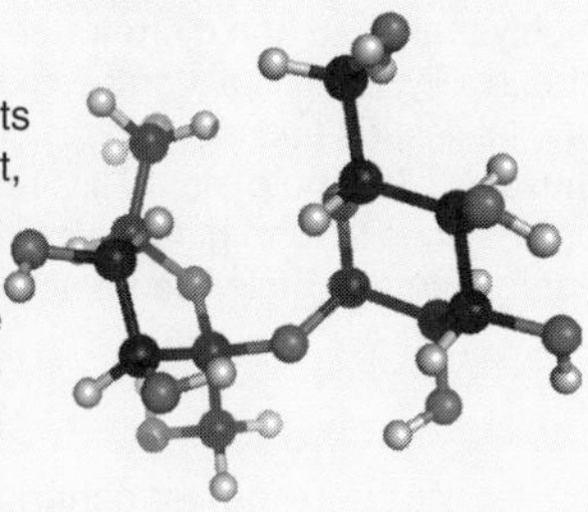

1. Explain briefly how disaccharide sugars are formed and broken down: ____________

____

____

____

2. On the diagram above, name the reaction occurring at points **A** and **B** and name the product that is formed:

____

____

3. On the lactose, maltose, and sucrose molecules (above right), circle the two monomers on each molecule.

© 2015 **BIOZONE** International
ISBN: 978-1-927309-31-5
Photocopying Prohibited

56 Polysaccharides

Key Idea: Polysaccharides consist of many monosaccharides joined by condensation. Their functional properties depend on composition and monosaccharide isomer involved.

Polysaccharides are macromolecules consisting of straight or branched chains of many monosaccharides. They can consist of one or more types of monosaccharides. The most common polysaccharides (cellulose, starch, and glycogen) contain only glucose, but their properties are very different. These differences are a function of the glucose isomer involved and the types of linkages joining the monomers. Different polysaccharides can thus be a source of readily available glucose or a structural material that resists digestion.

Cellulose

Cellulose is a structural material found in the cell walls of plants. It is made up of unbranched chains of β-glucose molecules held together by β-1,4 glycosidic links. As many as 10 000 glucose molecules may be linked together to form a straight chain. Parallel chains become cross-linked with hydrogen bonds and form bundles of 60-70 molecules called **microfibrils**. Cellulose microfibrils are very strong and are a major structural component of plants, e.g. as the cell wall. Few organisms can break the β-linkages so cellulose is an ideal structural material.

Public Domain

Cotton fibres contain more than 90% cellulose fibre.

The structure of polysaccharides (also called complex carbohydrates) can be compared using molecular visualisation software

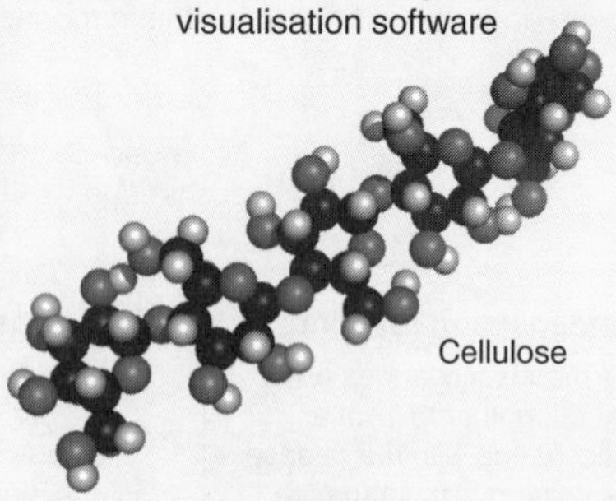

Cellulose

Starch

Starch is also a polymer of glucose, but it is made up of long chains of α-glucose molecules linked together. It contains a mixture of 25-30% amylose (unbranched chains linked by α-1,4 glycosidic bonds) and 70-75% amylopectin (branched chains with α-1, 6 glycosidic bonds every 24-30 glucose units). Starch is an energy storage molecule in plants and is found concentrated in insoluble starch granules within specialised plastids called amyloplasts in plant cells (see photo, right). Starch can be easily hydrolysed by enzymes to soluble sugars when required.

BF

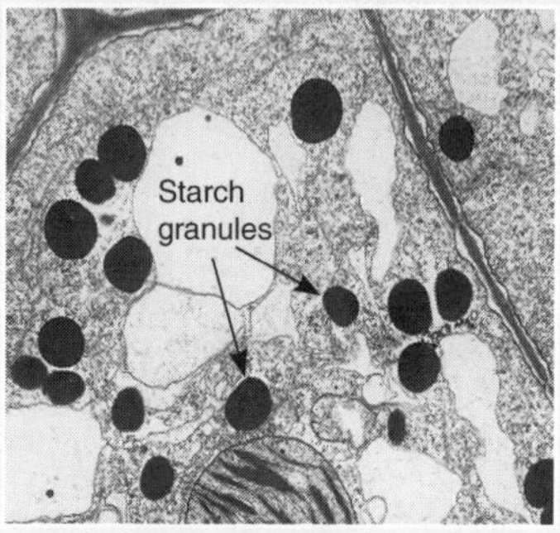

Starch
granules

Starch granules in a plant cell (TEM).

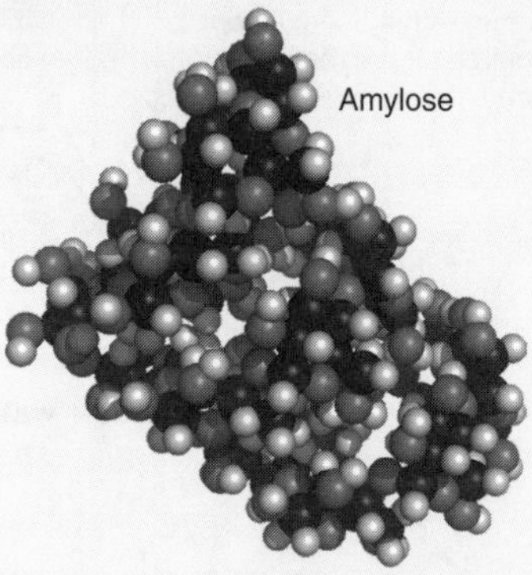

Amylose

Glycogen

Glycogen, like starch, is a branched polysaccharide. It is chemically similar to amylopectin, being composed of α-glucose molecules, but there are more α-1,6 glycosidic links mixed with α-1,4 links. This makes it more highly branched and more water-soluble than starch. Glycogen is a storage compound in animal tissues and is found mainly in liver and muscle cells (photo, right). It is readily hydrolysed by enzymes to form glucose making it an ideal energy storage molecule for active animals.

J. Miquel, D. Vilavella, Z.widerski, V. V. Shimalov and J. Torres

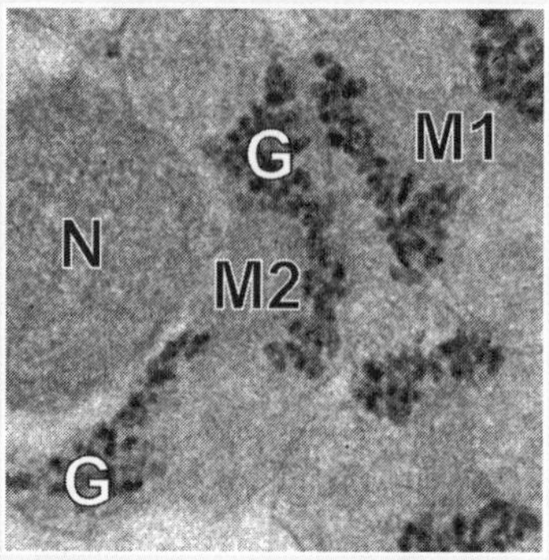

G
M1
N
M2
G

Glycogen (G) in the spermatozoa of a flatworm. M1, M2=mitochondria, N=nucleus.

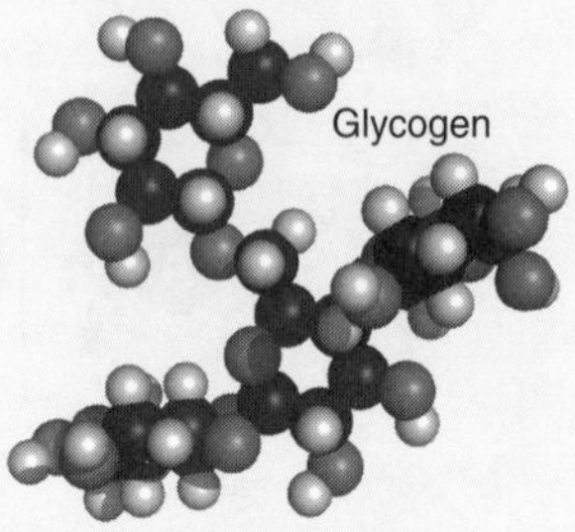

Glycogen

1. (a) Why are polysaccharides such a good source of energy? ______________________

   ____

   (b) How is the energy stored in polysaccharides mobilised? ______________________

   ____

2. Contrast the properties of the polysaccharides starch, cellulose, and glycogen and relate these to their roles in the cell:

   ____

   ____

   ____

   ____

   ____

© 2015 BIOZONE International
ISBN:978-1-927309-31-5
Photocopying Prohibited

57 Starch and Cellulose

Key Idea: Starch and cellulose are important polysaccharides in plants. Starch is a storage carbohydrate made up of two α-glucose polymers, amylose and amylopectin. Cellulose is a β-glucose polymer which forms the plant cell wall.

Glucose monomers can be linked in condensation reactions to form large structural and energy storage polysaccharides. The glucose isomer involved and the type of glycosidic linkage determines the properties of the molecule.

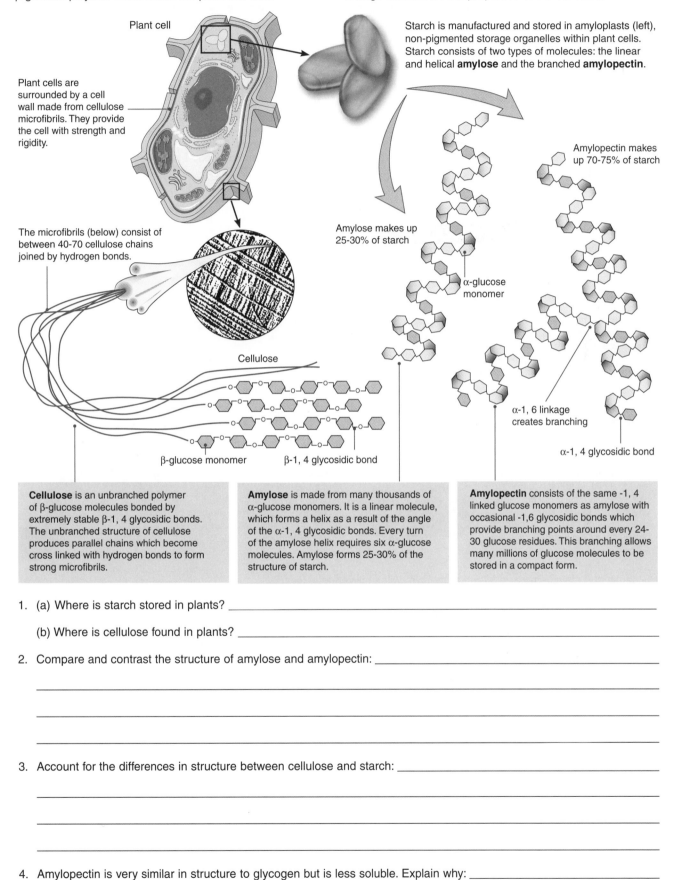

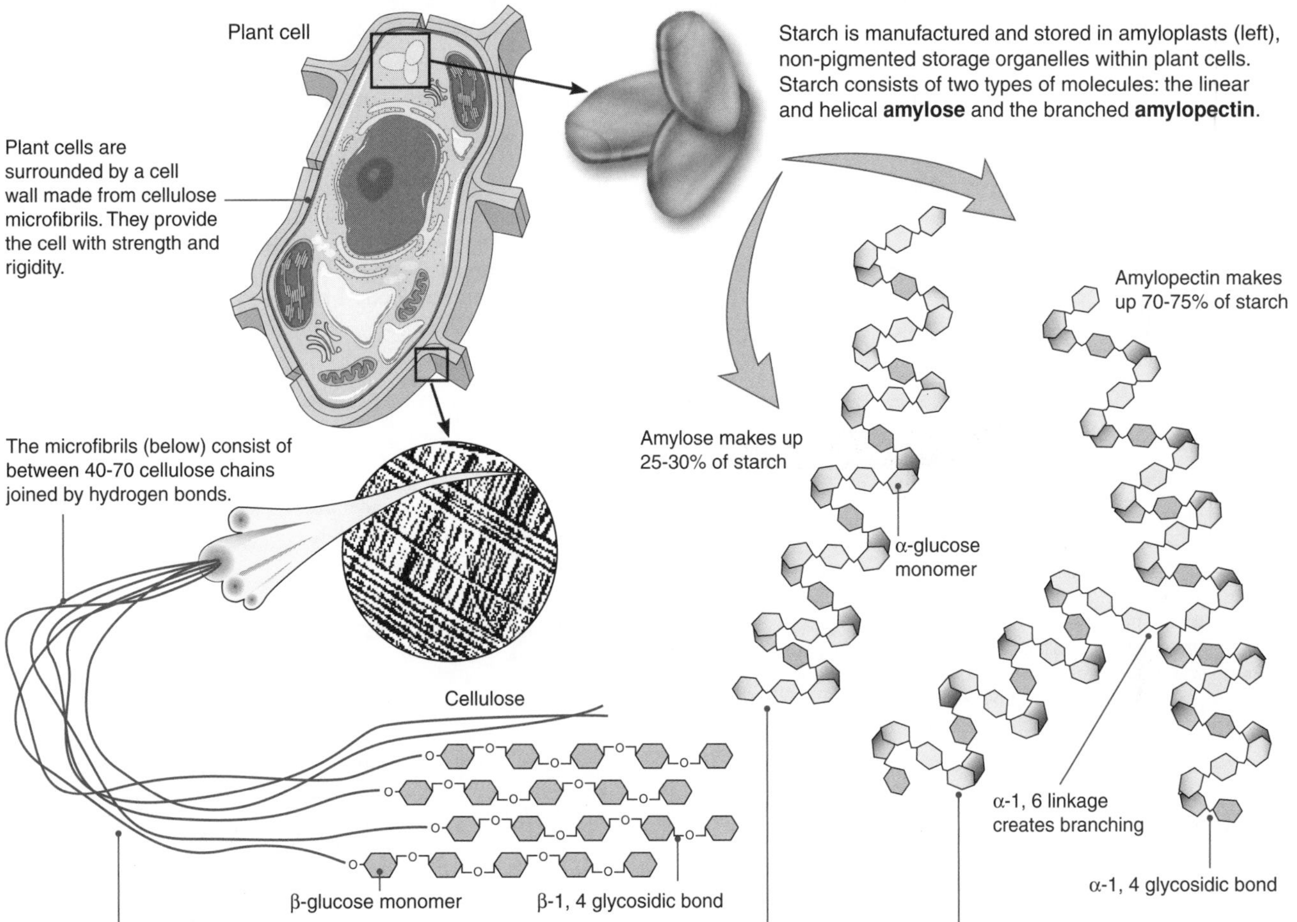
Plant cell
Plant cells are surrounded by a cell wall made from cellulose microfibrils. They provide the cell with strength and rigidity.
Starch is manufactured and stored in amyloplasts (left), non-pigmented storage organelles within plant cells. Starch consists of two types of molecules: the linear and helical **amylose** and the branched **amylopectin**.
Amylopectin makes up 70-75% of starch
Amylose makes up 25-30% of starch
α-glucose monomer
The microfibrils (below) consist of between 40-70 cellulose chains joined by hydrogen bonds.
Cellulose
α-1, 6 linkage creates branching
α-1, 4 glycosidic bond
β-glucose monomer
β-1, 4 glycosidic bond

Cellulose is an unbranched polymer of β-glucose molecules bonded by extremely stable β-1, 4 glycosidic bonds. The unbranched structure of cellulose produces parallel chains which become cross linked with hydrogen bonds to form strong microfibrils.

Amylose is made from many thousands of α-glucose monomers. It is a linear molecule, which forms a helix as a result of the angle of the α-1, 4 glycosidic bonds. Every turn of the amylose helix requires six α-glucose molecules. Amylose forms 25-30% of the structure of starch.

Amylopectin consists of the same -1, 4 linked glucose monomers as amylose with occasional -1,6 glycosidic bonds which provide branching points around every 24-30 glucose residues. This branching allows many millions of glucose molecules to be stored in a compact form.

1. (a) Where is starch stored in plants? ______________________

   (b) Where is cellulose found in plants? ______________________

2. Compare and contrast the structure of amylose and amylopectin: ______________________

____

____

____

3. Account for the differences in structure between cellulose and starch: ______________________

____

____

____

4. Amylopectin is very similar in structure to glycogen but is less soluble. Explain why: ______________________

____

© 2015 **BIOZONE** International
ISBN: 978-1-927309-31-5
Photocopying Prohibited

58 Lipids

Key Idea: Lipids are non-polar, hydrophobic organic molecules, which have many important biological functions. Fatty acids are the building blocks of more complex lipids.

Lipids are organic compounds which are mostly nonpolar (have no overall charge) and hydrophobic, so they do not readily dissolve in water. Lipids include fats, waxes, sterols, and phospholipids. Fatty acids are a major component of neutral fats and phospholipids. Most fatty acids consist of an even number of carbon atoms, with hydrogen bound along the length of the chain. The carboxyl group (–COOH) at one end makes them an acid. They are generally classified as saturated or unsaturated fatty acids (below).

Triglycerides

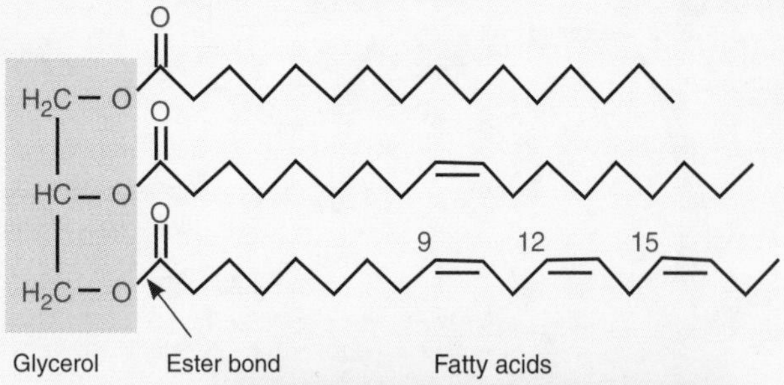

H_2C — O
HC — O
H_2C — O
9
12
15
Glycerol
Ester bond
Fatty acids

Triglyceride: an example of a neutral fat

Neutral fats and oils are the most abundant lipids in living things. They make up the fats and oils found in plants and animals. They consist of a glycerol attached to one (mono-), two (di-) or three (tri-) fatty acids by **ester bonds**. Lipids have a high proportion of hydrogen present in the fatty acid chains. When the molecule is metabolised, the chemical energy is released. Being so reduced and anhydrous, they are an economical way to store fuel reserves, and provide more than twice as much energy as the same quantity of carbohydrate.

Lipids containing a high proportion of saturated fatty acids tend to be solids at room temperature (e.g. butter). Lipids with a high proportion of unsaturated fatty acids are oils and tend to be liquid at room temperature (e.g. olive oil). This is because the unsaturation causes kinks in the straight chains so that the fatty acid chains do not pack closely together.

Saturated and unsaturated fatty acids

Fatty acids are carboxylic acids with long hydrocarbon chains. They are classed as either saturated or unsaturated. **Saturated fatty acids** contain the maximum number of hydrogen atoms. **Unsaturated fatty acids** contain some double-bonds between carbon atoms and are not fully saturated with hydrogens. A chain with only one double bond is called monounsaturated, whereas a chain with two or more double bonds is called polyunsaturated.

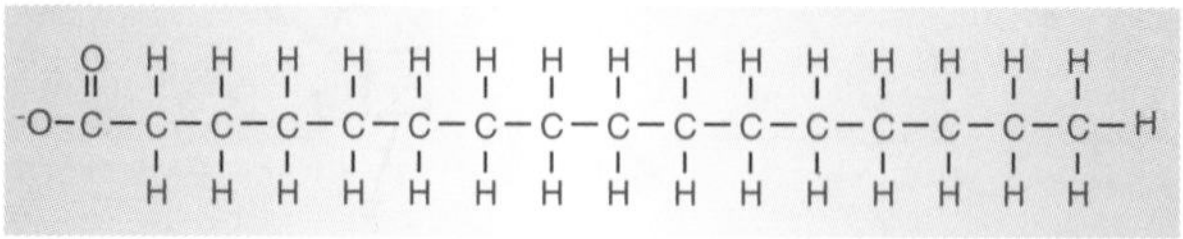

Formula (above) and molecular model (below) for a saturated fatty acid (palmitic acid).

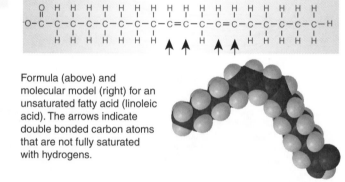

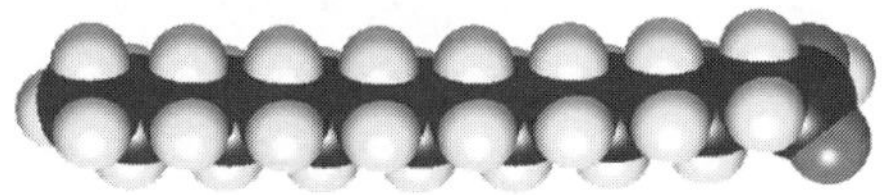

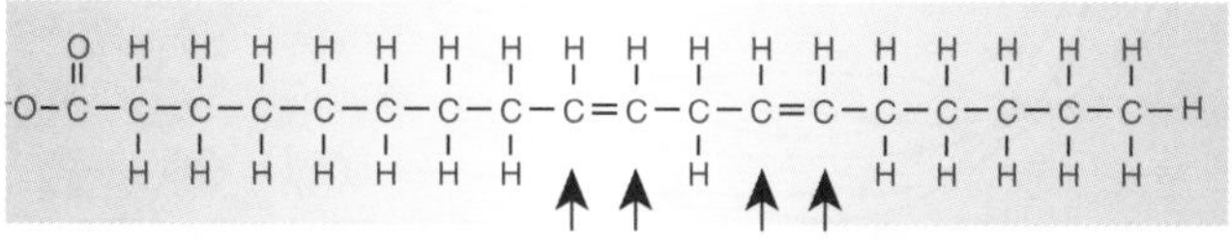

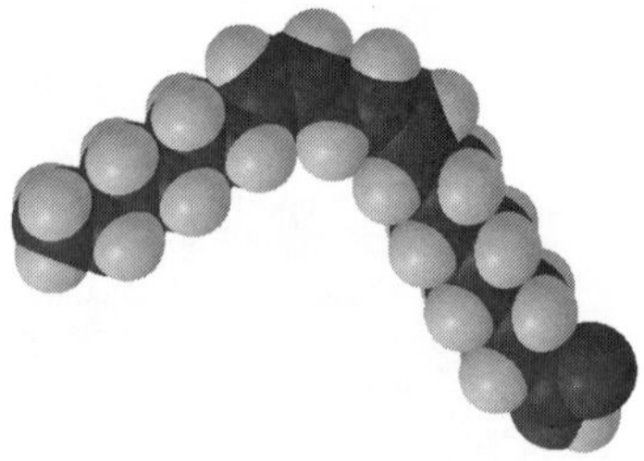

Formula (above) and molecular model (right) for an unsaturated fatty acid (linoleic acid). The arrows indicate double bonded carbon atoms that are not fully saturated with hydrogens.

1. Identify the main components (a-c) of the symbolic triglyceride below:

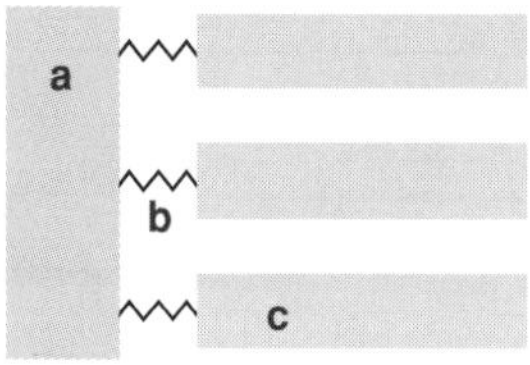

a
b
c

(a) ______________________

(b) ______________________

(c) ______________________

2. Why do lipids have such a high energy content? ______________________

____

____

3. (a) Distinguish between saturated and unsaturated fatty acids: ______________________

____

(b) Relate the properties of a neutral fat to the type of fatty acid present: ______________________

____

____

© 2015 **BIOZONE** International
ISBN:978-1-927309-31-5
Photocopying Prohibited

Triglycerides are formed by condensation reactions

Triglycerides form when glycerol bonds with three fatty acids. Glycerol is an alcohol containing three carbons. Each of these carbons is bonded to a hydroxyl (-OH) group.

When glycerol bonds with the fatty acid, an **ester bond** is formed and water is released. Three separate condensation reactions are involved in producing a triglyceride.

Esterification: A condensation reaction of an alcohol (e.g. glycerol) with an acid (e.g. fatty acid) to produce an ester and water. In the diagram right, the ester bonds are indicated by blue lines.

Lipolysis: The breakdown of lipids. It involves hydrolysis of triglycerides into glycerol molecules and free fatty acids.

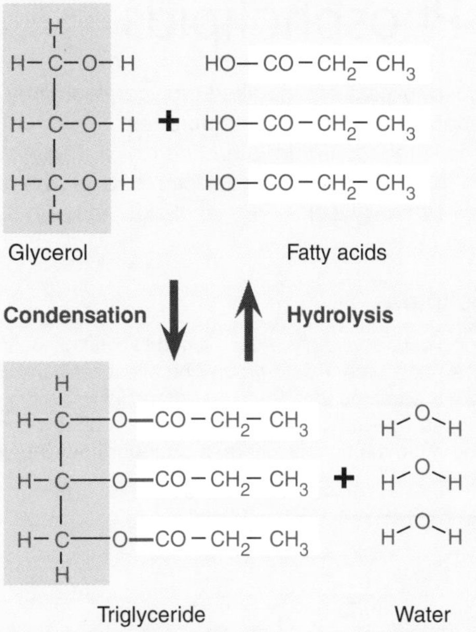
Glycerol
Fatty acids
Condensation
Hydrolysis
Triglyceride
Water

Biological functions of lipids

Lipids are concentrated sources of energy and provide fuel for aerobic respiration.

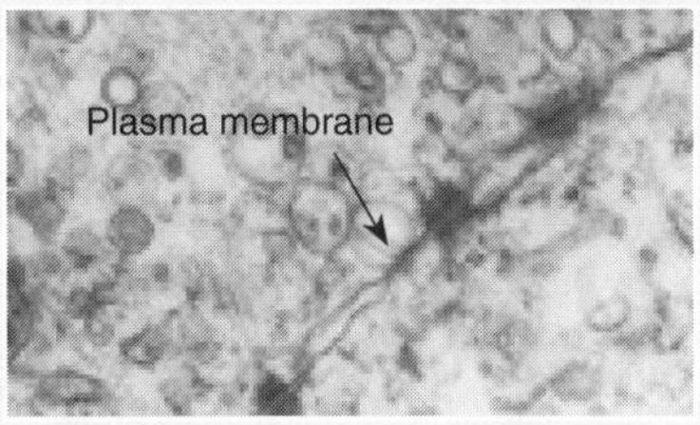
Plasma membrane

WMU

Phospholipids form the structure of cellular membranes in eukaryotes and prokaryotes.

Waxes and oils secreted onto surfaces provide waterproofing in plants and animals.

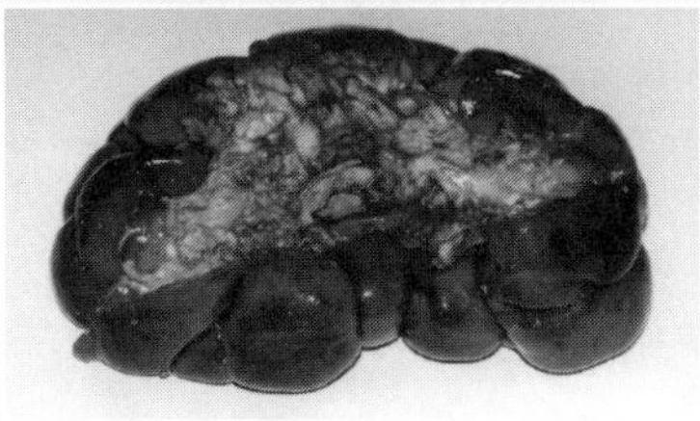

TG

Fat absorbs shocks. Organs that are prone to bumps and shocks (e.g. kidneys) are cushioned with a relatively thick layer of fat.

Lipids are a source of metabolic water. During respiration stored lipids are metabolized for energy, producing water and carbon dioxide.

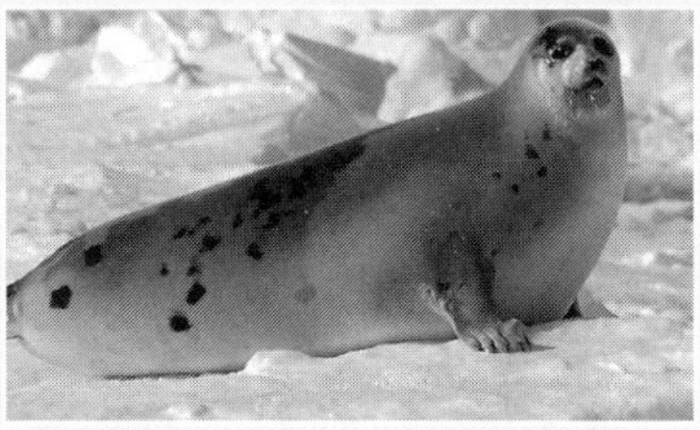

Stored lipids provide insulation. Increased body fat levels in winter reduce heat losses to the environment.

4. (a) Describe what happens during the esterification (condensation) process to produce a triglyceride:

(b) Describe what happens when a triglyceride is hydrolysed:

5. Discuss the biological role of lipids:

© 2015 **BIOZONE** International
ISBN: 978-1-927309-31-5
Photocopying Prohibited

59 Phospholipids

Key Idea: Phospholipids are modified triglycerides. They are important components of cellular membranes.

Phospholipids are similar in structure to a triglyceride except that a phosphate group replaces one of the fatty acids attached to the glycerol. Phospholipids naturally form bilayers in aqueous solutions and are the main component of all cellular membranes. The fatty acid tails can be saturated (forming straight chains) or unsaturated (kinked chains). The level of phospholipids with saturated or unsaturated tails affects the fluidity of the phospholipid bilayer.

Phospholipids

Phospholipids consist of a glycerol attached to two fatty acid chains and a phosphate (PO_4^{3-}) group. The phosphate end of the molecule is attracted to water (it is hydrophilic) while the fatty acid end is repelled (hydrophobic). The hydrophobic ends turn inwards in the membrane to form a **phospholipid bilayer.**

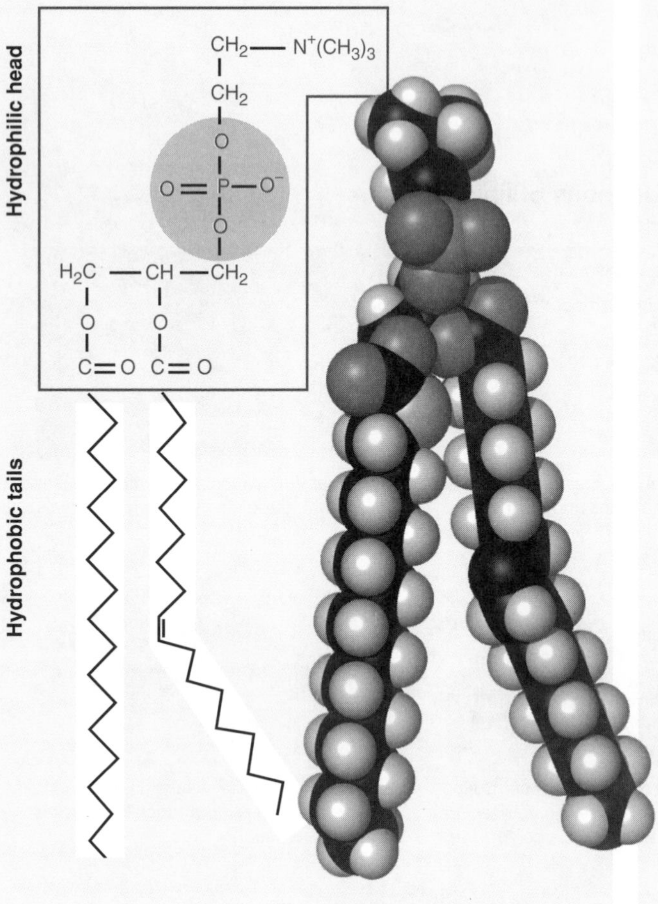
Hydrophilic head
Hydrophobic tails
CH_2— $N^+(CH_3)_3$
CH_2
O
O=P—O⁻
O
H_2C —CH —CH_2
O O
C=O C=O

Phospholipids and membranes

The amphipathic (having hydrophobic and hydrophilic ends) nature of phospholipids means that when in water they spontaneously form bilayers. This bilayer structure forms the outer boundary of cells or organelles. Modifications to the different hydrophobic ends of the phospholipids cause the bilayer to change its behaviour. The greater the number of double bonds in the hydrophobic tails, the greater the fluidity of the membrane.

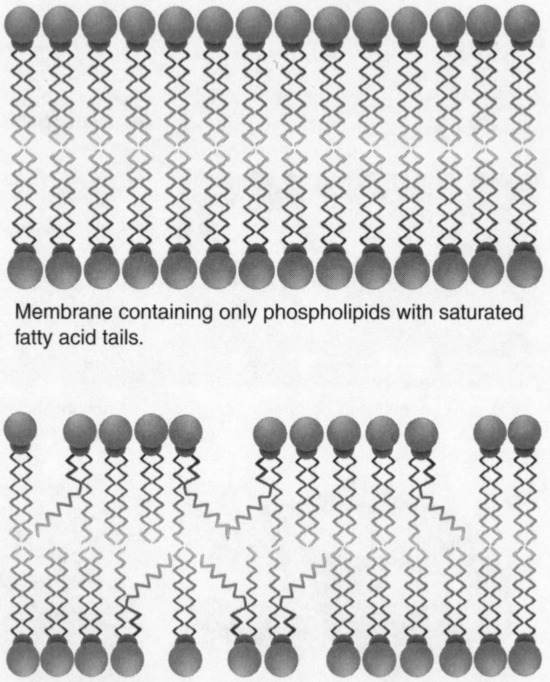

Membrane containing only phospholipids with saturated fatty acid tails.

Membrane containing phospholipids with unsaturated fatty acid tails. The fact that the phospholipids do not stack neatly together produces a more fluid membrane.

1. (a) Relate the structure of phospholipids to their chemical properties and their functional role in cellular membranes:

____

____

____

(b) Suggest how the cell membrane structure of an Arctic fish might differ from that of tropical fish species: _______________

____

____

2. Explain why phospholipid bilayers containing many phospholipids with unsaturated tails are particularly fluid:

____

____

____

© 2015 BIOZONE International
ISBN:978-1-927309-31-5
Photocopying Prohibited

60 Amino Acids

Key Idea: Amino acids join together in a linear chain by condensation reactions to form polypeptides. The sequence of amino acids in a protein is defined by a gene and encoded in the genetic code. In the presence of water, they can be broken apart by hydrolysis into their constituent amino acids.

Amino acids are the basic units from which proteins are made. Twenty amino acids commonly occur in proteins and they can be linked in many different ways by peptide bonds to form a huge variety of polypeptides. Proteins are made up of one or more polypeptide molecules.

The structure and properties of amino acids

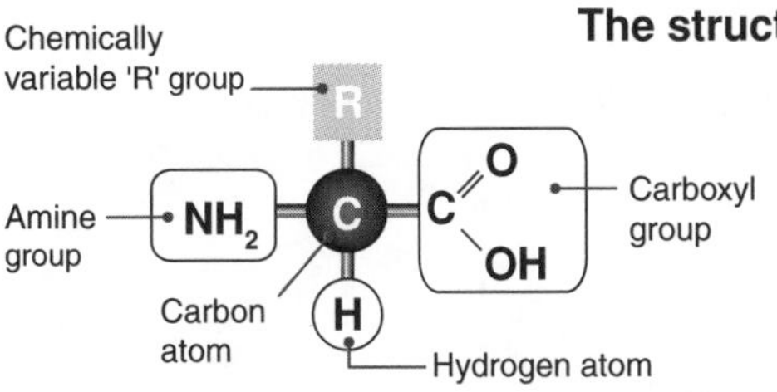
Chemically variable 'R' group
R
Amine group
NH2
C
Carbon atom
H
Hydrogen atom
C
O
OH
Carboxyl group

All amino acids have a common structure (above), but the R group is different in each kind of amino acid (right). The property of the R group determines how it will interact with other amino acids and ultimately determines how the amino acid chain folds up into a functional protein. For example, the hydrophobic R groups of soluble proteins are folded into the protein's interior, while the hydrophilic groups are arranged on the outside.

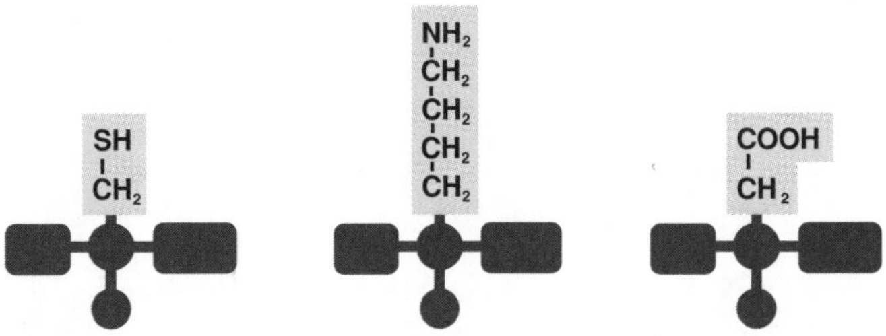
SH
CH2
NH2
CH2
CH2
CH2
CH2
COOH
CH2

Cysteine
This 'R' group can form **disulfide bridges** with other cysteines to create cross linkages in a polypeptide chain.

Lysine
This 'R' group gives the amino acid an **alkaline** property.

Aspartic acid
This 'R' group gives the amino acid an **acidic** property.

Condensation and hydrolysis reactions

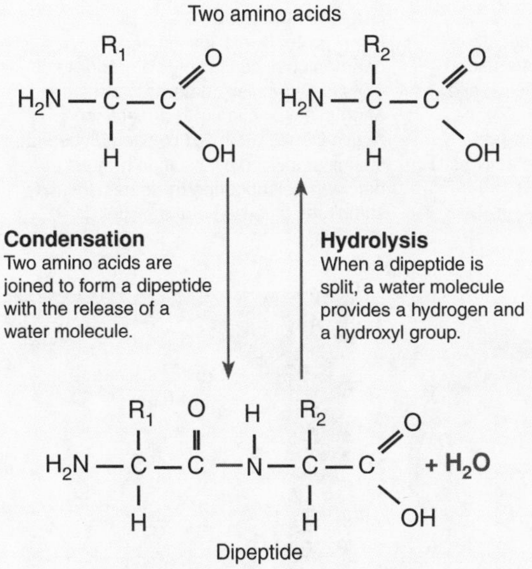
Two amino acids
R1
H2N — C — C
O
OH
H
R2
H2N — C — C
O
OH
H
Condensation
Two amino acids are joined to form a dipeptide with the release of a water molecule.
Hydrolysis
When a dipeptide is split, a water molecule provides a hydrogen and a hydroxyl group.
R1 O H R2
H2N — C — C — N — C — C
O
OH
H H
+ H2O
Dipeptide

Amino acids are linked by **peptide bonds** to form long **polypeptide chains** of up to several thousand amino acids. Peptide bonds form between the carboxyl group of one amino acid and the amine group of another (left). Water is formed as a result of this bond formation.

The sequence of amino acids in a polypeptide is called the **primary structure** and is determined by the order of nucleotides in DNA and mRNA (the gene sequence). The linking of amino acids to form a polypeptide occurs on ribosomes. Once released from the ribosome, a polypeptide will fold into a secondary structure determined by the composition and position of the amino acids making up the chain.

A polypeptide chain

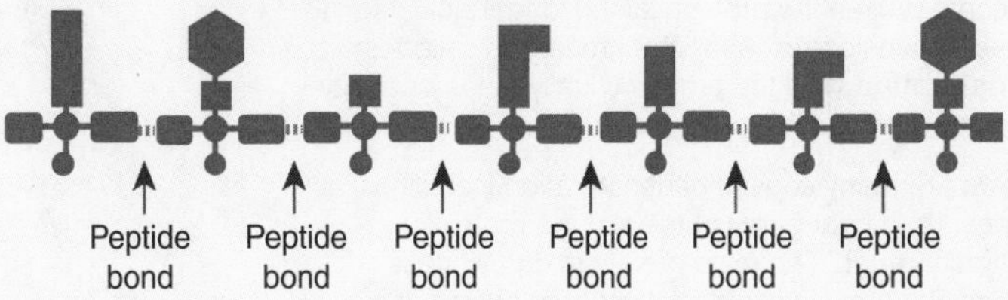
Peptide bond
Peptide bond
Peptide bond
Peptide bond
Peptide bond
Peptide bond

1. (a) What makes each of the amino acids in proteins unique? ______________________

(b) What is the primary structure of a protein? ______________________

(c) What determines the primary structure? ______________________

____

(d) How do the sequence and composition of amino acids in a protein influence how a protein folds up? ______________________

____

____

2. (a) What type of bond joins neighbouring amino acids together? ______________________

(b) How is this bond formed? ______________________

(c) Circle this bond in the dipeptide above:

(d) How are di- and polypeptides broken down? ______________________

© 2015 **BIOZONE** International
ISBN: 978-1-927309-31-5
Photocopying Prohibited

61 Protein Shape is Related to Function

Key idea: Interactions between amino acid R groups direct a polypeptide chain to fold into its functional shape. When a protein is denatured, it loses its functionality.

A protein may consist of one polypeptide chain, or several polypeptide chains linked together. Hydrogen bonds between amino acids cause it to form its **secondary structure**, either an α-helix or a β-pleated sheet. The interaction between R groups causes a polypeptide to fold into its **tertiary structure**, a three dimensional shape held by ionic bonds and disulfide bridges (bonds formed between sulfur containing amino acids). If bonds are broken (through denaturation), the protein loses its tertiary structure, and its functionality.

The shape of a protein reflects its biological role

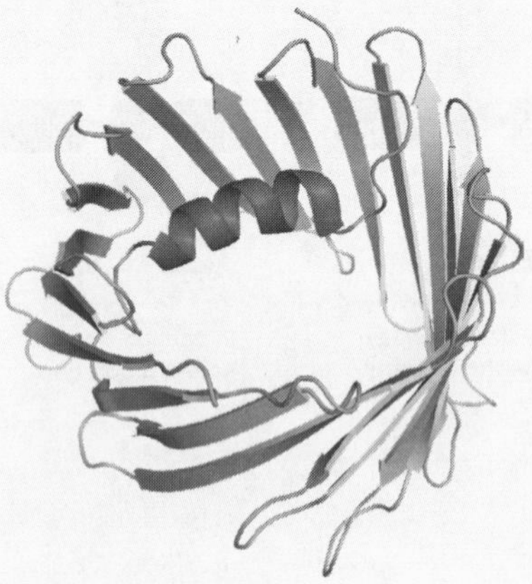

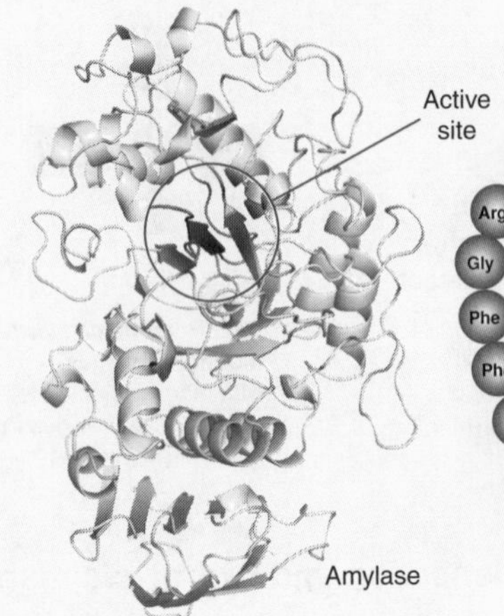
Active site
Amylase

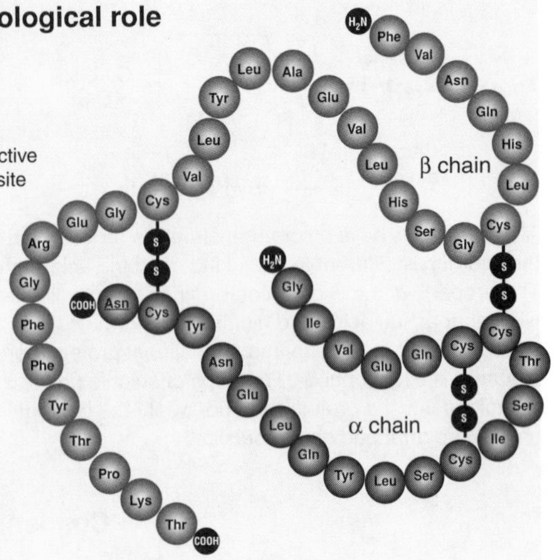
β chain
α chain

Channel proteins
Proteins that fold to form channels in the plasma membrane present non-polar R groups to the membrane and polar R groups to the inside of the channel. Hydrophilic molecules and ions are then able to pass through these channels into the interior of the cell. Ion channels are found in nearly all cells and many organelles.

Enzymes
Enzymes are globular proteins that catalyse specific reactions. Enzymes that are folded to present polar R groups at the active site will be specific for polar substances. Non-polar active sites will be specific for non-polar substances. Alteration of the active site by extremes of temperature or pH cause a loss of function.

Sub-unit proteins
Many proteins, e.g. insulin and haemoglobin, consist of two or more sub-units in a complex quaternary structure, often in association with a metal ion. Active insulin is formed by two polypeptide chains stabilised by disulfide bridges between neighbouring cysteines. Insulin stimulates glucose uptake by cells.

Protein denaturation

When the chemical bonds holding a protein together become broken the protein can no longer hold its three dimensional shape. This process is called **denaturation**, and the protein usually loses its ability to carry out its biological function.

There are many causes of denaturation including exposure to heat or pH outside of the protein's optimum range. The main protein in egg white is albumin. It has a clear, thick fluid appearance in a raw egg (right). Heat (cooking) denatures the albumin protein and it becomes insoluble, clumping together to form a thick white substance (far right).

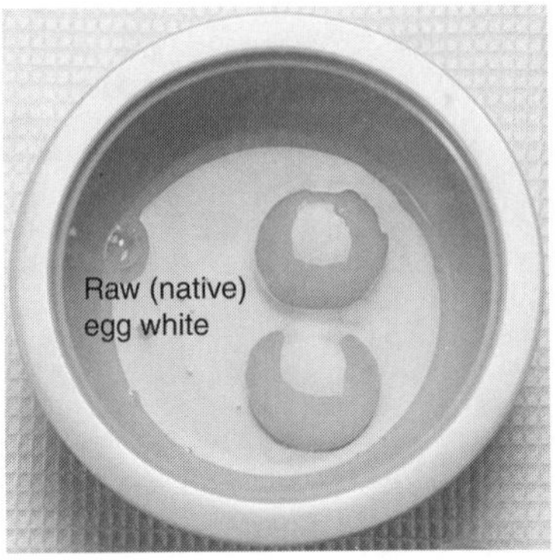
Raw (native) egg white

Cooked (denatured) egg white

1. Explain the importance of the amino acid sequence in protein folding: ______

2. Why do channel proteins often fold with non-polar R groups to the channel's exterior and polar R groups to its interior?

3. Why does **denaturation** often result in the loss of protein functionality? ______

© 2015 BIOZONE International
ISBN:978-1-927309-31-5
Photocopying Prohibited

62 Protein Structure

Key Idea: The sequence and type of animo acids in a protein determines the protein's three-dimensional shape and function.

Proteins are large, complex **macromolecules**, built up from a linear sequence of repeating units called **amino acids**. Proteins are molecules of central importance in the chemistry of life. They account for more than 50% of the dry weight of most cells, and they are important in virtually every cellular process. The folding of a protein into its functional form creates a three dimensional arrangement of the active 'R' groups. It is this **tertiary structure** that gives a protein its unique chemical properties. If a protein loses this precise structure (through **denaturation**), it is usually unable to carry out its biological function.

Primary (1°) structure
(amino acid sequence)

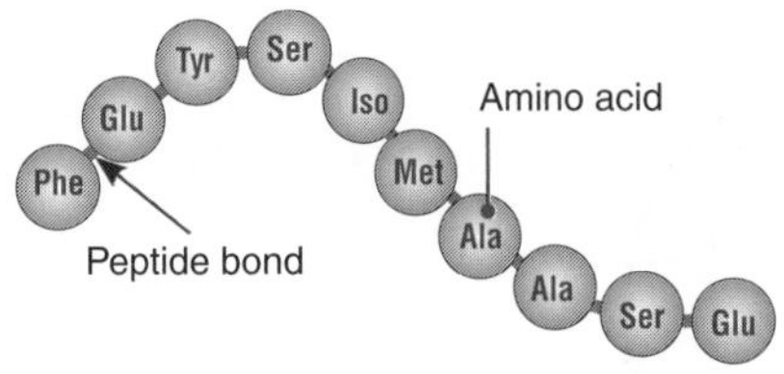

Phe
Glu
Tyr
Ser
Iso
Met
Ala
Ala
Ser
Glu
Amino acid
Peptide bond

Hundreds of amino acids are linked together by peptide bonds to form polypeptide chains. The attractive and repulsive charges on the amino acids determines the higher levels of organisation in the protein and its biological function.

Secondary (2°) structure
(α-helix or β pleated sheet)

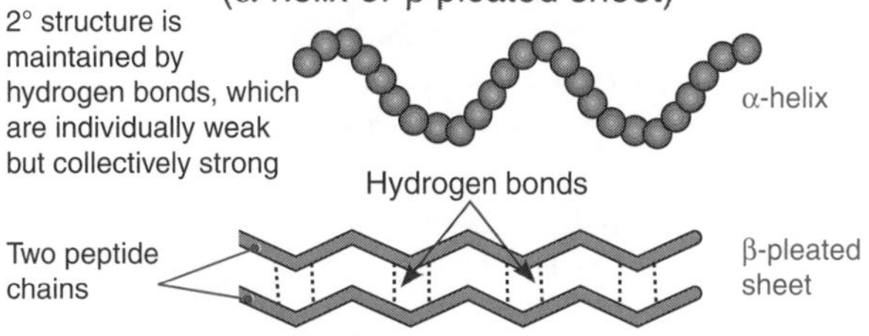

2° structure is maintained by hydrogen bonds, which are individually weak but collectively strong
α-helix
Hydrogen bonds
Two peptide chains
β-pleated sheet

Polypeptides fold into a secondary (2°) structure, usually a coiled α-helix or a β-pleated sheet. Secondary structures are maintained by hydrogen bonds between neighbouring CO and NH groups. Most globular proteins contain regions of α-helices together with β-sheets.

Tertiary (3°) structure
(folding of the **2**° structure)

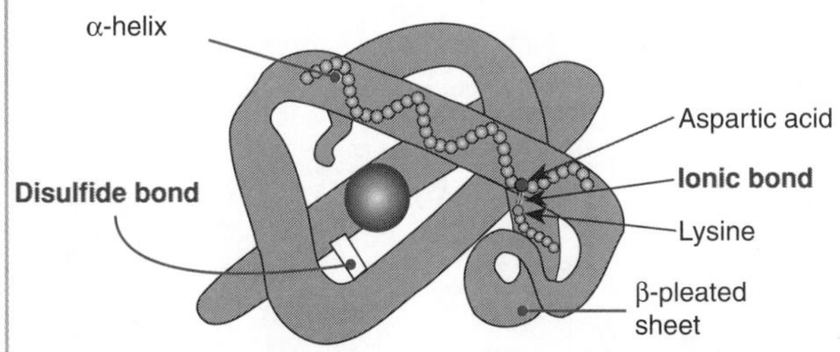

α-helix
Disulfide bond
Aspartic acid
Ionic bond
Lysine
β-pleated sheet

A protein's tertiary structure is the three-dimensional shape it forms when the secondary structure folds up. Chemical bonds such as **disulfide bridges** between cysteine amino acids, ionic bonds, hydrogen bonds, and hydrophobic interactions result in protein folding. These bonds can be destroyed by heavy metals or some solvents, and extremes of pH and temperature.

Quaternary (4°) structure

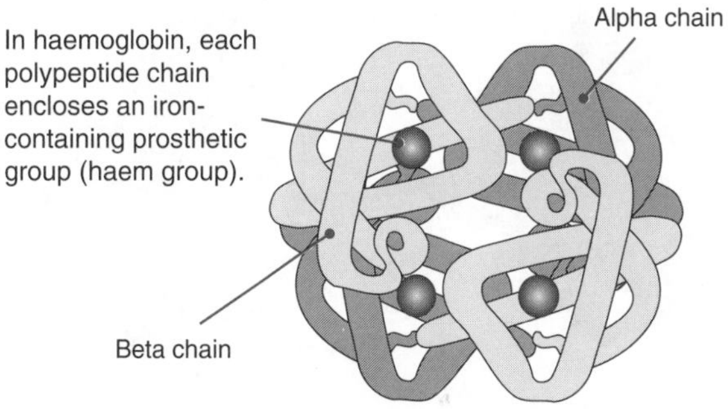

In haemoglobin, each polypeptide chain encloses an iron-containing prosthetic group (haem group).
Alpha chain
Beta chain

Many complex proteins exist as groups of polypeptide chains. The arrangement of the polypeptide chains into a functional protein is termed the quaternary structure. The example (above) shows haemoglobin, which has a quaternary structure comprising two alpha and two beta polypeptide chains, each enclosing a complex iron-containing prosthetic group.

1. Describe the main features that aid the formation of each part of a protein's structure:

   (a) Primary structure: ______________________

   (b) Secondary structure: ______________________

   (c) Tertiary structure: ______________________

   (d) Quaternary structure: ______________________

2. How are proteins built up into a functional structure? ______________________

© 2015 BIOZONE International
ISBN: 978-1-927309-31-5
Photocopying Prohibited

63 Comparing Globular and Fibrous Proteins

Key Idea: Protein structure is related to its biological function. Proteins can be classified according to their structure or their function. **Globular proteins** are spherical and soluble in water (e.g. enzymes). **Fibrous proteins** have an elongated structure and are not water soluble. They are often made up of repeating units and provide stiffness and rigidity to the more fluid components of cells and tissues. They have important structural and contractile roles.

Globular proteins

Properties
- Easily water soluble
- Tertiary structure critical to function
- Polypeptide chains folded into a spherical shape

Function
- Catalytic, *e.g. enzymes*
- Regulatory, *e.g. hormones (insulin)*
- Transport, *e.g. haemoglobin*
- Protective, *e.g. immunoglobulins (antibodies)*

Haemoglobin is an oxygen-transporting protein found in vertebrate red blood cells. One haemoglobin molecule consists of four polypeptide chains (two identical alpha chains and two identical beta chains). Each polypeptide subunit contains a non-protein prosthetic group, an iron-containing haem group, which binds oxygen, enabling oxygen to be transported around the body.

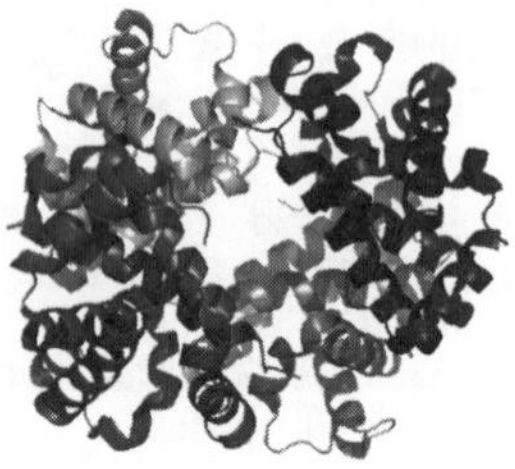
Haemoglobin

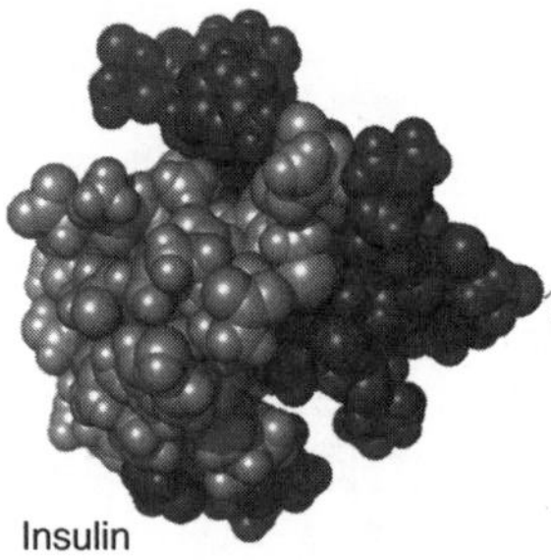
Insulin

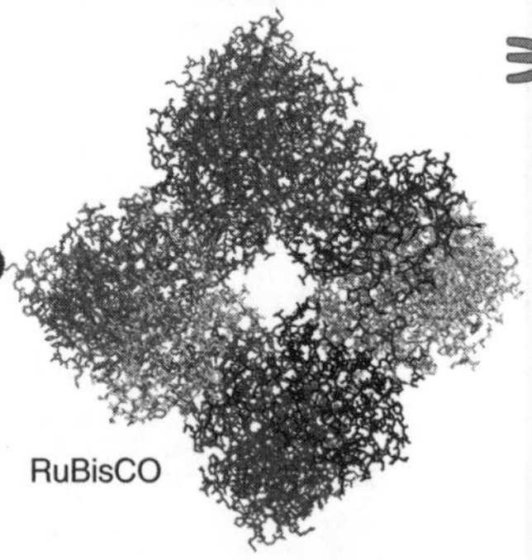
RuBisCO

Insulin is a peptide hormone involved in the regulation of blood glucose. Insulin is composed of two peptide chains (the A chain and the B chain) linked together by two disulfide bonds.

RuBisCo is a large multi-unit enzyme found in green plants and catalyses the first step of carbon fixation in the Calvin cycle. It consists of 8 large (L) and 8 small (S) subunits arranged as 4 dimers. RuBisCO is the most abundant protein on Earth.

Fibrous proteins

Properties
- Water insoluble
- Very tough physically; may be supple or stretchy
- Parallel polypeptide chains in long fibres or sheets

Function
- Structural role in cells and organisms e.g. *collagen in connective tissues, skin, and blood vessel walls.*
- Contractile e.g. *myosin, actin*

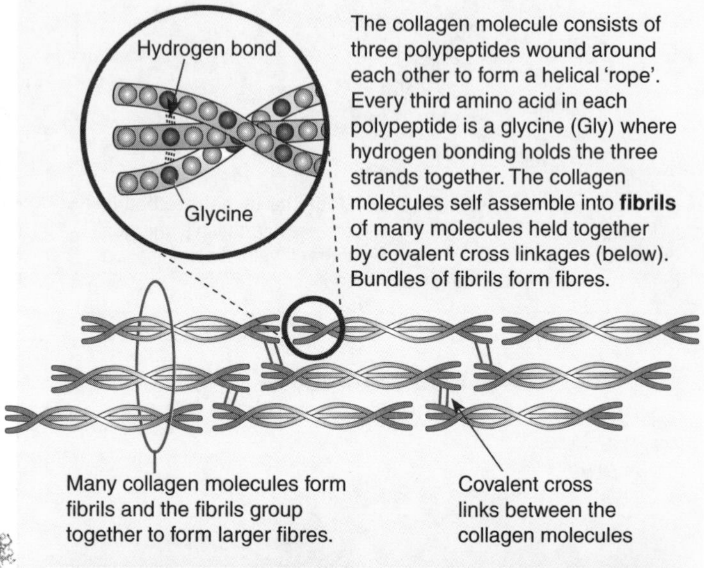
Hydrogen bond
Glycine
Many collagen molecules form fibrils and the fibrils group together to form larger fibres.
Covalent cross links between the collagen molecules

The collagen molecule consists of three polypeptides wound around each other to form a helical 'rope'. Every third amino acid in each polypeptide is a glycine (Gly) where hydrogen bonding holds the three strands together. The collagen molecules self assemble into **fibrils** of many molecules held together by covalent cross linkages (below). Bundles of fibrils form fibres.

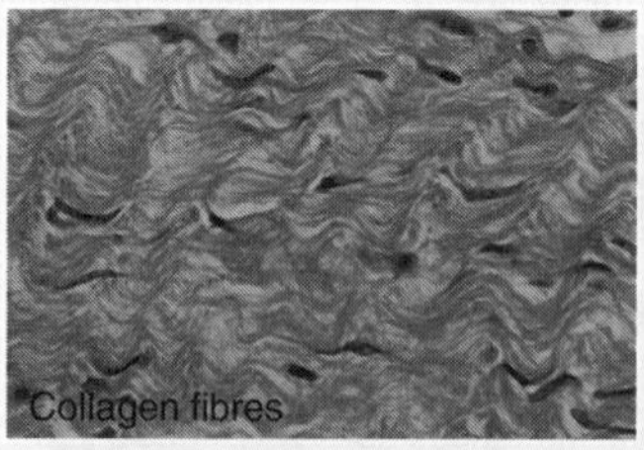
Collagen fibres

This rhinoceros' horn is keratin

Collagen is the main component of connective tissue, and is mostly found in fibrous tissues (e.g. tendons, ligaments, and skin). **Keratin** is found in hair, nails, horn, hooves, wool, feathers, and the outer layers of the skin. The polypeptide chains of keratin are arranged in parallel sheets held together by hydrogen bonding.

1. How are proteins involved in the following roles? Give examples to help illustrate your answer:

   (a) Structural tissues of the body: ______________________

   (b) Catalysing metabolic reactions in cells: ______________________

2. How does the shape of a fibrous protein relate to its functional role? ______________________

3. How does the shape of a catalytic protein (enzyme) relate to its functional role? ______________________

© 2015 BIOZONE International
ISBN:978-1-927309-31-5
Photocopying Prohibited

64 Water

Key Idea: Water forms bonds between other water molecules and also with ions allowing water to act as a medium for transporting molecules and the biological reactions of life.

Water (H_2O) is the main component of living things, and typically makes up about 70% of any organism. Water is important in cell chemistry as it takes part in, and is a common product of, many reactions. Water can form bonds with other water molecules, and also with other ions (charged molecules). Because of this chemical ability, water is regarded as the universal solvent.

Water forms hydrogen bonds

A water molecule is polar, meaning it has a positively and a negatively charged region. In water, oxygen has a slight negative charge and each of the hydrogens have a slight positive charge. Water molecules have a weak attraction for each other, forming large numbers of weak hydrogen bonds with other water molecules (far right).

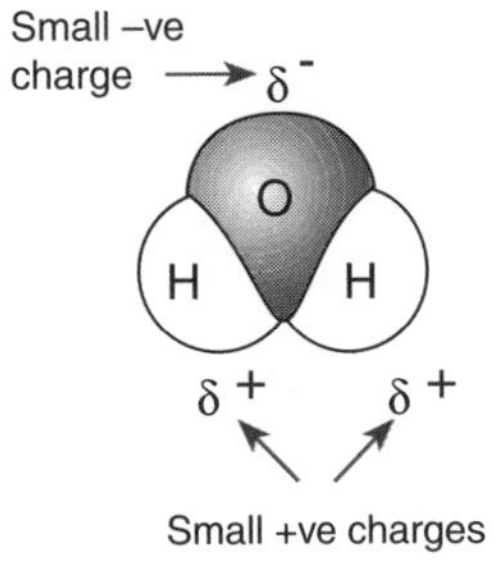
Small –ve charge
δ-
O
H
H
δ+
δ+
Small +ve charges

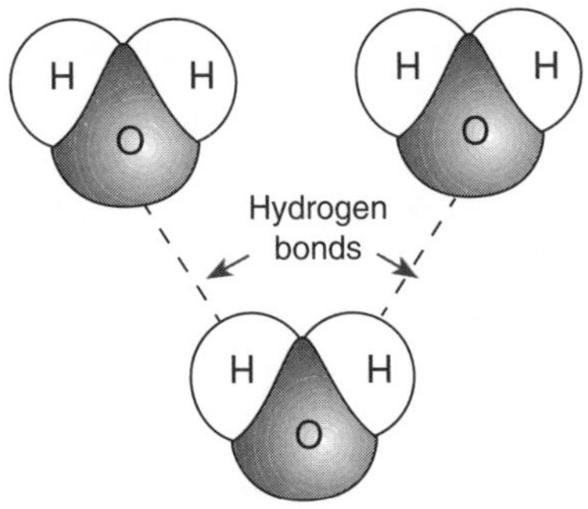
H
H
O
H
H
O
Hydrogen bonds
H
H
O

Intermolecular bonds between water and other polar molecules or ions are important for biological systems. Inorganic ions may have a positive or negative charge (e.g sodium ion is positive, chloride ion is negative). The charged water molecule is attracted to the charged ion and surrounds it (right). This formation of intermolecular bonds between water and the ions is what keeps the ions dissolved in water. Polar molecules such as amino acids and carbohydrates also dissolve readily in water.

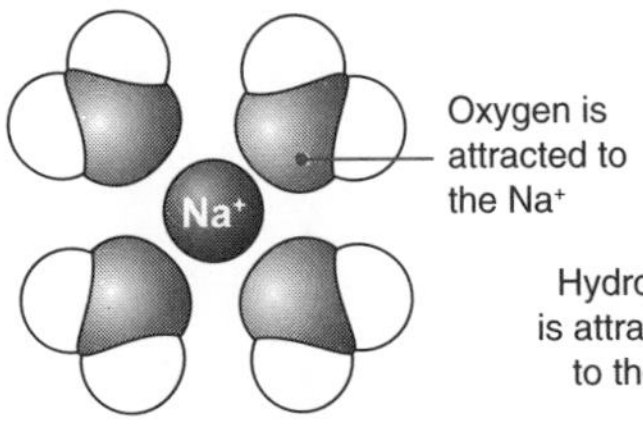
Na^+
Oxygen is attracted to the Na^+

Water surrounding a positive ion (Na^+)

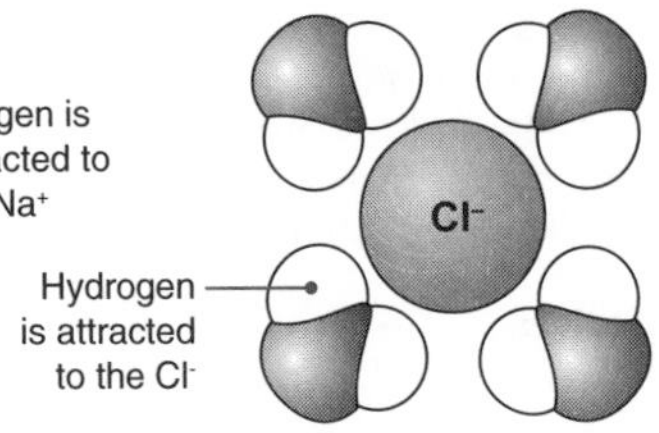
Cl^-
Hydrogen is attracted to the Cl^-

Water surrounding a negative ion (Cl^-)

The importance of water

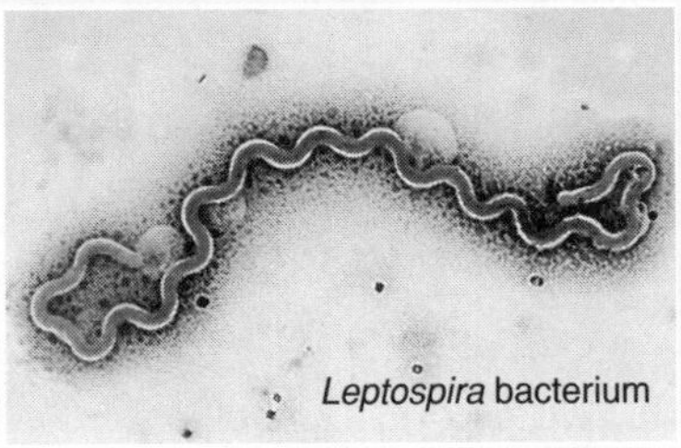

Leptospira bacterium

The metabolic reactions carried out by all organisms depend on dissolved reactants (solutes) coming into contact. Water provides the medium for metabolic reactions. Water can also act as an acid (donating H^+) or a base (receiving H^+) in chemical reactions.

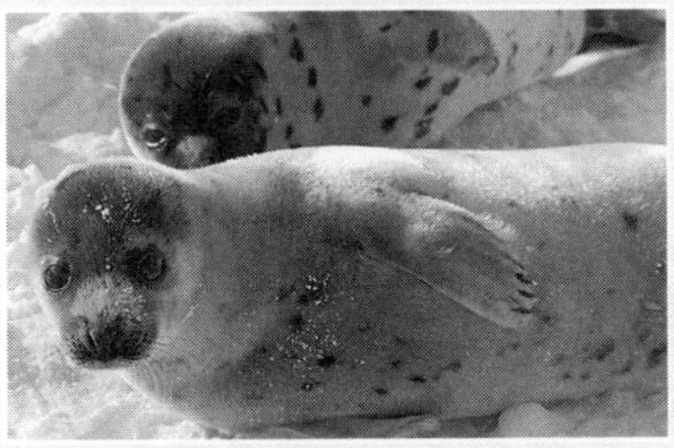

Water provides an aquatic environment for organisms to live in. Ice is less dense than water and floats, insulating the underlying water and maintaining the aquatic habitat. A lot of energy is needed for water to change state, so water has a buffering effect on climate.

Water is colourless, with a high transmission of visible light. Light penetrates aquatic environments, allowing photosynthesis to continue at depth. Water also has a high heat capacity, absorbing and releasing energy slowly. This means large bodies of water are thermally stable.

1. The diagram at the top of the page shows a positive sodium ion and a negative chloride ion surrounded by water molecules. On the diagram, draw on the charge of the water molecules.

2. Explain the formation of hydrogen bonds between water and other polar molecules: ______________________

____

____

____

____

3. Explain the central role of water in metabolic processes: ______________________

____

____

____

© 2015 **BIOZONE** International
ISBN: 978-1-927309-31-5
Photocopying Prohibited

65 The Properties of Water

Key Idea: Water's chemical properties influence its physical properties and account for its central role in life's processes. Water's cohesive, adhesive, thermal, and solvent properties come about because of its polarity and its ability to form hydrogen bonds with other polar molecules. Water's physical and chemical properties are essential for sustaining life.

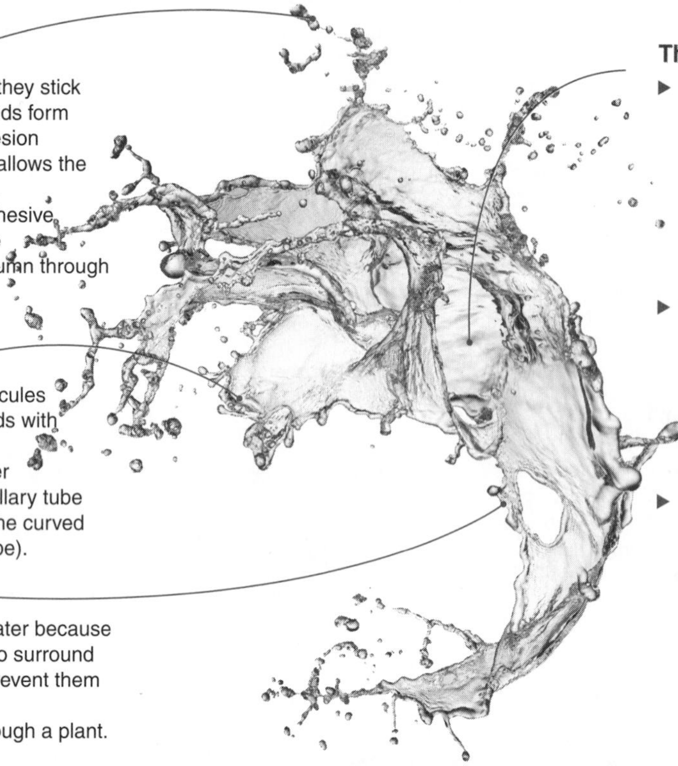

Cohesive properties

Water molecules are cohesive, they stick together because hydrogen bonds form between water molecules. Cohesion allows water to form drops and allows the development of surface tension.
Example: The cohesive and adhesive properties of water allow it to be transported as an unbroken column through the xylem of plants.

Adhesive properties

Water is attracted to other molecules because it forms hydrogen bonds with other polar molecules.
Example: The adhesion of water molecules to the sides of a capillary tube is responsible for a meniscus (the curved upper surface of a liquid in a tube).

Solvent properties

Other substances dissolve in water because water's dipolar nature allows it to surround other charged molecules and prevent them from clumping together.
Example: Mineral transport through a plant.

Thermal properties

- Water has the highest heat capacity of all liquids, so it takes a lot of energy before it will change temperature. As a result, water heats up and cools down slowly, so large bodies of water maintain a relatively stable temperature.
- Water is liquid at room temperature and has a high boiling point because a lot of energy is needed to break the hydrogen bonds. The liquid environment supports life and metabolic processes.
- Water has a high latent heat of vaporisation, meaning it takes a lot of energy to transform it from the liquid to the gas phase. In sweating, the energy is provided by the body, so sweat has a cooling effect.

Reef corals secrete calcium carbonate to form a hard skeleton

Water is known as the universal solvent, because many substances will dissolve in it. In natural waters, dissolved minerals, such as calcium, are available to aquatic organisms, e.g. corals. Blood plasma is about 92% water and transports many water-soluble substances, including ions, glucose, and amino acids, around the body.

Many aquatic organisms depend on a thermally stable environment

Water has a high heat capacity, meaning a lot of energy is needed before it will change temperature. This means that large water bodies will maintain a relatively stable temperature, even when the air temperature fluctuates. It also allows temperature sensitive metabolic reactions to take place within organisms.

Sweating cools by evaporation

Water's high latent heat of vaporisation means that a lot of energy is needed for water to change state (e.g from liquid to gas). Sweating is therefore an effective cooling mechanism. As the water in sweat evaporates from the skin's surface, heat from the body is transferred to the air, cooling the body.

1. What is the biological significance of water having a high heat capacity? ______________________

____

____

2. How does water act as a coolant during sweating? ______________________

____

____

3. (a) What is the significance of water's solvent properties within organisms? ______________________

____

(b) What is the significance of water's solvent properties in natural water bodies? ______________________

____

© 2015 BIOZONE International
ISBN:978-1-927309-31-5
Photocopying Prohibited

66 Chapter Review

Summarise what you know about this topic under the headings provided. You can draw diagrams or mind maps, or write short notes to organise your thoughts. Use the images and hints to help you and refer back to the introduction to check the points covered:

Analytical tests for biological molecules:
HINT: Describe how analytical tests can be used to identify and quantify biological molecules.

Lipids:
HINT: Compare the structure and biological role of different lipids.

Carbohydrates:
HINT: Relate carbohydrate structure to function.

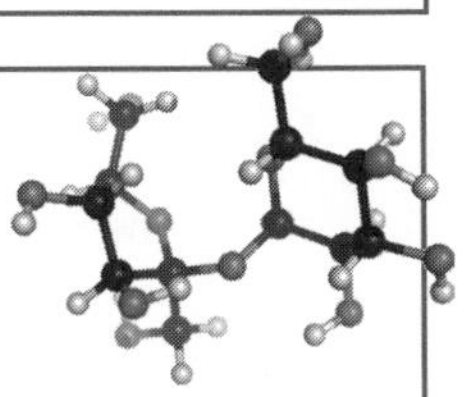

Proteins and water:
HINT: Relate the structure of fibrous and globular proteins to their contrasting roles. Explain the significance of water's properties.

© 2015 **BIOZONE** International
ISBN: 978-1-927309-31-5
Photocopying Prohibited

67 KEY TERMS AND IDEAS: Did You Get It?

1. Test your vocabulary by matching each term to its correct definition, as identified by its preceding letter code.

amino acids	A	The loss of a protein's three dimensional functional structure is called this.
carbohydrates	B	A class of organic compounds with an oily, greasy, or waxy consistency. Important as energy storage molecules and as components of cellular membranes.
condensation	C	The sequence of amino acids in a polypeptide.
denaturation	D	The building blocks of proteins.
fibrous proteins	E	Proteins with a rod or wire-like structure that are important in structure or storag.
globular proteins	F	Long carbohydrate molecules made up of monosaccharide units joined together by glycosidic bonds.
hydrogen bond	G	The splitting of a molecule into smaller components by addition of a water molecule.
hydrolysis	H	A general term for a reaction in which water is released.
lipids	I	Carbohydrate monomers. Examples include fructose and glucose.
monosaccharides	J	Fatty acids containing less than the maximum number of possible hydrogen atoms because of the presence of double bonded carbon atoms.
polypeptides	K	Water soluble proteins with a spherical tertiary structure. They are involved in many cellular functions including as catalysts and in transport and regulation.
polysaccharides	L	Organic compounds, usually linear polymers, made of amino acids linked together by peptide bonds.
primary structure	M	Weak attractive interaction between polar molecules.
saturated fatty acids	N	The structure of a protein maintained by disulfide bonds and hydrophilic and hydrophobic interactions.
tertiary structure	O	Organic molecules consisting only of carbon, hydrogen and oxygen that serve as structural components in cells and as energy sources.
unsaturated fatty acids	P	Fatty acids containing the maximum number of hydrogen bonds.

2. The diagram (right) symbolically represents a phospholipid.

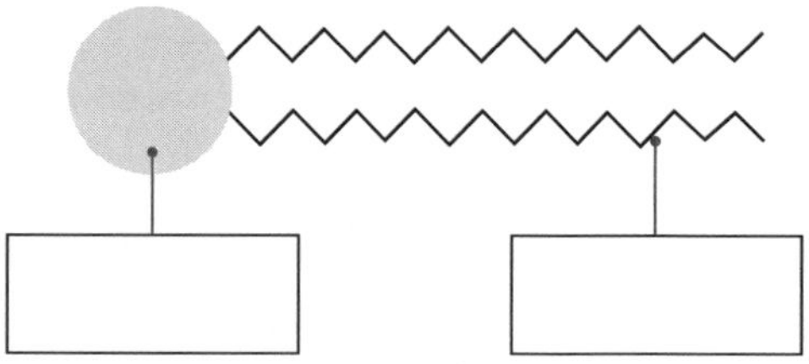

(a) Label the hydrophobic and hydrophilic regions of the phospholipid.

(b) Explain how the properties of the phospholipid molecule result in the bilayer structure of membranes:

____

____

3. (a) What general reaction combines two molecules to form a larger molecule? ____________________

(b) What general reaction cleaves a larger molecule by the addition of water? ____________________

4. (a) Which class of biological molecules contains carbon, hydrogen, and oxygen only: ____________________

(b) In addition to carbon, hydrogen, and oxygen, name the other element that all proteins contain: ____________________

(c) Some proteins also contain sulfur. What is the effect of sulfur on a protein's structure: ____________________

____

© 2015 BIOZONE International
ISBN:978-1-927309-31-5
Photocopying Prohibited

Topic 3 Enzymes

Key terms

- activation energy
- active site
- catalyst
- denaturation
- enzyme
- enzyme-product complex
- enzyme-substrate complex
- enzyme inhibition
- extracellular
- induced fit model
- intracellular
- lock-and-key model
- metabolic pathway
- metabolism
- Michaelis-Menten constant (K_m)
- optimum (for enzyme)
- reversible inhibitor
- specificity
- V_{max}

3.1 Mode of action of enzymes

Learning outcomes

Activity number

- ☐ 1 Explain the role of enzymes in catalysing the many reactions that regulate metabolism. Relate the specificity of enzymes to their substrates to the efficient function of cells and organisms. — 68
- ☐ 2 Explain that enzymes are globular proteins that catalyse metabolic reactions. — 68
- ☐ 3 Describe the role of enzymes in catalysing both intracellular an extracellular reactions, e.g. catalase (intracellular) and amylase (extracellular). — 68
- ☐ 4 Describe the mode of action of enzymes, including reference to the enzyme's tertiary structure and the role of the active site, specificity, formation of the enzyme-substrate (ES) complex, and lowering of activation energy. — 69
- ☐ 5 Explain the lock-and-key and induced fit models of enzyme action, with reference to the ES complex, enzyme-product complex, and product formation. — 70
- ☐ 6 **PRAC** Investigate the progress of an enzyme-catalysed reaction by measuring rates of product formation (e.g. using catalase) or rates of substrate disappearance (e.g. using amylase). — 72 73

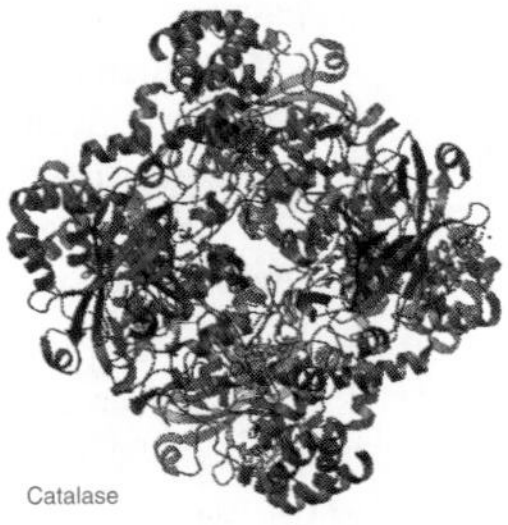

Catalase

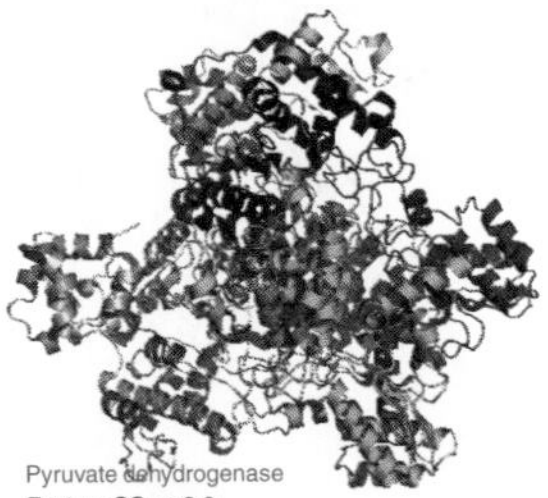

Pyruvate dehydrogenase
FontanaCG cc 3.0

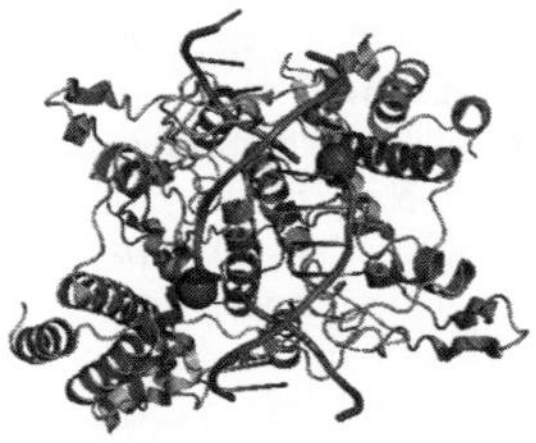

Restriction enzyme

3.2 Factors affecting enzyme activity

Learning outcomes

Activity number

- ☐ 7 Describe the effect of pH, temperature, substrate concentration, and enzyme concentration on enzyme activity. Recognise that enzymes can be denatured. — 71
- ☐ 8 **PRAC** Investigate the effects of pH, temperature, substrate concentration, enzyme concentration or inhibitor concentration on the rate of an enzyme catalysed reaction. If appropriate, prepare enzyme and substrate dilutions using serial dilution technique. — 72 73
- ☐ 9 Understand that the maximum rate of reaction (V_{max}) is used to derive the Michaelis-Menten constant (K_m), which can be used to compare the affinity of different enzymes for their substrates. — 74
- ☐ 10 Describe the effects of reversible inhibitors on the rate of enzyme-controlled reactions. Include reference to competitive and non-competitive inhibition and identify these on graphs of reaction rate vs substrate concentration. — 75
- ☐ 11 Investigate and explain the effect of immobilising an enzyme, such as lactase (β-galactosidase) on its activity as compared with its activity free in solution. — 76

68 Enzymes

Key Idea: Enzymes are biological catalysts. The active site is critical to this functional role.

Most enzymes are globular proteins. Enzymes are biological catalysts because they speed up biochemical reactions, but the enzyme itself remains unchanged. The substrate in a reaction binds to a region of the enzyme called the active site, which is formed by the precise folding of the enzyme's amino acid chain. Enzymes control metabolic pathways. One enzyme will act on a substance to produce the next reactant in a pathway, which will be acted on by a different enzyme.

The active site

Enzymes have an **active site** to which specific substrates bind. The shape and chemistry of the active site is specific to an enzyme, and is a function of the polypeptide's complex tertiary structure.

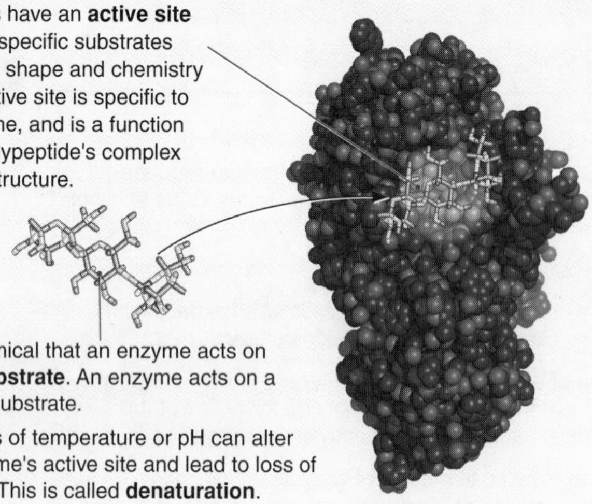

The chemical that an enzyme acts on is the **substrate**. An enzyme acts on a specific substrate.

Extremes of temperature or pH can alter the enzyme's active site and lead to loss of function. This is called **denaturation**.

Substrates collide with an enzyme's active site

For a reaction to occur reactants must collide with sufficient speed and with the correct orientation. Enzymes enhance reaction rates by providing a site for reactants to come together in such a way that a reaction will occur. They do this by orientating the reactants so that the reactive regions are brought together. They may also destabilise the bonds within the reactants making it easier for a reaction to occur.

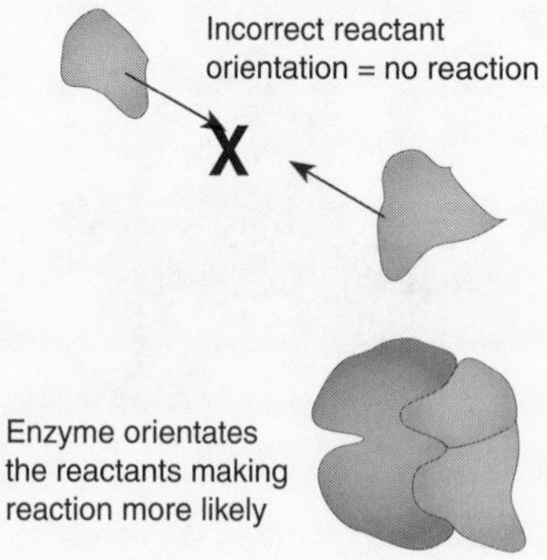
Incorrect reactant orientation = no reaction
X
Enzyme orientates the reactants making reaction more likely

Enzymes can be intracellular or extracellular

Enzymes can be defined based on where they are produced relative to where they are active.

An **intracellular enzyme** is an enzyme that performs its function within the cell that produces it. Most enzymes are intracellular enzymes, e.g. respiratory enzymes.

Example: Catalase.

Many metabolic processes produce hydrogen peroxide, which is harmful to cells. Catalase converts hydrogen peroxide into water and oxygen (below) to prevent damage to cells and tissues.

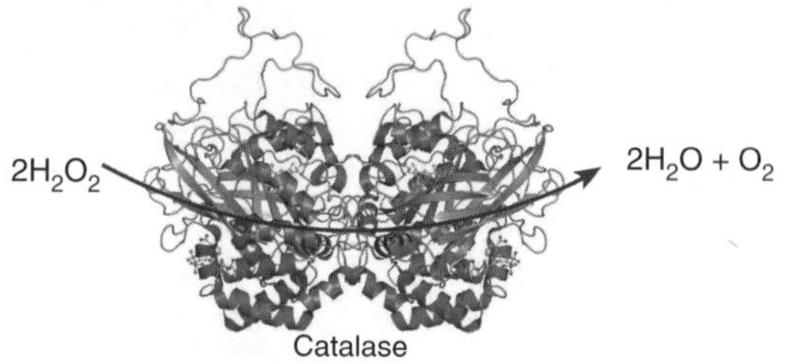
$2H_2O_2$
$2H_2O + O_2$
Catalase

An **extracellular enzyme** is an enzyme that functions outside the cell from which it originates (i.e. it is produced in one location but active in another).

Examples: Amylase and trypsin.

Amylase is a digestive enzyme produced in the salivary glands and pancreas in humans. However, it acts in the mouth and small intestine respectively to hydrolyse starch into sugars.

Trypsin is a protein-digesting enzyme and hydrolyses the peptide bond immediately after a basic residue (e.g. arginine). It is produced in an inactive form (called trypsinogen) and secreted into the small intestine by the pancreas. It is activated in the intestine by the enzyme enteropeptidase to form trypsin. Active trypsin can convert more trypsinogen to trypsin.

1. (a) What is meant by the **active site** of an enzyme and relate it to the enzyme's tertiary structure: ____________________

(b) Why are enzymes specific to one substrate (or group of closely related substrates)? ____________________

2. How do substrate molecules come into contact with an enzyme's active site? ____________________

3. (a) Suggest why digestion (the breakdown of large macromolecules) is largely performed by extracellular enzymes:

____

(b) Why would an extracellular enzyme be produced and secreted in an inactive form? ____________________

© 2015 BIOZONE International
ISBN:978-1-927309-31-5
Photocopying Prohibited

69 How Enzymes Work

Key Idea: Enzymes increase the rate of biological reactions by lowering the reaction's activation energy.

Chemical reactions in cells are accompanied by energy changes. The amount of energy released or taken up is directly related to the tendency of a reaction to run to completion (for all the reactants to form products). Any reaction needs to raise the energy of the substrate to an unstable transition state before the reaction will proceed (below). The amount of energy needed to do this is the **activation energy** (*Ea*). Enzymes lower the *Ea* by destabilising bonds in the substrate so that it is more reactive. Enzyme reactions can break down a single substrate molecule into simpler substances (catabolic reactions), or join two or more substrate molecules together (anabolic reactions).

Lowering the activation energy

The presence of an enzyme simply makes it easier for a reaction to take place. All catalysts speed up reactions by influencing the stability of bonds in the reactants. They may also provide an alternative reaction pathway, thus lowering the activation energy (E_a) needed for a reaction to take place (see the graph below).

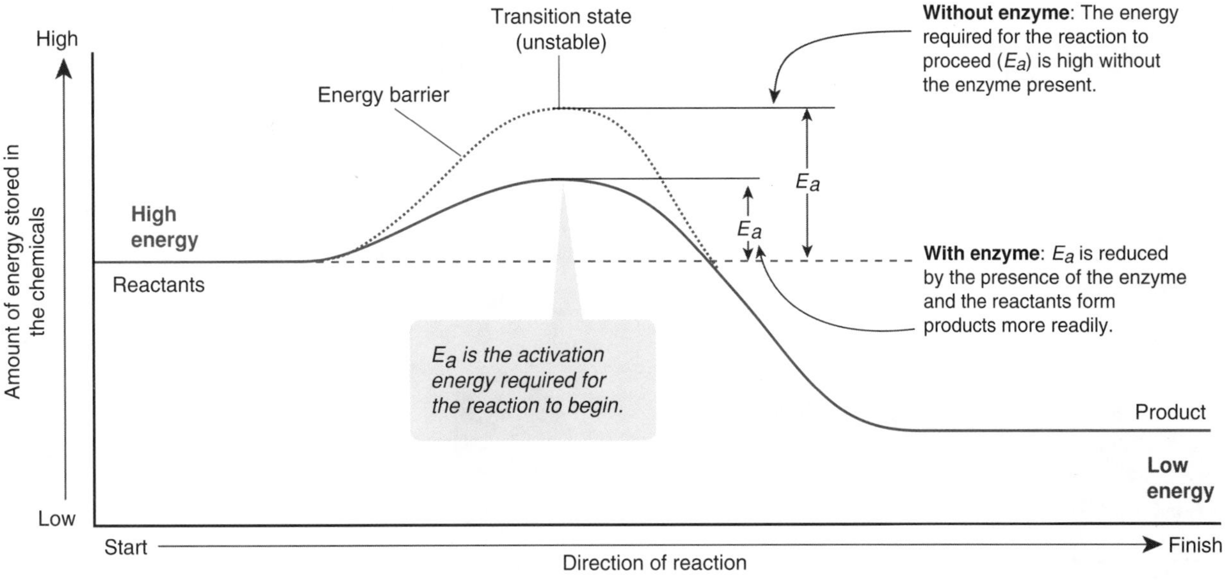

Transition state (unstable)
Without enzyme: The energy required for the reaction to proceed (Ea) is high without the enzyme present.
High
Energy barrier
Ea
Ea
High energy
Reactants
With enzyme: Ea is reduced by the presence of the enzyme and the reactants form products more readily.
Amount of energy stored in the chemicals
Ea is the activation energy required for the reaction to begin.
Product
Low energy
Low
Start
Finish
Direction of reaction

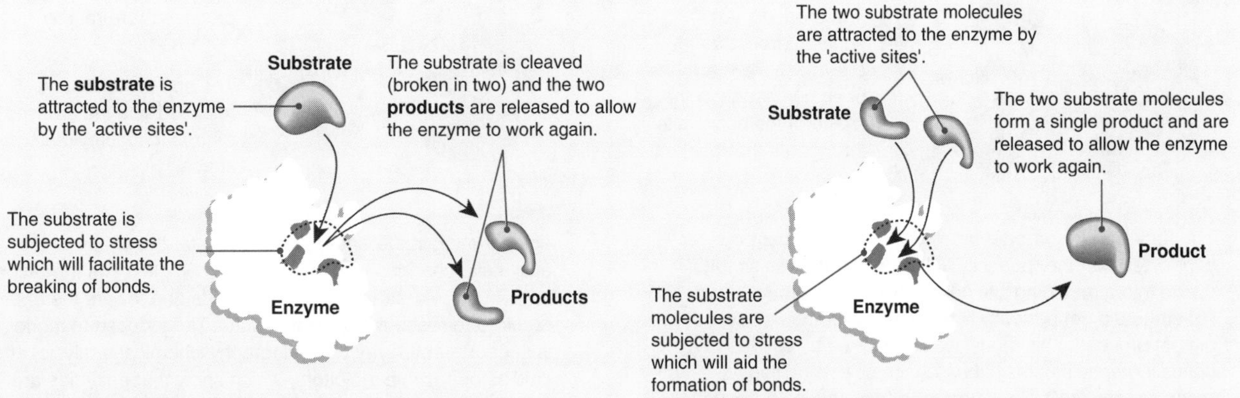

Substrate
The substrate is attracted to the enzyme by the 'active sites'.
The substrate is cleaved (broken in two) and the two products are released to allow the enzyme to work again.
The substrate is subjected to stress which will facilitate the breaking of bonds.
Enzyme
Products
The two substrate molecules are attracted to the enzyme by the 'active sites'.
Substrate
The two substrate molecules form a single product and are released to allow the enzyme to work again.
Product
The substrate molecules are subjected to stress which will aid the formation of bonds.
Enzyme

Catabolic reactions

Some enzymes can cause a single substrate molecule to be drawn into the active site. Chemical bonds are broken, causing the substrate molecule to break apart to become two separate molecules. Catabolic reactions break down complex molecules into simpler ones and involve a net release of energy, so they are called exergonic.
Examples: *hydrolysis, cellular respiration.*

Anabolic reactions

Some enzymes can cause two substrate molecules to be drawn into the active site. Chemical bonds are formed, causing the two substrate molecules to form bonds and become a single molecule. Anabolic reactions involve a net use of energy (they are endergonic) and build more complex molecules and structures from simpler ones.
Examples: *protein synthesis, photosynthesis.*

1. How do enzymes lower the activation energy for a reaction? ______________________

____

____

2. Describe the difference between a catabolic and anabolic reaction: ______________________

____

© 2015 BIOZONE International
ISBN: 978-1-927309-31-5
Photocopying Prohibited

70 Models of Enzyme Activity

Key Idea: Enzymes catalyse reactions by providing a reaction site for a substrate. The model that describes the behaviour of enzymes the best is the induced fit model.

The initial model of enzyme activity was the lock and key model proposed by Emil Fischer in the 1890s. Fischer proposed enzymes were rigid structures, similar to a lock, and the substrate was the key. While some aspects of Fischer's model were correct, for example, substrates align with enzymes in a way that is likely to make a reaction more likely, the model has been adapted as techniques to study molecular structures have developed. The current 'induced-fit' model of enzyme function is supported by studies of enzyme inhibitors, which show that enzymes are flexible and change shape when interacting with the substrate.

The lock and key model of enzyme function

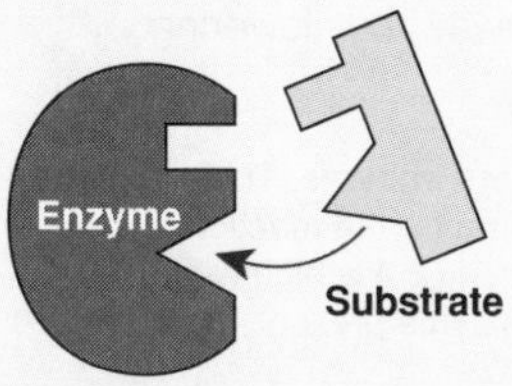
Enzyme
Substrate

1. The substrate molecule is drawn into site of the enzyme. The enzyme's active site does not change shape.

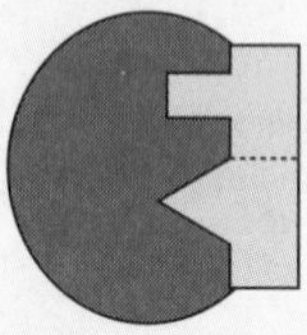

2. The enzyme-substrate (ES) complex is formed.

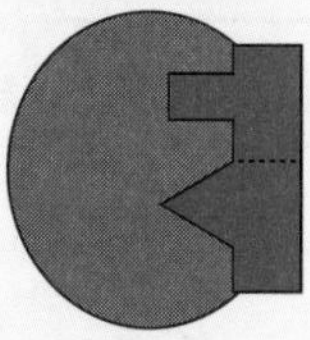

3. The enzyme reaction takes place to form the enzyme-product (EP) complex.

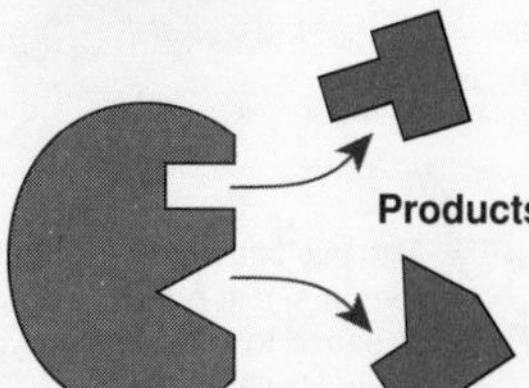
Products

4. The products are released from the enzyme. Note there has been no change in the shape of the active site throughout the reaction.

The **lock and key model** proposed earlier last century suggested that the (perfectly fitting) substrate was simply drawn into a matching site on the enzyme molecule. If the substrate did not perfectly fit the active site, the reaction did not proceed. This model was supported by early X-ray crystallography studies but has since been modified to recognise the flexibility of enzymes (the induced fit model).

The current induced fit model

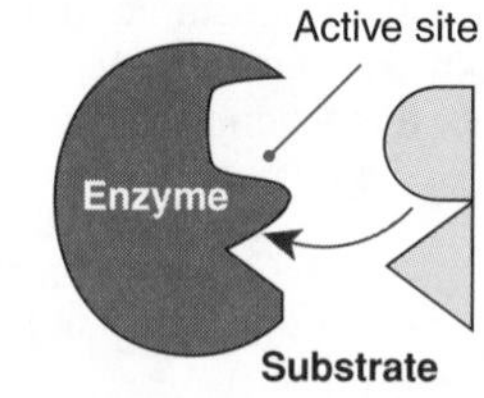
Active site
Enzyme
Substrate

1. A substrate molecule is drawn into the enzyme's active site, which is like a cleft into which the substrate molecule(s) fit.

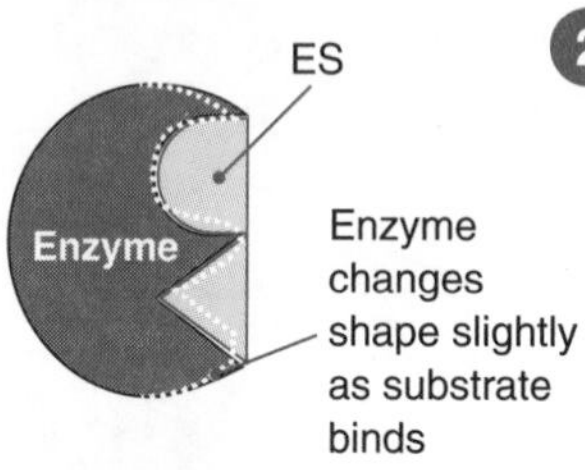
ES
Enzyme
Enzyme changes shape slightly as substrate binds

2. The enzyme changes shape as the substrate binds, forming an enzyme-substrate (ES) complex. The shape change makes the substrate more amenable to alteration. In this way, the enzyme's interaction with its substrate is best regarded as an induced fit.

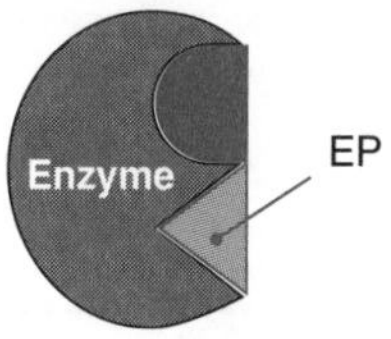
Enzyme
EP

3. The ES interaction results in an intermediate enzyme-product (EP) complex. The substrate becomes bound to the enzyme by weak chemical bonds, straining bonds in the substrate and allowing the reaction to proceed more readily.

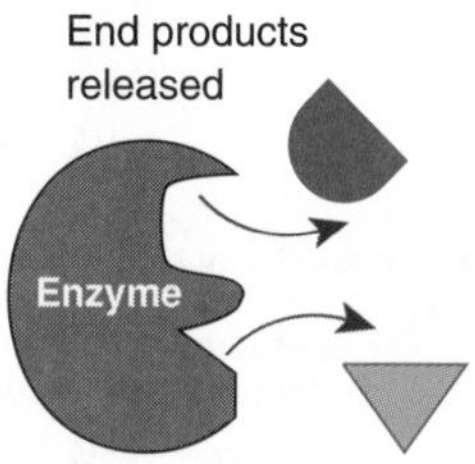
End products released
Enzyme

4. The end products are released and the enzyme returns to its previous shape.

Once the substrate enters the active site, the shape of the active site changes to form an active complex. The formation of an ES complex strains substrate bonds and lowers the energy required to reach the transition state. The induced-fit model is supported by X-ray crystallography, chemical analysis, and studies of enzyme inhibitors, which show that enzymes are flexible and change shape when interacting with the substrate.

1. Describe the key features of the '**lock and key**' model of enzyme action and explain its deficiencies as a working model:

2. How does the current '**induced fit**' model of enzyme action differ from the lock and key model?

© 2015 BIOZONE International
ISBN:978-1-927309-31-5
Photocopying Prohibited

71 Enzyme Reaction Rates

Key idea: Enzymes operate most effectively within a narrow range of conditions. The rate of enzyme catalysed reactions is influenced by both enzyme and substrate concentration.

Enzymes usually have an optimum set of conditions (e.g. of pH and temperature) under which their activity is greatest. Many plant and animal enzymes show little activity at low temperatures. Enzyme activity increases with increasing temperature, but falls off after the optimum temperature is exceeded and the enzyme is denatured. Extremes in pH can also cause denaturation. Within their normal operating conditions, enzyme reaction rates are influenced by enzyme and substrate concentration in a predictable way (below).

In the graphs below, the rate of reaction or degree of enzyme activity is plotted against each of four factors that affect enzyme performance. Answer the questions relating to each graph:

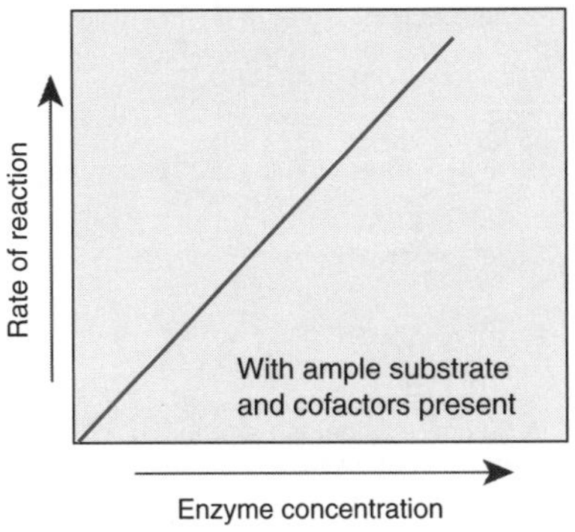
Rate of reaction
With ample substrate and cofactors present
Enzyme concentration

1. **Enzyme concentration**

(a) Describe the change in the rate of reaction when the enzyme concentration is increased (assuming substrate is not limiting):

(b) Suggest how a cell may vary the amount of enzyme present in a cell:

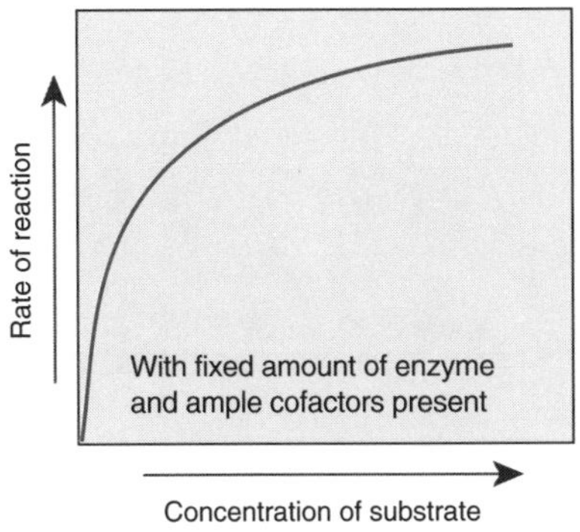
Rate of reaction
With fixed amount of enzyme and ample cofactors present
Concentration of substrate

2. **Substrate concentration**

(a) Describe the change in the rate of reaction when the substrate concentration is **increased** (assuming a fixed amount of enzyme):

(b) Explain why the rate changes the way it does:

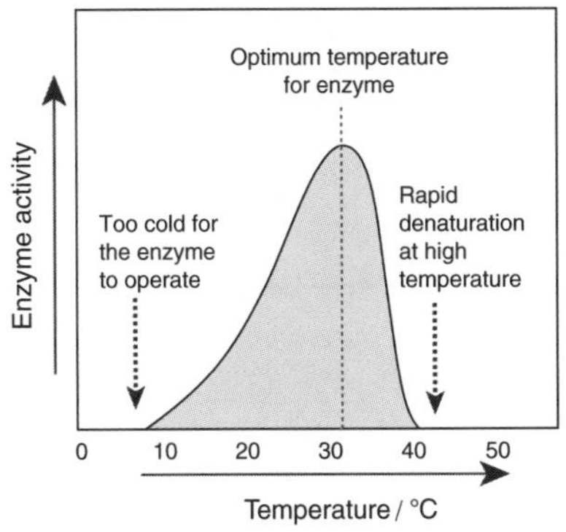
Optimum temperature for enzyme
Too cold for the enzyme to operate
Rapid denaturation at high temperature
Enzyme activity
0
10
20
30
40
50
Temperature / °C

3. **Temperature**

Higher temperatures speed up all reactions, but few enzymes can tolerate temperatures higher than 50–60°C. The rate at which enzymes are **denatured** (change their shape and become inactive) increases with higher temperatures.

(a) Describe what is meant by an *optimum temperature* for enzyme activity:

(b) Explain why most enzymes perform poorly at low temperatures:

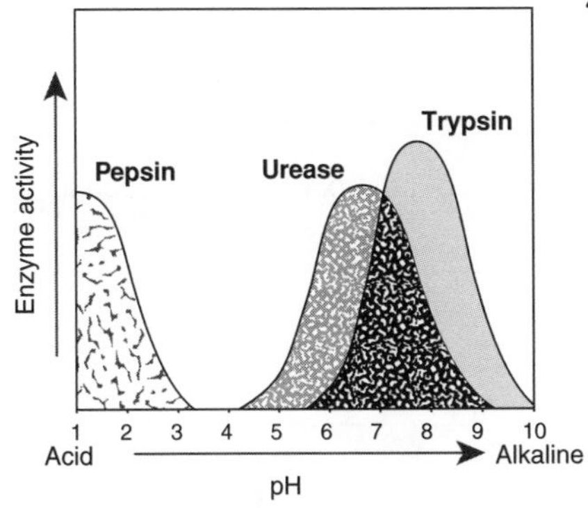
Enzyme activity
Pepsin
Urease
Trypsin
1
2
3
4
5
6
7
8
9
10
Acid
Alkaline
pH

4. **Acidity or alkalinity (pH)**

Like all proteins, enzymes are **denatured** by *extremes* of **pH** (very acid or alkaline). Within these extremes, most enzymes are still influenced by pH. Each enzyme has a preferred pH range for optimum activity.

(a) State the optimum pH for each of the enzymes:

Pepsin: ______ Trypsin: ______ Urease: ______

(b) Pepsin acts on proteins in the stomach. Explain how its optimum pH is suited to its working environment:

© 2015 **BIOZONE** International
ISBN: 978-1-927309-31-5
Photocopying Prohibited

72 Investigating Catalase Activity

Key Idea: Enzyme reaction rate can be determined indirectly by measuring the volume of reaction products.

A group of students decided to use cubes of potato, which naturally contain the enzyme catalase, placed in hydrogen peroxide to test the effect of enzyme concentration on reaction rate. The reaction rate could be measured by the volume of oxygen produced as the hydrogen peroxide was decomposed into oxygen and water.

Aim

To investigate the effect of potato mass (and therefore enzyme concentration) on the rate of H_2O_2 decomposition.

Hypothesis

A greater mass of potato will have more enzyme present and will produce a greater reaction rate.

Method

The students cut raw potato into cubes with a mass of one gram. These were placed a conical flask with excess hydrogen peroxide (right). The reaction was left for five minutes and the volume of oxygen produced recorded. The students recorded the results for three replicates each of 1, 2, 3, 4, and 5 cubes of potato below:

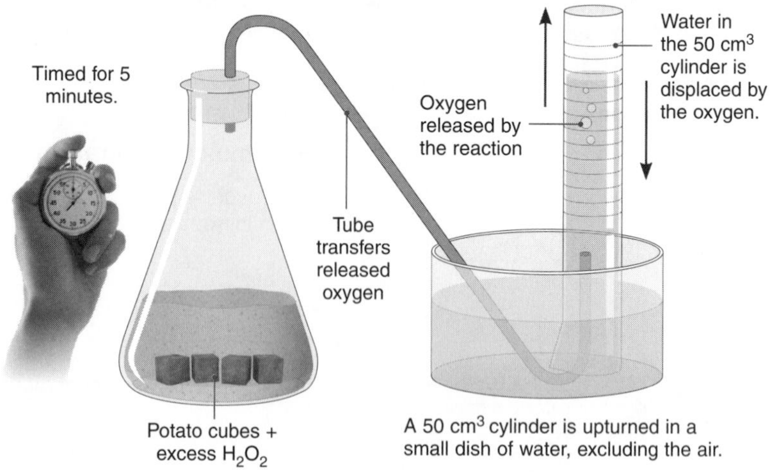

Timed for 5 minutes.
Water in the 50 cm³ cylinder is displaced by the oxygen.
Oxygen released by the reaction
Tube transfers released oxygen
Potato cubes + excess H₂O₂
A 50 cm³ cylinder is upturned in a small dish of water, excluding the air.

Mass of potato / g	Volume oxygen / cm^3 (5 minutes)			Mean	Mean rate of O_2 production / $cm^3\ min^{-1}$
	Test 1	Test 2	Test 3		
1	6	5	6		
2	10	9	9		
3	14	15	15		
4	21	20	20		
5	24	23	25		

1. Complete the table by filling in the mean volume of oxygen produced and the rate of oxygen production.

2. Plot the mass of the potato vs the rate of production on the grid (right):

3. Relate the rate of the reaction to the amount of enzyme present.

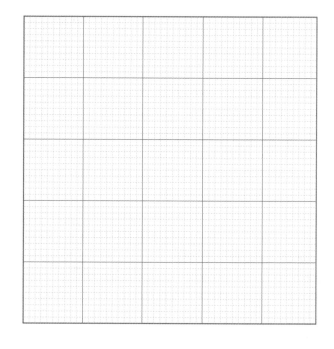

4. Why did the students add excess H_2O_2 to the reaction?

5. State one extra reaction that should have been carried out by the students:

6. (a) The students decide to cook some potato and carry out the test again with two grams of potato. Predict the result:

   (b) Explain this result:

© 2015 BIOZONE International
ISBN:978-1-927309-31-5
Photocopying Prohibited

73 Investigating Amylase Activity

Key Idea: Salivary amylase works optimally at the pH and temperature conditions of the human body. Enzyme activity outside these conditions decreases.

Amylase is a digestive enzyme that hydrolyses (breaks down) starch into the sugars maltose (a disaccharide) and glucose (a monosaccharide). In mammals, amylase is secreted by the salivary gland into the saliva and by the pancreas into the small intestine. Like all enzymes, amylase works best under certain conditions. In the experiments below, students looked at how pH and temperature affected amylase activity.

Aim

To determine the optimum pH for salivary amylase.

Hypothesis

If the normal pH for saliva is 6.5-7.5, then the optimum pH for salivary amylase should be approximately pH 7.

Background

Iodine solution (I_2/KI) is a yellow/orange colour, but in the presence of starch, it turns a blue/black colour. When the iodine solution no longer changes colour after the sample is added (i.e. remains yellow), all the starch has been hydrolysed.

Method

The experiment was performed at room temperature. A single drop of 0.1 M iodine solution was placed into the wells of spotting plates. 2 cm^3 of 1% amylase solution and 1 cm^3 of a buffered solution, pH 4, were added to the test tube. The solutions were mixed and 2 cm^3 of a 1% starch solution was added. A timer was immediately started. After 10 seconds a plastic pipette was used to remove a small amount of solution. A single drop was added to the first well of the **spotting plate** (right) and the remaining solution inside the pipette returned to the test tube. This action was repeated at 10 second intervals, adding a drop of the reaction solution into a new well until the iodine solution no longer changed colour (remained yellow/orange). The experiment was repeated using buffer solutions of pH 5, 6, 7, and 8.

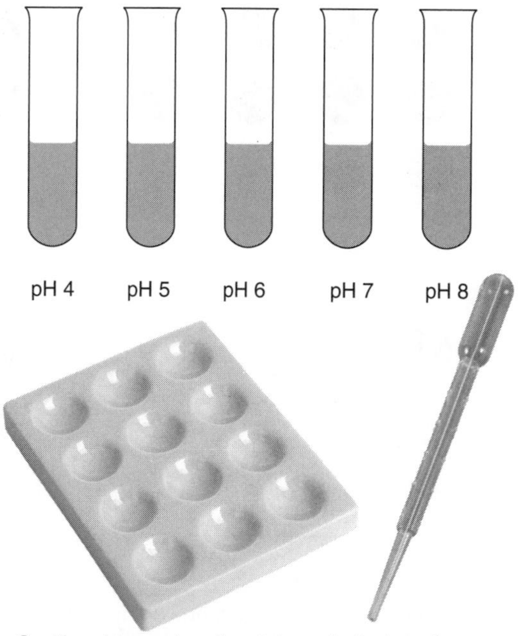
pH 4
pH 5
pH 6
pH 7
pH 8

Spotting plate: each well contains a single drop of 0.1 M iodine solution (iodine dissolved in a solution of potassium iodide). Multiple spotting plates were set up to accommodate the number of tests required.

Results

The table below shows how many drops it took until there was no colour change (the iodine solution remained yellow).

pH	Number of drops until no colour change occurred	Number of seconds until no colour change occurred	Reaction rate / s^{-1}
4	19	190	
5	12	120	
6	10	100	
7	6	60	
8	29	290	

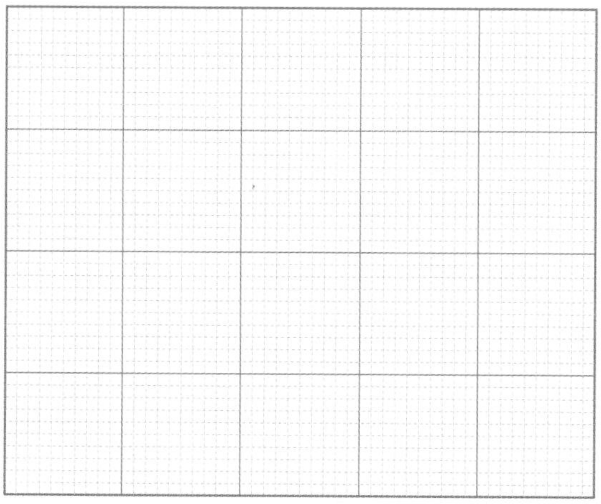

1. Why was it important to add the buffer and enzyme together before adding the starch?

2. Complete the table (left) by calculating the reaction rate for each pH (1 ÷ seconds):

3. (a) Graph the reaction rate vs pH on the grid.

   (b) Identify the pH where amylase activity was the highest:

   (c) Is this what you had expected? Explain:

4. The students repeated the experiment at pH 1. Each sample turned blue/black when added to the iodine even after five minutes of sampling. Explain what has happened here:

© 2015 BIOZONE International
ISBN: 978-1-927309-31-5
Photocopying Prohibited

LINK 74 KNOW

In a second experiment, students wanted to determine the temperature optimum for salivary amylase. Spotting plates were set up by adding a single drop of 0.1 M iodine solution. To a test tube, 2 cm^3 of 1% amylase solution and 1 cm^3 of a buffered pH 7 solution was added. The test tubes were placed in a water bath at one the appropriate temperature and left for five minutes until it was at the required temperature. Once the temperature had been reached 2 cm^3 of a 1% starch solution was added. A timer was immediately started. After one minute a plastic pipette was used to remove a small amount of solution. A single drop was added to the spotting plate and the colour change observed. Samples were repeated at one minute intervals until no colour change was seen. The experiment was repeated at 10, 20, 30, 40, 50, and 60°C. The results are shown below.

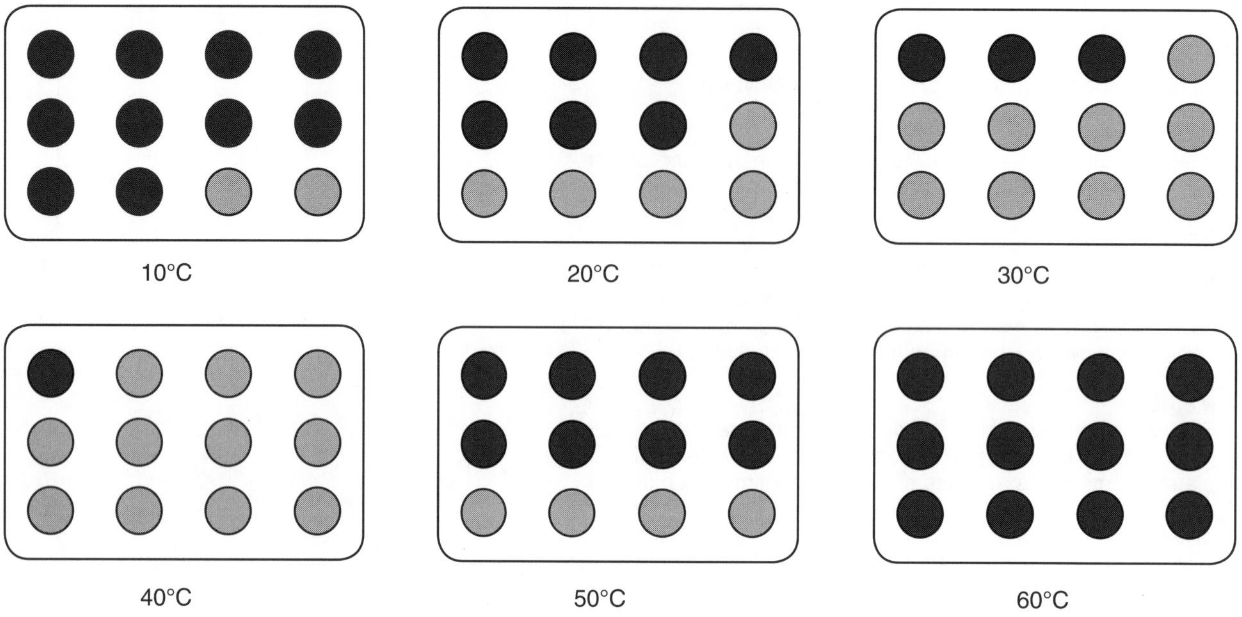
10°C
20°C
30°C
40°C
50°C
60°C

5. The students did not use any controls when they investigated the effect of pH on salivary amylase activity. What would a suitable control have been?

6. Why was the temperature investigation experiment carried out at pH 7?

7. Identify the temperature at which amylase shows no activity (the enzyme is denatured):

8. On the grid, plot the time taken for all the starch to be digested against temperature (do not plot 60°C):

9. Identify the optimum temperature for amylase:

10. Describe how temperature affects the activity of amylase:

11. Predict amylase activity below 10°C and give a reason for your prediction:

© 2015 **BIOZONE** International
ISBN:978-1-927309-31-5
Photocopying Prohibited

74 Enzyme Kinetics

Key Idea: The rate of enzyme activity and the affinity of an enzyme for its substrate can be determined from a graph.

As we have seen, the rate of catalysis for many enzymes varies with substrate concentration. At a fixed concentration of enzyme, the reaction rate is fastest at the beginning, but falls off as all the active sites are engaged in catalysis.

The kinetics of this type of enzyme-catalysed reaction is described by the Michaelis-Menten model (below). Two values are important in describing an enzyme-catalysed reaction under this model: the maximal rate, Vmax, and the Michaelis-Menten constant, Km. These can be derived from the reaction rate at different substrate concentrations (below).

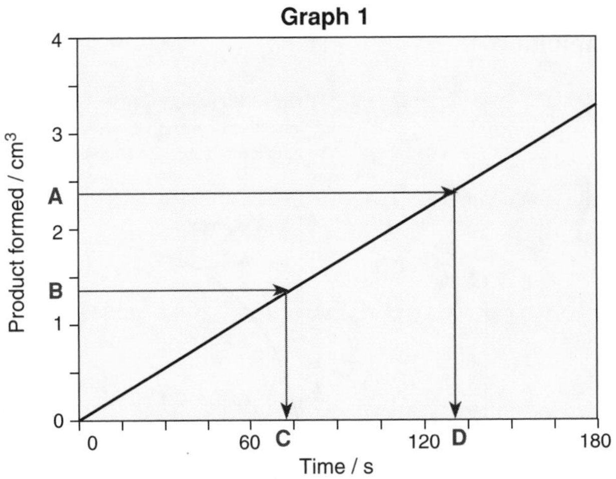

Graph 1
Product formed / cm^3
Time / s
0
1
2
3
4
A
B
C
D
60
120
180

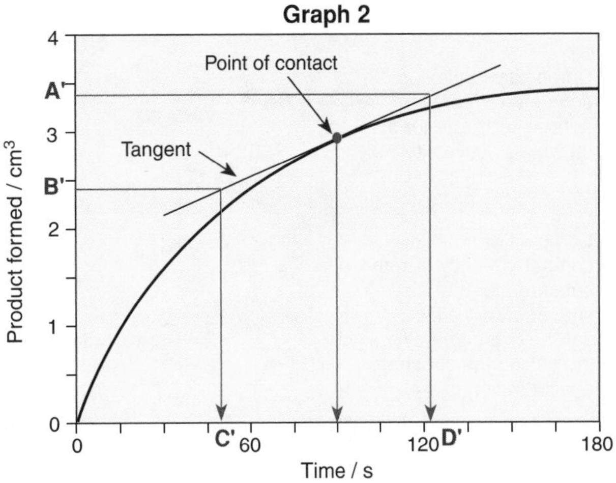

Graph 2
Point of contact
Tangent
A'
B'
C'
D'
Product formed / cm^3
Time / s
0
1
2
3
4
60
120
180

The rate of a reaction can be calculated from the amount of product produced during a given time period. For a reaction in which the rate does not vary (graph 1) the reaction rate calculated at any one point in time will be the same. For example: B/C = A/D = A-B/D-C = (Δp/Δt) (the change in product divided by the change in time).

In a reaction in which the rate varies (graph 2) a reaction rate can be calculated for any instantaneous moment in time by using a tangent. The tangent must touch the curve at only one point. The gradient of the tangent can then be used to calculate the rate of reaction at that point in time (A'-B'/D'-C').

Michaelis-Menten enzyme kinetics

The Michaelis-Menten equation is used to study the kinetics of enzyme-catalysed reactions. Usually, the reaction rate is measured at different concentrations of substrate [S], producing a plot.

Two values can be obtained from this plot.

1. $\mathbf{V_{max}}$ is the is the maximum reaction rate at saturating substrate concentrations.

2. $\mathbf{K_m}$ is the substrate concentration at which the reaction rate is exactly half of V_{max}. K_m is also called the Michaelis-Menten constant.

The K_m is loosely related to the enzyme's affinity for the substrate. The higher the K_m, the lower the fraction of enzyme with bound substrate. An enzyme with a high K_m has a low affinity for its substrate. An enzyme with a low K_m has a high affinity for its substrate.

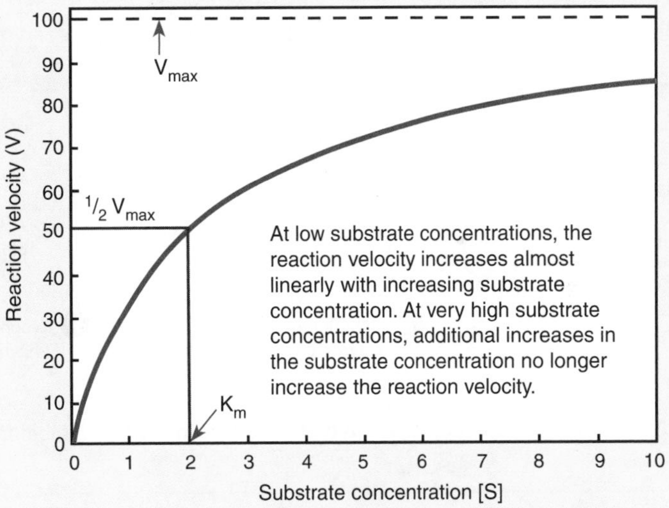

V_{max}
$^1/_2\ V_{max}$
K_m
Reaction velocity (V)
Substrate concentration [S]
0
10
20
30
40
50
60
70
80
90
100
1
2
3
4
5
6
7
8
9
10
At low substrate concentrations, the reaction velocity increases almost linearly with increasing substrate concentration. At very high substrate concentrations, additional increases in the substrate concentration no longer increase the reaction velocity.

1. Calculate the reaction rate in graph 1: ______________________

2. For graph 2 calculate:

   (a) The reaction rate at 90 seconds: ______________________

   (b) The reaction rate at 30 seconds: ______________________

3. (a) For an enzyme that follows Michaelis-Menten kinetics, what is K_m equal to? ______________________

   (b) What is the relationship between K_m and the affinity of the enzyme for its substrate? ______________________

4. What does the shape of the curve demonstrate: ______________________

© 2015 BIOZONE International
ISBN: 978-1-927309-31-5
Photocopying Prohibited

75 Enzyme Inhibitors

Key Idea: Enzyme activity can be reduced or stopped by inhibitors. These may be competitive or non-competitive.

Enzyme activity can be stopped, temporarily or permanently, by chemicals called enzyme inhibitors. Reversible inhibitors can be displaced from the enzyme and have a role as enzyme regulators in metabolic pathways. **Competitive inhibitors** compete directly with the substrate for the active site and their effect can be overcome by increasing the concentration of available substrate. A **non-competitive inhibitor** does not occupy the active site, but distorts it so that the substrate and enzyme can no longer interact. The type of inhibition involved can be deduced from the kinetics of the reaction.

Competitive inhibition

Competitive inhibitors compete with the normal substrate for the enzyme's active site.

Competitive inhibitors compete directly with the substrate for the active site, and their effect can be overcome by increasing the substrate concentration.

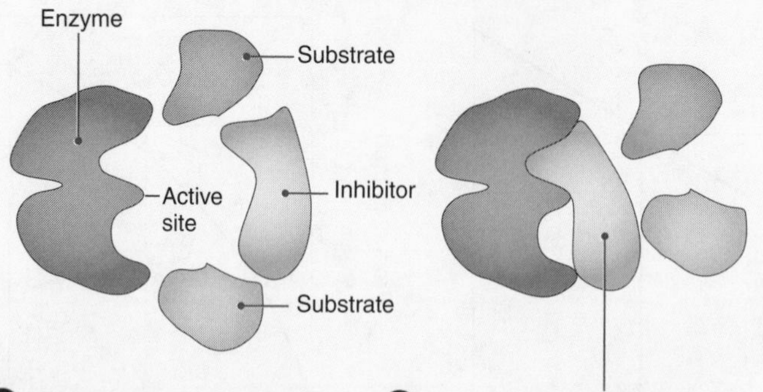
Enzyme
Substrate
Active site
Inhibitor
Substrate

1. Inhibitor is present in the cell (or solution) with the substrate
2. Inhibitor temporarily binds to the active site, blocking it so that the substrate cannot bind

Fig.1 Effect of competitive inhibition on enzyme reaction rate at different substrate concentration

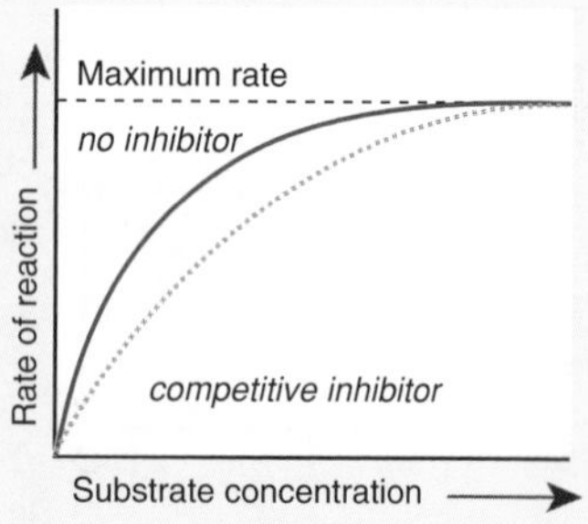
Maximum rate
no inhibitor
Rate of reaction
competitive inhibitor
Substrate concentration

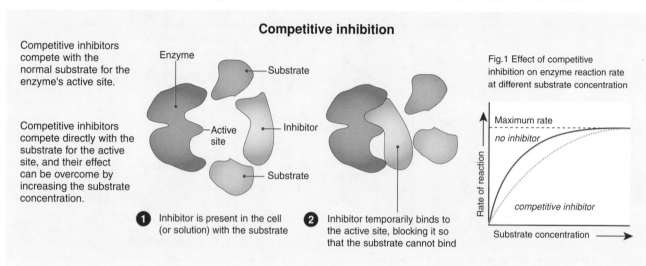

Non-competitive inhibition

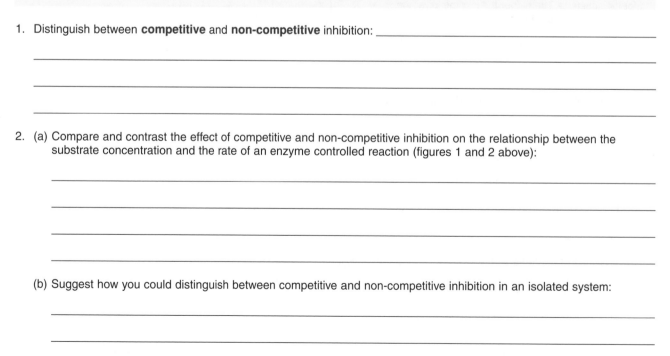

Non-competitive inhibitors bind with the enzyme at a site other than the active site.

They inactivate the enzyme by altering its shape so that the substrate and enzyme can no longer interact.

Non-competitive inhibition cannot be overcome by increasing the substrate concentration.

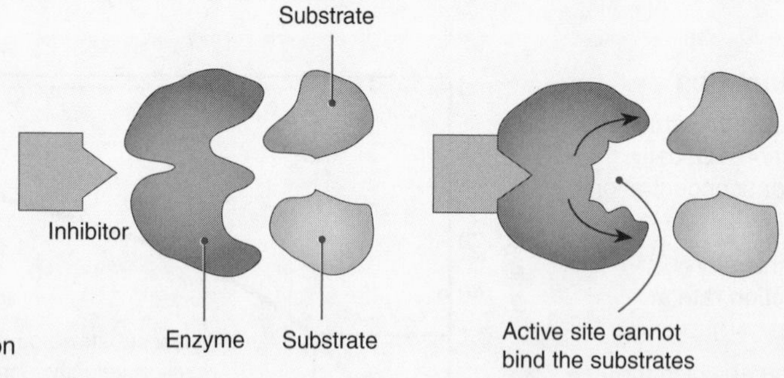
Substrate
Inhibitor
Enzyme
Substrate
Active site cannot bind the substrates

1. Without the inhibitor bound, the enzyme can bind the substrate
2. When the inhibitor binds, the enzyme changes shape.

Fig.2 Effect of non-competitive inhibition on enzyme reaction rate at different substrate concentration

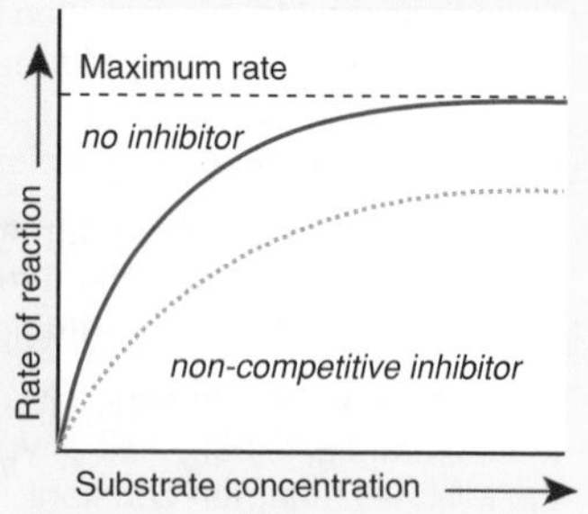
Maximum rate
no inhibitor
Rate of reaction
non-competitive inhibitor
Substrate concentration

1. Distinguish between **competitive** and **non-competitive** inhibition: ______________________

____

____

____

2. (a) Compare and contrast the effect of competitive and non-competitive inhibition on the relationship between the substrate concentration and the rate of an enzyme controlled reaction (figures 1 and 2 above):

____

____

____

____

(b) Suggest how you could distinguish between competitive and non-competitive inhibition in an isolated system:

____

____

© 2015 BIOZONE International
ISBN:978-1-927309-31-5
Photocopying Prohibited

76 Immobilised Enzymes

Key idea: Immobilised lactase is used to remove lactose from milk, making it suitable for people with lactose intolerance.

An **immobilised enzyme** is an enzyme that has been bound to a stationary support. Substrate is passed over the bound enzyme and the product is collected. The immobilised enzyme can be reused many times and, because it is bound, the final product is enzyme-free. One application of this technology is in the production of lactose-free milk. Milk is a high quality food, containing proteins, fats, and the sugar lactose. As people age, they can become lactose intolerant (cannot digest lactose) and so they avoid milk and milk products and miss out on their dietary benefits. The production of lactose-free milk allows these people to benefit from including milk and milk products in their diet.

Removing lactose from milk

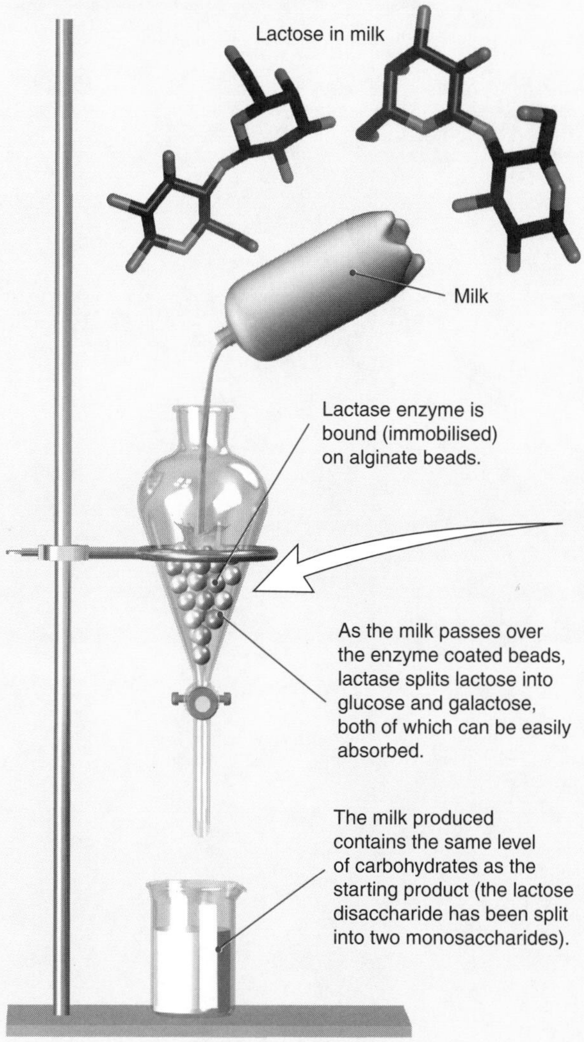
Lactose in milk
Milk
Lactase enzyme is bound (immobilised) on alginate beads.
As the milk passes over the enzyme coated beads, lactase splits lactose into glucose and galactose, both of which can be easily absorbed.
The milk produced contains the same level of carbohydrates as the starting product (the lactose disaccharide has been split into two monosaccharides).

The effect of temperature on free and alginate immobilised lactase enzyme

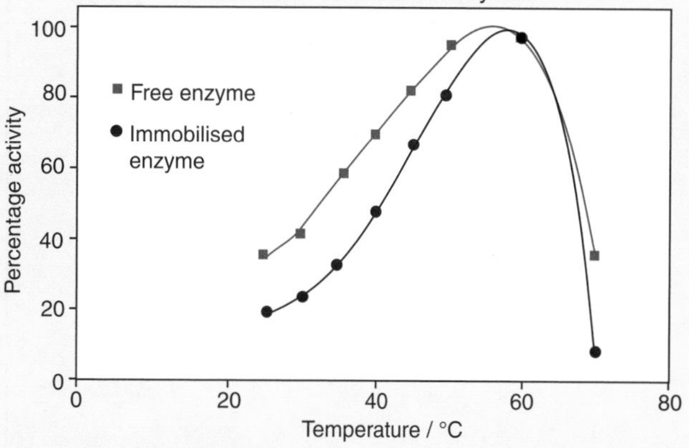
Free enzyme
Immobilised enzyme
Percentage activity
Temperature / °C
0
20
40
60
80
100

Data source: Mohy Eldin, M.S *et al.* (2005)

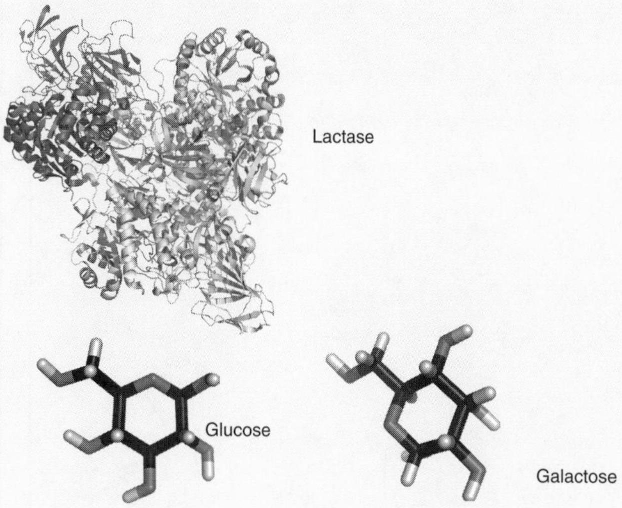
Lactase
Glucose
Galactose

1. What is an immobilised enzyme? ______________________________

____

2. How is lactase used to produce lactose-free milk? ______________________________

____

____

____

3. Compare the activity of free lactase and immobilised lactase as shown in the graph above: ______________________________

____

____

____

© 2015 **BIOZONE** International
ISBN: 978-1-927309-31-5
Photocopying Prohibited

77 Chapter Review

Summarise what you know about this topic under the headings provided. You can draw diagrams or mind maps, or write short notes to organise your thoughts. Use the images and hints to help you and refer back to the introduction to check the points covered:

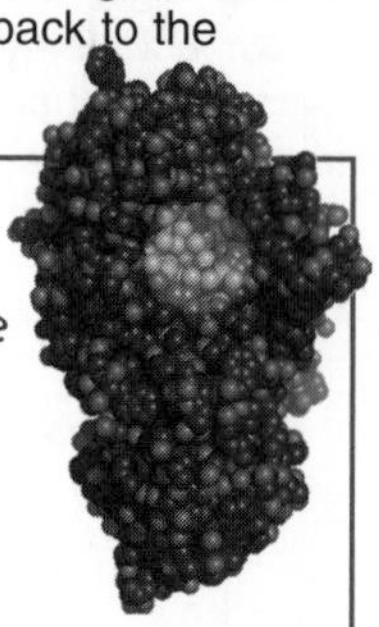

The action of enzymes

HINT: Describe how enzymes catalyse reactions.

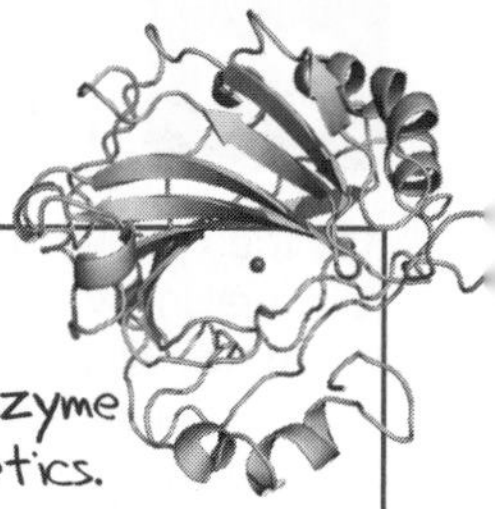

Enzyme reaction rates

HINT: Describe factors affecting enzyme activity and models of enzyme kinetics.

Enzyme inhibitors

HINT: Describe the action of inhibitors on enzyme activity.

© 2015 **BIOZONE** International
ISBN:978-1-927309-31-5
Photocopying Prohibited

78 KEY TERMS AND IDEAS: Did You Get It?

1. Test your vocabulary by matching each term to its correct definition, as identified by its preceding letter code.

activation energy	A	The energy that must be overcome in order for a chemical reaction to occur.
active site	B	Any reagent that increases the rate of a chemical reaction but is itself not consumed by the reaction.
anabolic reactions	C	The conditions at which an enzyme works best (e.g. a specific pH or temperature).
catabolic reactions	D	Reactions that build larger molecules from smaller ones.
catalyst	E	Biological catalysts, usually globular proteins.
denaturation	F	The currently accepted model for enzyme function.
enzymes	G	Reactions that break up larger molecules into their component parts.
induced fit model	H	The loss of a protein's three dimensional functional structure is called this.
optimum (for enzyme)	I	The region of an enzyme responsible for substrate binding and reaction catalysis.

2. (a) Label the graph, right, with appropriate axes and the following labels: Reactants, products, activation energy, transition state.

   (b) Assume the reaction has had no enzyme added. Draw the shape of the graph if an enzyme was added to the reaction mix.

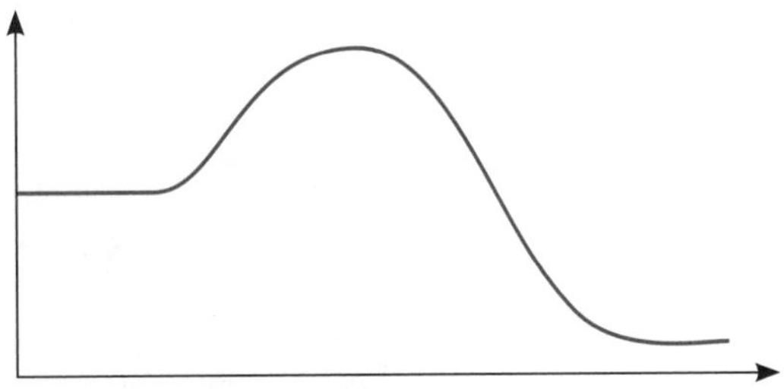

3. The graph (right) shows the effect of an enzyme inhibitor in enzyme reaction rate.

   (a) It show competitive inhibition/non-competitive inhibition (delete one).

   (b) Circle the diagram below that illustrates your choice in (a):

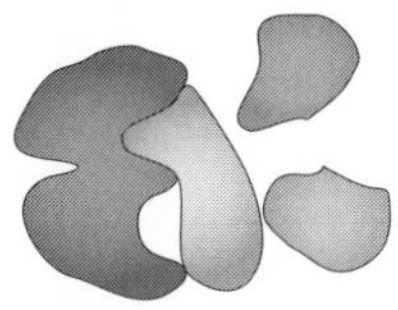

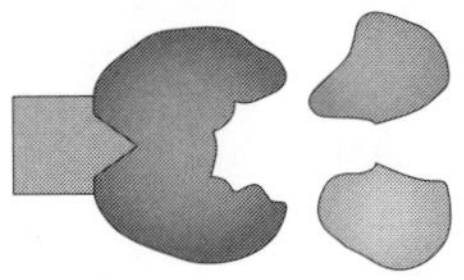

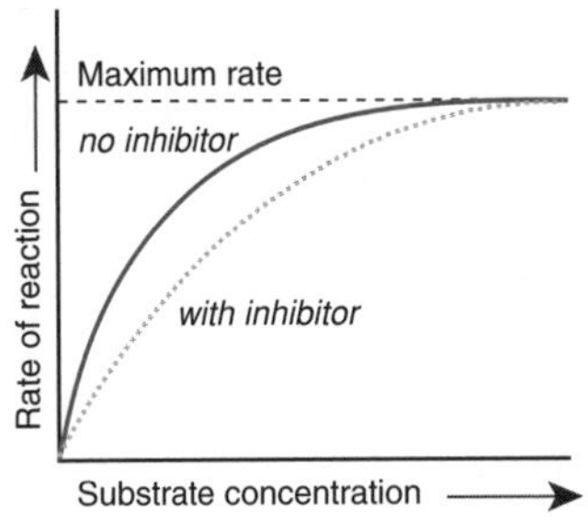

Maximum rate
no inhibitor
with inhibitor
Rate of reaction
Substrate concentration

4. The graph (right) shows reaction velocity versus substrate concentration for two enzymes (x and y). Both enzymes have the same substrate and the same V_{max}.

   (a) Determine the ½V_{max} for enzyme x: ______________________

   (b) Determine the ½V_{max} for enzyme y: ______________________

   (c) Determine K_m for enzyme x: ______________________

   (d) Determine K_m for enzyme y: ______________________

   (e) Compare the two K_m values and comment on the affinity of each enzyme for the substrate:

   ____

   ____

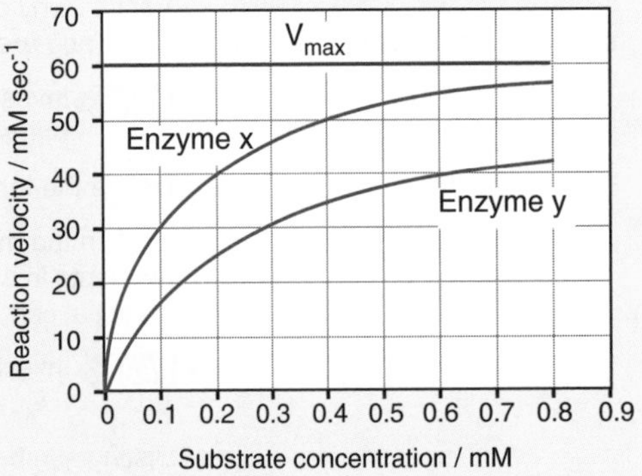

V_{max}
Enzyme x
Enzyme y
Reaction velocity / mM sec^{-1}
0
10
20
30
40
50
60
70
0
0.1
0.2
0.3
0.4
0.5
0.6
0.7
0.8
0.9
Substrate concentration / mM

© 2015 BIOZONE International
ISBN: 978-1-927309-31-5
Photocopying Prohibited

Topic 4 Cell membranes and transport

Key terms

- active transport
- carrier protein
- channel protein
- cholesterol
- cell signalling
- cell surface (=plasma) membrane
- concentration gradient
- diffusion
- endocytosis
- exocytosis
- facilitated diffusion
- fluid mosaic model
- glycolipid
- glycoprotein
- hypertonic
- hypotonic
- ion pump
- isotonic
- ligand
- osmolarity
- osmosis
- osmotic potential
- partially permeable
- passive transport
- phagocytosis
- phospholipid
- pinocytosis
- plasma membrane
- plasmolysis
- solute potential
- surface area: volume ratio
- turgor
- water potential

4.1 Fluid mosaic membranes

Learning outcomes — **Activity number**

- ☐ 1 Describe and explain the fluid mosaic model of membrane structure, including the roles of phospholipids, cholesterol, glycolipids, proteins, and glycoproteins. Include reference to membrane stability, fluidity, cellular communication, and cellular transport. Relate phospholipid structure to the formation of a lipid bilayer. — 80 81
- ☐ 2 Outline the roles of cell surface membranes with reference to carrier proteins, channel proteins, cell surface receptors, and cell surface antigens. — 79 80
- ☐ 3 Use your understanding of membrane structure to explain the effect of temperature or solvents on membrane structure and permeability. — 80
- ☐ 4 **PRAC** Investigate factors affecting membrane structure and permeability. — 82
- ☐ 5 Outline the process of cell signalling involving the release of chemical signal molecules (ligands) that combine with cell surface receptors on target cells to bring about a specific response. — 83

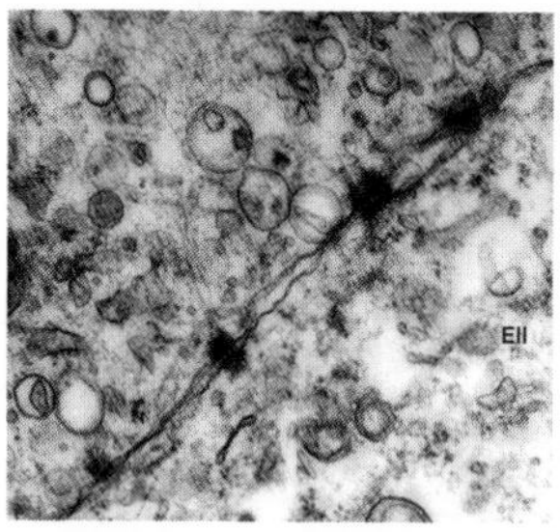

Ell

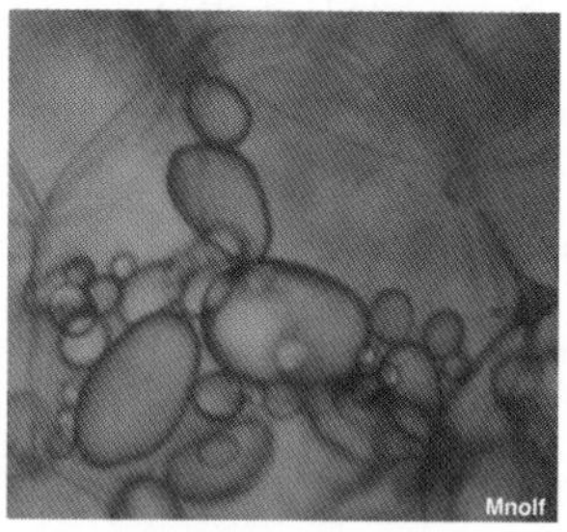

Mnolf

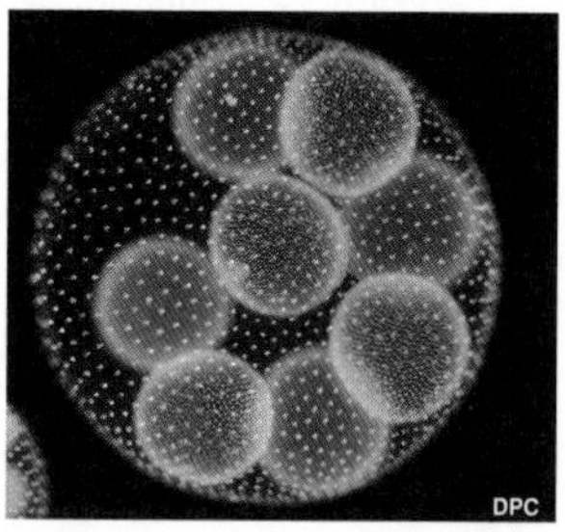

DPC

4.2 Movement of substances into and out of cells

Learning outcomes — **Activity number**

- ☐ 6 Describe the movement of molecules across membranes by diffusion and facilitated diffusion, identifying them as passive transport processes. Explain factors affecting diffusion rates across membranes: membrane thickness, surface area, and concentration gradient. — 84
- ☐ 7 **PRAC** Investigate factors affecting diffusion rates in plant tissues and non-living materials, such as Visking tubing or agar. — 85
- ☐ 8 Calculate surface areas and volumes of simple shapes to show how surface area to volume ratios decrease with increasing size. — 86
- ☐ 9 Explain why cell size is limited by the rate of diffusion. Explain the significance of surface area to volume ratio to cells and relate this to organism size. — 87
- ☐ 10 **PRAC** Investigate the effect of changing surface area to volume rate on diffusion using agar blocks of different sizes. — 87
- ☐ 11 Define the terms osmosis and osmotic potential. — 88
- ☐ 12 Explain the movement of water across membranes by osmosis with reference to gradients in water potential. Explain the effects that solutions of different water potential can have on plant and animal cells. — 89
- ☐ 13 **PRAC** Investigate the effects of solutions of different water potential on plant tissues, using the results to estimate the water potential of the tissues. — 90 91
- ☐ 14 Distinguish between passive transport and active transport, identifying the involvement of membrane proteins and energy in active transport processes. — 92 95
- ☐ 15 Using examples, describe and explain active transport processes in cells, including ion pumps, endocytosis, and exocytosis. — 92 93 94

79 The Role of the Cell Surface Membrane

Key Idea: Many of the functions of the cell surface membrane, including transport, communication, and cell recognition are a function of the membrane's integral proteins.

The cell surface (or plasma) membrane encloses the cell's contents and regulates many of the cell's activities. Within the cell, membranes enable reactions to be compartmentalised.

Roles of the cell surface membrane

Cell communication
Integral membrane proteins act as receptors for signal molecules such as hormones (e.g. adrenaline, dopamine).

Transport through pores
Channel proteins are pore-forming membrane proteins present in all cells. They enable the rapid movement of ions across the membrane and are important in nerve impulse transmission and in regulating cell volume.

Transport by carriers
Carrier proteins are integral trans-membrane proteins involved in the transport of ions, small molecules, or macromolecules (such as sugars and proteins) across the membrane by facilitated diffusion or by active transport.

Cell recognition
Cell surface antigens, such as the MHC antigens, allow the body to distinguish between self (its own tissues) and non-self (foreign tissues).

Roles of internal membranes

The internal membranes within cells create compartments enabling specific metabolic reactions to occur in discrete locations. This creates greater efficiency of function.

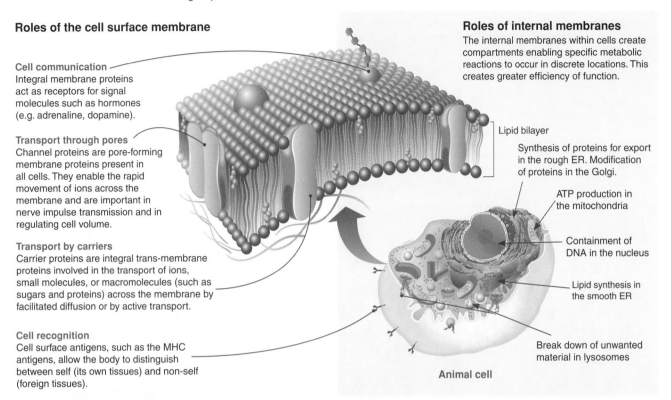

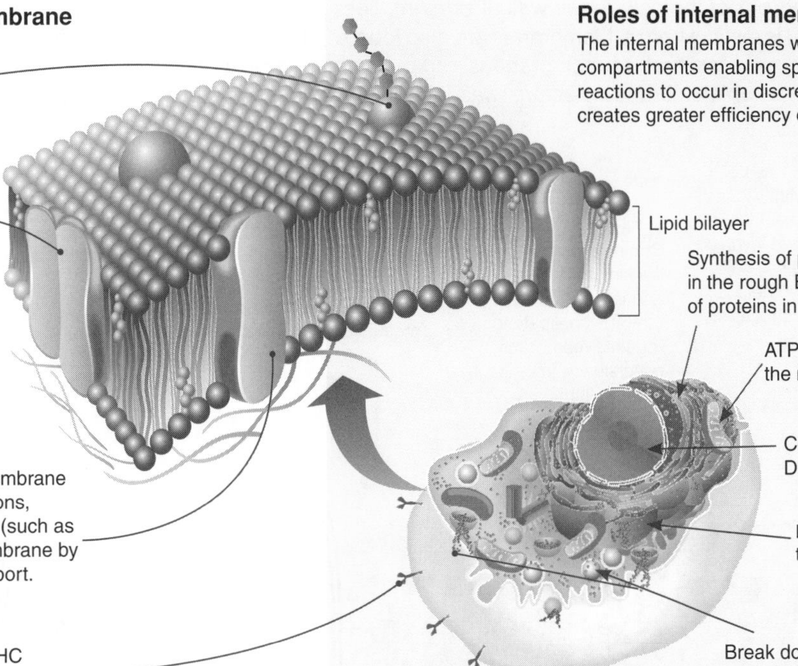
Lipid bilayer
Synthesis of proteins for export in the rough ER. Modification of proteins in the Golgi.
ATP production in the mitochondria
Containment of DNA in the nucleus
Lipid synthesis in the smooth ER
Break down of unwanted material in lysosomes
Animal cell

What do proteins in the cell surface membrane really look like?

The tertiary structure of membrane proteins enables them to perform their particular function in transport, cell signalling, and cell recognition. The proteins are integral to the membrane, and often have parts of their structure projecting from both internal and external sides of the membrane.

Vossman cc 3.0

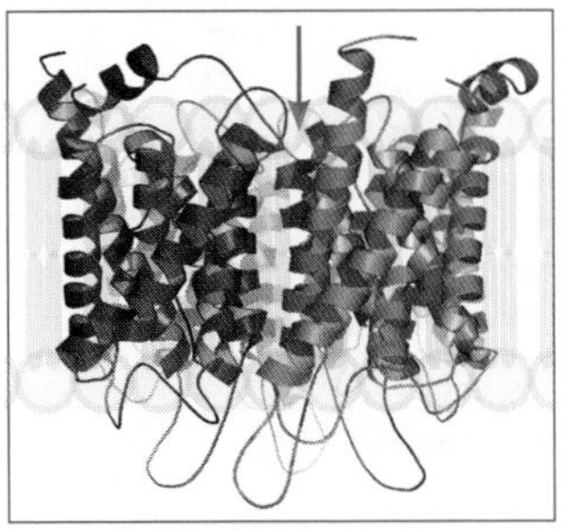

Aquaporins are a special type of channel protein that speed up the passage of water molecules across the membrane. Their tertiary structure creates a pore through the centre of the protein through which molecules can pass.

A2-33 cc 3.0

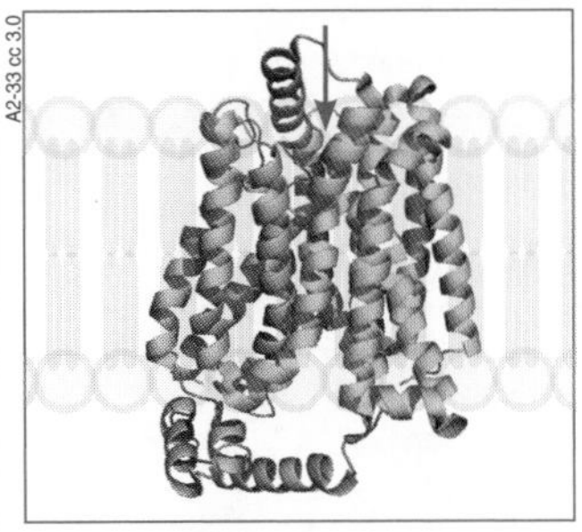

The GLUT1 glucose transporter is a carrier protein that facilitates the transport of glucose across the cell surface membranes of mammalian cells. It speeds up the transport of glucose into cells by 50 000 times over unaided transport.

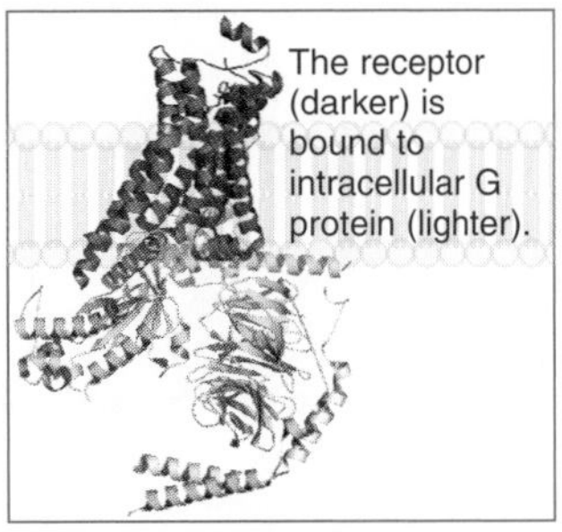
The receptor (darker) is bound to intracellular G protein (lighter).

G-protein coupled receptors are proteins involved in signalling pathways. A signal molecule binds to the receptor protein outside the cell to trigger a reaction involving intracellular G protein. The receptor in this example binds to adrenaline.

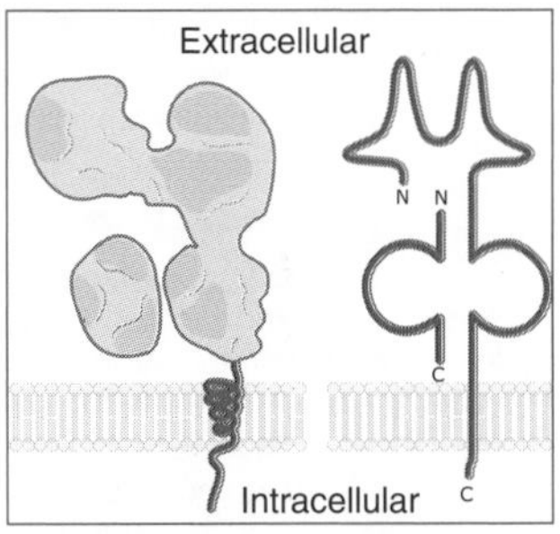
Extracellular
N
N
C
Intracellular
C

Cell surface antigens provide a recognisable cell signature so that the body can distinguish between its own cells and foreign molecules. They are often glycoproteins. The image above shows how the antigens project from the membrane.

1. Summarise the role of different membrane proteins in the transport of different substances into and out of the cell:

___

___

___

2. Summarise the role of the cell surface membrane in the following processes, identifying the components involved:

(a) Cell communication: ___

___

(b) Recognition of self and non-self: ___

___

© 2015 BIOZONE International
ISBN: 978-1-927309-31-5
Photocopying Prohibited

80 The Structure of Membranes

Key Idea: The plasma (cell surface) membrane is composed of a lipid bilayer with proteins moving freely within it.

All cells have a cell surface (or plasma) membrane, which forms the outer limit of the cell and regulates the passage of materials into and out of the cell. A cell wall, if present, lies outside this, and it is distinct from it. Membranes are also found inside eukaryotic cells as part of membranous organelles. The original model of membrane structure was as a lipid bilayer coated with protein. This model was modified after the discovery that the protein molecules were embedded within the bilayer rather than coating the outside. The now-accepted **fluid-mosaic model** of membrane structure (below) satisfies the observed properties of membranes. The self-orientating properties of the phospholipids allows cellular membranes to reseal themselves when disrupted. The double layer of lipids is also quite fluid, and proteins move quite freely within it.

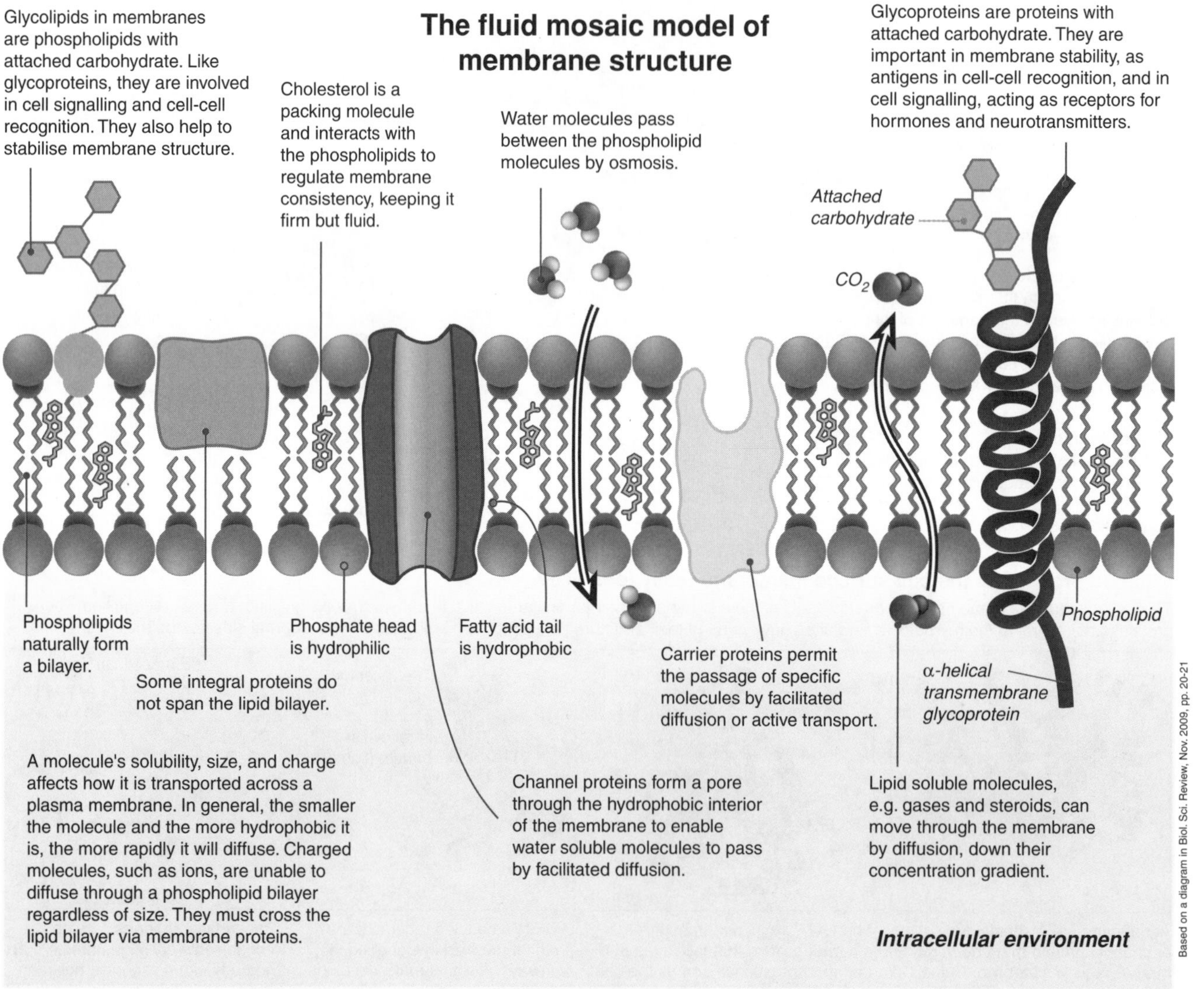
The fluid mosaic model of membrane structure
Glycolipids in membranes are phospholipids with attached carbohydrate. Like glycoproteins, they are involved in cell signalling and cell-cell recognition. They also help to stabilise membrane structure.
Cholesterol is a packing molecule and interacts with the phospholipids to regulate membrane consistency, keeping it firm but fluid.
Water molecules pass between the phospholipid molecules by osmosis.
Glycoproteins are proteins with attached carbohydrate. They are important in membrane stability, as antigens in cell-cell recognition, and in cell signalling, acting as receptors for hormones and neurotransmitters.
Attached carbohydrate
CO_2
Phospholipids naturally form a bilayer.
Some integral proteins do not span the lipid bilayer.
Phosphate head is hydrophilic
Fatty acid tail is hydrophobic
Carrier proteins permit the passage of specific molecules by facilitated diffusion or active transport.
α-helical transmembrane glycoprotein
Phospholipid
A molecule's solubility, size, and charge affects how it is transported across a plasma membrane. In general, the smaller the molecule and the more hydrophobic it is, the more rapidly it will diffuse. Charged molecules, such as ions, are unable to diffuse through a phospholipid bilayer regardless of size. They must cross the lipid bilayer via membrane proteins.
Channel proteins form a pore through the hydrophobic interior of the membrane to enable water soluble molecules to pass by facilitated diffusion.
Lipid soluble molecules, e.g. gases and steroids, can move through the membrane by diffusion, down their concentration gradient.
Intracellular environment
Based on a diagram in Biol. Sci. Review, Nov. 2009, pp. 20-21

1. Identify the component(s) of the plasma membrane involved in:

   (a) Facilitated diffusion: ____________ (c) Cell signalling: ____________

   (b) Active transport: ____________ (d) Regulating membrane fluidity: ____________

2. How do the properties of phospholipids contribute to their role in forming the structural framework of membranes?

   ____

   ____

3. (a) Describe the modern fluid mosaic model of membrane structure: ____________

   ____

   ____

   ____

© 2015 BIOZONE International
ISBN:978-1-927309-31-5
Photocopying Prohibited

(b) Explain how the fluid mosaic model accounts for the observed properties of cellular membranes:

4. Explain the importance of each of the following to cellular function:

(a) Carrier proteins in the plasma membrane:

(b) Channel proteins in the plasma membrane:

5. Non-polar (lipid-soluble) molecules diffuse more rapidly through membranes than polar (lipid-insoluble) molecules:

(a) Explain the reason for this:

(b) Discuss the implications of this to the transport of substances into the cell through the plasma membrane:

6. Describe the purpose of cholesterol in plasma membranes:

7. List three substances that need to be transported **into** all kinds of animal cells, in order for them to survive:

(a) (b) (c)

8. List two substances that need to be transported **out** of all kinds of animal cells, in order for them to survive:

(a) (b)

9. Use the symbol for a phospholipid molecule (below) to draw a **simple labelled diagram** to show the structure of a plasma membrane (include features such as lipid bilayer and various kinds of proteins):

Symbol for phospholipid

© 2015 BIOZONE International
ISBN: 978-1-927309-31-5
Photocopying Prohibited

81 How Do We Know? Membrane Structure

Key Idea: The freeze-fracture technique for preparing and viewing cellular membranes has provided evidence to support the fluid mosaic model of the plasma membrane.

Cellular membranes play many extremely important roles in cells and understanding their structure is central to understanding cellular function. Moreover, understanding the structure and function of membrane proteins is essential to understanding cellular transport processes, and cell recognition and signalling. Cellular membranes are far too small to be seen clearly using light microscopy, and certainly any detail is impossible to resolve. Since early last century, scientists have known that membranes were composed of a lipid bilayer with associated proteins. The original model of membrane structure, proposed by Davson and Danielli, was the unit membrane (a lipid bilayer coated with protein). This model was later modified by Singer and Nicolson after the discovery that the protein molecules were embedded *within* the bilayer rather than coating the outside. But how did they find out just how these molecules were organised?

The answers were provided with electron microscopy, and one technique in particular – **freeze fracture**. As the name implies, freeze fracture, at its very simplest level, is the freezing of a cell and then fracturing it so the inner surface of the membrane can be seen using electron microscopy. Membranes are composed of two layers of phospholipids held together by weak intermolecular bonds. These split apart during fracture.

The procedure involves several steps:

- Cells are immersed in chemicals that alter the strength of the internal and external regions of the plasma membrane and immobilise any mobile macromolecules.
- The cells are passed through a series of glycerol solutions of increasing concentration. This protects the cells from bursting when they are frozen.
- The cells are mounted on gold supports and frozen using liquid propane.
- The cells are fractured in a helium-vented vacuum at -150°C. A razor blade cooled to -170° C acts as both a cold trap for water and the fracturing instrument.
- The surface of the fractured cells may be evaporated a little to produce some relief on the surface (known as etching) so that a three-dimensional effect occurs.
- For viewing under an electron microscope (EM), a replica of the cells is made by coating them with gold or platinum to ~3 nm thick. A layer of carbon around 30 nm thick is used to provide contrast and stability for the replica.
- The samples are then raised to room temperature and placed into distilled water or digestive enzymes, which separates the replica from the sample. The replica is then rinsed in distilled water before it is ready for viewing.

The freeze fracture technique provided the necessary supporting evidence for the current fluid mosaic model of membrane structure. When cleaved, proteins in the membrane left impressions that showed they were embedded into the membrane and not a continuous layer on the outside as earlier models proposed.

Cleaving the membrane

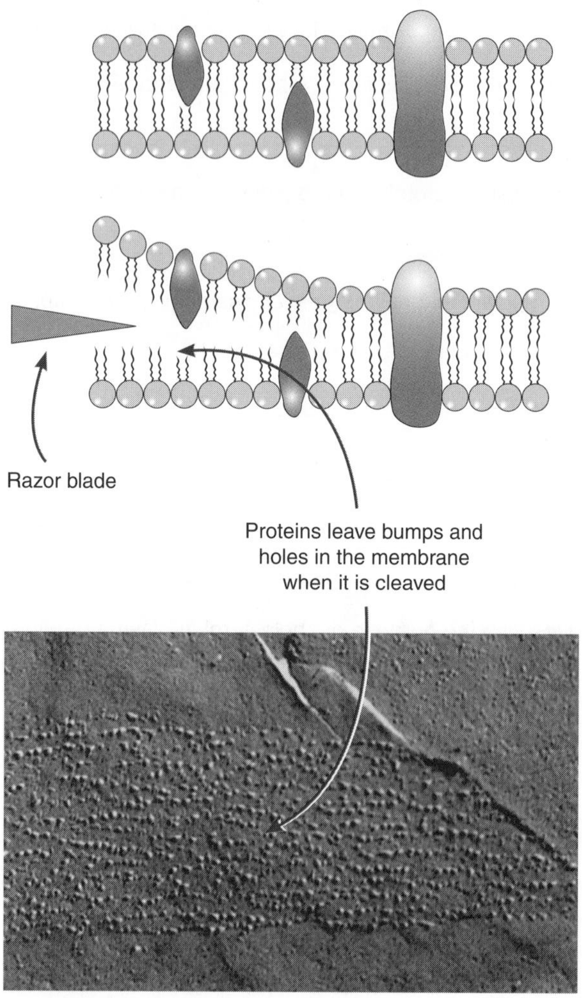
Razor blade
Proteins leave bumps and holes in the membrane when it is cleaved

50 nm — Photo: Louisa Howard and Chuck Daghlian, Dartmouth College

1. Explain how freeze-fracture studies provided evidence for our current model of membrane structure:

2. The Davson and Danielli model of membrane structure was the unit membrane; a phospholipid bilayer with a protein coat. Explain how the freeze-fracture studies showed this model to be flawed:

© 2015 BIOZONE International
ISBN:978-1-927309-31-5
Photocopying Prohibited

82 Factors Altering Membrane Permeability

Key Idea: Temperature and solvents can disrupt the structure of cellular membranes and alter their permeability.

Membrane permeability can be disrupted if membranes are subjected to high temperatures or solvents. At temperatures above the optimum, the membrane proteins become denatured. Alcohols, e.g. ethanol, can also denature proteins. In both instances, the denatured proteins no longer function properly and the membrane loses its selective permeability and becomes leaky. In addition, the combination of alcohol and high temperature can also dissolve lipids.

Beetroot cubes

The aim and hypothesis

To investigate the effect of temperature on membrane permeability. The students hypothesised that the amount of pigment leaking from the beetroot cubes would increase with increasing temperature.

Background

Plant cells often contain a large central vacuole surrounded by a membrane called a **tonoplast**. In beetroot plants, the vacuole contains a water-soluble red pigment called betacyanin, which gives beetroot its colour. If the tonoplast is damaged, the red pigment leaks out into the surrounding environment. The amount of leaked pigment relates to the amount of damage to the tonoplast.

Experimental method

Raw beetroot was cut into uniform cubes using a cork borer with a 4 mm internal diameter. The cubes were trimmed to 20 mm lengths and placed in a beaker of distilled water for 30 minutes.

Five cm^3 of distilled water was added to 15 clean test tubes. Three were placed into a beaker containing ice. These were the 0°C samples. Three test tubes were placed into water baths at 20, 40, 60, or 90°C and equilibrated for 30 minutes. Once the tubes were at temperature, the beetroot cubes were removed from the distilled water and blotted dry on a paper towel. One beetroot cube was added to each of the test tubes. After 30 minutes, they were removed. The colour of the solution in each test tube was observed by eye and then the absorbance of each sample was measured at 530 nm. Results are given in the table below.

Absorbance of beetroot samples at varying temperatures

Temperature / °C	Observation	Absorbance at 530 nm			Mean
		Sample 1	Sample 2	Sample 3	
0	No colour	0	0.007	0.004	
20	Very pale pink	0.027	0.022	0.018	
40	Very pale pink	0.096	0.114	0.114	
60	Pink	0.580	0.524	0.509	
90	Red	3	3	3	

1. Why is it important to wash the beetroot cubes in distilled water prior to carrying out the experiment? ______________________

2. (a) Complete the table above by calculating the mean absorbance for each temperature:

   (b) Based on the results in the table above, describe the effect of temperature on membrane permeability: ______________________

   (c) Explain why this effect occurs: ______________________

© 2015 **BIOZONE** International
ISBN: 978-1-927309-31-5
Photocopying Prohibited

Method for determining effect of ethanol concentration on membrane permeability

Beetroot cubes were prepared the same way as described on the previous page. The following ethanol concentrations were prepared using serial dilution: 0, 6.25, 12.5, 25, 50, and 100%. Eighteen clean test tubes were divided into six groups of three and labelled with one of the six ethanol concentrations. Three cm^3 of the appropriate ethanol solution was placed into each test tube. A dried beetroot cube was added to each test tube. The test tubes were covered with parafilm (plastic paraffin film with a paper backing) and left at room temperature. After one hour the beetroot cubes were removed and the absorbance measured at 477 nm.
Results are given in the table, right.

	Absorbance of beetroot samples at varying ethanol concentrations			
Ethanol concentration / %	**Absorbance at 477 nm**			**Mean**
	Sample 1	**Sample 2**	**Sample 3**	
0	0.014	0.038	0.038	
6.25	0.009	0.015	0.023	
12.5	0.010	0.041	0.018	
25	0.067	0.064	0.116	
50	0.945	1.100	0.731	
100	1.269	1.376	0.907	

3. What was the purpose of the 0% ethanol solution in the experiment described above?

4. (a) Why do you think the tubes were covered in parafilm?

(b) How could the results have been affected if the test tubes were not covered with parafilm?

5. (a) Complete the table above by calculating the mean absorbance for each ethanol concentration:

(b) Plot a line graph of ethanol concentration against mean absorbance on the grid (above):

(c) Describe the effect of ethanol concentration on the membrane permeability of beetroot:

6. How does ethanol affect membrane permeability?

© 2015 BIOZONE International
ISBN:978-1-927309-31-5
Photocopying Prohibited

83 Cell Signalling and Receptors

Key Idea: Cells use signals (chemical messengers) to communicate and to gather information about, and respond to, changes in their cellular environment.

Cells communicate and bring about responses by producing and reacting to signal molecules (chemical messengers). The chemical messenger binds to a specific type of receptor on the target cell to bring about a response. Only cells with the correct receptor will respond to the chemical messenger. Three main pathways for cell signalling exist, operating over different distances within the body.

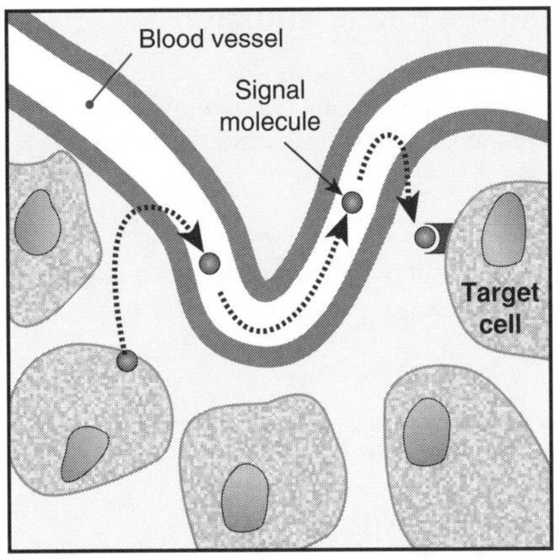
Blood vessel
Signal molecule
Target cell

Endocrine signalling: Hormone signals are released by endocrine glands and are carried in the blood through the body to reach specific target cells. Examples include sex hormones, growth factors, and neurohormones such as dopamine.

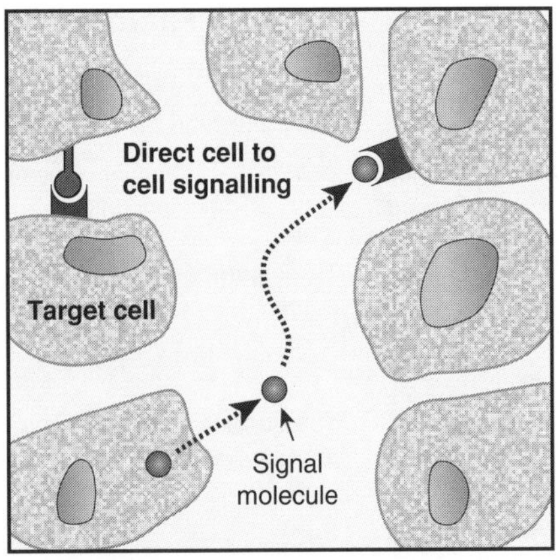
Direct cell to cell signalling
Target cell
Signal molecule

Paracrine signalling: Signals released from a cell act on target cells close by. The messenger can be transferred through the extracellular fluid (e.g. at synapses) or directly between cells. Examples include neurotransmitters and histamine.

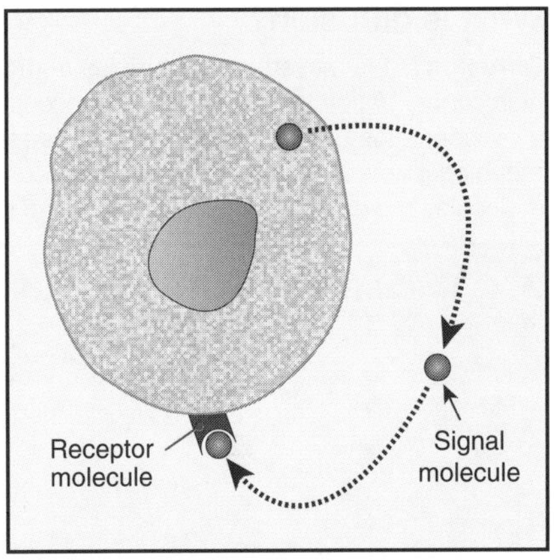
Receptor molecule
Signal molecule

Autocrine signalling: Cells produce and react to their own signals. In vertebrates, when a foreign antibody enters the body, some T-cells produce a growth factor to stimulate their own production. The increased number of T-cells helps to fight the infection.

Signalling receptors and signalling molecules

Histamine is a paracrine signal molecule involved in local immune responses.

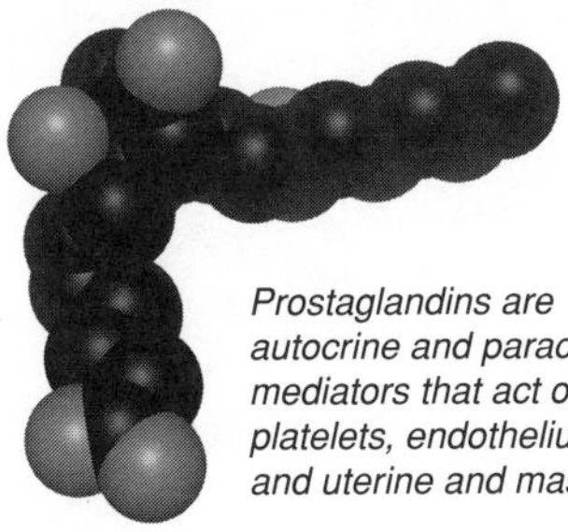

Prostaglandins are autocrine and paracrine mediators that act on platelets, endothelium, and uterine and mast cells.

Examples of cell signalling molecules

The binding sites of cell receptors are specific only to certain signal molecules (**ligands**). This stops them reacting to every signal the cell encounters. Receptors generally fall into two main categories:

▶ **Cytoplasmic receptors**

Cytoplasmic receptors, located within the cell cytoplasm, bind ligands, which are able to cross the plasma membrane unaided.

▶ **Transmembrane receptors**

These span the cell membrane and bind ligands which cannot cross the plasma membrane on their own. They have an extra-cellular domain outside the cell, and an intracellular domain within the cell cytosol.

Ion channels, protein kinases and G-protein coupled receptors are examples of transmembrane receptors (see diagram on right).

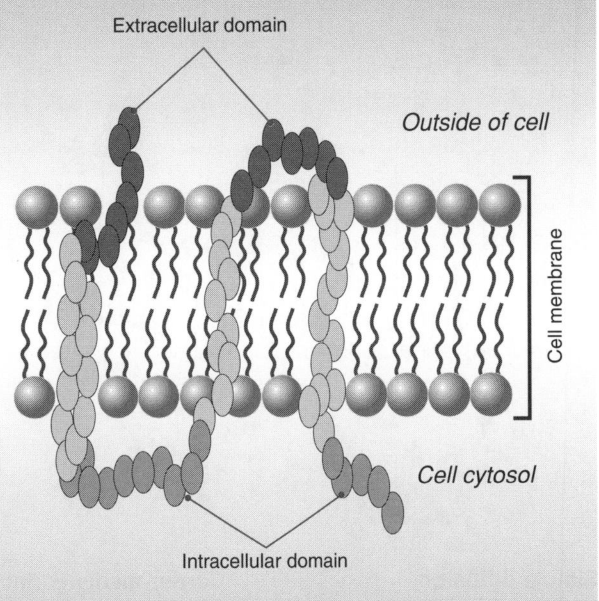
Extracellular domain
Outside of cell
Cell membrane
Cell cytosol
Intracellular domain

Structure of a transmembrane receptor

1. Briefly describe the three types of cell signalling:

(a) ______________________________

(b) ______________________________

(c) ______________________________

2. Identify the components that all three cell signalling types have in common: ______________________________

____

____

© 2015 **BIOZONE** International
ISBN: 978-1-927309-31-5
Photocopying Prohibited

84 Diffusion

Key Idea: Diffusion is the movement of molecules from higher concentration to a lower concentration (i.e. down a concentration gradient).

The molecules that make up substances are constantly moving about in a random way. This random motion causes molecules to disperse from areas of high to low concentration. This dispersal is called **diffusion** and it requires no energy. Each type of molecule moves down its own concentration gradient. Diffusion is important in allowing exchanges with the environment and in the regulation of cell water content.

What is diffusion?

Diffusion is the movement of particles from regions of high concentration to regions of low concentration (down a concentration gradient). Diffusion is a **passive process**, meaning it needs no input of energy to occur. During diffusion, molecules move randomly about, becoming evenly dispersed.

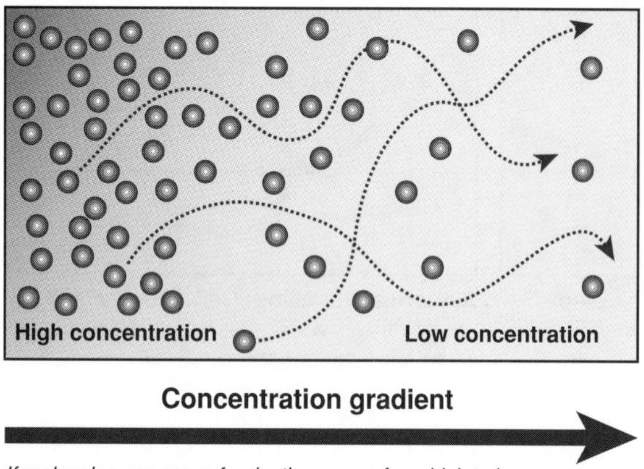
High concentration
Low concentration
Concentration gradient

If molecules can move freely, they move from high to low concentration (down a concentration gradient) until evenly dispersed.

Factors affecting the rate of diffusion

Concentration gradient	The rate of diffusion is higher when there is a greater difference between the concentrations of two regions.
The distance moved	Diffusion over shorter distance occurs at a greater rate than over a larger distance.
The surface area involved	The larger the area across which diffusion occurs, the greater the rate of diffusion.
Barriers to diffusion	Thick barriers have a slower rate of diffusion than thin barriers.
Temperature	Particles at a high temperature diffuse at a greater rate than at a low temperature.

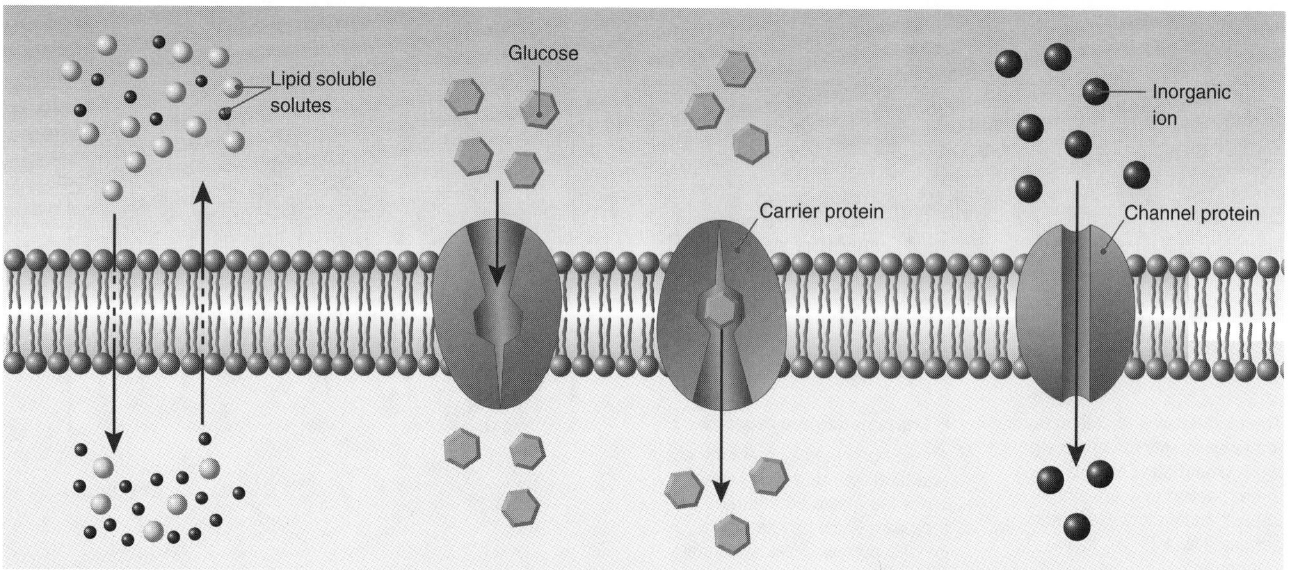
Lipid soluble solutes
Glucose
Carrier protein
Inorganic ion
Channel protein

Simple diffusion
Molecules move directly through the membrane without assistance.
Example: O_2 diffuses into the blood and CO_2 diffuses out.

Carrier-mediated facilitated diffusion
Carrier proteins allow large lipid-insoluble molecules that cannot cross the membrane by simple diffusion to be transported into the cell.
Example: the transport of glucose into red blood cells.

Channel-mediated facilitated diffusion
Channels (hydrophilic pores) in the membrane allow inorganic ions to pass through the membrane.
Example: K^+ ions exiting nerve cells to restore resting potential.

1. What is diffusion? ______________________________

____

2. What do the three types of diffusion described above all have in common? ______________________________

____

3. How does facilitated diffusion differ from simple diffusion? ______________________________

____

© 2015 BIOZONE International
ISBN:978-1-927309-31-5
Photocopying Prohibited

85 Investigating Diffusion

Key Idea: Dialysis tubing can be used to model the diffusion of glucose down its concentration gradient.

Diffusion through a partially permeable membrane can be modelled using dialysis tubing. The pores of the dialysis tubing determine the size of the molecules that can pass through. The experiment described below demonstrates how glucose will diffuse down its concentration gradient from a high glucose concentration to a low glucose concentration.

The aim

To demonstrate diffusion through a semipermeable membrane.

Hypothesis

If there is no glucose outside the dialysis tubing, then glucose will diffuse down its concentration gradient from the dialysis tubing into the distilled water until the glucose concentrations are equal.

Background

Dialysis tubing acts as a partially (or selectively) permeable membrane. It comes in many pore sizes, and only allows molecules smaller than the size of the pore to pass through.

Lugol's indicator contains iodine, and turns blue/black in the presence of starch.

The presence of glucose can be tested using a glucose dipstick test. If glucose is present, the indicator window will change colour. The colour change can be compared against a reference to determine the level of glucose present.

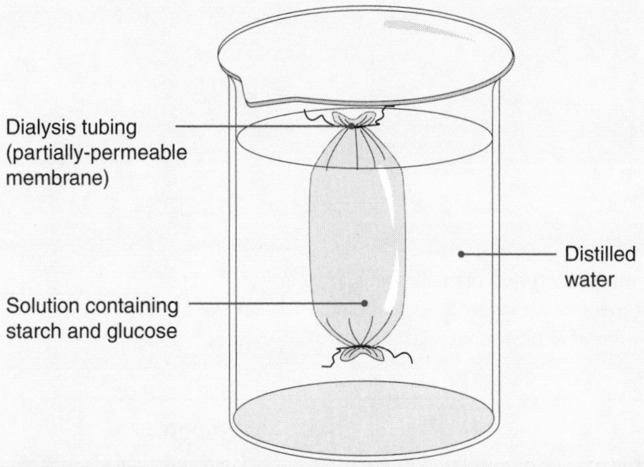
Dialysis tubing (partially-permeable membrane)
Distilled water
Solution containing starch and glucose

Method

Dialysis tubing was filled with 5 cm^3 each of a 1% starch solution and a 10% glucose solution. A 1 cm^3 sample was removed and tested for the presence of starch using Lugol's indicator, and glucose using a glucose dipstick.

The dialysis tubing was tied, and the outside of the tubing washed with distilled water to remove any starch or glucose that spilled on to the outer surface during filling. The tubing was placed into a beaker of distilled water.

After 30 minutes, the solution inside the dialysis tubing and the distilled water were tested for the presence of starch and glucose.

1. Why was it important to wash the dialysis tubing before placing it into the beaker of distilled water? ____________________

____

2. What part of a cell does the dialysis tubing represent?

____

3. The results for the experiment are presented in the table on the right.

	Dialysis tubing start	Beaker start	Dialysis tubing end	Beaker end
Starch	++	-	++	-
Glucose	++	-	+	+

(S) Starch (G) Glucose

(a) In the spaces provided (below, right) draw the distribution of starch and glucose at the start and at the end of the experiment. Use the symbols shown under the table to represent starch and glucose:

Dialysis tubing start	Beaker start

Dialysis tubing end	Beaker end

(b) Describe why glucose has moved across the partially permeable membrane during the experiment:

____

____

____

____

(c) Why was there no starch present in the beaker at the end of the experiment?

____

____

© 2015 BIOZONE International
ISBN: 978-1-927309-31-5
Photocopying Prohibited

86 Properties of Geometric Shapes

Key Idea: Circumference, surface area, and volume are useful calculations that can be applied in biological situations. Biology often requires you to evaluate the effect of a physical property, such as cell volume, on function. For example, how does surface area to volume ratio influence the transport of materials into a cell? The cells of organisms, and sometimes the organisms themselves, are often rather regular shapes, so their physical properties (e.g. cell volume or surface area) can be calculated (or approximated) using the simple formulae applicable to standard geometric shapes.

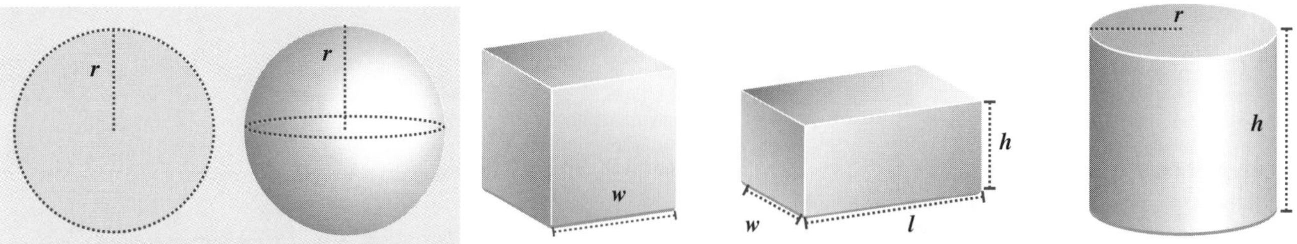
r
r
w
h
w
l
r
h

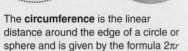

The **circumference** is the linear distance around the edge of a circle or sphere and is given by the formula $2\pi r$

r = radius l = length w = width h = height $\pi = 3.14$

	Sphere	Cube	Rectangular prism	Cylinder
Biological example	*Staphylococcus* bacterial cell	Kidney tubule cell	Intestinal epithelial cell	Axon of neuron
Surface area: The sum of all areas of all shapes covering an object's surface.	$4\pi r^2$	$6w^2$	$2(lh + lw + hw)$	$(2\pi r^2) + (2\pi rh)$
Volume: The amount that a 3-dimensional shape can hold.	$\frac{4}{3}\pi r^3$	w^3	lwh	$\pi r^2 h$

1. For a sphere with a radius of 2 cm, calculate the:

   (a) Circumference: ____

   (b) Surface area: ____

   (c) Volume: ____

2. For a rectangular prism with the dimensions l = 3 mm, w = 0.3 mm, and h = 2 mm calculate the:

   (a) Surface area: ____

   (b) Volume: ____

3. For a cylinder with a radius of 4.9 cm and height of 11 cm, calculate the:

   (a) Surface area: ____

   (b) Volume: ____

4. Find the height of a rectangular prism with a volume of 48 cm^3, a length of 4 cm, and a width of 2.5 cm: ____

5. Find the radius of a cylinder with a volume of 27 cm^3 and a height of 3 cm: ____

6. A spherical bacterium with a radius of 0.2 µm divides in two. Each new cell has a radius that is 80% of the original cell.

   (a) Calculate the surface area of the 'parent' bacterial cell: ____

   (b) Calculate the volume of the 'parent' bacterial cell: ____

   (c) Calculate the surface area of each new cell: ____

   (d) Calculate the volume of each new cell: ____

   (e) Which cell has the greatest surface area to volume ratio: ____

© 2015 **BIOZONE** International
ISBN:978-1-927309-31-5
Photocopying Prohibited

87 Diffusion and Cell Size

Key Idea: Diffusion is less efficient in cells with a small surface area relative to their volume than in cells with a large surface area relative to their volume.
When an object (e.g. a cell) is small it has a large surface area in comparison to its volume. Diffusion is an effective way to transport materials (e.g. gases) into the cell. As an object becomes larger, its surface area compared to its volume is smaller. Diffusion is no longer an effective way to transport materials to the inside. This places a physical limit on the size a cell can grow, with the effectiveness of diffusion being the controlling factor. Larger organisms overcome this constraint by becoming multicellular.

Single-celled organisms

Single-celled organisms (e.g. *Amoeba*), are small and have a large surface area relative to the cell's volume. The cell's requirements can be met by the diffusion or active transport of materials into and out of the cell (below).

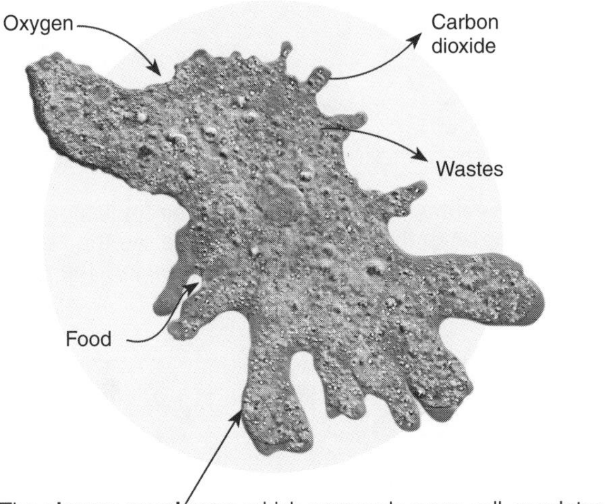
Oxygen
Carbon dioxide
Wastes
Food

The **plasma membrane**, which surrounds every cell, regulates movements of substances into and out of the cell. For each square micrometre of membrane, only so much of a particular substance can cross per second.

Multicellular organisms

Multicellular organisms (e.g. plants and animals) are often quite large and large organisms have a small surface area compared to their volume. They require specialised systems to transport the materials they need to and from the cells and tissues in their body.

In a multicellular organism, such as an elephant, the body's need for respiratory gases cannot be met by diffusion through the skin.

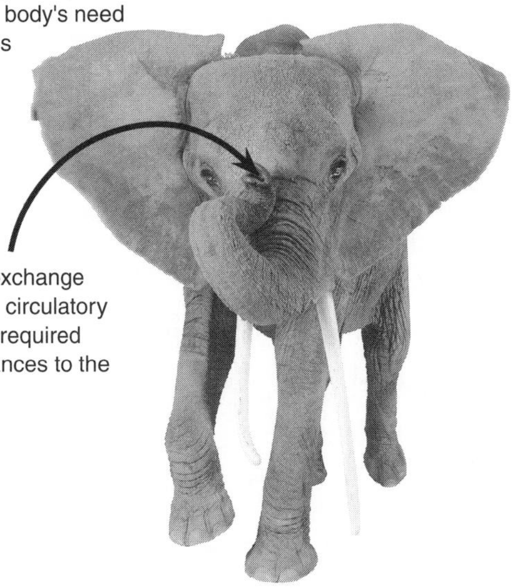

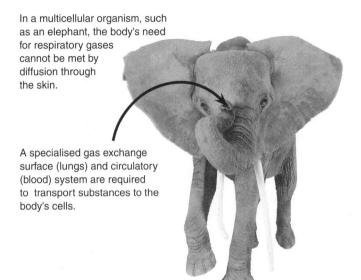

A specialised gas exchange surface (lungs) and circulatory (blood) system are required to transport substances to the body's cells.

The diagram below shows four hypothetical cells of different sizes. They range from a small 2 cm cube to a 5 cm cube. This exercise investigates the effect of cell size on the efficiency of diffusion.

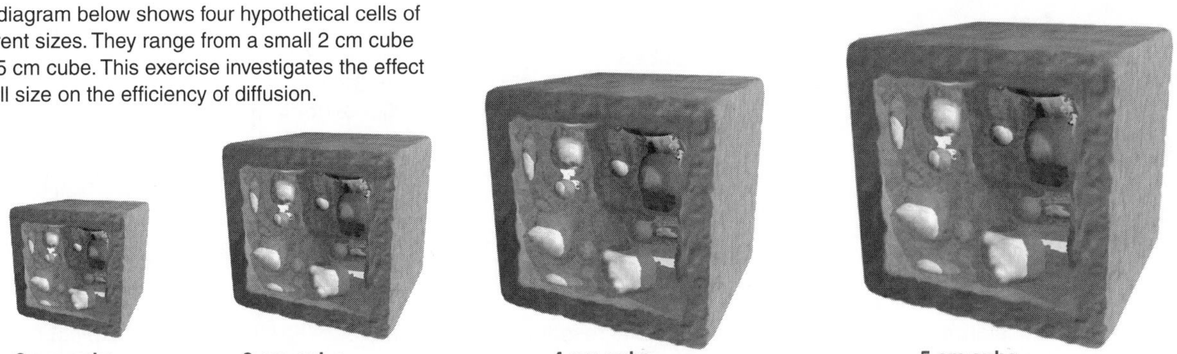
2 cm cube
3 cm cube
4 cm cube
5 cm cube

1. Calculate the volume, surface area and the ratio of surface area to volume for each of the four cubes above (the first has been done for you). When completing the table below, show your calculations.

Cube size	Surface area	Volume	Surface area to volume ratio
2 cm cube	2 x 2 x 6 = 24 cm^2 (2 cm x 2 cm x 6 sides)	2 x 2 x 2 = 8 cm^3 (height x width x depth)	24 to 8 = 3:1
3 cm cube			
4 cm cube			
5 cm cube			

© 2015 **BIOZONE** International
ISBN: 978-1-927309-31-5
Photocopying Prohibited

2. Create a graph, plotting the surface area against the volume of each cube, on the grid on the right. Draw a line connecting the points and label axes and units.

3. Which increases the fastest with increasing size: the **volume** or the **surface area**?

4. Explain what happens to the ratio of surface area to volume with increasing size.

5. The diffusion of molecules into a cell can be modelled by using agar cubes infused with phenolphthalein indicator and soaked in sodium hydroxide (NaOH). Phenolphthalein turns a pink colour when in the presence of a base. As the NaOH diffuses into the agar, the phenolphthalein changes to pink and thus indicates how far the NaOH has diffused into the agar. By cutting an agar block into cubes of various sizes, it is possible to show the effect of cell size on diffusion.

(a) Use the information below to fill in the table on the right:

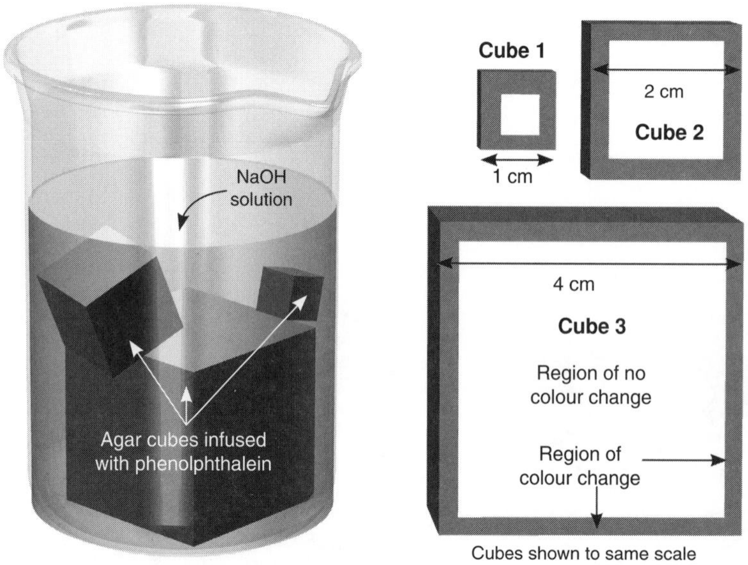
NaOH
solution
Agar cubes infused
with phenolphthalein
Cube 1
1 cm
2 cm
Cube 2
4 cm
Cube 3
Region of no
colour change
Region of
colour change
Cubes shown to same scale

Cube	1	2	3
1. Total volume / cm^3			
2. Volume not pink / cm^3			
3. Diffused volume / cm^3 (subtract value 2 from value 1)			
4. Percentage diffusion			

(b) Diffusion of substances into and out of a cell occurs across the plasma membrane. For a cuboid cell, explain how increasing cell size affects the effective ability of diffusion to provide the materials required by the cell:

6. Explain why a single large cell of 2 cm x 2 cm x 2 cm is less efficient in terms of passively acquiring nutrients than eight cells of 1 cm x 1 cm x 1 cm:

© 2015 **BIOZONE** International
ISBN:978-1-927309-31-5
Photocopying Prohibited

88 Osmosis

Key Idea: Osmosis is the term describing the diffusion of water molecules down their concentration gradient across a partially permeable membrane.

The diffusion of water down its concentration gradient across a partially permeable membrane is called **osmosis** and it is the principal mechanism by which water moves in and out of living cells. A partially permeable membrane, such as the plasma membrane, allows some molecules, but not others, to pass through. Water molecules can diffuse directly through the lipid bilayer, but movement is aided by specific protein channels called aquaporins. There is a net movement of water molecules until an equilibrium is reached and net movement is then zero. Osmosis is a passive process and does not require any energy input.

Demonstrating osmosis

Osmosis can be demonstrated using dialysis tubing in a simple experiment (described below). Dialysis tubing, like all cellular membranes, is a partially permeable membrane.

A sucrose solution (high solute concentration) is placed into dialysis tubing, and the tubing is placed into a beaker of water (low solute concentration). The difference in concentration of sucrose (solute) between the two solutions creates an osmotic gradient. Water moves by osmosis into the sucrose solution and the volume of the sucrose solution inside the dialysis tubing increases.

The dialysis tubing acts as a partially permeable membrane, allowing water to pass freely, while keeping the sucrose inside the dialysis tubing.

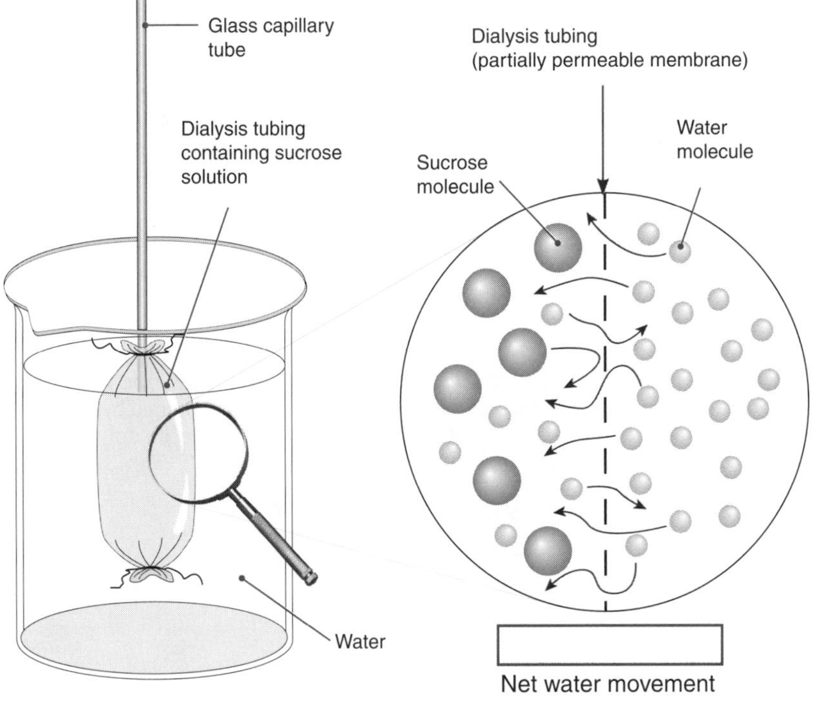
Glass capillary tube
Dialysis tubing (partially permeable membrane)
Dialysis tubing containing sucrose solution
Sucrose molecule
Water molecule
Water
Net water movement

Osmotic potential

Osmotic potential is a term often used when studying animal cells. The presence of solutes (dissolved substances) in a solution increases the tendency of water to move into that solution. This tendency is called the osmotic potential or osmotic pressure. The greater a solution's concentration (i.e. the more total dissolved solutes it contains) the greater the osmotic potential.

Describing solutions

Water movements in cells, particularly plant cells, are often explained in terms of water potential (see next activity). But you will often see other terms used to compare solutions of different solute concentration, especially in animal biology:

Isotonic solution: Having the same solute concentration relative to another solution (e.g. the cell's contents).

Hypotonic solution:
Having a lower solute concentration relative to another solution.

Hypertonic solution:
Having a higher solute concentration relative to another solution.

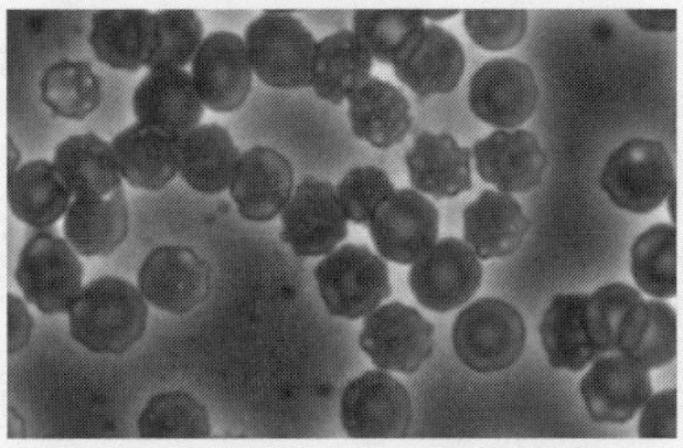

Zephyris

The red blood cells above were placed into a hypertonic solution. As a result, the cells have lost water and have begun to shrink, losing their usual discoid shape.

1. What is osmosis? ______

2. (a) In the blue box on the diagram above, draw an arrow to show the direction of net water movement.

(b) Why did water move in this direction? ______

3. What would happen to the height of the water in the capillary tube if the sucrose concentration was increased?

______

© 2015 BIOZONE International
ISBN: 978-1-927309-31-5
Photocopying Prohibited

89 Water Movement in Plant Cells

Key Idea: Water potential explains the tendency of water to move from one region to another by osmosis. Water molecules moves to regions of lower water potential.

The water potential of a solution (denoted by ψ) is the term given to the tendency for water molecules to enter or leave a solution by osmosis. The tendency for water to move in any particular direction can be calculated on the basis of the water potential of the cell sap relative to its surrounding environment. The use of water potential to express the water relations of plant cells is used in preference to osmotic potential and osmotic pressure although these terms are still frequently used in areas of animal physiology and medicine.

Water potential and water movement

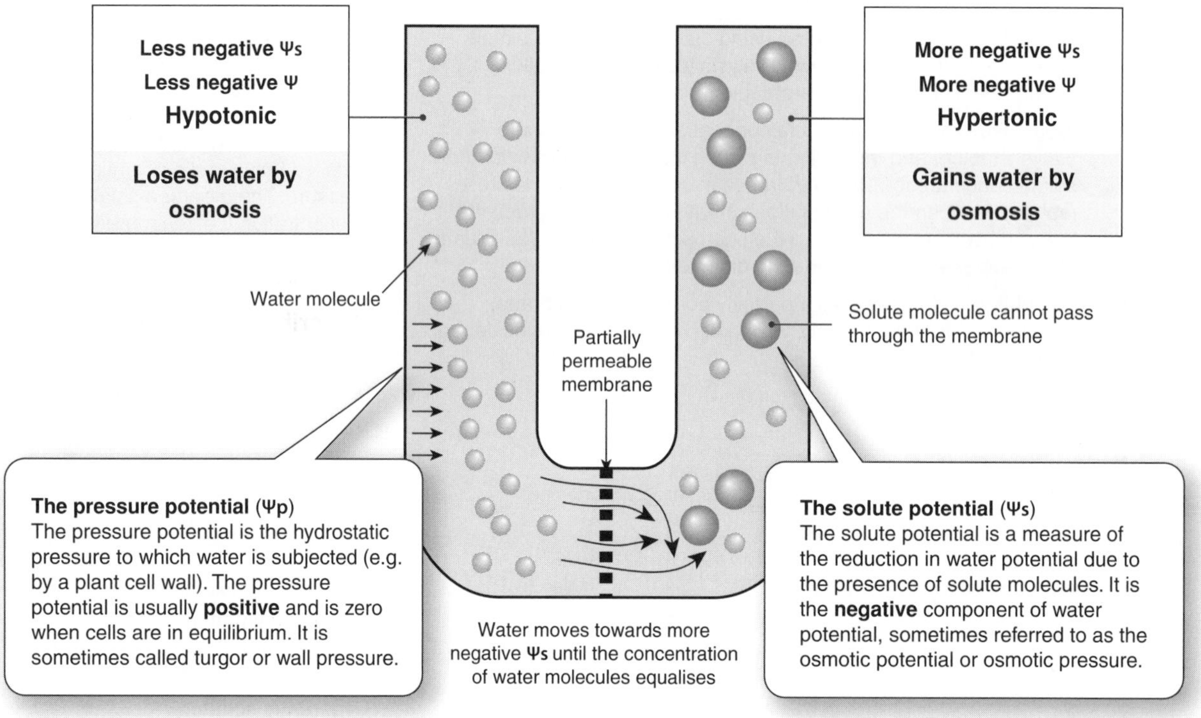

Less negative Ψs
Less negative Ψ
Hypotonic
Loses water by osmosis
More negative Ψs
More negative Ψ
Hypertonic
Gains water by osmosis
Water molecule
Partially permeable membrane
Solute molecule cannot pass through the membrane
The pressure potential (Ψp)
The pressure potential is the hydrostatic pressure to which water is subjected (e.g. by a plant cell wall). The pressure potential is usually positive and is zero when cells are in equilibrium. It is sometimes called turgor or wall pressure.
Water moves towards more negative Ψs until the concentration of water molecules equalises
The solute potential (Ψs)
The solute potential is a measure of the reduction in water potential due to the presence of solute molecules. It is the negative component of water potential, sometimes referred to as the osmotic potential or osmotic pressure.

As water molecules move around some collide with the plasma membrane and create pressure on the membrane called **water potential** (ψ). The greater the movement of water molecules, the higher their water potential. The presence of solutes (e.g. sucrose) lowers water potential because the solutes restrict the movement of water molecules. Pure water has the highest water potential (zero). Dissolving any solute in water lowers the water potential (makes it more negative).

Water always diffuses from regions of less negative to more negative water potential. Water potential is determined by two components: the **solute potential**, ψs (of the cell sap) and the **pressure potential**, ψp, expressed by:

$$\psi cell = \psi s + \psi p$$

The closer a value is to zero, the higher its water potential.

1. What is the water potential of pure water? ______________________

2. The diagrams below show three hypothetical situations where adjacent cells have different water potentials. Draw arrows on each pair of cells (a)-(c) to indicate the net direction of water movement and calculate ψ for each side:

(a)

A	B
ψs = –400 kPa	ψs = –500 kPa
ψp = 300 kPa	ψp = 300 kPa

(b)

A	B
ψs = –500 kPa	ψs = –600 kPa
ψp = 100 kPa	ψp = 100 kPa

(c)

A	B
ψs = –600 kPa	ψs = –500 kPa
ψp = 200 kPa	ψp = 300 kPa

ψ for side A: ______________ ______________ ______________

ψ for side B: ______________ ______________ ______________

© 2015 BIOZONE International
ISBN:978-1-927309-31-5
Photocopying Prohibited

When the contents of a plant cell push against the cell wall they create **turgor** (tightness) which provides support for the plant body. When cells lose water, there is a loss of turgor and the plant wilts. Complete loss of turgor from a cell is called plasmolysis and is irreversible. The diagram below shows two situations: when the external water potential is less negative than the cell and when it is more negative than the cell. When the external water potential is the same as that of the cell, there is no net movement of water.

Plasmolysis in a plant cell

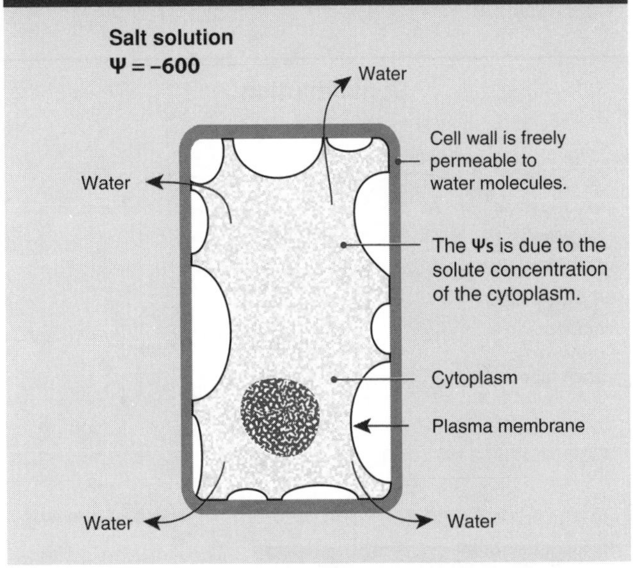
Salt solution
Ψ = –600
Water
Water
Cell wall is freely permeable to water molecules.
The Ψs is due to the solute concentration of the cytoplasm.
Cytoplasm
Plasma membrane
Water
Water

When external water potential is more negative than the water potential of the cell (Ψcell = Ψs + Ψp), water leaves the cell and, because the cell wall is rigid, the plasma membrane shrinks away from the cell wall. This process is termed **plasmolysis** and the cell becomes flaccid (Ψp = 0). Full plasmolysis is irreversible; the cell cannot recover by taking up water.

Turgor in a plant cell

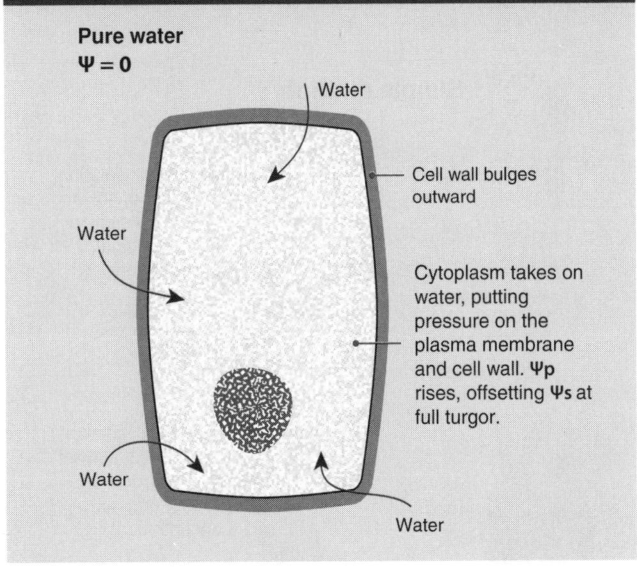
Pure water
Ψ = 0
Water
Cell wall bulges outward
Water
Cytoplasm takes on water, putting pressure on the plasma membrane and cell wall. Ψp rises, offsetting Ψs at full turgor.
Water
Water

When the external water potential is less negative than the Ψcell, water enters the cell. A pressure potential is generated when sufficient water has been taken up to cause the cell contents to press against the cell wall. Ψp rises progressively until it offsets Ψs. Water uptake stops when the Ψcell = 0. The rigid cell wall prevents cell rupture. Cells in this state are **turgid**.

3. What is the effect of dissolved solutes on water potential? ______________________

4. Why don't plant cells burst when water enters them? ______________________

5. (a) Distinguish between plasmolysis and turgor: ______________________

   (b) Describe the state of the plant in the photo on the right and explain your reasoning:

6. (a) Explain the role of pressure potential in generating cell turgor in plants: ______________________

   (b) Explain the purpose of cell turgor to plants: ______________________

© 2015 **BIOZONE** International
ISBN: 978-1-927309-31-5
Photocopying Prohibited

90 Making Dilutions

Key Idea: Dilution reduces the concentration of a stock solution by a known factor.

A dilution reduces the concentration of a solution by a known value. **Simple dilutions** are based on ratios, and involve taking a volume of stock solution and adding it to an appropriate volume of solvent to achieve the desired dilution.

Simple dilutions are often used to produce calibration curves. A **serial dilution** is a stepwise dilution that quickly amplifies the dilution factor. Serial dilutions are useful when you require a volume or amount that is too small to measure accurately, or when you need to quickly dilute a solution that is very concentrated to begin with (e.g. bacterial cells in a solution).

Simple dilution

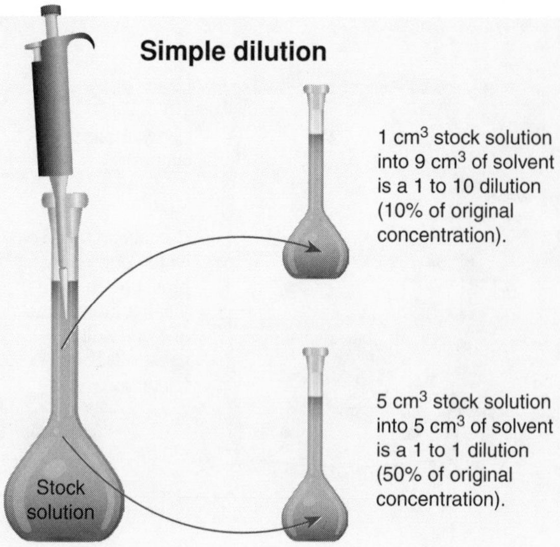

Stock solution
1 cm³ stock solution into 9 cm³ of solvent is a 1 to 10 dilution (10% of original concentration).
5 cm³ stock solution into 5 cm³ of solvent is a 1 to 1 dilution (50% of original concentration).

The following equation is used to calculate the volume needed to make a simple dilution:

$$C1 \times V1 = C2 \times V2$$

C1 = initial concentration of stock solution

V1 = initial volume of stock solution

C2= final concentration required

V2= final volume required

You will always know three of the values, so by rearranging the equation you can determine what volume of stock solution is needed to achieve the desired final concentration.

$$V1 = (C2 \times V2) \div C1$$

Serial dilution

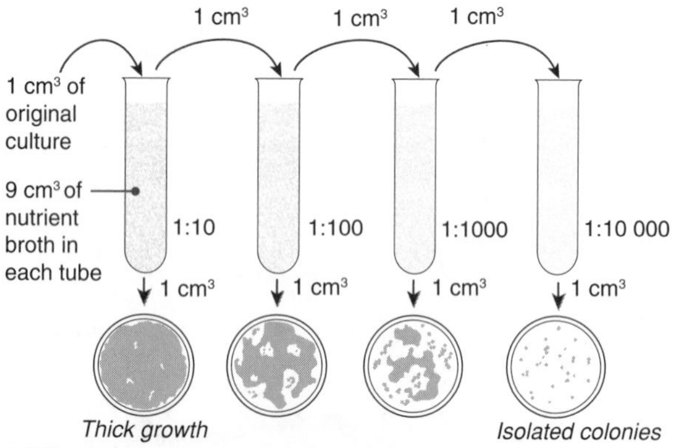

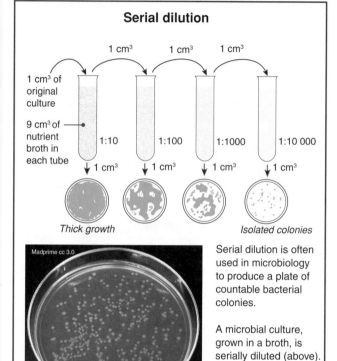

1 cm³
1 cm³
1 cm³
1 cm³ of original culture
9 cm³ of nutrient broth in each tube
1:10
1:100
1:1000
1:10 000
1 cm³
1 cm³
1 cm³
1 cm³
Thick growth
Isolated colonies

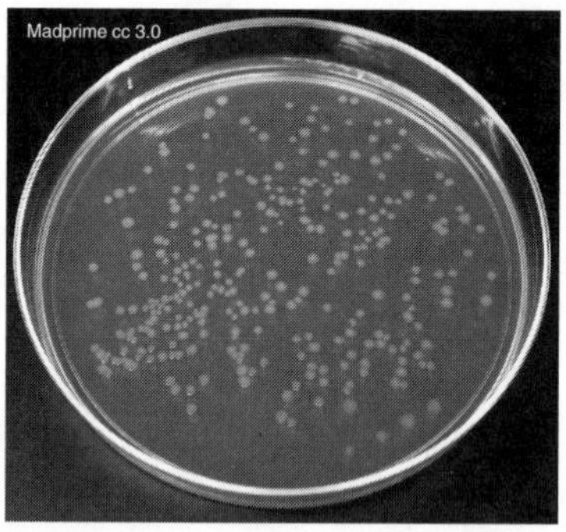

Madprime cc 3.0

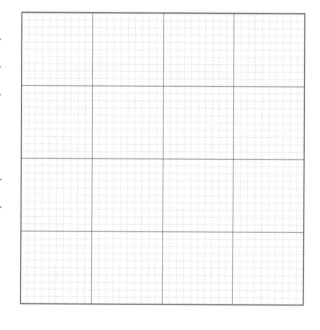

Serial dilution is often used in microbiology to produce a plate of countable bacterial colonies.

A microbial culture, grown in a broth, is serially diluted (above). The diluted culture is plated onto agar (left). this technique is called dilution plating.

When a culture has been sufficiently diluted, the colonies are discrete and can easily be counted. Each colony arises from a single cell.

1. A student had a 1.00 mol dm^{-3} stock solution of sucrose. Calculate the dilutions required to produce 5 cm^3 of sucrose solution at the following concentrations:

   (a) 0.75 mol dm^{-3}: ______________________

   (b) 0.50 mol dm^{-3}: ______________________

   (c) 0.25 mol dm^{-3}: ______________________

2. (a) Use the equation below to calculate the solute potential (ψs) of the solutions in (1) and also of the 1.00 mol dm^{-3} solution (the solutions were at 22°C):

   0.75 mol dm^{-3}: __________ 0.50 mol dm^{-3}: __________

   0.25 mol dm^{-3}: __________ 1.00 mol dm^{-3}: __________

$$\psi_s = -iCRT$$

i = ionisation constant (for sucrose, this is 1)
C = molar concentration
R = pressure constant = 8.31 dm^3 kPa K^{-1}mol^{-1}
T = temperature (°K) = 273 + °C of solution.

   (b) Plot sucrose concentration vs solute potential on the grid.

© 2015 BIOZONE International
ISBN:978-1-927309-31-5
Photocopying Prohibited

91 Estimating Osmolarity

Key Idea: A cell placed in a hypotonic solution will gain water while a cell placed in a hypertonic solution will lose water. The osmolarity (which is directly proportional to the solute potential) of a cell or tissue can be estimated by placing the tissue into a series of solutions of known concentration and observing if the tissue loses or gains water. The solution in which the tissue remains unchanged indicates the osmolarity of the tissue. At this point, the wall pressure (ψp) is zero.

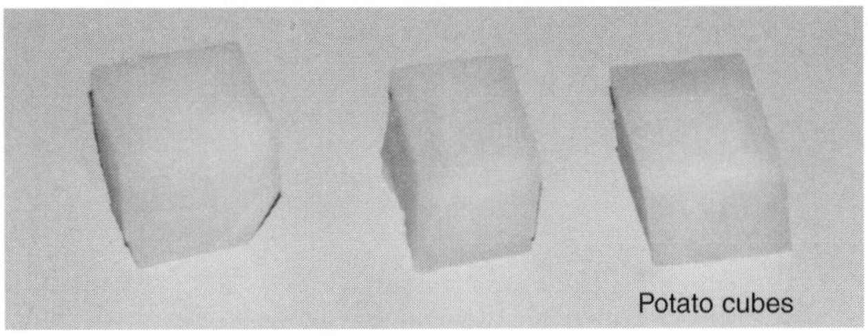
Potato cubes

KP

The aim

To determine the solute potential of potatoes by placing potato cubes in varying solutions of sucrose, $C_{12}H_{22}O_{11}$ (table sugar).

The method

Fifteen identical 1.5 cm^3 cubes of potato where cut and weighed in grams to two decimal places. Five solutions of sucrose were prepared in the following range (in mol dm^{-3}): 0.00, 0.25, 0.50, 0.75, 1.00. Three potato cubes were placed in each solution, at 22°C, for two hours, stirring every 15 minutes. The cubes were then retrieved, patted dry on blotting paper and weighed again.

1. Complete the table (right) by calculating the total mass of the potato cubes, the total change in mass, and the total % change in mass for all the sucrose concentrations:

2. Use the grid below to draw a line graph of the sucrose concentration vs total percentage change in mass:

The results

	Potato sample	Initial mass (I) / g	Final mass (F) / g
[Sucrose] 0.00 mol dm^{-3}	1	5.11	6.00
	2	5.15	6.07
	3	5.20	5.15
Total			
Change (C) (F-I) / g			
% Change (C/I x 100)			
[Sucrose] 0.25 mol dm^{-3}	1	6.01	4.98
	2	6.07	5.95
	3	7.10	7.00
Total			
Change (C) (F-I) / g			
% Change (C/I x 100)			
[Sucrose] 0.50 mol dm^{-3}	1	6.12	5.10
	2	7.03	6.01
	3	5.11	5.03
Total			
Change (C) (F-I) / g			
% Change (C/I x 100)			
[Sucrose] 0.75 mol dm^{-3}	1	5.03	3.96
	2	7.10	4.90
	3	7.03	5.13
Total			
Change (C) (F-I) / g			
% Change (C/I x 100)			
[Sucrose] 1.00 mol dm^{-3}	1	5.00	4.03
	2	5.04	3.95
	3	6.10	5.02
Total			
Change (C) (F-I) / g			
% Change (C/I x 100)			

3. (a) Use this graph to estimate the osmolarity of the potato (the point where there is no change in mass):

   (b) Use the calibration curve (opposite) to determine the solute potential (ψs) of your potato (in kPa):

   (c) What is the pressure potential (ψp) of the potato cells at equilibrium?

   (d) Use the equation ψ = ψs + ψp to determine the water potential of the potato cells at equilibrium:

© 2015 **BIOZONE** International
ISBN: 978-1-927309-31-5
Photocopying Prohibited

92 Active Transport

Key Idea: Active transport uses energy to transport molecules against their concentration gradient across a partially permeable membrane.

Active transport is the movement of molecules (or ions) from regions of low concentration to regions of high concentration across a cellular membrane by a transport protein. Active transport needs energy to proceed because molecules are being moved against their concentration gradient.

- The energy for active transport comes from **ATP** (adenosine triphosphate). Energy is released when ATP is hydrolysed (water is added) forming ADP (adenosine diphosphate) and inorganic phosphate (Pi).
- Transport (carrier) proteins in the membrane are used to actively transport molecules from one side of the membrane to the other (below).
- Active transport can be used to move molecules into and out of a cell.
- Active transport can be either primary or secondary. Primary active transport directly uses ATP for the energy to transport molecules. In secondary active transport, energy is stored in a concentration gradient. The transport of one molecule is coupled to the movement of another down its concentration gradient, ATP is not directly involved in the transport process.

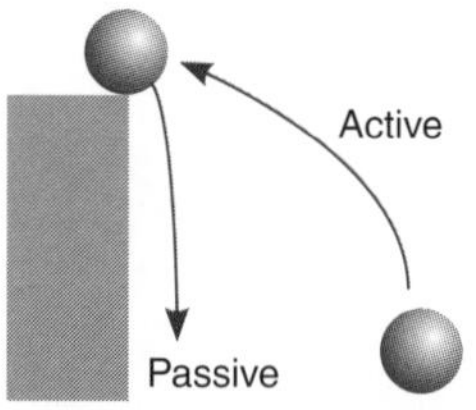
Active
Passive

A ball falling is a passive process (it requires no energy input). Replacing the ball requires active energy input.

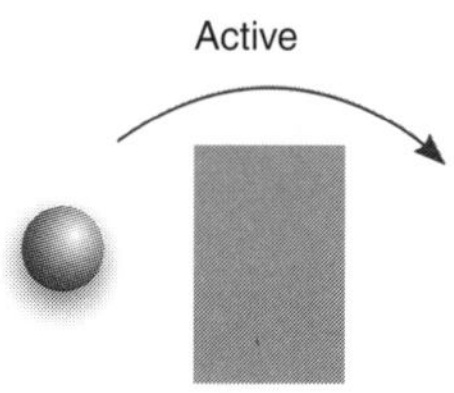
Active

It requires energy to actively move an object across a physical barrier.

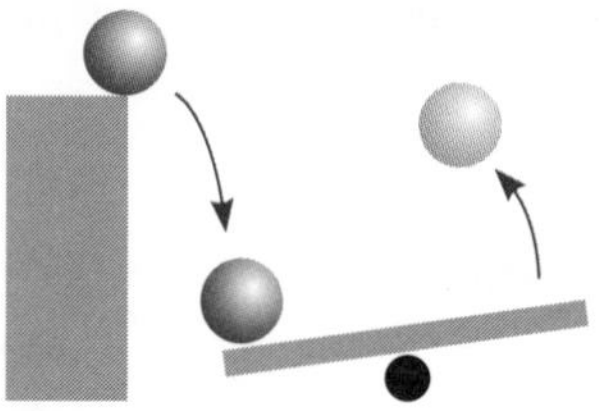

Sometimes the energy of a passively moving object can be used to actively move another. For example, a falling ball can be used to catapult another (left).

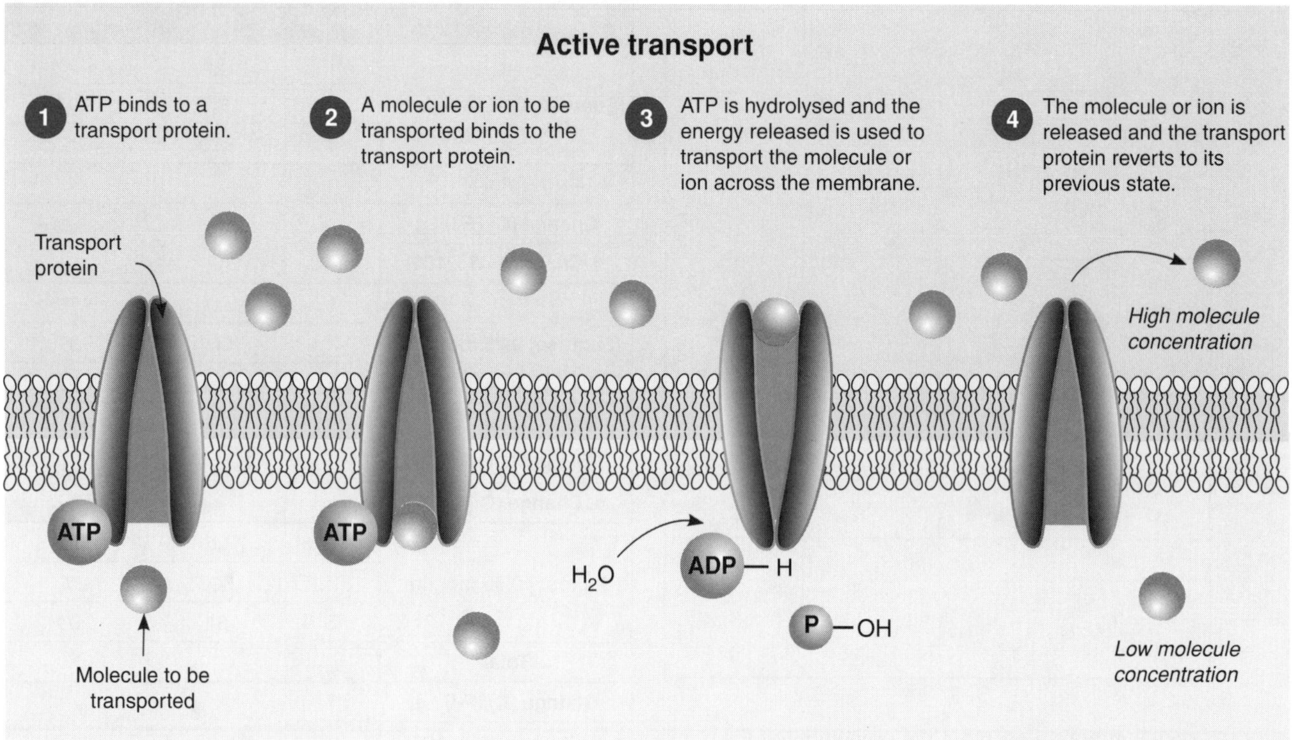
Active transport
1 ATP binds to a transport protein.
2 A molecule or ion to be transported binds to the transport protein.
3 ATP is hydrolysed and the energy released is used to transport the molecule or ion across the membrane.
4 The molecule or ion is released and the transport protein reverts to its previous state.
Transport protein
ATP
ATP
Molecule to be transported
H2O
ADP — H
P — OH
High molecule concentration
Low molecule concentration

1. What is **active transport**? ______________________________

____

____

____

2. Where does the energy for active transport come from? ______________________________

3. What is the difference between primary active transport and secondary active transport? ______________________________

____

____

____

© 2015 BIOZONE International
ISBN:978-1-927309-31-5
Photocopying Prohibited

93 Ion Pumps

Key Idea: Ion pumps are transmembrane proteins that use energy to move ions and molecules across a membrane against their concentration gradient.

Sometimes molecules or ions are needed in concentrations that diffusion alone cannot supply to the cell, or they cannot diffuse through the plasma membrane. In this case ion pumps move ions (and some molecules) across the plasma membrane. The sodium-potassium pump (below) is found in almost all animal cells and is common in plant cells also. The concentration gradient created by ion pumps is often coupled to the transport of other molecules such as glucose across the membrane.

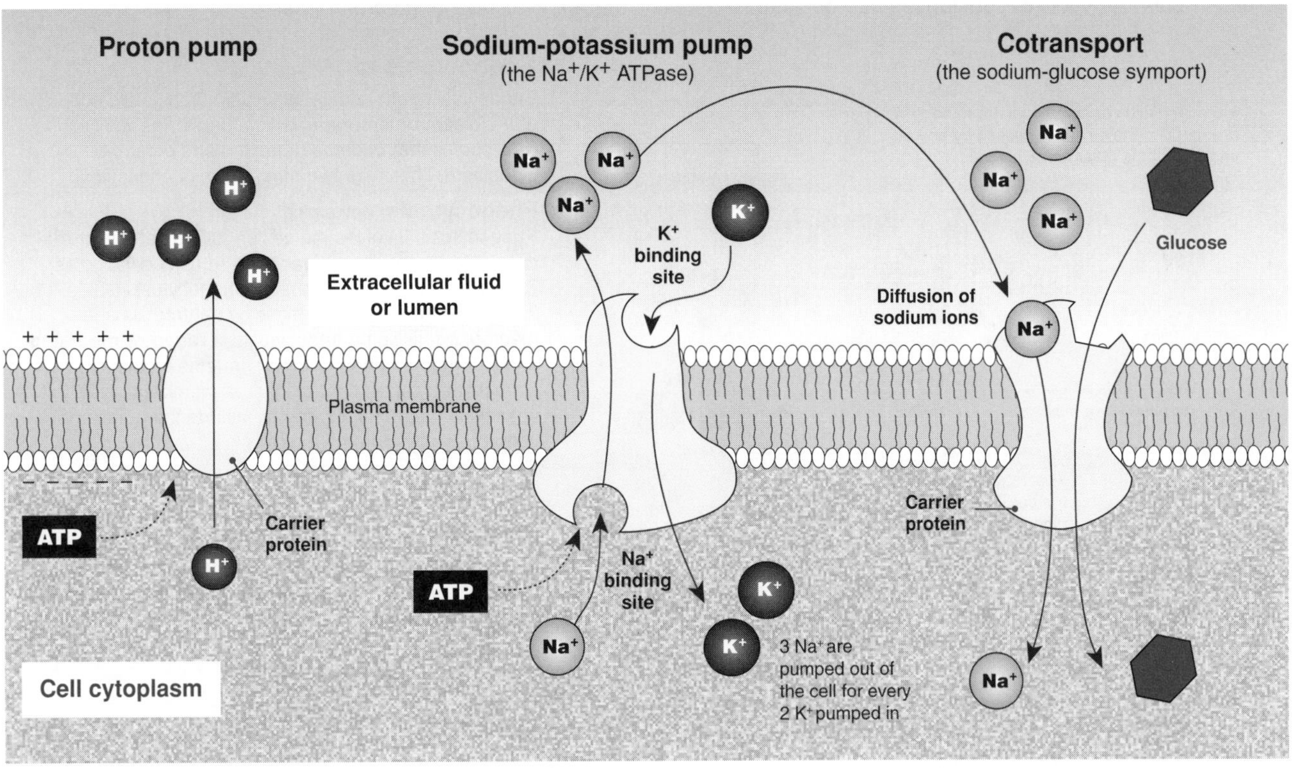

Proton pump
Sodium-potassium pump
(the Na+/K+ ATPase)
Cotransport
(the sodium-glucose symport)
H+
Extracellular fluid or lumen
Na+
K+
K+ binding site
Glucose
Diffusion of sodium ions
+ + + + +
Plasma membrane
− − − − −
ATP
Carrier protein
Na+ binding site
3 Na+ are pumped out of the cell for every 2 K+ pumped in
Cell cytoplasm

Proton pumps

ATP driven proton pumps use energy to remove hydrogen ions (H^+) from inside the cell to the outside. This creates a large difference in the proton concentration either side of the membrane, with the inside of the plasma membrane being negatively charged. This potential difference can be coupled to the transport of other molecules.

Sodium-potassium pump

The sodium-potassium pump is a specific protein in the membrane that uses energy in the form of ATP to exchange sodium ions (Na^+) for potassium ions (K^+) across the membrane. The unequal balance of Na^+ and K^+ across the membrane creates large concentration gradients that can be used to drive transport of other substances (e.g. cotransport of glucose).

Cotransport (coupled transport)

A gradient in sodium ions drives the active transport of **glucose** in intestinal epithelial cells. The specific transport protein couples the return of Na^+ down its concentration gradient to the transport of glucose into the intestinal epithelial cell. A low intracellular concentration of Na^+ (and therefore the concentration gradient) is maintained by a sodium-potassium pump.

1. Why is ATP required for membrane pump systems to operate? __________

2. (a) Explain what is meant by cotransport: __________

   (b) How is cotransport used to move glucose into the intestinal epithelial cells? __________

   (c) What happens to the glucose that is transported into the intestinal epithelial cells? __________

3. Describe two consequences of the extracellular accumulation of sodium ions: __________

© 2015 BIOZONE International
ISBN: 978-1-927309-31-5
Photocopying Prohibited

94 Exocytosis and Endocytosis

Key Idea: Endocytosis and exocytosis are active transport processes. Endocytosis involves the cell engulfing material. Exocytosis involves the cell expelling material.

Most cells carry out **cytosis**, a type of active transport in which the plasma membrane folds around a substance to transport it across the plasma membrane. The ability of cells to do this is a function of the flexibility of the plasma membrane. Cytosis results in bulk transport of substances into or out of the cell and is achieved through the localised activity of the cell's cytoskeleton. **Endocytosis** involves material being engulfed and taken into the cell. It typically occurs in protozoans and some white blood cells of the mammalian defence system (phagocytes). **Exocytosis** is the reverse of endocytosis and involves expelling material from the cell in vesicles that fuse with the plasma membrane. Exocytosis is common in cells that export material (secretory cells).

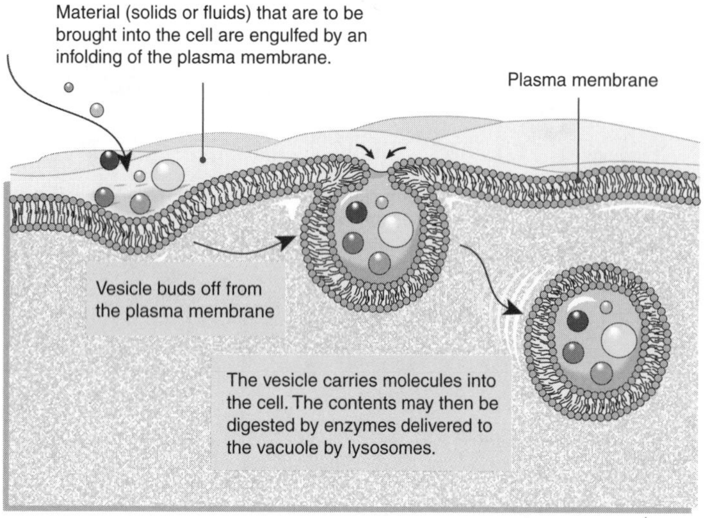
Material (solids or fluids) that are to be brought into the cell are engulfed by an infolding of the plasma membrane.
Plasma membrane
Vesicle buds off from the plasma membrane
The vesicle carries molecules into the cell. The contents may then be digested by enzymes delivered to the vacuole by lysosomes.

Endocytosis

Endocytosis (left) occurs by invagination (infolding) of the plasma membrane, which then forms vesicles or vacuoles that become detached and enter the cytoplasm. There are two main types of endocytosis:

Phagocytosis: 'cell-eating'

Phagocytosis involves the cell engulfing **solid material** to form large vesicles or vacuoles (e.g. food vacuoles). Examples: Feeding in *Amoeba*, phagocytosis of foreign material and cell debris by neutrophils and macrophages. Some endocytosis is **receptor mediated** and is triggered when receptor proteins on the extracellular surface of the plasma membrane bind to specific substances. Examples include the uptake of lipoproteins by mammalian cells.

Pinocytosis: 'cell-drinking'

Pinocytosis involves the non-specific uptake of **liquids** or fine suspensions into the cell to form small pinocytic vesicles. Pinocytosis is used primarily for absorbing extracellular fluid. Examples: Uptake in many protozoa, some cells of the liver, and some plant cells.

Both endocytosis and exocytosis require energy in the form of ATP.

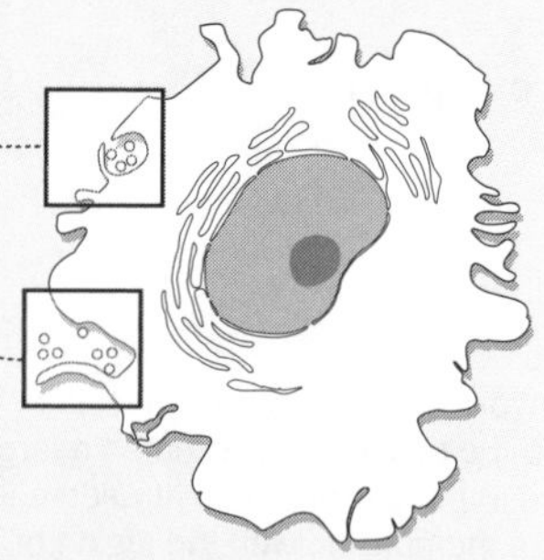
Areas of enlargement

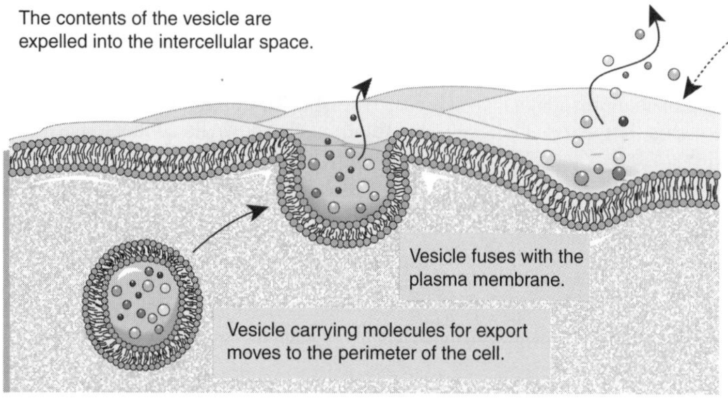
The contents of the vesicle are expelled into the intercellular space.
Vesicle fuses with the plasma membrane.
Vesicle carrying molecules for export moves to the perimeter of the cell.

Exocytosis

Exocytosis (left) is the reverse process to endocytosis. In multicellular organisms, various types of cells are specialised to manufacture and export products, such as proteins, from the cell to elsewhere in the body or outside it. Exocytosis occurs by fusion of the vesicle membrane and the plasma membrane, followed by release of the vesicle contents to the outside of the cell.

1. Distinguish between **phagocytosis** and **pinocytosis**: ______________________

____

____

2. Describe an example of phagocytosis and identify the cell type involved: ______________________

____

3. Describe an example of exocytosis and identify the cell type involved: ______________________

____

4. How does each of the following substances enter a living macrophage:

(a) Oxygen: ______________________ (c) Water: ______________________

(b) Cellular debris: ______________________ (d) Glucose: ______________________

© 2015 BIOZONE International
ISBN:978-1-927309-31-5
Photocopying Prohibited

95 Active and Passive Transport Summary

Key Idea: Cells move materials into and out of the cell by either passive transport, which does not require energy, or by active transport which requires energy, often as ATP.

Cells need to move materials into and out of the cell. Molecules needed for metabolism must be accumulated from outside the cell, where they may be in low concentration. Waste products and molecules for use in other parts of the organism must be 'exported' out of the cell. Some materials (e.g. gases and water) move into and out of the cell by passive transport processes, without energy expenditure. Other molecules (e.g. sucrose) are moved into and out of the cell using active transport. Active transport processes involve the expenditure of energy in the form of ATP, and therefore use oxygen.

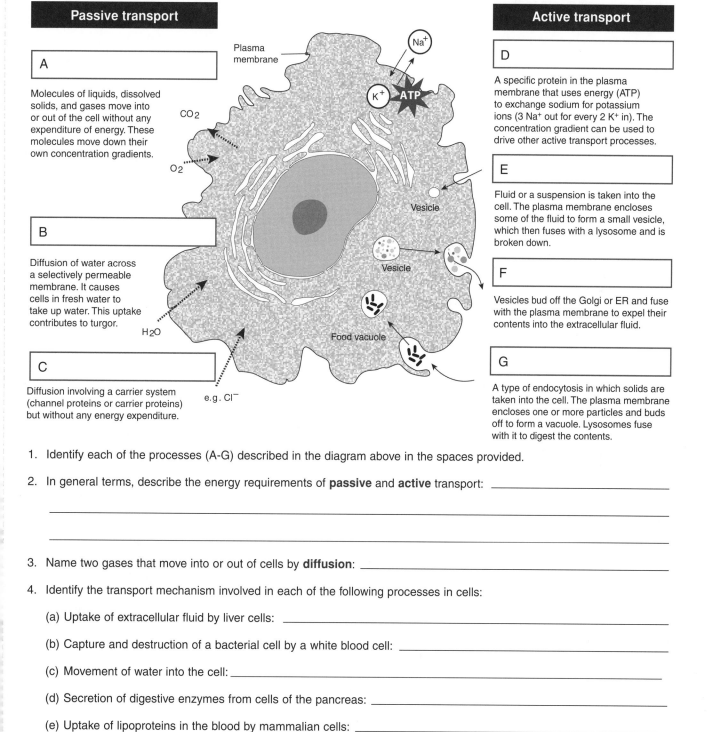

Passive transport

A

Molecules of liquids, dissolved solids, and gases move into or out of the cell without any expenditure of energy. These molecules move down their own concentration gradients.

B

Diffusion of water across a selectively permeable membrane. It causes cells in fresh water to take up water. This uptake contributes to turgor.

C

Diffusion involving a carrier system (channel proteins or carrier proteins) but without any energy expenditure.

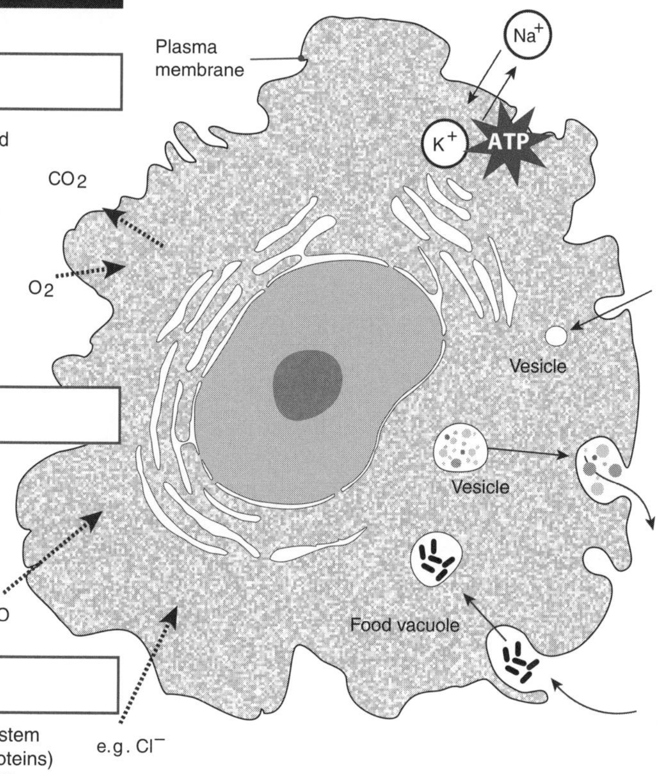
Plasma membrane
Na^+
K^+
ATP
CO_2
O_2
Vesicle
Vesicle
H_2O
Food vacuole
e.g. Cl^-

Active transport

D

A specific protein in the plasma membrane that uses energy (ATP) to exchange sodium for potassium ions (3 Na^+ out for every 2 K^+ in). The concentration gradient can be used to drive other active transport processes.

E

Fluid or a suspension is taken into the cell. The plasma membrane encloses some of the fluid to form a small vesicle, which then fuses with a lysosome and is broken down.

F

Vesicles bud off the Golgi or ER and fuse with the plasma membrane to expel their contents into the extracellular fluid.

G

A type of endocytosis in which solids are taken into the cell. The plasma membrane encloses one or more particles and buds off to form a vacuole. Lysosomes fuse with it to digest the contents.

1. Identify each of the processes (A-G) described in the diagram above in the spaces provided.

2. In general terms, describe the energy requirements of **passive** and **active** transport: ____________________

3. Name two gases that move into or out of cells by **diffusion**: ____________________

4. Identify the transport mechanism involved in each of the following processes in cells:

   (a) Uptake of extracellular fluid by liver cells: ____________________

   (b) Capture and destruction of a bacterial cell by a white blood cell: ____________________

   (c) Movement of water into the cell: ____________________

   (d) Secretion of digestive enzymes from cells of the pancreas: ____________________

   (e) Uptake of lipoproteins in the blood by mammalian cells: ____________________

   (f) Ingestion of a food particle by a protozoan: ____________________

   (g) Transport of chloride ions into a cell: ____________________

   (h) Uptake of glucose into red blood cells: ____________________

   (i) Establishment of a potential difference across the membrane of a nerve cell: ____________________

© 2015 **BIOZONE** International
ISBN: 978-1-927309-31-5
Photocopying Prohibited

96 Chapter Review

Summarise what you know about this topic under the headings provided. You can draw diagrams or mind maps, or write short notes to organise your thoughts. Use the images and hints to help you and refer back to the introduction to check the points covered:

Passive transport processes

HINT: Include reference to the concentration gradient

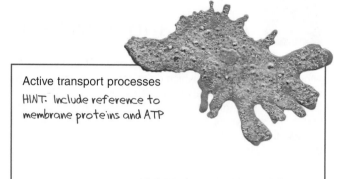

Active transport processes

HINT: Include reference to membrane proteins and ATP

Membrane structure

HINT: Define the fluid mosaic model and draw a cell surface membrane. What factors alter membrane permeability?

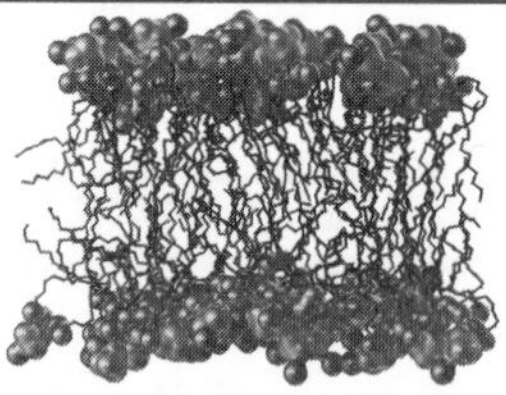

© 2015 BIOZONE International
ISBN:978-1-927309-31-5
Photocopying Prohibited

97 KEY TERMS AND IDEAS: Did You Get It?

1. Match each term to its definition, as identified by its preceding letter code.

active transport	A	A partially-permeable phospholipid bilayer forming the boundary of all cells.
carrier protein	B	The movement of substances across a biological membrane without energy expenditure.
cell surface membrane	C	The passive movement of molecules from high to low concentration.
concentration gradient	D	A measure of the tendency of water to move from one area to another by osmosis. Its components are solute potential and pressure potential.
diffusion	E	A membrane-bound protein involved in the transport of a specific molecule across the membrane either by active transport or facilitated diffusion.
endocytosis	F	The energy-requiring movement of substances across a biological membrane against a concentration gradient.
facilitated diffusion	G	Active transport in which molecules are engulfed by the plasma membrane, forming a phagosome or food vacuole within the cell.
fluid mosaic model	H	Passive movement of water molecules across a partially permeable membrane down a concentration gradient.
ion pump	I	A transmembrane protein that moves ions across a plasma membrane against their concentration gradient.
osmosis	J	Gradual change in the concentration of solutes as a function of distance through the solution. In biology, this usually results from unequal distribution of ions across a membrane.
passive transport	K	The model for membrane structure which proposes a double phospholipid bilayer in which proteins and cholesterol are embedded.
surface area: volume ratio	L	This relationship determines capacity for effective diffusion in a cell.
water potential	M	A type of passive transport facilitated by transport proteins.

2. Match the statements in the table below to form a complete paragraph. The left hand column is in the correct order, the right hand column is not.

Transport of molecules though the plasma membrane...	....to the movement of molecules or ions against their concentration gradient.
Active transport requires the input of energy...	...high concentration to low concentration (down a concentration gradient).
Passive transport involves the movement of molecules from...	...can be active or passive.
Simple diffusion can occur...	...directly across the membrane.
Facilitated diffusion involves proteins in the plasma membrane...	...which help molecules or ions to move through.
Active transport involves membrane proteins, which couple the energy provided by ATP...	...whereas passive transport does not.

3. The diagrams below depict what happens when a red blood cell is placed into three solutions with differing water potentials. Describe the water potential of the solution (in relation to the cell) and describe what is happening:

A

B

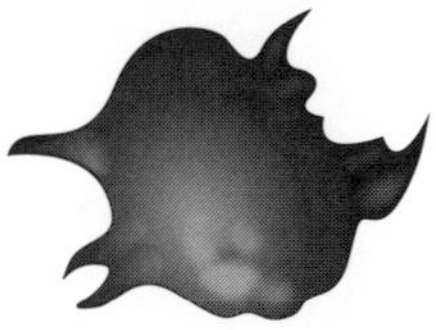

C

© 2015 BIOZONE International
ISBN: 978-1-927309-31-5
Photocopying Prohibited

Topic 5 The mitotic cell cycle

Key terms

cellular differentiation
centromere
chromatid
chromosome
cytokinesis
interphase
G1 phase
G2 phase
histone
metaphase
mitosis
multicellular
multipotent
pluripotent
prophase
S phase
spindle fibres
stem cell
telomere
telophase
totipotent

5.1 Replication and division of nuclei and cells

Learning outcomes

		Activity number
☐	1 Describe the structure of eukaryotic chromosomes, with reference to chromatids, the centromere, and telomeres, and the role of histone proteins in packaging DNA.	98
☐	2 Describe the outcome of mitotic division and explain the significance and roles of mitosis in eukaryotic life cycles.	99 103
☐	3 Describe stages in the eukaryotic cell cycle: interphase, mitosis, cytokinesis. Outline the events occurring during interphase stages: G1, S, and G2. Distinguish between the events of cytokinesis in plant and animal cells.	100
☐	4 Outline the significance of telomeres in allowing continued replication of DNA and in preventing the loss of genes.	101
☐	5 Explain what is meant by a stem cell. Describe the properties of stem cells and distinguish between levels of potency and its significance. Describe the role of mitosis and differentiation of stem cells in development and in cell replacement and tissue repair.	105-107
☐	6 Appreciate that the cell cycle is tightly regulated and describe how uncontrolled cell division can result in the formation of a tumour.	108 109

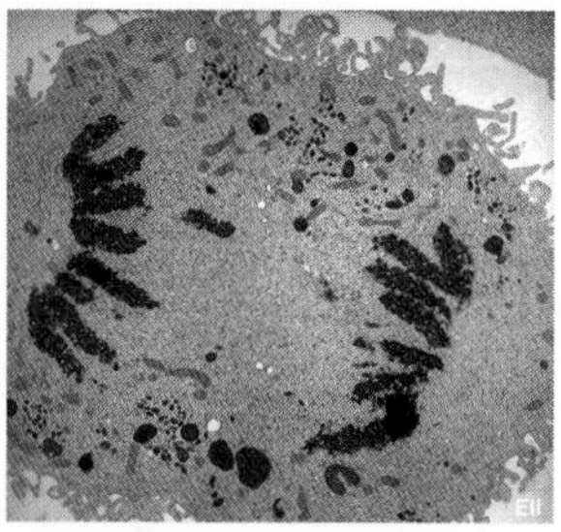
EII

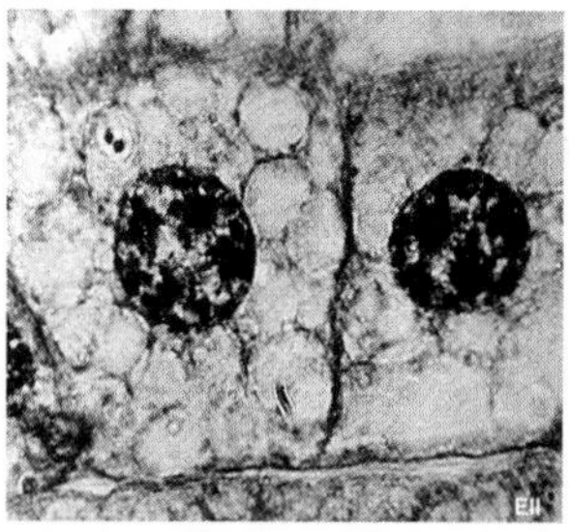
EII

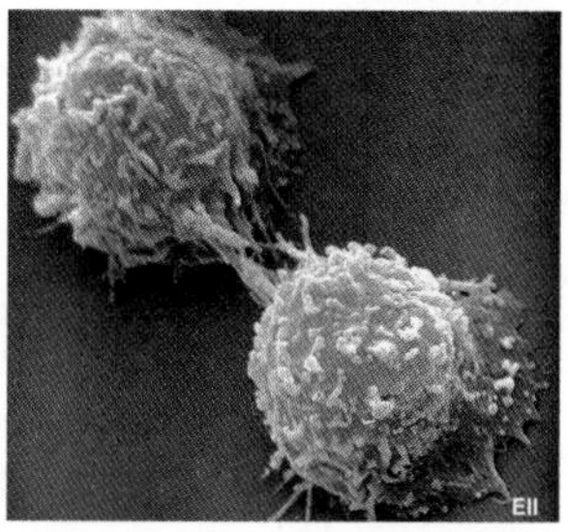
EII

5.2 Chromosome behaviour in mitosis

Learning outcomes

		Activity number
☐	7 Describe mitosis as a continuous process, with distinct stages. Using photomicrographs and diagrams to help you, describe the behaviour of chromosomes in plant and animal cells during the mitotic cell cycle. Include reference to the main stages of mitosis (prophase, metaphase, anaphase, telophase) and the behaviour of the nuclear envelope, cell surface membrane, and the mitotic spindle.	102
☐	8 PRAC Observe and draw the mitotic stages visible in stained sections and temporary squashes of plant tissue viewed with a light microscope.	103 104

98 Eukaryotic Chromosome Structure

Key Idea: Eukaryotic DNA is located in the cell nucleus. A DNA molecule is very long. It must be wound up to fit into the cell's nucleus.

Eukaryotes package their DNA as discrete linear chromosomes. The number of chromosomes varies from species to species. The way the DNA is packaged changes during the life cycle of the cell, but classic chromosome structures (below) appear during metaphase of mitosis.

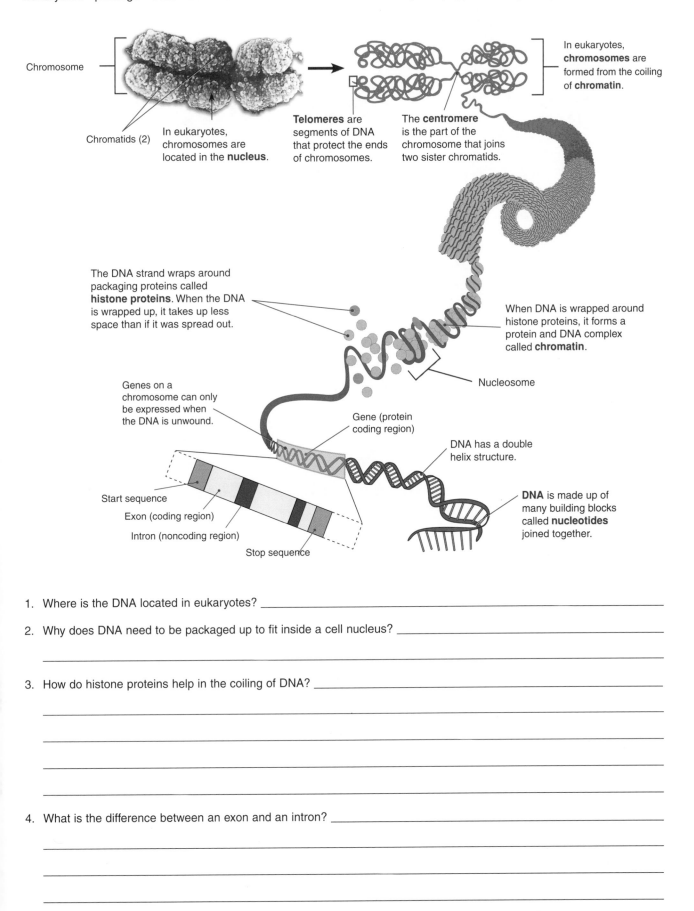

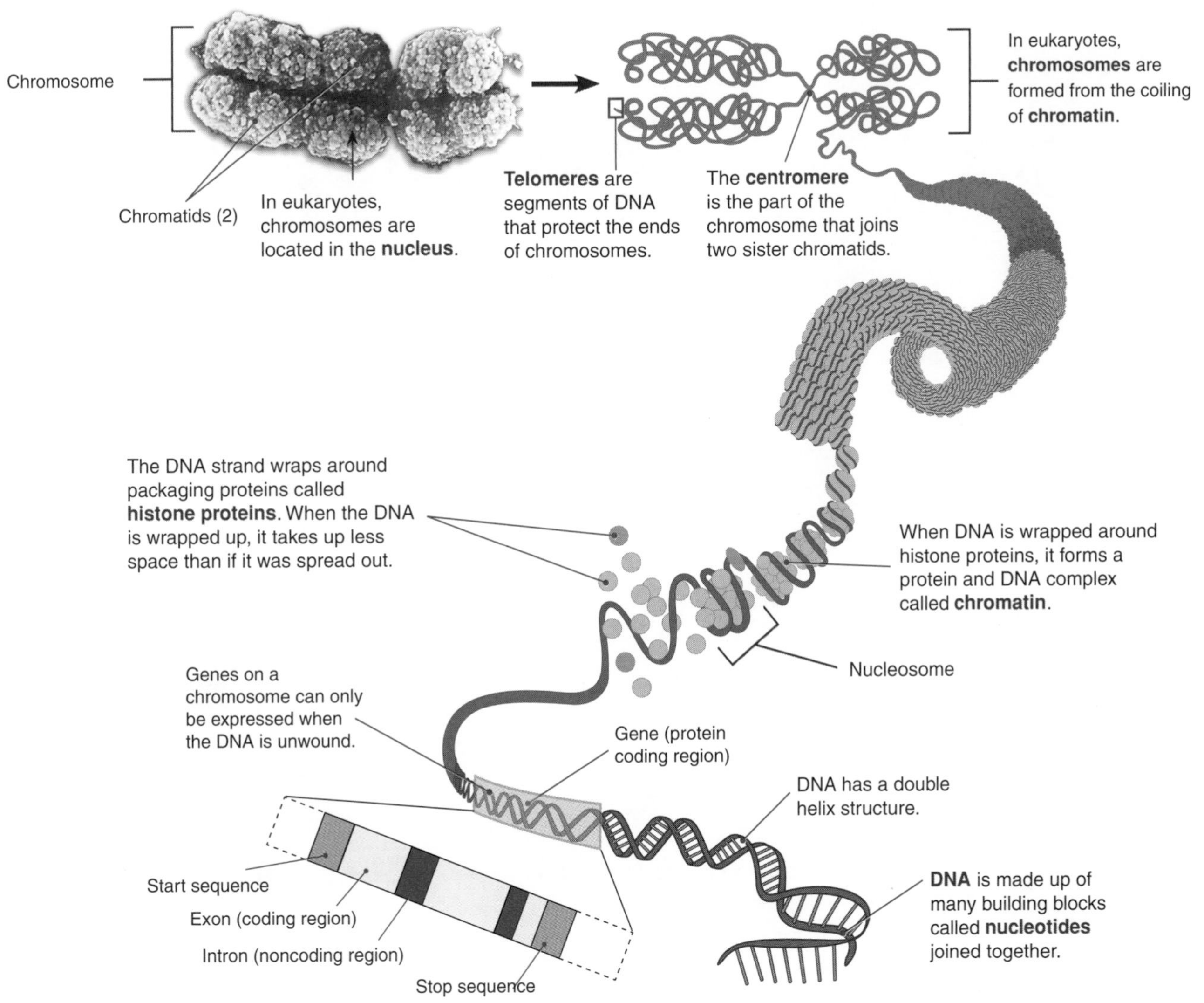
Chromosome
Chromatids (2)
In eukaryotes, chromosomes are located in the **nucleus**.
Telomeres are segments of DNA that protect the ends of chromosomes.
The **centromere** is the part of the chromosome that joins two sister chromatids.
In eukaryotes, **chromosomes** are formed from the coiling of **chromatin**.
The DNA strand wraps around packaging proteins called **histone proteins**. When the DNA is wrapped up, it takes up less space than if it was spread out.
When DNA is wrapped around histone proteins, it forms a protein and DNA complex called **chromatin**.
Nucleosome
Genes on a chromosome can only be expressed when the DNA is unwound.
Gene (protein coding region)
DNA has a double helix structure.
DNA is made up of many building blocks called **nucleotides** joined together.
Start sequence
Exon (coding region)
Intron (noncoding region)
Stop sequence

1. Where is the DNA located in eukaryotes? ______________________________

2. Why does DNA need to be packaged up to fit inside a cell nucleus? ______________________________

____

3. How do histone proteins help in the coiling of DNA? ______________________________

____

____

____

____

4. What is the difference between an exon and an intron? ______________________________

____

____

____

© 2015 **BIOZONE** International
ISBN: 978-1-927309-31-5
Photocopying Prohibited

99 The Role of Mitosis

Key Idea: Mitosis has three primary functions: growth of the organism, replacement of damaged or old cells, and asexual reproduction (in some organisms).

Mitotic cell division produces daughter cells that are genetically identical to the parent cell. It has three purposes: growth, repair, and reproduction. Multicellular organisms grow from a single fertilised cell into a mature organism that may consist of several thousand to several trillion cells. Repair occurs by replacing damaged and old cells with new cells. Some unicellular eukaryotes (such as yeasts) and some multicellular organisms (e.g. *Hydra*) reproduce asexually by mitotic division.

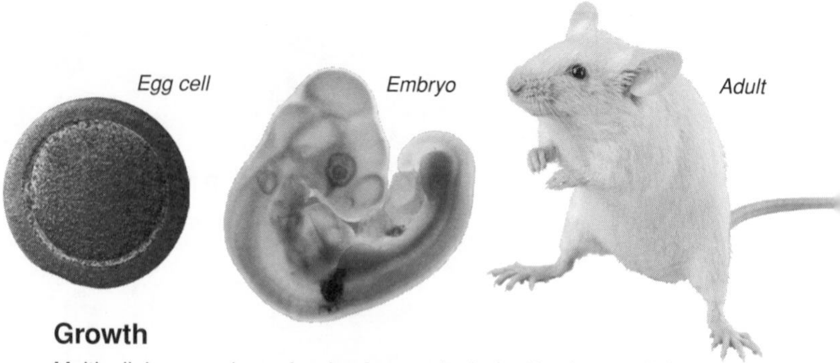
Egg cell
Embryo
Adult

Asexual reproduction

Some simple eukaryotic organisms reproduce asexually by mitosis. Yeasts (such as baker's yeast) can reproduce by budding. The parent cell buds to form a daughter cell (right) which eventually separates from the parent cell. Prokaryotes divide by binary fission, a different but superficially similar process.

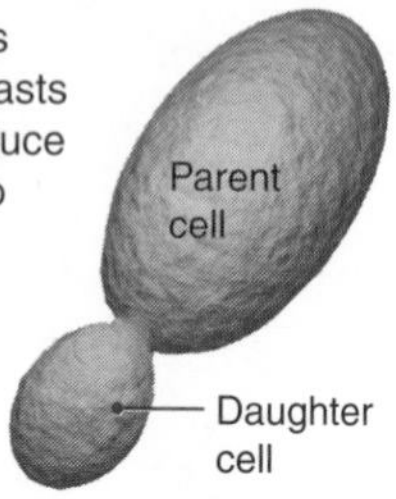
Parent cell
Daughter cell

Growth

Multicellular organisms develop from a single fertilised egg cell (above, left) and grow by increasing cell numbers. Cells complete a cell cycle, in which the cell copies its DNA and then divides to produce two identical cells. During the period of growth, the production of new cells is faster than the death of old ones. Organisms, such as the 12 day old mouse embryo (above, middle), grow by increasing their total cell number and the cell become specialised as part of development. Cell growth is highly regulated and once the mouse reaches its adult size (above, right), physical growth stops and the number of cell deaths equals the number of new cells produced.

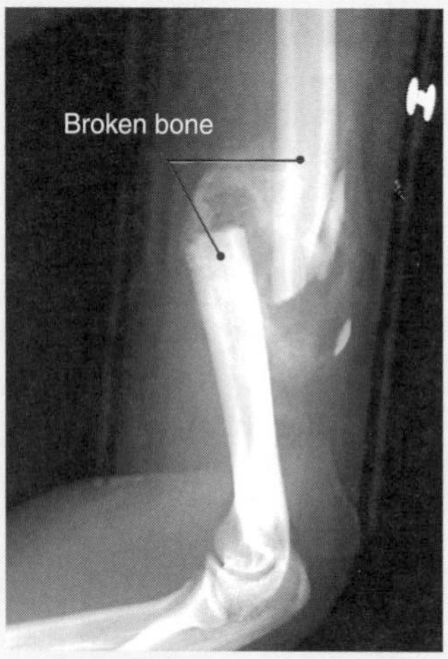
Broken bone

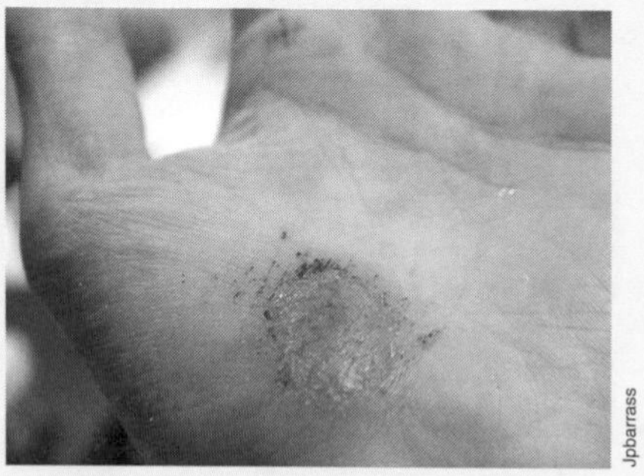
Jpbarrass

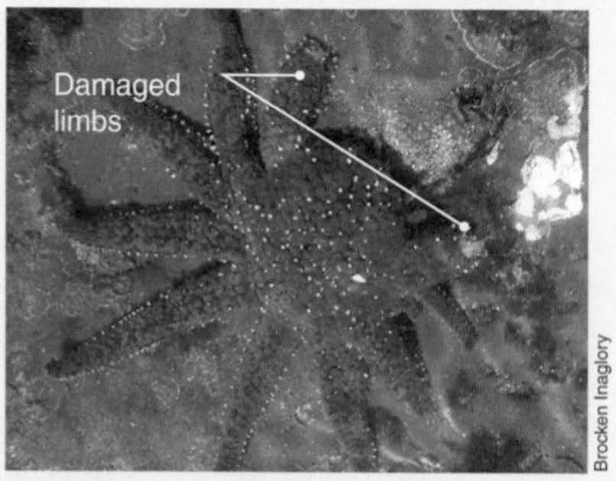
Damaged limbs
Brocken Inaglory

Repair

Cell division is responsible for the repair and replacement of damaged cells in multicellular organisms. When you break a bone, or graze your skin, new cells are generated to repair the damage. Some organisms, like the sea star (above right) are able to generate new limbs if they are broken off.

1. Use examples to explain the role of cell division in:

   (a) Growth of an organism: ______________________________

   ____

   ____

   ____

   (b) Replacement of damaged cells: ______________________________

   ____

   ____

   ____

   (c) Asexual reproduction: ______________________________

   ____

   ____

© 2015 BIOZONE International
ISBN:978-1-927309-31-5
Photocopying Prohibited

100 The Cell Cycle in Eukaryotes

Key Idea: The cell cycle of eukaryotes has four main phases. There are also three checkpoints that regulate the progression to the next phase of the cell cycle.

The cell cycle can be divided into interphase and M phase. The cell spends 90% of its time in interphase. Interphase is the time between cell divisions when the cell is not in M-phase. It can be further divided into three phases: G1, S-phase, and G2. M-phase includes mitosis (nuclear division involving the separation of replicated DNA) and cytokinesis (the division of the cell into two new cells). The duration of the cell cycle varies between organisms and between cell types and is fastest in the cells of early embryos.

The cell cycle

Interphase

Cells spend most of their time in interphase. Interphase is divided into three stages (right):

- The first gap phase.
- The S-phase.
- The second gap phase.

During interphase the cell grows, carries out its normal activities, and replicates its DNA in preparation for cell division.
Interphase is not a stage in mitosis.

Mitosis and cytokinesis (M-phase)

Mitosis and cytokinesis occur during M-phase. During mitosis, the cell nucleus (containing the replicated DNA) divides in two equal parts. Cytokinesis occurs at the end of M-phase. During cytokinesis the cell cytoplasm divides, and two new daughter cells are produced.

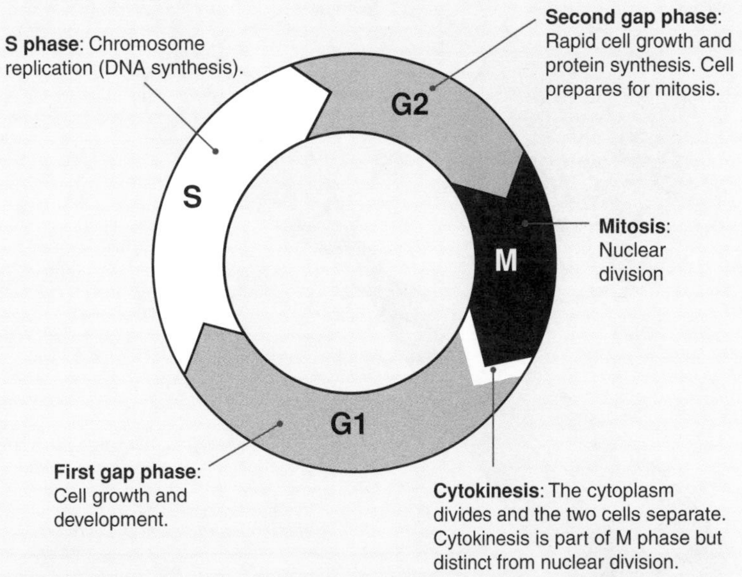
S phase: Chromosome replication (DNA synthesis).
Second gap phase: Rapid cell growth and protein synthesis. Cell prepares for mitosis.
G2
S
M
Mitosis: Nuclear division
G1
First gap phase: Cell growth and development.
Cytokinesis: The cytoplasm divides and the two cells separate. Cytokinesis is part of M phase but distinct from nuclear division.

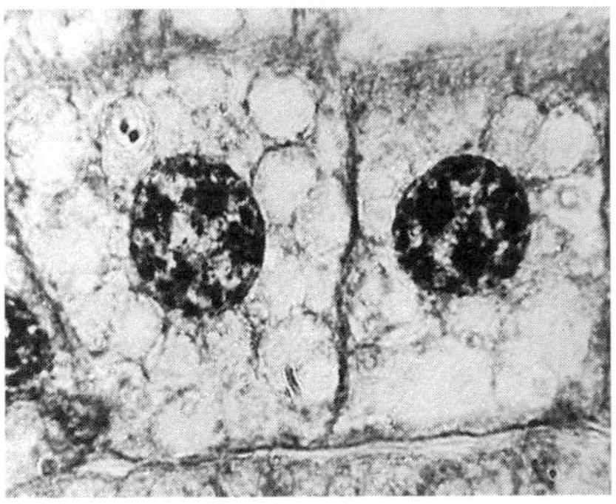

During interphase, the cell grows and acquires the materials needed to undergo mitosis. It also prepares the nuclear material for separation by replicating it.

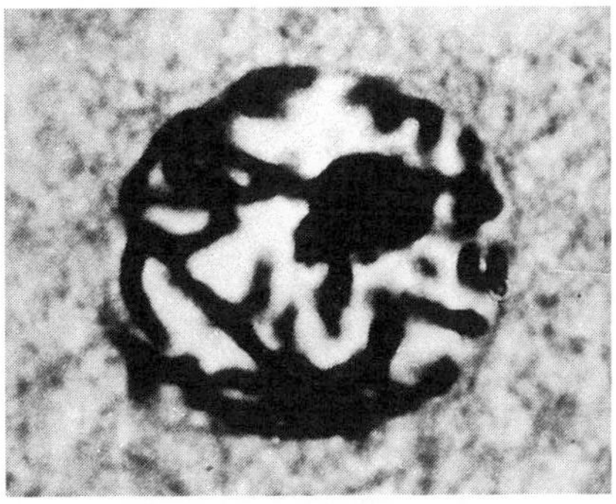

During interphase the nuclear material is unwound. As mitosis approaches, the nuclear material begins to reorganise in readiness for nuclear division.

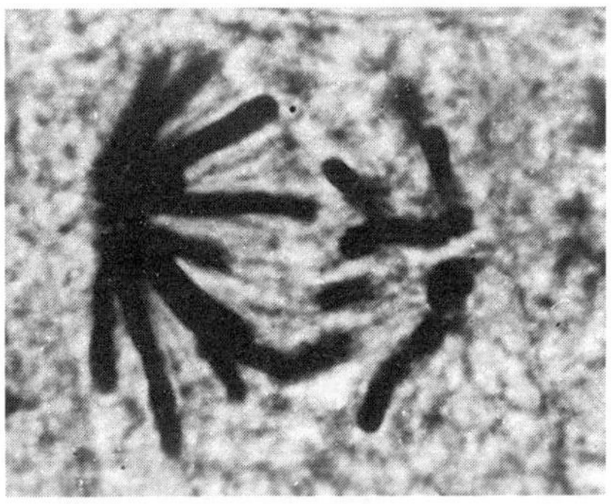

During mitosis the chromosomes are separated. Mitosis is a highly organised process and the cell must pass "checkpoints" before it proceeds to the next phase.

1. Briefly outline what occurs during the following phases of the cell cycle:

(a) Interphase: ______________________

____

____

____

(b) Mitosis: ______________________

____

____

(c) Cytokinesis: ______________________

____

© 2015 BIOZONE International
ISBN: 978-1-927309-31-5
Photocopying Prohibited

101 The Role of Telomeres

Key Idea: Telomeres are segments of DNA that protect the ends of chromosomes.

Telomeres are repeating segments of DNA found at the tips of chromosomes. They protect the chromosomes from degradation (and subsequent loss of genes) and incorrect recombination. However, during DNA replication, the very ends of the telomeres are unable to be copied. Thus the telomeres become shorter with each round of replication. Eventually the telomeres are depleted, which leads to a cessation of cell division or to programmed cell death. This telomeric shortening gives a way of regulating the life span of a dividing cell. Enzymes called telomerases can maintain the length of the telomeres. Telomerases are active in stem cells, hair follicles, and cancerous cells.

Telomere position and structure

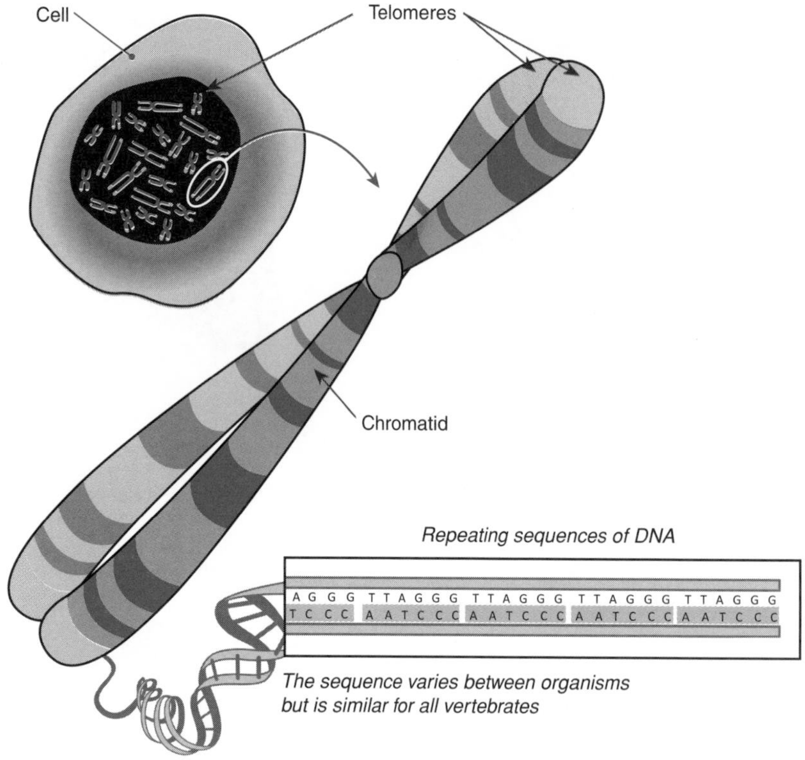
Cell
Telomeres
Chromatid
Repeating sequences of DNA
AGGG TTAGGG TTAGGG TTAGGG TTAGGG
TCCC AATCCC AATCCC AATCCC AATCCC

The sequence varies between organisms but is similar for all vertebrates

How telomeres work

In vertebrates, telomeres consist of the DNA sequence TTAGGG (below left) that may repeat several hundred to several thousand times (2500 times in humans). During replication, the enzymes that copy the DNA cannot continue all the way to the end of chromosome. Part of the telomere is therefore left out during each replication. When the telomeres become particularly short, it signals to the cell to stop dividing. At this stage, the cell may enter cellular old age (senescence), or begin programmed cell self-destruction (apoptosis).

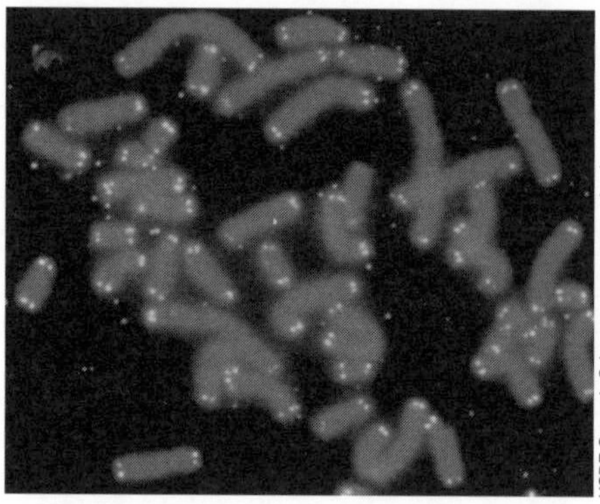

USDE Genomic Science program, genomicscience.energy.gov

The image above shows the telomeres as bright dots at the ends of the chromosomes.

Telomeres and telomerase

All cells employ the enzyme telomerase to extend the length of the telomeres. However these enzymes are not particularly active and the shortening of the telomeres is greater than their regeneration. In rapidly dividing cells such as stem cells, some blood cells, and hair follicles, there is greater telomerase activity which increases the dividing life of the cell.

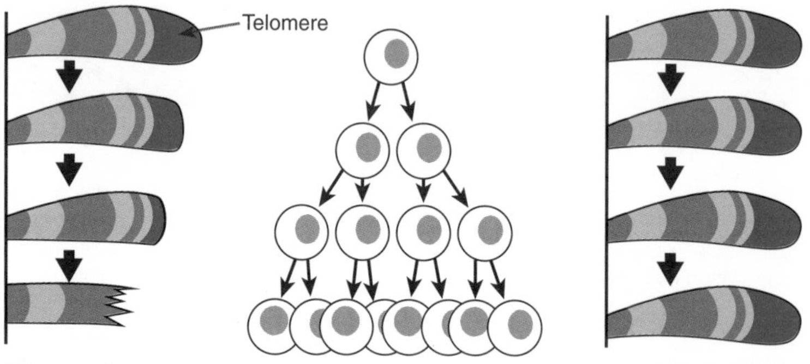
Telomere

Telomeres in somatic cell

Cell divisions

Telomeres in cells with telomerase, such as stem cells.

1. What is a telomere? ______________________________

____

2. What is the repeated sequence in human telomeres? ______________________________

3. Explain how telomere length is linked to cell age: ______________________________

____

4. Explain why telomerase is more active in stem cells than ordinary somatic cells: ______________________________

____

____

© 2015 BIOZONE International
ISBN:978-1-927309-31-5
Photocopying Prohibited

102 Mitosis and Cytokinesis

Key Idea: Mitosis is part of the cell cycle in which an existing cell (the parent cell) divides into two (the daughter cells). **Mitosis** results in the separation of the nuclear material and division of the cell. It does not result in a change of chromosome number and the daughter cells are identical to the parent cell. Although mitosis is part of a continuous cell cycle, it is often divided into stages to help differentiate the processes occurring. Mitosis is one of the shortest stages of the cell cycle. Cytokinesis (the division of the newly formed cells) is part of M-phase but distinct from nuclear division.

The animal cell cycle and stages of mitosis

Interphase

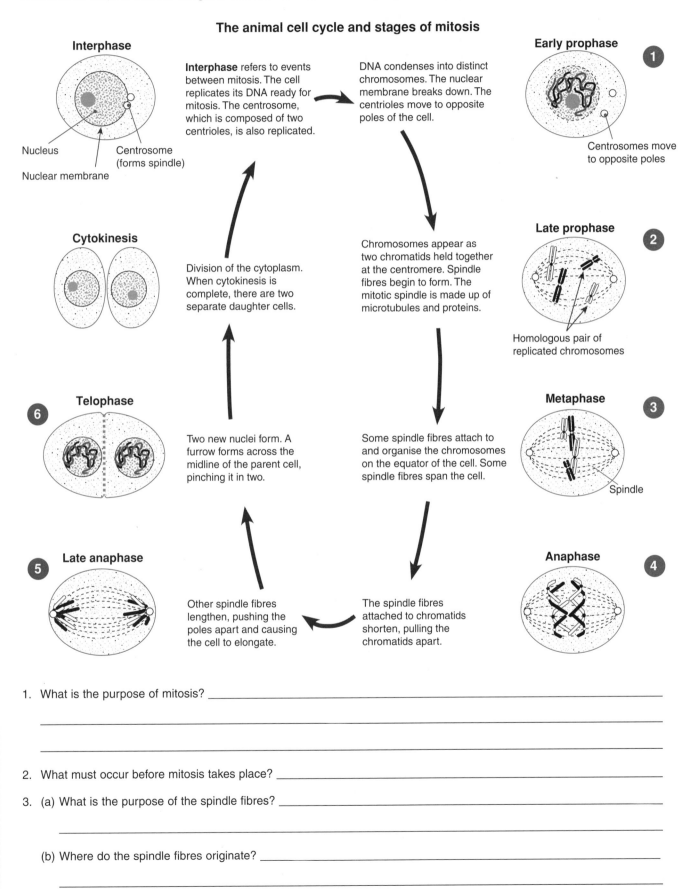

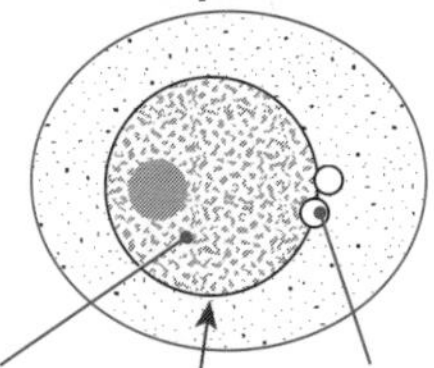
Nucleus
Centrosome (forms spindle)
Nuclear membrane

Interphase refers to events between mitosis. The cell replicates its DNA ready for mitosis. The centrosome, which is composed of two centrioles, is also replicated.

1 Early prophase

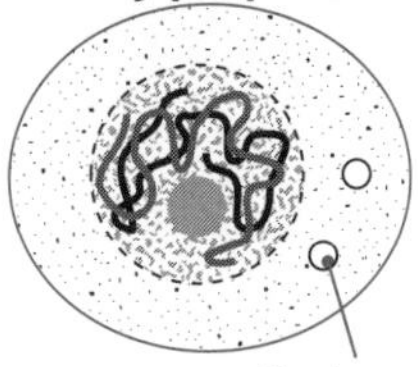
Centrosomes move to opposite poles

DNA condenses into distinct chromosomes. The nuclear membrane breaks down. The centrioles move to opposite poles of the cell.

2 Late prophase

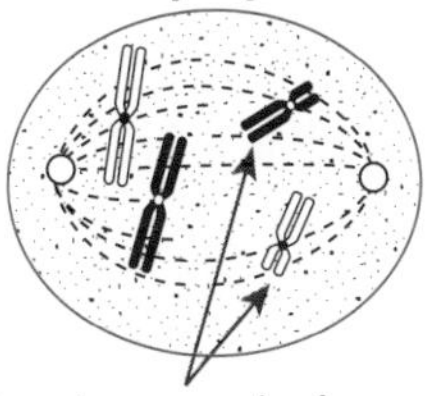
Homologous pair of replicated chromosomes

Chromosomes appear as two chromatids held together at the centromere. Spindle fibres begin to form. The mitotic spindle is made up of microtubules and proteins.

3 Metaphase

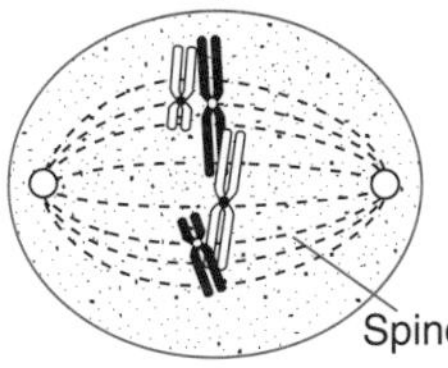
Spindle

Some spindle fibres attach to and organise the chromosomes on the equator of the cell. Some spindle fibres span the cell.

4 Anaphase

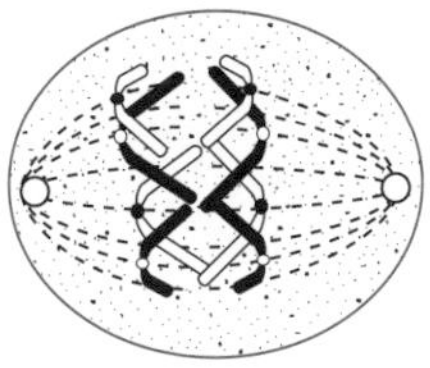

The spindle fibres attached to chromatids shorten, pulling the chromatids apart.

5 Late anaphase

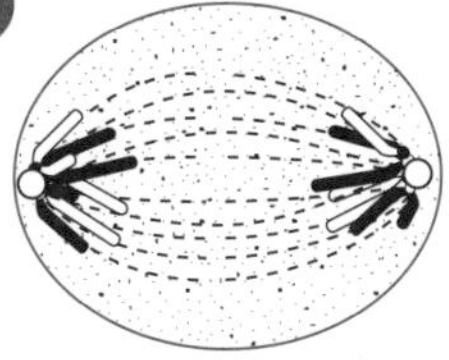

Other spindle fibres lengthen, pushing the poles apart and causing the cell to elongate.

6 Telophase

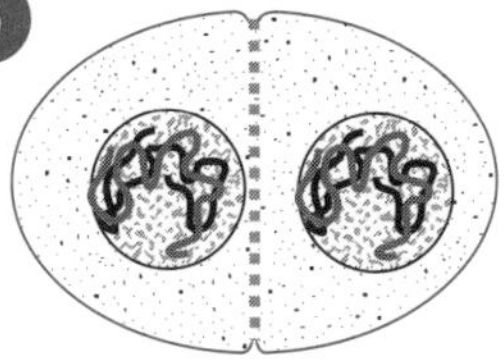

Two new nuclei form. A furrow forms across the midline of the parent cell, pinching it in two.

Cytokinesis

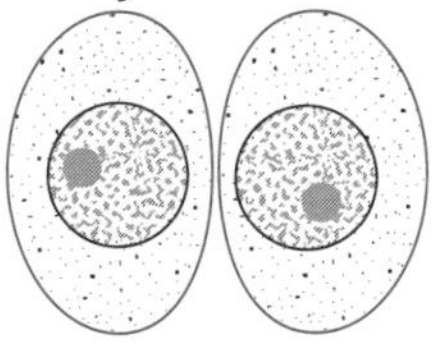

Division of the cytoplasm. When cytokinesis is complete, there are two separate daughter cells.

1. What is the purpose of mitosis? ______________________________

____

____

2. What must occur before mitosis takes place? ______________________________

3. (a) What is the purpose of the spindle fibres? ______________________________

____

(b) Where do the spindle fibres originate? ______________________________

____

© 2015 BIOZONE International
ISBN: 978-1-927309-31-5
Photocopying Prohibited

Cytokinesis

In plant cells (below right), cytokinesis (division of the cytoplasm) involves construction of a cell plate (a precursor of the new cell wall) in the middle of the cell. The cell wall materials are delivered by vesicles derived from the Golgi. The vesicles join together to become the plasma membranes of the new cell surfaces. Animal cell cytokinesis (below left) begins shortly after the sister chromatids have separated in anaphase of mitosis. A ring of microtubules assembles in the middle of the cell, next to the plasma membrane, constricting it to form a cleavage furrow. In an energy-using process, the cleavage furrow moves inwards, forming a region of separation where the two cells will separate.

Wadsworth Center- New York State Department of Health

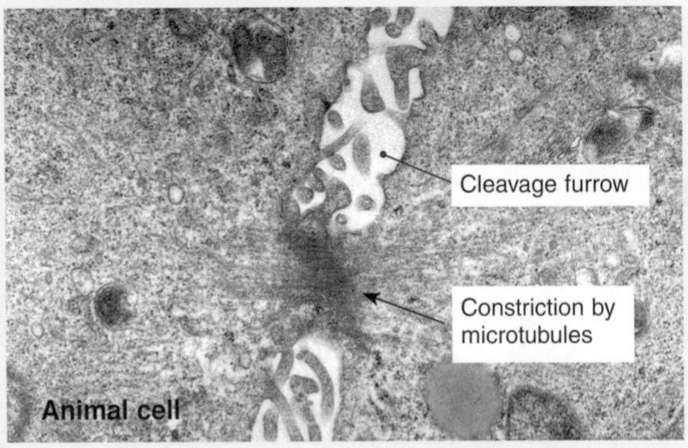
Cleavage furrow
Constriction by microtubules
Animal cell

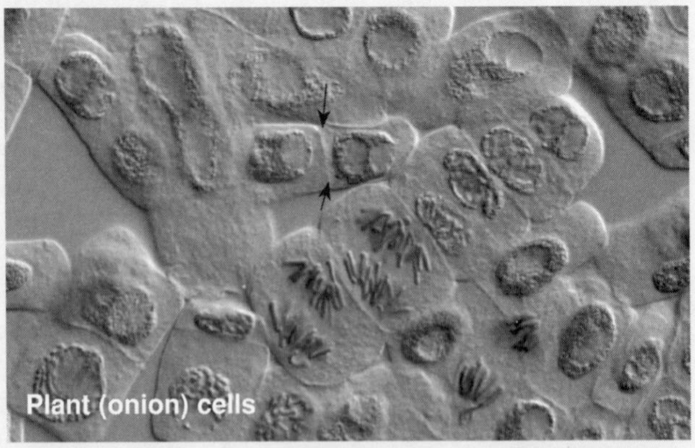
Plant (onion) cells

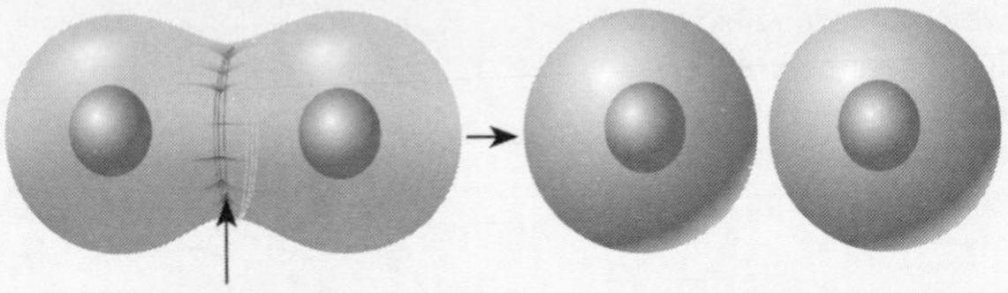
Cleavage furrow

Cytokinesis in an animal cell

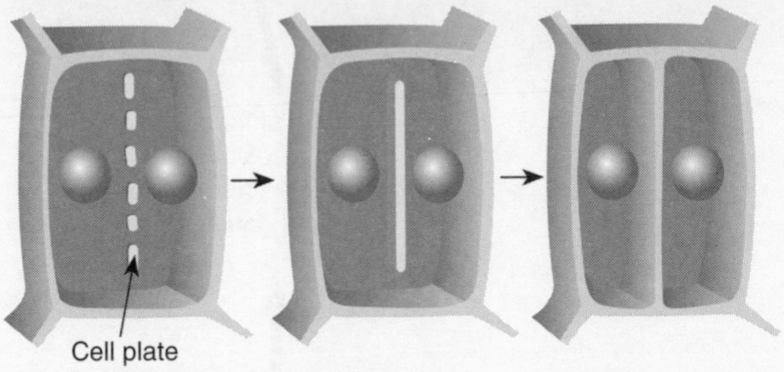
Cell plate forming

Cytokinesis in an plant cell

4. Summarise what happens in each of the following phases:

   (a) Prophase: ______________________________

   (b) Metaphase: ______________________________

   (c) Anaphase: ______________________________

   (d) Telophase: ______________________________

5. (a) What is the purpose of cytokinesis? ______________________________

   (b) Describe the differences between cytokinesis in an animal cell and a plant cell: ______________________________

© 2015 BIOZONE International
ISBN:978-1-927309-31-5
Photocopying Prohibited

103 Mitosis in Plants

Key Idea: In plants, mitosis occurs in the meristems. Beyond this zone, cells elongate and then become specialised.

In plants, mitosis occurs only in the meristems, where the cells are undifferentiated and totipotent. Cell elongation and specialisation occurs in regions away from the meristem. Primary growth (increase in length) occurs in the apical meristems (growing tips) of every stem and root. Plants that show lateral (side) growth also have lateral meristems where growth in diameter occurs. The zones of cell division, expansion, and specialisation in a root are shown below. Similar zones occur in stem tips, which produce all above-ground plant organs.

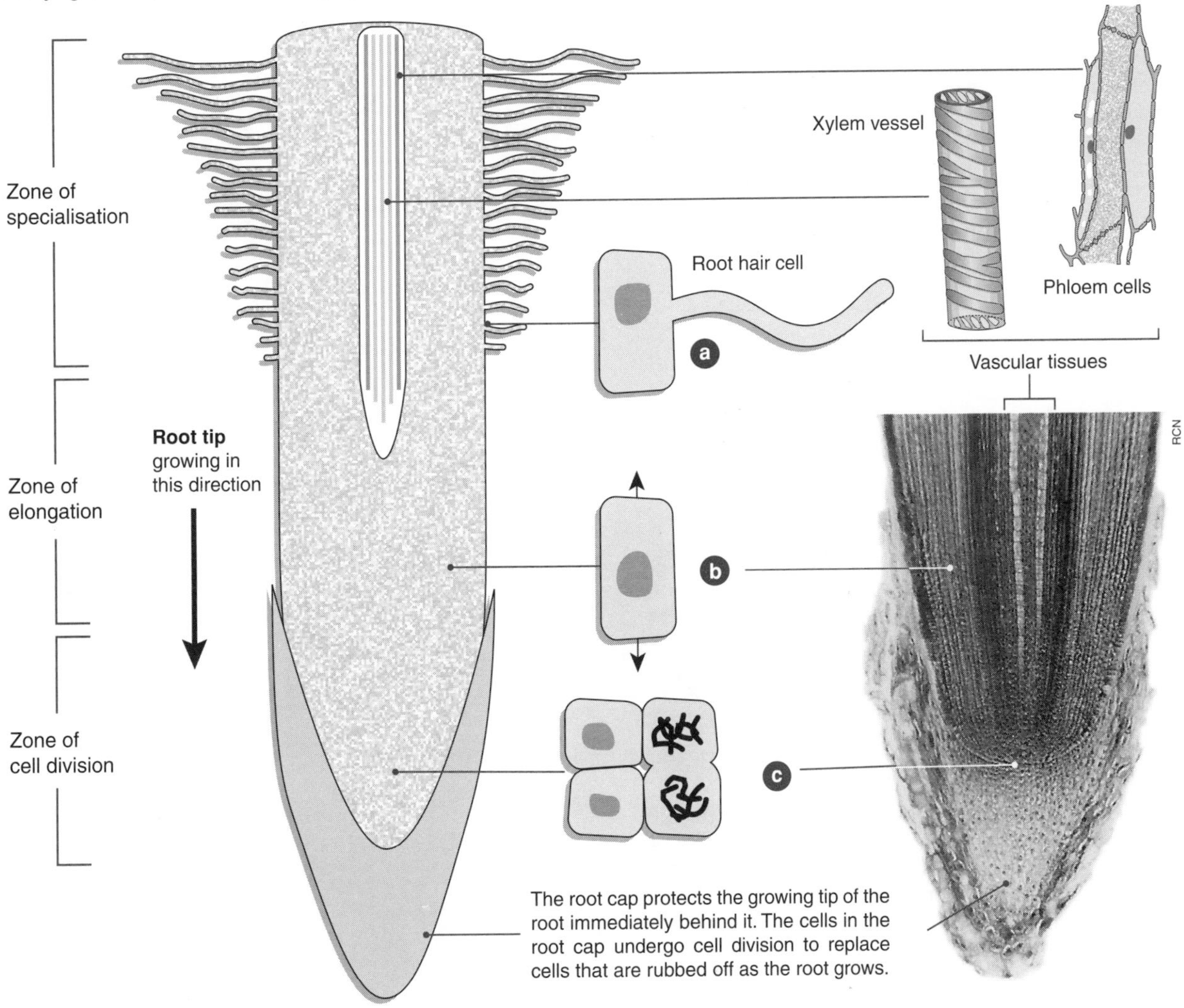

Zone of specialisation
Zone of elongation
Zone of cell division
Root tip growing in this direction
Xylem vessel
Phloem cells
Root hair cell
Vascular tissues
a
b
c
RCN
The root cap protects the growing tip of the root immediately behind it. The cells in the root cap undergo cell division to replace cells that are rubbed off as the root grows.

1. What is happening to the plant cells at each of the points labelled (**a**) to (**c**) in the diagram above?

   (a) ___

   (b) ___

   (c) ___

2. The light micrograph (below) shows a section of the cells of an onion root tip, stained to show up the chromosomes.

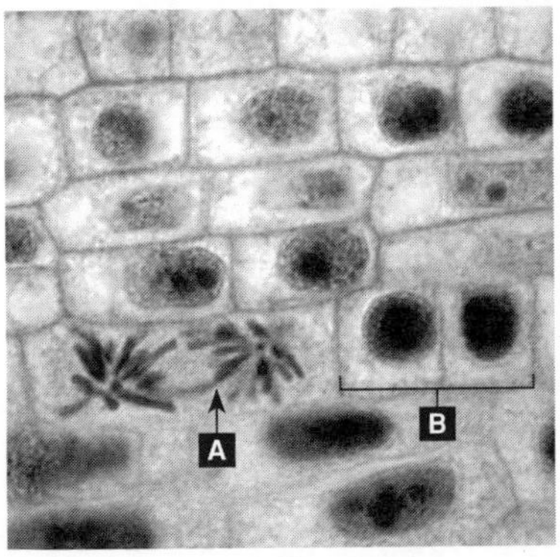

A
B

   (a) State the mitotic stage of the cell labelled **A** and explain your answer:

   ___

   (b) State the mitotic stage just completed in the cells labelled **B** and explain:

   ___

   (c) If, in this example, 250 cells were examined and 25 were found to be in the process of mitosis, what proportion of the cell cycle is occupied by mitosis:

   ___

© 2015 **BIOZONE** International
ISBN: 978-1-927309-31-5
Photocopying Prohibited

104 Recognising Stages in Mitosis

Key Idea: The stages of mitosis can be recognised by the organisation of the cell and chromosomes.

Although mitosis is a continuous process, it is divided into four stages (prophase, anaphase, metaphase, and telophase) to more easily describe the processes occurring during its progression.

The mitotic index

The mitotic index measures the ratio of cells in mitosis to the number of cells counted. It is a measure of cell proliferation and can be used to diagnose cancer. In areas of high cell growth the mitotic index is high such as in plant apical meristems or the growing tips of plant roots. The mitotic index can be calculated using the formula:

$$\text{Mitotic index} = \frac{\text{Number of cells in mitosis}}{\text{Total number of cells}}$$

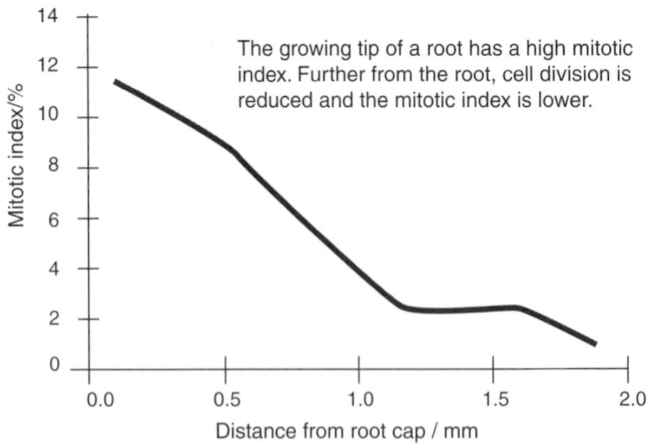

The growing tip of a root has a high mitotic index. Further from the root, cell division is reduced and the mitotic index is lower.
Mitotic index/%
14
12
10
8
6
4
2
0
0.0
0.5
1.0
1.5
2.0
Distance from root cap / mm

1. Use the information on the previous page to identify which stage of mitosis is shown in each of the photographs below:

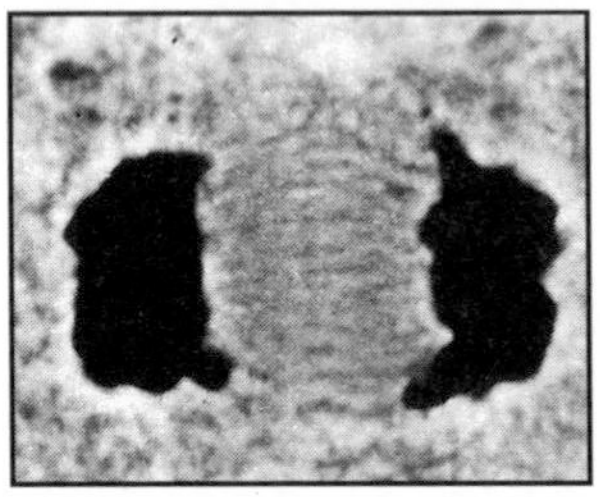

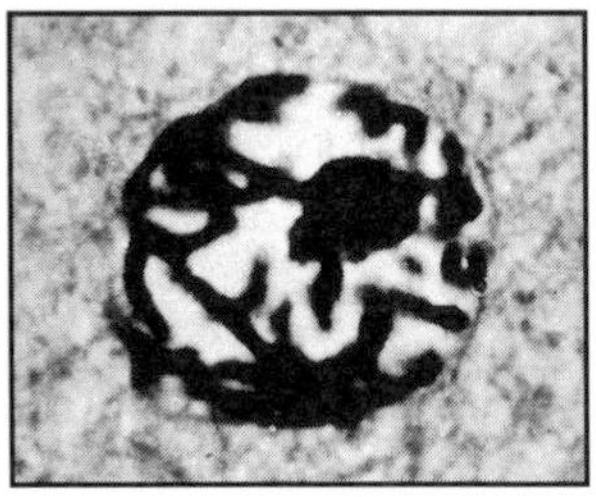

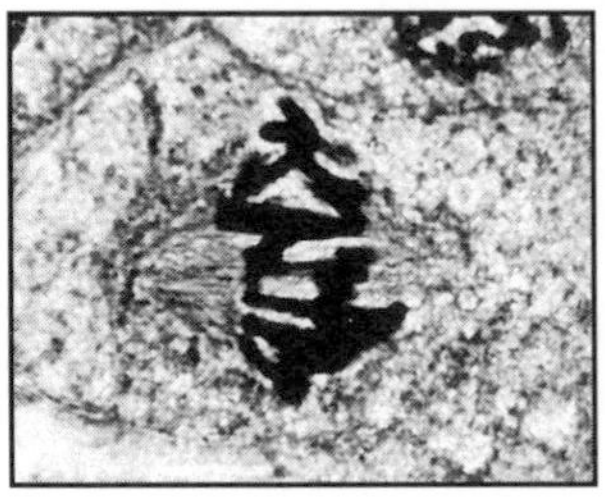

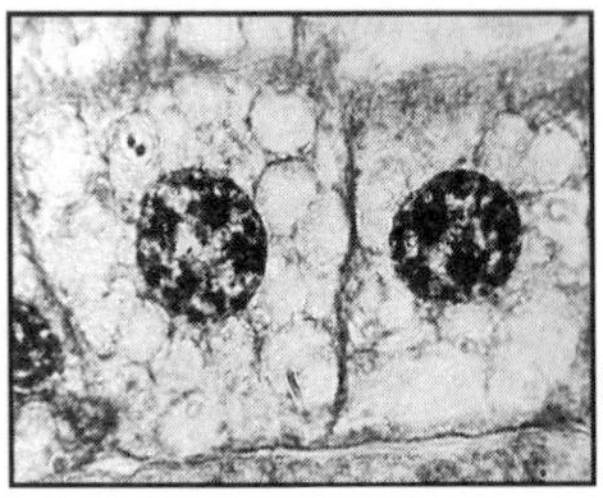

Photos: RCN

(a) ______________ (b) ______________ (c) ______________ (d) ______________

2. (a) The light micrograph (right) shows a section of cells in an onion root tip. These cells have a cell cycle of approximately 24 hours. The cells can be seen to be in various stages of the cell cycle. By counting the number of cells in the various stages it is possible to calculate how long the cell spends in each stage of the cycle. Count and record the number of cells in the image that are in mitosis and those that are in interphase. Cells in cytokinesis can be recorded as in interphase. Estimate the amount of time a cell spends in each phase.

Stage	No. of cells	% of total cells	Estimated time in stage
Interphase			
Mitosis			
Total		100	

(b) Use your counts from 2(a) to calculate the mitotic index for this section of cells.

____

____

3. What would you expect to happen to the mitotic index of a population of cells that loses the ability to divide as they mature?

____

____

Onion root tip cells

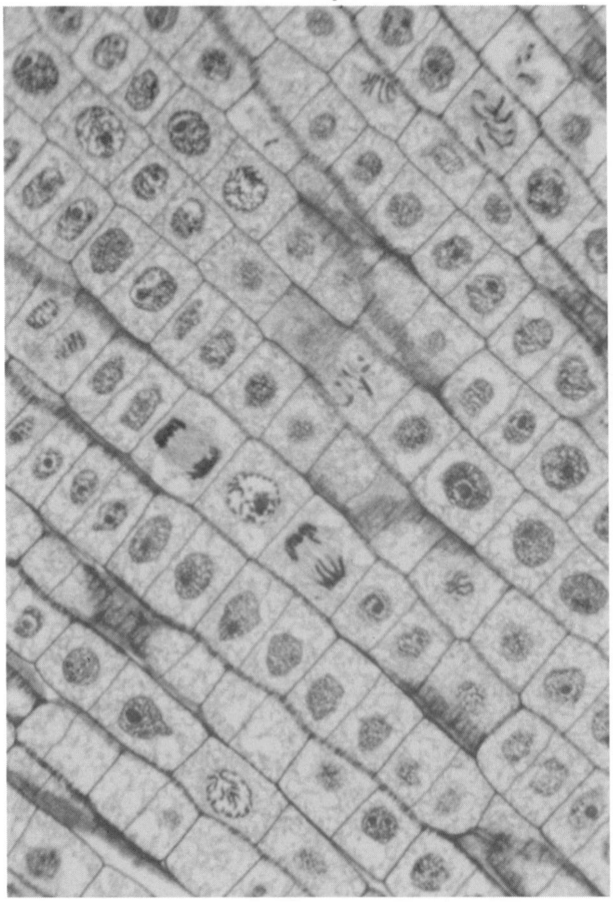

© 2015 **BIOZONE** International
ISBN:978-1-927309-31-5
Photocopying Prohibited

105 Stem Cells and Differentiation

Key Idea: Stem cells are undifferentiated cells found in multicellular organisms. They are characterised by the properties of self renewal and potency.

A zygote can differentiate into many different types of cells because early on it divides into stem cells. Stem cells are unspecialised and can give rise to the many cell types that make up the tissues and organs of a multicellular organism. The differentiation of multipotent stem cells in bone marrow gives rise to all the cell types that make up blood, a fluid connective tissue. Multipotent (or adult) stem cells are found in most body organs, where they replace old or damaged cells and replenish the body's cells throughout life.

Stem cells and blood cell production

New blood cells are produced in the red bone marrow, which becomes the main site of blood production after birth, taking over from the fetal liver. All types of blood cells develop from a single cell type: called a **multipotent stem cell**. These cells are capable of mitosis and of differentiation into 'committed' precursors of each of the main types of blood cell. Each of the different cell lines is controlled by a specific **growth factor**. When a stem cell divides, one of its daughters remains a stem cell, while the other becomes a precursor cell, either a **lymphoid cell** or **myeloid cell**. These cells continue to mature into the various specialised cell types.

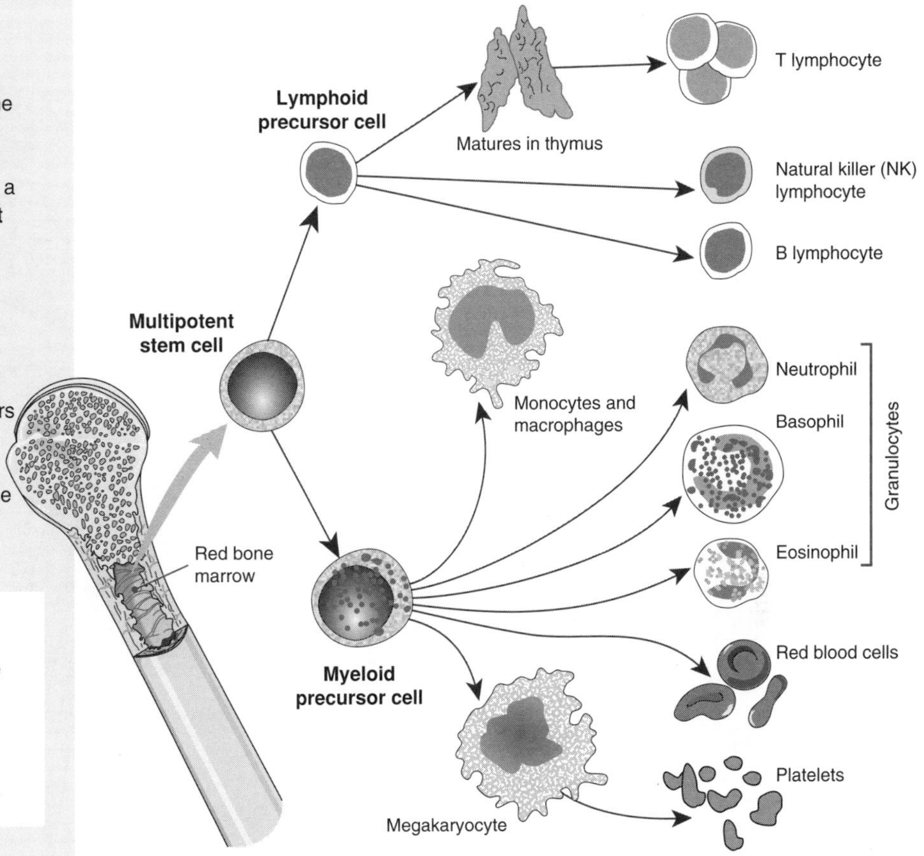
Lymphoid precursor cell
Matures in thymus
T lymphocyte
Natural killer (NK) lymphocyte
B lymphocyte
Multipotent stem cell
Monocytes and macrophages
Neutrophil
Basophil
Eosinophil
Granulocytes
Red bone marrow
Myeloid precursor cell
Red blood cells
Platelets
Megakaryocyte

Properties of stem cells

Self renewal: The ability to divide many times while maintaining an unspecialised state.

Potency: The ability to differentiate into specialised cells.

Categories of stem cells

Totipotent stem cells

These stem cells can differentiate into all the cells in an organism. Example: In humans, the zygote and its first few divisions. The meristematic tissue of plants is also totipotent.

Pluripotent stem cells

These stem cells can give rise to any cells of the body, except extra-embryonic cells (e.g. placenta and chorion). Example: Embryonic stem cells (ESC).

Multipotent stem cells

These adult stem cells (ASC) can give rise a limited number of cell types, related to their tissue of origin. Example: Bone marrow stem cells, epithelial stem cells, bone stem cells (osteoblasts).

1. Describe the two defining features of stem cells:

   (a) ______________________

   (b) ______________________

2. Explain the role of stem cells in the development of specialised tissues in multicellular organisms: ______________________

____

____

____

____

© 2015 BIOZONE International
ISBN: 978-1-927309-31-5
Photocopying Prohibited

106 Stem Cells and Skin Renewal

Key Idea: The skin is being constantly renewed as pluripotent stem cells in the basal layers divide and move towards the surface, replacing the dead cells that are sloughed off.

The skin is the body's largest organ and acts as an essential physical barrier against infection and physical damage of the underlying tissues. It is made up of two parts: the epidermis, which forms a layered barrier, and the dermis, which supports and nourishes the epidermis. Different types of skin stem cells maintain the skin's epidermis and contribute to its healing after damage. As a result of constant renewal from the base and loss from the surface, the skin is completely renewed every 4 weeks.

The skin is largely composed of cells called keratinocytes. They have a life cycle of about 4 weeks, formed by division of stem cells at the basal layer and differentiating to form the various types of cells making up the uppermost layers of the epidermis.

Keratinised layer
Surface layer of dead flattened cells completely filled with the waterproof keratin.

Granular layer
Layer of cells containing obvious granules of the protein keratin.

Prickle cell layer
Layer of polyhedral cells tightly bound to one another, making them appear spiky. Keratin synthesis begins in this layer.

Basal layer
The basal layer of keratinocyte stem cells. These divide continually to form the cells of the stratum spinosum. Pigment producing cells are also found in this layer.

The bulge region of the hair follicle outer root sheath contains multipotent stem cells, which supply cells for the hair follicle, sebaceous glands, and epidermis. They are important during wound healing.

Stem cells in the matrix are responsible for hair production. Cell division in the matrix forms the major structures of the hair fibre and the inner root sheath.

The region beneath the dermis is not part of the skin, but contains fat cells, which act as cushioning and protection for the tissues underneath.

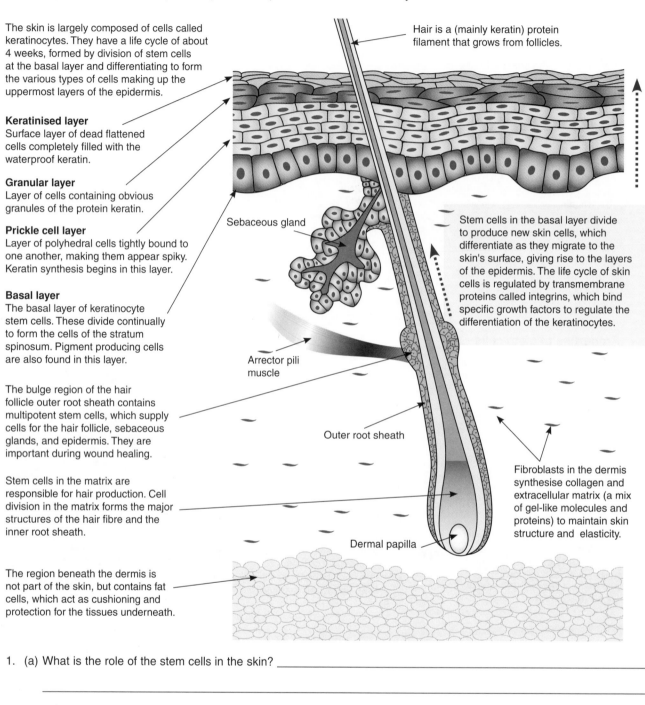

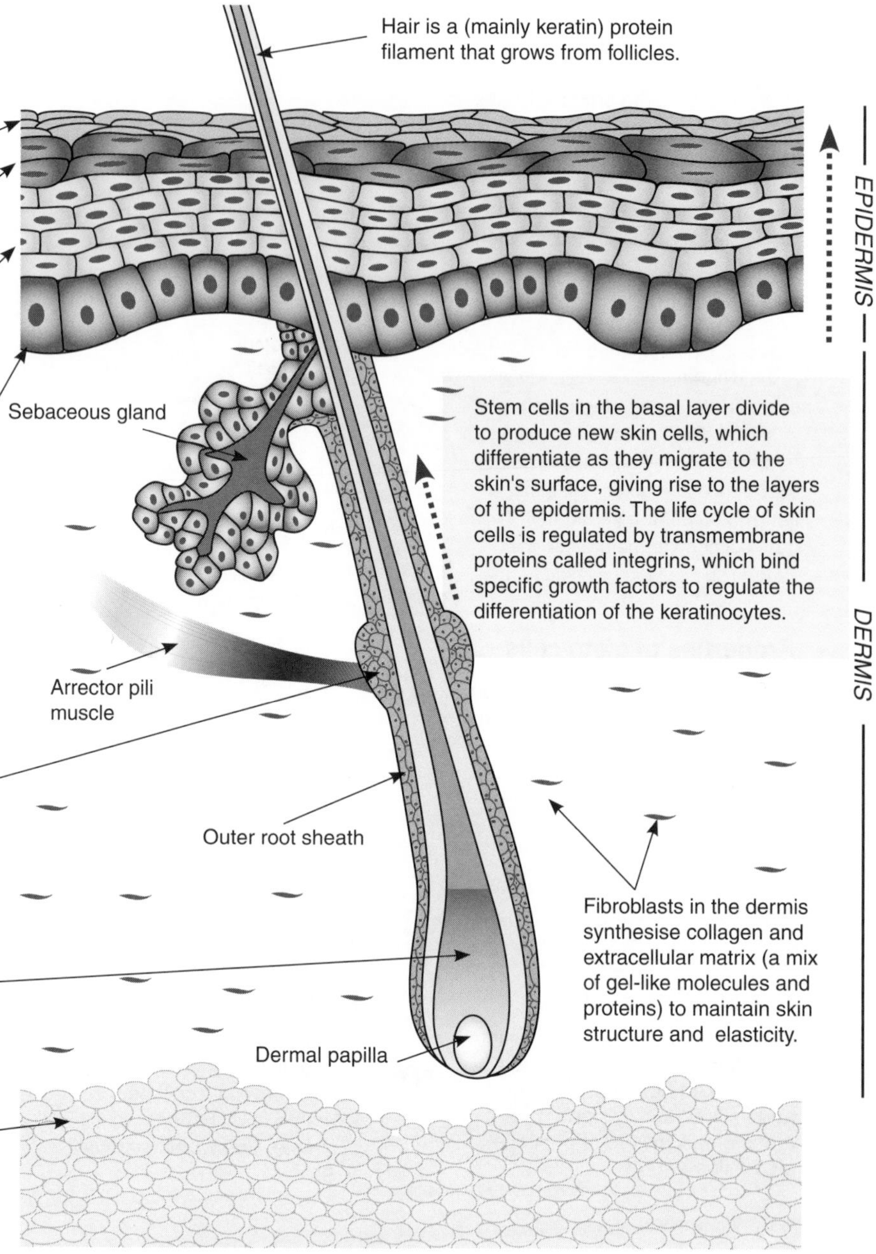
Hair is a (mainly keratin) protein filament that grows from follicles.
EPIDERMIS
Sebaceous gland
Stem cells in the basal layer divide to produce new skin cells, which differentiate as they migrate to the skin's surface, giving rise to the layers of the epidermis. The life cycle of skin cells is regulated by transmembrane proteins called integrins, which bind specific growth factors to regulate the differentiation of the keratinocytes.
DERMIS
Arrector pili muscle
Outer root sheath
Fibroblasts in the dermis synthesise collagen and extracellular matrix (a mix of gel-like molecules and proteins) to maintain skin structure and elasticity.
Dermal papilla

1. (a) What is the role of the stem cells in the skin? ______________________

____

(b) Where are these stem cells located? ______________________

(c) What is the potency of these cells? ______________________

2. What is the role of transmembrane receptors and growth factors in the life cycle of skin cells? ______________________

____

3. Drugs that treat cancer target rapidly dividing cells. Why is it that people undergoing cancer treatment lose their hair?

____

____

© 2015 BIOZONE International
ISBN:978-1-927309-31-5
Photocopying Prohibited

107 Using Stem Cells to Treat Disease

Key Idea: Stem cells have the potential to treat a variety of diseases or replace damaged tissue.

The properties of self renewal and potency that characterise stem cells make them potentially suitable for the treatment of many diseases, including growing new tissue to replace damaged tissue. The greatest potential for stem cell therapies comes from embryonic stem cells (ESC), because they are pluripotent, but there are ethical issues to address when human embryos are used as the source because harvesting the ESC involves destroying the embryo. Although tissue engineering is still a new technology, engineered skin is already widely used to treat burns and other skin injuries. The adult stem cells (ASC) for this process are obtained from discarded tissue, so there are few barriers to its use.

Engineering a living skin

New technologies such as cell replacement therapy and tissue engineering require a disease-free and plentiful supply of cells of specific types. Tissue engineering, for example, involves inducing living cells to grow on a scaffold of natural or synthetic material to produce a three-dimensional tissue such as bone or skin.

In 1998, an artificial skin called **Apligraf** became the first product of this type to be approved for use as a biomedical device. It is now widely used in place of skin grafts to treat diabetic ulcers and burns, with the patient's own cells and tissues helping to complete the biological repair. Producing Apligraf is a three stage process (right), which results in a bilayered, living structure capable of stimulating wound repair through its own growth factors and proteins. The cells used to start the culture are usually obtained from discarded neonatal foreskins collected after circumcision.

The key to future tissue engineering will be the developments in stem cell research. ESC from very early embryos have the most potential, because they are pluripotent, but ASC can also be used.

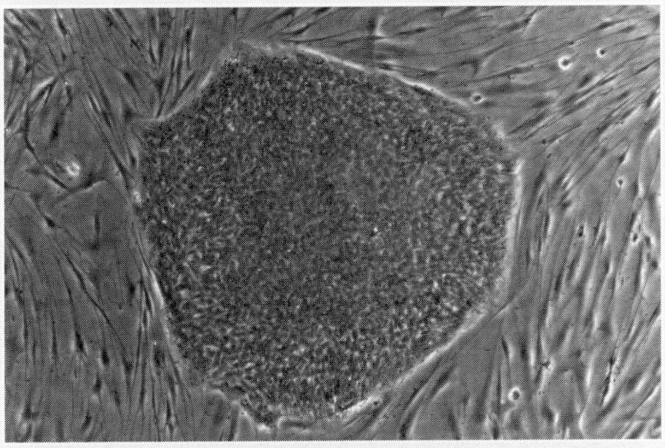

NIH

Human embryonic stem cells (ESC) growing on mouse embryonic fibroblasts. The mouse fibroblasts act as feeder cells for the culture, releasing nutrients and providing a surface for the ESC to grow on.

Human dermal cells

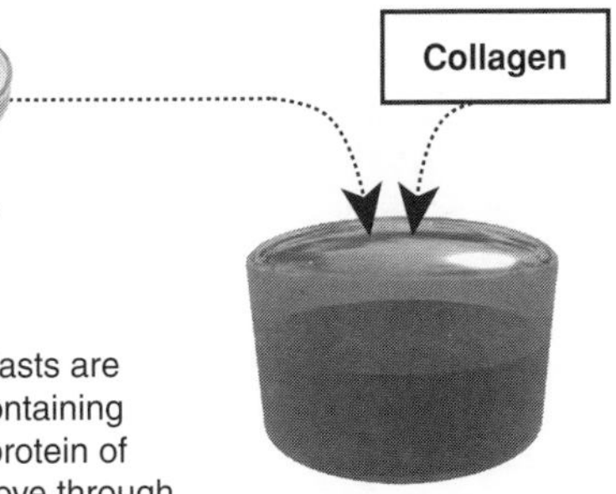
Collagen

Step 1
Form the lower dermal layer

Day 0

Undifferentiated fibroblasts are combined with a gel containing collagen, the primary protein of skin. The fibroblasts move through the gel, rearranging the collagen to produce a fibrous, living matrix similar to the natural dermis.

Human epidermal cells

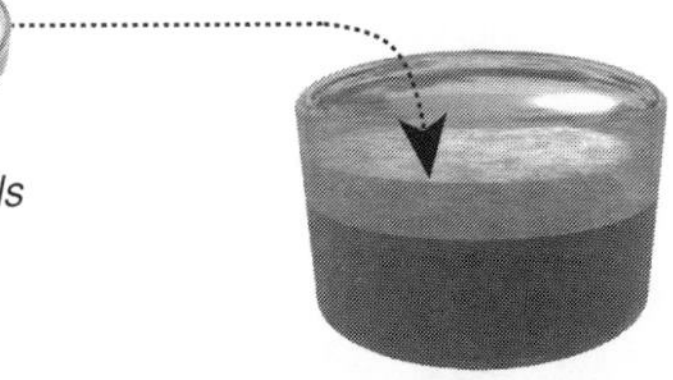

Step 2
Form the upper epidermal layer

Day 6

Human epidermal cells (keratinocytes) are placed on top of the dermal layer. These cells multiply to cover the dermal layer.

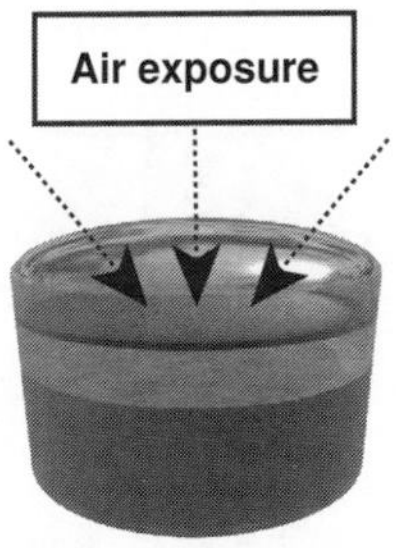
Air exposure

Step 3
Form the outer layer

Day 10

Exposing the culture to air induces the epidermal cells to form the outer protective (keratinised) layer of skin. The final size of the Apligraf product is about 75 mm. From this, many thousands of pieces of skin can be made.

1. Describe the benefits of using an engineered skin product, such as Apligraf, to treat wounds that require grafts:

2. (a) Why is the collection of ESCs from early embryos controversial?

   (b) The stem cells used to produce Apligraf often come from discarded neonatal foreskins. Explain why this is less controversial than using young embryos:

© 2015 **BIOZONE** International
ISBN: 978-1-927309-31-5
Photocopying Prohibited

108 Regulation of the Cell Cycle

Key Idea: The cell cycle is regulated by checkpoints, which ensure the cell has met certain conditions before it continues to the next phase of the cell cycle.

The cell cycle is an orderly sequence of events, but its duration varies enormously between cells of different species and between cell types in one organism. For example, human intestinal cells normally divide around twice a day, whereas cells in the liver typically divide once a year. However, if these tissues are damaged, cell division increases to repair the damage. Some cells, such as neurones in the central nervous system, are unable to divide, and cannot be repaired if damaged. Progression through the cell cycle is controlled by regulatory checkpoints, which ensure the cell has met the conditions required to successfully complete the next phase.

Checkpoints during the cell cycle

There are three **checkpoints** during the cell cycle. A checkpoint is a critical regulatory point in the cell cycle. At each checkpoint, a set of conditions determines whether or not the cell will continue into the next phase. For example, cell size is important in regulating whether or not the cell can pass through the G_1 checkpoint.

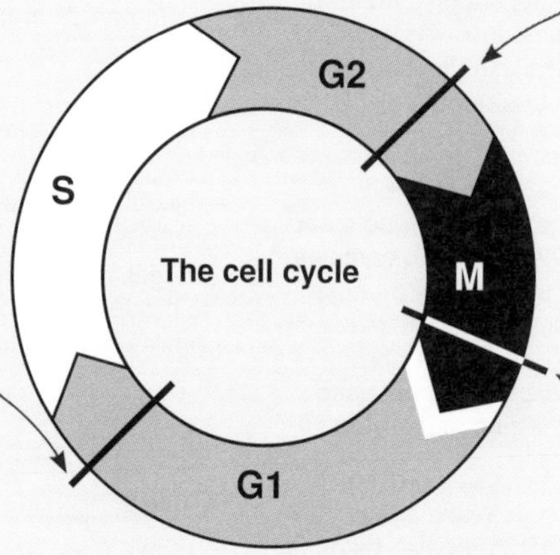
G2
S
The cell cycle
M
G1

G_2 checkpoint:
Pass this checkpoint if:
- Cell size is large enough.
- Replication of chromosomes has been successfully completed.
- Proteins required for mitosis have been synthesised.

G_1 checkpoint
Pass this checkpoint if:
- Cell size is large enough.
- Sufficient nutrients are available.
- Signals from other cells have been received.

Metaphase checkpoint
Pass this checkpoint if:
- All chromosomes are attached to the mitotic spindle.

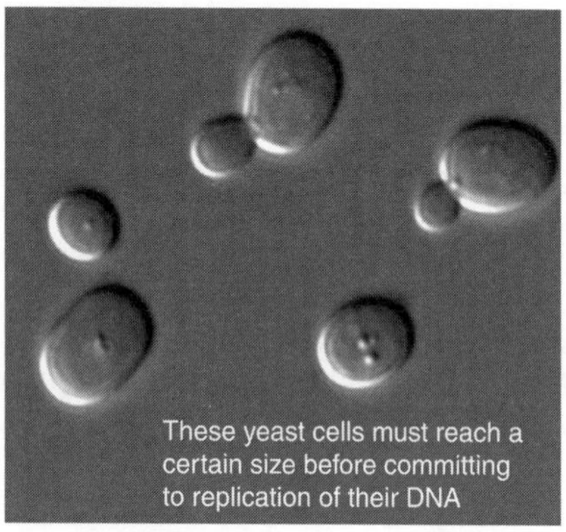
These yeast cells must reach a certain size before committing to replication of their DNA

The G_1 checkpoint is the critical regulatory point in cells. At this checkpoint, the cell decides whether to commit to the cell cycle or to enter an arrested phase called G_0. Once sufficient nutrients or cell size is reached and the checkpoint is passed the cell is committed to replication of the nuclear material. Most cells that pass G_1 complete the cell cycle.

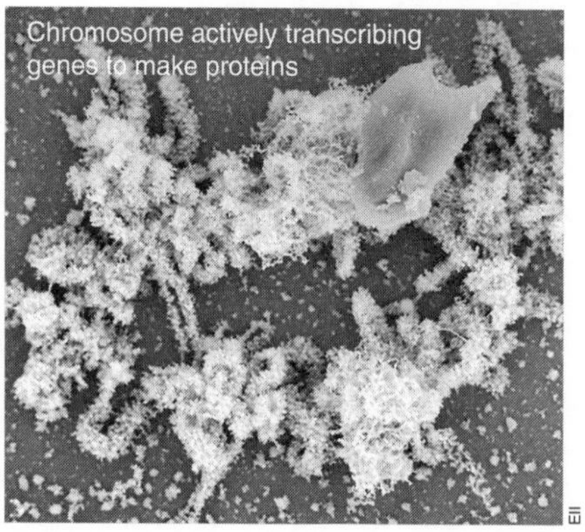
Chromosome actively transcribing genes to make proteins
EII

The G_2 checkpoint determines if DNA synthesis was completed correctly, that the necessary proteins for mitosis have been synthesised, and that the cell has reached a size suitable for cell division. Damage to the DNA prevents entry to M phase. The entry into M phase is controlled by a protein called cyclin B, which reaches a concentration peak at the G_2-M phase boundary.

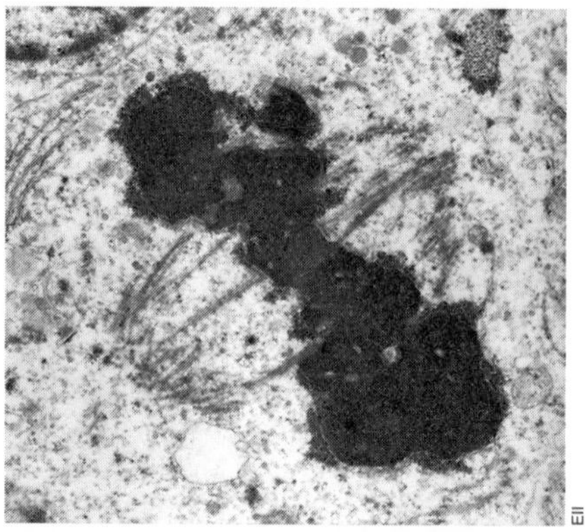
EII

The metaphase checkpoint, or spindle checkpoint, checks that all the chromatids are attached to the spindle fibres and under the correct tension. At this point, cyclin B is degraded, ultimately resulting in the sister chromatids separating and the cell entering anaphase, pulling the chromatids apart. The cell then begins cytokinesis and produces two new daughter cells.

1. What is the general purpose of cell cycle checkpoints? ______________________

____

____

2. (a) What is the purpose of the metaphase checkpoint? ______________________

____

(b) Why is this checkpoint important? ______________________

____

3. What would happen if the cell cycle was not regulated? ______________________

____

© 2015 **BIOZONE** International
ISBN:978-1-927309-31-5
Photocopying Prohibited

109 Cancer: Cells out of Control

Key Idea: Cancerous cells have lost their normal cellular control mechanisms, and grow uncontrollably.

Cells that become damaged beyond repair will normally undergo a programmed cell death (apoptosis), which is part of the cell's normal control system. Some cells evade the control system and become immortal, continuing to divide without any regulation. Such cells are called **cancer cells**. They form tissue masses called tumours, and spread through blood and lymph to invade other tissues, eventually causing damage to the affected tissue. Any one of a number of cancer-causing factors (including defective genes) may interact to disrupt the cell cycle and result in cancer.

How cancer cells form

Changes to DNA (mutations) can be caused by external agents called mutagens. Carcinogens are mutagens that cause cancer. Cancerous cells form when the genes controlling cell growth and multiplication are changed by carcinogens into oncogenes (genes that can cause cancer). Damaged cells usually fail to meet the checkpoints required for cell division to continue and are destroyed. However, cancerous cells evade the cell cycle checkpoints and divide rapidly, forming a tumour. A cancerous cell no longer carries out its designated role and instead takes on a parasitic 'lifestyle', taking from the body what it needs in the way of nutrients and contributing nothing in return. The rate of cell division is greater than in normal cells in the same tissue because there is no resting phase between divisions.

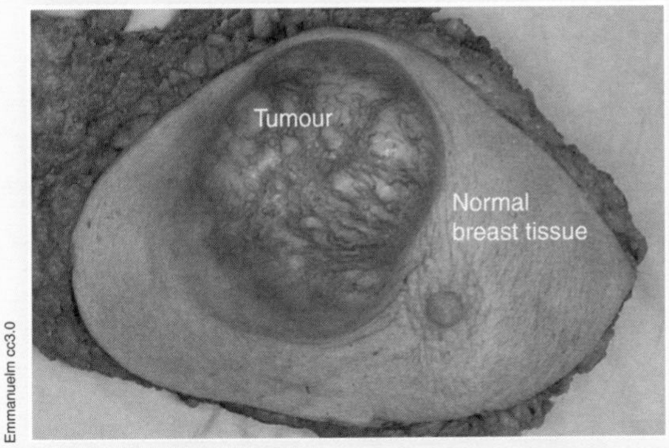
Tumour
Normal breast tissue
Emmanuelm cc3.0

The photo above shows a large tumour in the breast of a patient with breast cancer. The breast was surgically removed as part of treatment. Changes to the cell chemistry of cancerous cells encourage capillary formation. New capillaries grow into the tumour, providing it with nutrients so it can grow rapidly. Note how the cancerous tissue has grown rapidly compared to the normal breast tissue surrounding it.

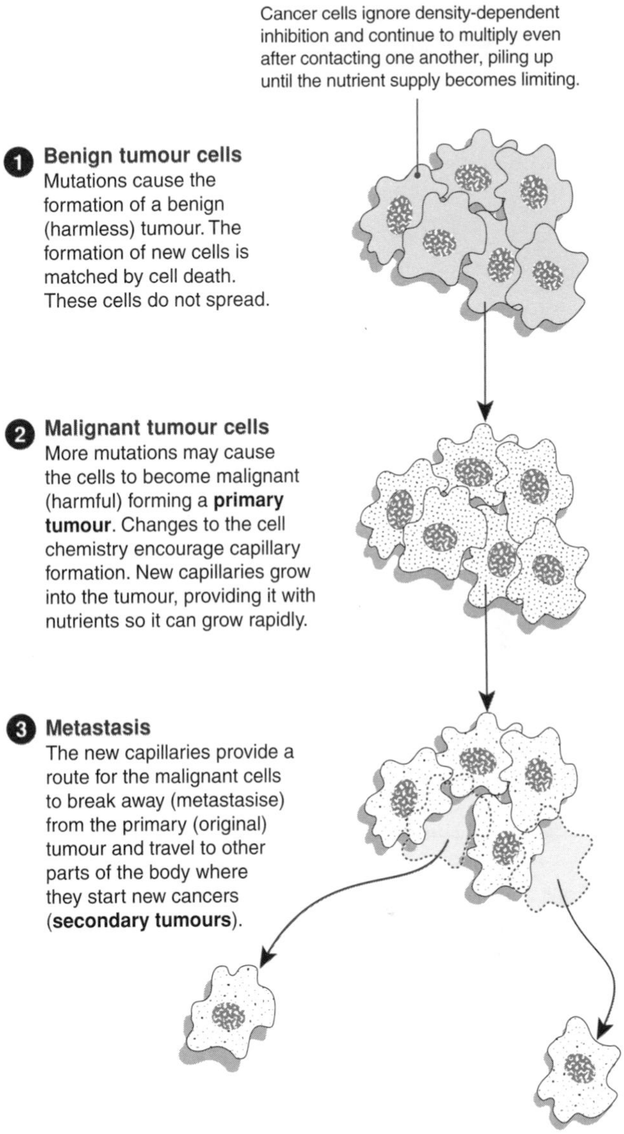
Cancer cells ignore density-dependent inhibition and continue to multiply even after contacting one another, piling up until the nutrient supply becomes limiting.
1 **Benign tumour cells** Mutations cause the formation of a benign (harmless) tumour. The formation of new cells is matched by cell death. These cells do not spread.
2 **Malignant tumour cells** More mutations may cause the cells to become malignant (harmful) forming a **primary tumour**. Changes to the cell chemistry encourage capillary formation. New capillaries grow into the tumour, providing it with nutrients so it can grow rapidly.
3 **Metastasis** The new capillaries provide a route for the malignant cells to break away (metastasise) from the primary (original) tumour and travel to other parts of the body where they start new cancers (**secondary tumours**).

1. (a) What distinguishes a cancerous cell from a normal cell? ______________________________

____

____

____

(b) Why can cancer cells grow rapidly? ______________________________

____

____

2. In a general way, explain how a tumour typically forms? ______________________________

____

____

____

© 2015 BIOZONE International
ISBN: 978-1-927309-31-5
Photocopying Prohibited

110 Chapter Review

Summarise what you know about this topic under the headings provided. You can draw diagrams or mind maps, or write short notes to organise your thoughts. Use the images and hints to help you and refer back to the introduction to check the points covered:

Eukaryotic chromosomes:
HINT: Describe eukaryotic chromosome structure, including the role of telomeres.

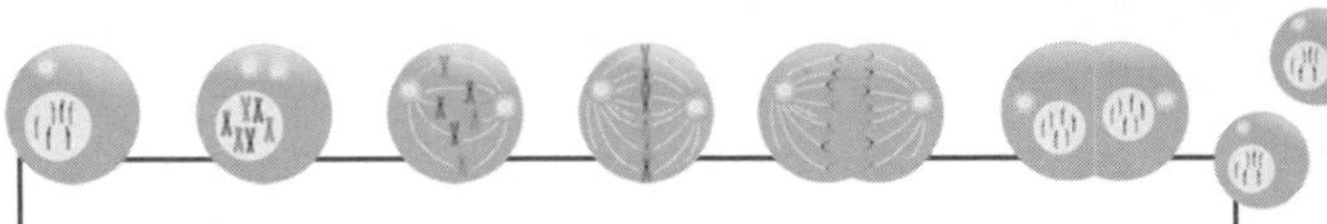

Mitosis:
HINT: Describe the stages of mitosis.

The cell cycle:
HINT: Describe the cell cycle and its regulation.

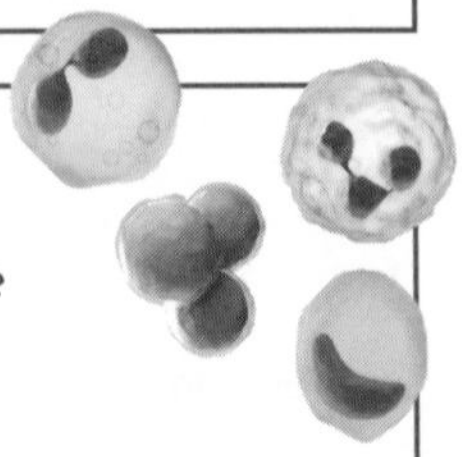

Stem cells:
HINT: Describe the role of stem cells in adult tissues. What are the applications of stem cells?

© 2015 **BIOZONE** International
ISBN:978-1-927309-31-5
Photocopying Prohibited

111 KEY TERMS AND IDEAS: Did You Get It?

1. Eukaryotic cells undergo mitosis before cell division.

   (a) What is the purpose of mitosis? ____________________

   ____

   ____

   (b) Use the space below to draw a labelled sequence of mitosis, including the important stages:

2. Test your vocabulary by matching each term to its definition, as identified by its preceding letter code.

cancer	A	An undifferentiated cell with the properties of self renewal and potency.
cell cycle	B	A general term for any cell mass in which the cells grow in an uncontrolled way and invade nearby tissue.
cellular differentiation	C	The phase of a cell cycle involving nuclear division in which the replicated chromosomes in a cell nucleus are separated into two identical sets.
cell division	D	Able to differentiate into a limited number of cell types related to the tissue of origin.
centromere	E	The stage in the cell cycle between divisions.
chromosome	F	Terminal segments of DNA that protect the ends of chromosomes.
histone	G	The process by which a less specialised cell becomes a more specialised cell type.
interphase	H	The region on a chromosome where two sister chromatids are joined.
mitosis	I	The changes that take place in a cell in the period between its formation as a product of cell division and its own subsequent division.
multipotent	J	Able to differentiate into all the cell types in an organism.
pluripotent	K	A protein found in eukaryotic cell nuclei that is involved in packaging DNA.
stem cell	L	Process by which a parent cell divides into two or more daughter cells..
telomeres	M	Single piece of DNA that contains many genes and associated regulatory elements and proteins. Found within the nucleus in eukaryotes.
totipotent	N	Able to give rise to any cells of the body, except extra-embryonic cells

© 2015 **BIOZONE** International
ISBN: 978-1-927309-31-5
Photocopying Prohibited

Topic 6 Nucleic acids and protein synthesis

Key terms

anticodon
ATP
base-pairing rule
coding strand
codon (on mRNA)
DNA
double-helix
exons
gene
gene expression
genetic code
hydrogen bonding
introns
mutation
nucleic acids
nucleotides
phosphodiester bond
polynucleotide
protein
purine
pyrimidine
ribosome
RNA (mRNA, rRNA, tRNA)
template strand
transcription
translation
triplet (on DNA)

6.1 Structure and replication of DNA

Learning outcomes — Activity number

- ☐ 1 Describe the structure of nucleotides, including the structure of the phosphorylated nucleotide derivative, ATP. Use an annotated diagram to help you. **112**
- ☐ 2 Describe the basic structure of nucleic acids (DNA and RNA), identifying differences between them. Explain the importance of base pairing, hydrogen bonding between bases, and the basic differences between purines (adenine and guanine) and pyrimidines (cytosine, thymine, and uracil). **113**
- ☐ 3 Demonstrate an understanding of the Watson-Crick double-helix model of DNA, including the base-pairing rule and the significance of the anti-parallel strands. **115**
- ☐ 4 Extension: Understand the evidence for the structure of DNA. In what way did the structure of DNA provide a mechanism for its self-replication? **114**
- ☐ 5 Describe the semi-conservative replication of DNA during interphase, including the role of helicase and DNA polymerase. Explain the role of proofreading in DNA replication and the importance of this. **116 117**
- ☐ 6 Extension: Analyse the results of Meselson and Stahl's experiments on DNA replication and use modelling to reproduce these for yourself. **118 119**

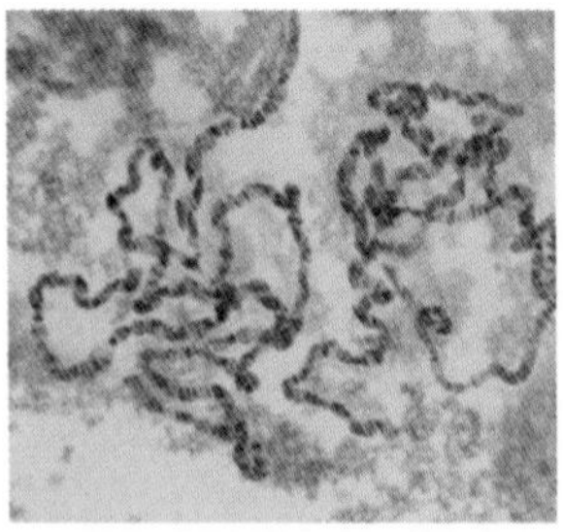

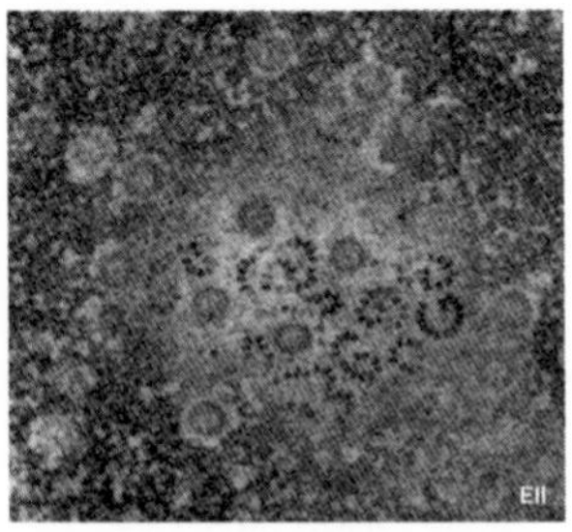

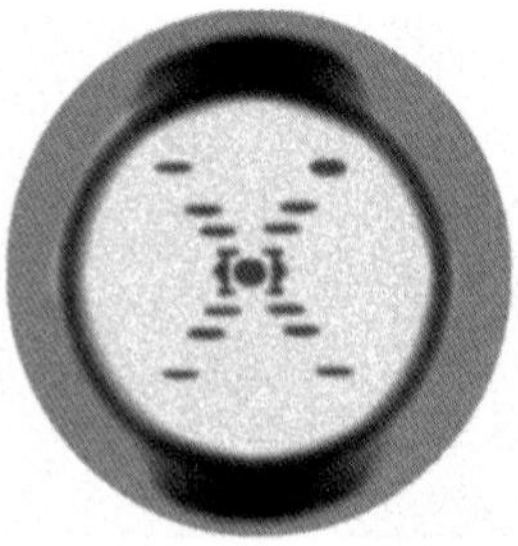

6.2 Protein synthesis

Learning outcomes — Activity number

- ☐ 7 Explain the features of the genetic code, including: **120**
    - The 4-letter alphabet and the 3-letter triplet code (codon) of base sequences.
    - The non-overlapping, linear nature of the code, which is read from start to finish in one direction. The specific punctuation codons and their significance.
    - The universal nature and degeneracy of the code.
- ☐ 8 Explain what is meant by a gene and explain how a gene determines the sequence of amino acids in a polypeptide (the primary structure of a protein). **121**
- ☐ 9 Explain what is meant by a gene mutation and describe how a change in the DNA sequence may result in a change in the polypeptide produced. **122 123**
- ☐ 10 Describe how a nucleotide sequence codes for the amino acid sequence in a polypeptide with reference to the nucleotide sequence for Hb^A (normal) and Hb^S (sickle cell) alleles for the gene for the β-globin polypeptide. **123**
- ☐ 11 Recognise transcription and translation as the two stages of gene expression. Describe the simple one gene-one polypeptide model for gene expression, understanding that this model has been modified in light of current understanding. **121**
- ☐ 12 Recall the structure of RNA and describe the range of RNA molecules and their roles in cellular activities. **113**
- ☐ 13 Describe the formation of mRNA in transcription, including the role of RNA polymerase and the significance of the coding strand and template strands. **124 126**
- ☐ 14 Describe translation (protein synthesis), including the role of tRNA, anticodons, and the general structure and role of ribosomes. Use the genetic code to determine the amino acids encoded by different codons. **125 126**

112 Nucleotides

Key Idea: Nucleotides make up nucleic acids. A nucleotide is made up of a base, a sugar, and a phosphate group.

Nucleotides are the building blocks of the nucleic acids DNA and RNA, which are involved in the transmission of inherited information. Nucleotide derivatives, such as ATP and GTP, are involved in energy transfers in cells. A nucleotide has three components: a base, a sugar, and a phosphate group. Nucleotides may contain one of five bases. The combination of bases in the nucleotides making up DNA or RNA stores the information controlling the cell's activity. The bases in DNA are the same as RNA except that thymine (T) in DNA is replaced with uracil (U) in RNA.

Pyrimidines

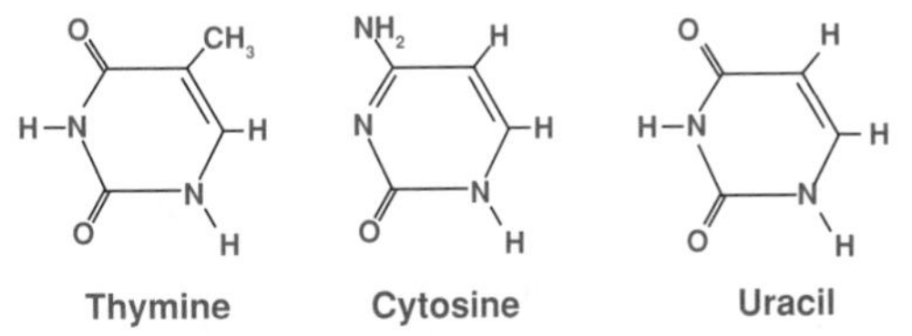

Thymine
Cytosine
Uracil

Pyrimidines are single ringed bases. DNA contains the pyrimidines cytosine (C) and thymine (T). RNA contains the pyrimidines cytosine and uracil (U).

Purines

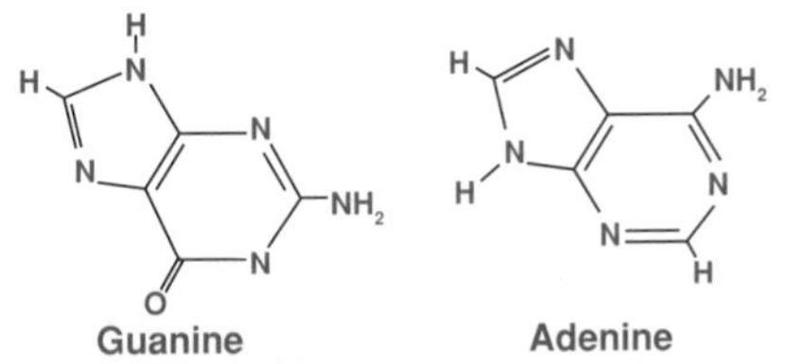

Guanine
Adenine

Purines are double ringed bases. Both DNA and RNA contain the purines adenine (A) and guanine (G).

Phosphate

Phosphate groups are represented by circles. Along with the pentose sugar they form the "backbone" of the DNA or RNA molecule.

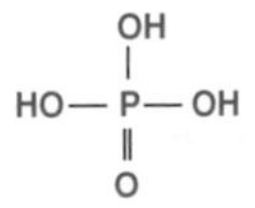

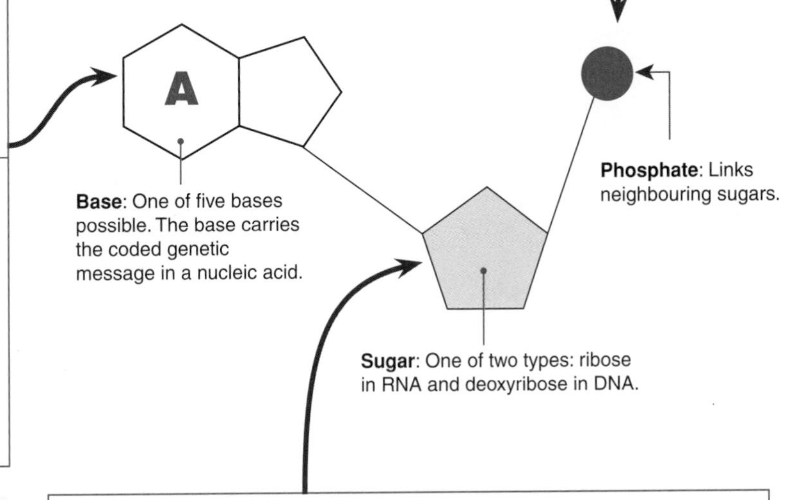

A
Base: One of five bases possible. The base carries the coded genetic message in a nucleic acid.
Phosphate: Links neighbouring sugars.
Sugar: One of two types: ribose in RNA and deoxyribose in DNA.

Sugars

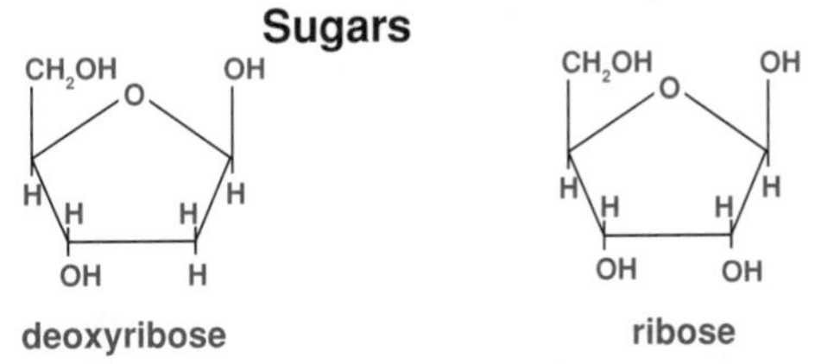

deoxyribose
ribose

Nucleotides contain one of two different sorts of sugars. **Deoxyribose** sugar is only found in DNA. **Ribose** sugar is found in RNA.

Nucleotide derivatives

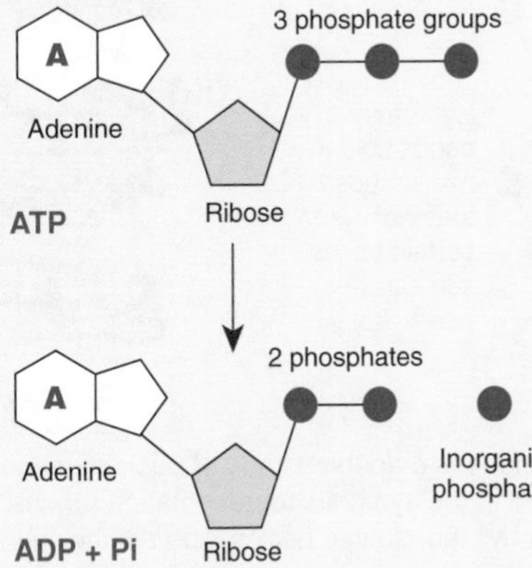

3 phosphate groups
A
Adenine
ATP
Ribose
2 phosphates
A
Adenine
Inorganic phosphate
ADP + Pi
Ribose

ATP is a nucleotide derivative used to provide chemical energy for metabolism. It consists of an adenine linked to a ribose sugar and 3 phosphate groups. Energy is made available when a phosphate group is transferred to a target molecule. Other nucleoside triphosphates (NTPs) have similar roles.

Nucleotide formation

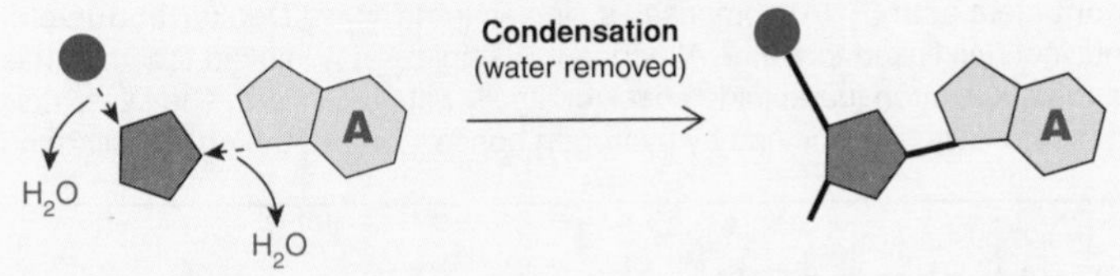

Condensation
(water removed)
A
A

Phosphoric acid and a base are chemically bonded to a sugar molecule by a **condensation** reaction in which water is given off. The reverse reaction is **hydrolysis**.

1. List the nucleotide bases present:

   (a) In DNA: ________________

   (b) In RNA: ________________

2. Name the sugar present: (a) In DNA: ____________ (b) In RNA: ____________

3. How can simple nucleotide units combine to store genetic information? ________________

© 2015 **BIOZONE** International
ISBN: 978-1-927309-31-5
Photocopying Prohibited

113 Nucleic Acids

Key Idea: Nucleic acids are macromolecules made up of long chains of nucleotides, which store and transmit genetic information. DNA and RNA are nucleic acids.

DNA and RNA are nucleic acids involved in the transmission of inherited information. Nucleic acids have the capacity to store the information that controls cellular activity. The central nucleic acid is called **deoxyribonucleic acid** (DNA). **Ribonucleic acids** (RNA) are involved in the 'reading' of the DNA information. All nucleic acids are made up of nucleotides linked together to form chains or strands. The strands vary in the sequence of the bases found on each nucleotide. It is this sequence which provides the 'genetic code' for the cell.

Joining nucleotides

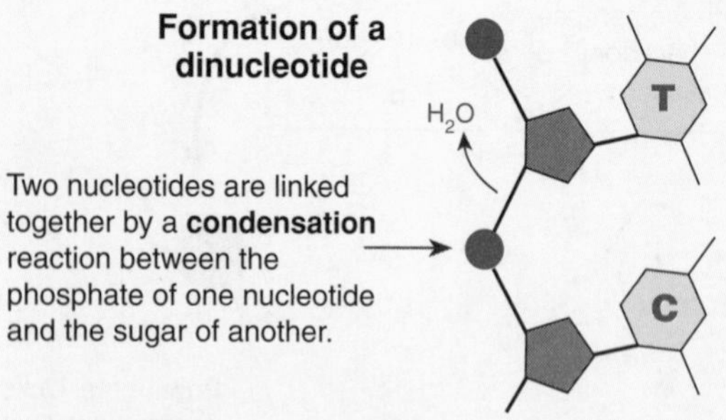

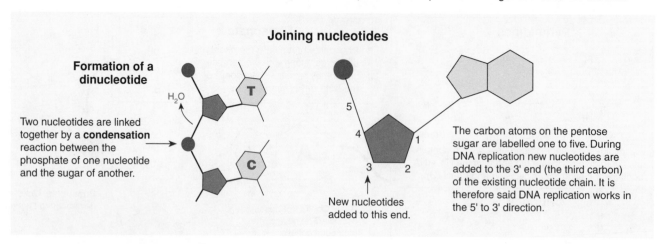

Formation of a dinucleotide
H_2O
T
C
Two nucleotides are linked together by a **condensation** reaction between the phosphate of one nucleotide and the sugar of another.

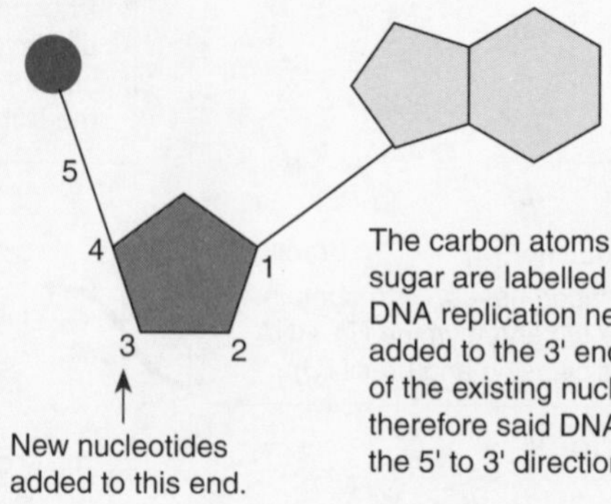

5
4
1
3
2
New nucleotides added to this end.

The carbon atoms on the pentose sugar are labelled one to five. During DNA replication new nucleotides are added to the 3' end (the third carbon) of the existing nucleotide chain. It is therefore said DNA replication works in the 5' to 3' direction.

RNA molecule

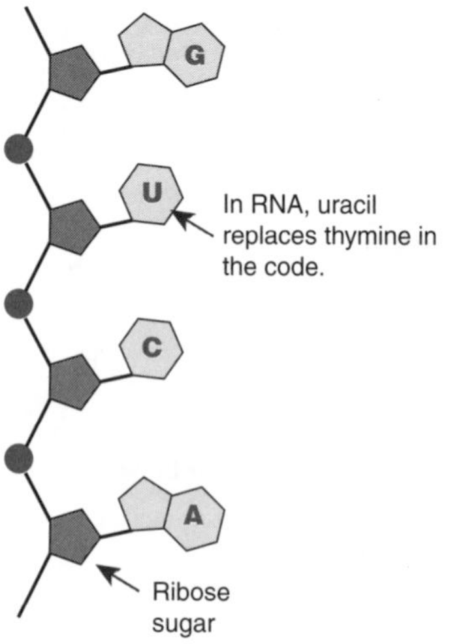

G
U
In RNA, uracil replaces thymine in the code.
C
A
Ribose sugar

DNA molecule

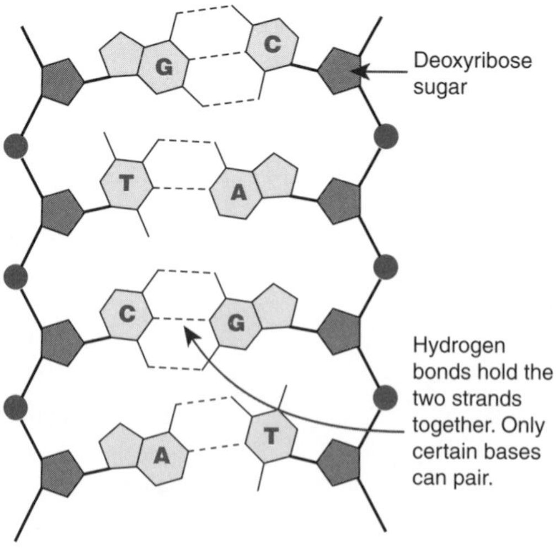

G
C
Deoxyribose sugar
T
A
C
G
Hydrogen bonds hold the two strands together. Only certain bases can pair.
A
T

Symbolic representation

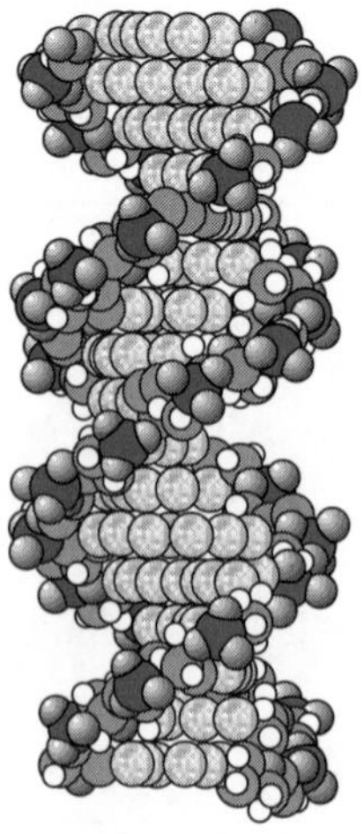

Space filling model

Ribonucleic acid (RNA) comprises a single strand of nucleotides linked together. Although it is single stranded, it is often found folded back on itself, with complementary bases joined by hydrogen bonds.

Deoxyribonucleic acid (DNA) comprises a double strand of nucleotides linked together. It is shown unwound in the symbolic representation (above left). The DNA molecule takes on a twisted, double helix shape as shown in the space filling model above right.

Double-stranded DNA

The double-helix structure of DNA is like a ladder twisted into a corkscrew shape around its longitudinal axis. It is 'unwound' here to show the relationships between the bases.

- The DNA backbone is made up of alternating phosphate and sugar molecules, giving the DNA molecule an asymmetrical structure.
- The asymmetrical structure gives a DNA strand **direction**. Each strand runs in the opposite direction to the other.
- The ends of a DNA strand are labelled the 5' (five prime) and 3' (three prime) ends. The **5'** end has a terminal phosphate group (off carbon 5), the **3'** end has a terminal hydroxyl group (off carbon 3).
- The way the pairs of bases come together to form hydrogen bonds is determined by the number of bonds they can form and the configuration of the bases.

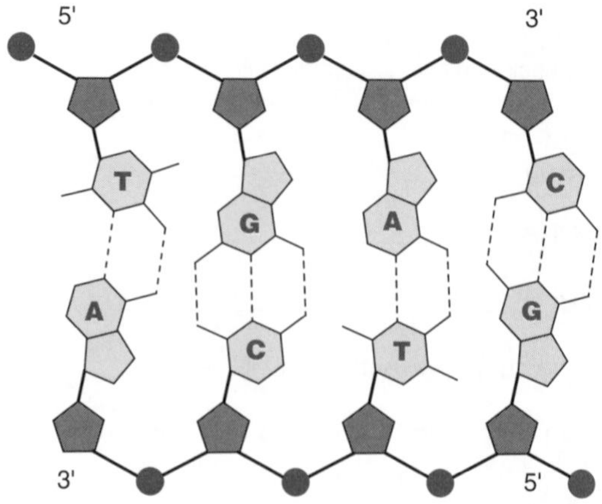

5'
3'
T
G
A
C
A
C
T
G
3'
5'

© 2015 **BIOZONE** International
ISBN:978-1-927309-31-5
Photocopying Prohibited

RNAs are involved in decoding the genetic information in DNA, as messenger RNA (mRNA), transfer RNA (tRNA), and ribosomal RNA (rRNA). RNA is also involved in modifying mRNA after transcription and in regulating translation.

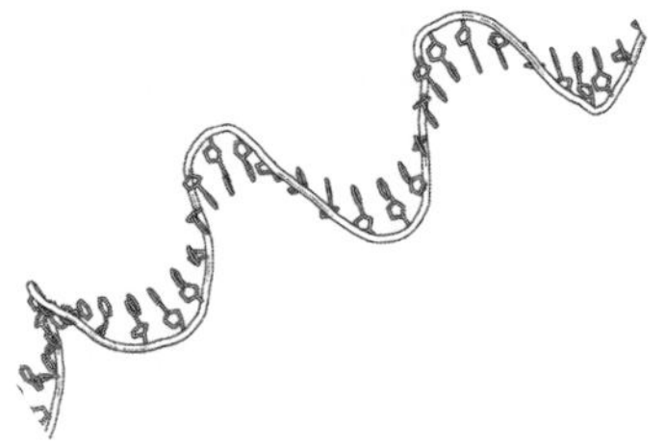

Messenger RNA (above) is transcribed (written) from DNA. It carries a copy of the genetic instructions from the DNA to ribosomes in the cytoplasm, where it is translated into a polypeptide chain.

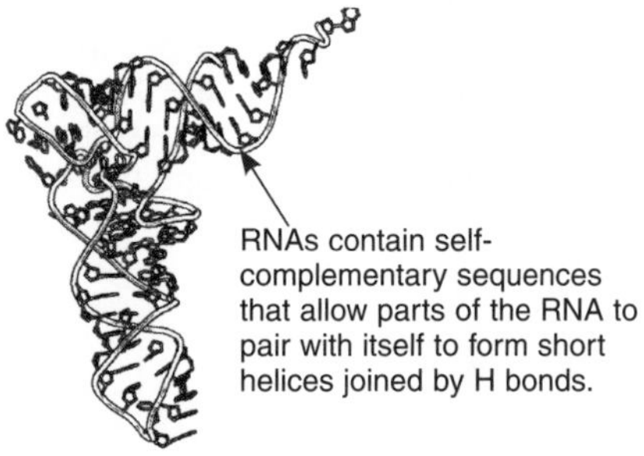
RNAs contain self-complementary sequences that allow parts of the RNA to pair with itself to form short helices joined by H bonds.

Transfer RNA (above) carries amino acids to the growing polypeptide chain. One end of the tRNA carries the genetic code in a three-nucleotide sequence called the **anticodon**. The amino acid links to the 3' end of the tRNA.

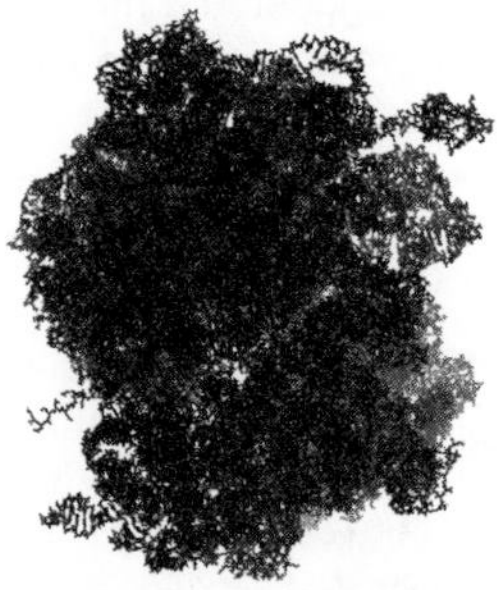

Ribosomal RNA (above) forms ribosomes from two separate ribosomal components (the large and small subunits) and assembles amino acids into a polypeptide chain.

1. Label the following parts on the diagram of the double-stranded DNA molecule at the bottom of page 92:
   (a) Deoxyribose (b) Phosphate (c) Hydrogen bonds (d) Purine bases (e) Pyrimidine bases

2. (a) Explain the **base-pairing rule** that applies in double-stranded DNA: ______________________

   (b) How is the base-pairing rule for mRNA different? ______________________

   (c) What is the purpose of the hydrogen bonds in double-stranded DNA? ______________________

3. Briefly describe the roles of RNA: ______________________

4. (a) If you wanted to use a radioactive or fluorescent tag to label only the RNA in a cell and not the DNA, what molecule(s) would you label?

   ____

   (b) If you wanted to use a radioactive or fluorescent tag to label only the DNA in a cell and not the RNA, what molecule(s) would you label?

   ____

5. (a) Why do the DNA strands have an asymmetrical structure? ______________________

   (b) What are the differences between the 5' and 3' ends of a DNA strand? ______________________

6. Complete the following table summarising the differences between DNA and RNA molecules:

	DNA	RNA
Sugar present		
Bases present		
Number of strands		
Relative length		

© 2015 **BIOZONE** International
ISBN: 978-1-927309-31-5
Photocopying Prohibited

114 Determining the Structure of DNA

Key Idea: Once the structure of DNA was known, it immediately suggested a mechanism for its replication.

DNA is easily extracted and isolated from cells (see below). This was first done in 1869, but it took the work of many scientists working in different areas many years to determine DNA's structure. The final pieces of evidence came from a photographic technique called X-ray crystallography in which X-rays are shone through crystallised molecules to produce a pattern on a film. The pattern can be used to understand the structure of the molecule. The focus of much subsequent research on DNA has been on DNA products, i.e. proteins and non-protein regulatory molecules (regulatory RNAs).

Discovering the structure of DNA

Although James Watson and Francis Crick are often credited with the discovery of the structure of DNA, at least two other scientists were instrumental in acquiring the images on which Watson and Crick based their discovery.

Maurice Wilkins and Rosalind Franklin produced X-ray diffraction patterns of the DNA molecule. The patterns provided measurements of different parts of the molecule and the position of different groups of atoms. Wilkins showed Franklin's X-ray image (photo 51) to Watson and Crick who then correctly interpreted the image and produced a model of the DNA molecule.

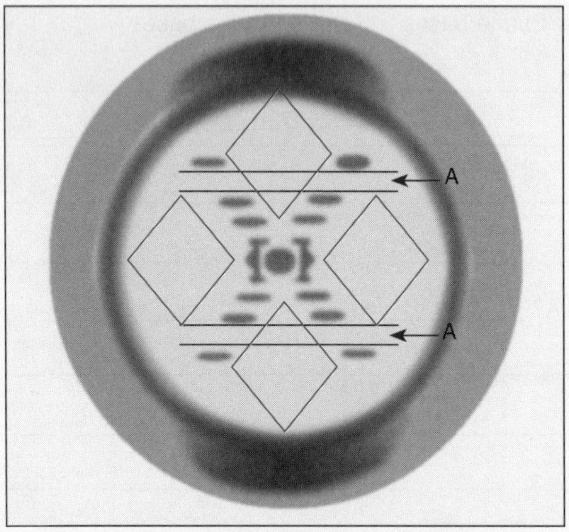
A
A

Diagram representing the image produced by Rosalind Franklin

Numerous distinct parts of the X-ray image indicate specific qualities of the DNA. The distinct X pattern indicates a helix structure, but Watson and Crick realised that the apparent gaps in the X (labelled **A**) were due to the repeating pattern of a *double* helix. The diamond shapes (in blue) indicate the helix is continuous and of constant dimensions and that the sugar-phosphate backbone is on the outside of the helix. The distance between the dark horizontal bands allows the calculation of the length of one full turn of the helix.

Structure and replication

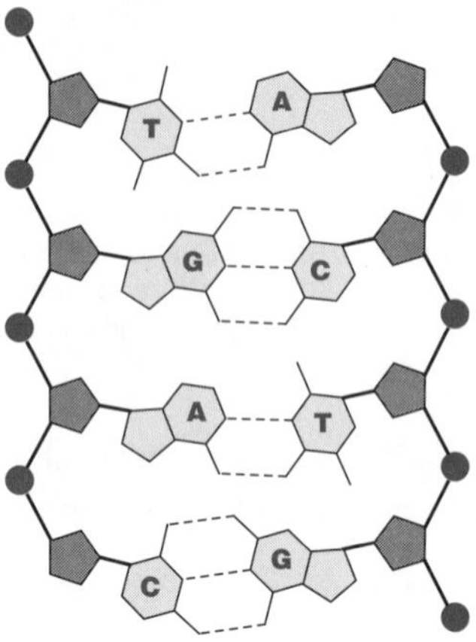
T
A
G
C
A
T
C
G

The realisation that DNA was a double helix consisting of antiparallel strands made of bases that followed a strict base pairing rule suggested a mechanism for its replication.

Watson and Crick hypothesised that each strand served as a template and that DNA replication was semi-conservative, producing two daughter strands consisting of half new and half parent material. This was confirmed by Meselson and Stahl.

DNA extraction by ethanol precipitation

DNA is easily extracted and precipitated out of solution using ice cold ethanol. Tissue is macerated in an extraction buffer and then cold ethanol is added so that the DNA precipitates out of the filtered suspension as visible whitish, glue-like strands (below left). The DNA can then be centrifuged with ethanol to form a pellet. Full methodologies are readily available through texts and online.

DNA extraction buffer contains water, detergent, and salt. The **detergent** helps to dissolve the cellular membranes of the tissue and deactivate DNases, which would chop up the DNA. The **salt** helps to remove the proteins bound to the DNA and keeps them in solution. Cations in the salt also neutralises the negative charge of the DNA. **Ethanol** causes the DNA to precipitate out by removing the water from around the molecule. Low temperatures speed up the precipitation and limit DNase activity.

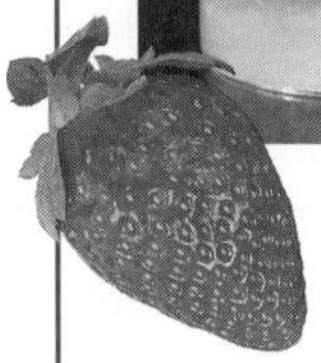

Strawberries are good candidates for DNA because they are octaploid (8 sets of chromosomes) and their colour makes it easy to see the precipitating DNA.

1. What made Watson and Crick realise that DNA was a double helix? ______

2. In the extraction and isolation of DNA:

   (a) Why is it necessary to dissolve the cellular membranes? ______

   (b) Why does the DNA precipitate out in ethanol? ______

   (c) For a DNA extraction, why is it helpful that strawberries are octaploid? ______

3. In a DNA extraction, student A obtained DNA in long threads, whereas student B obtained DNA that appeared fluffy. Account for the differences in these two results and suggest what student B might have done incorrectly?

______

© 2015 BIOZONE International
ISBN:978-1-927309-31-5
Photocopying Prohibited

115 Constructing a DNA Model

Key Idea: Nucleotides pair together in a specific way called the base pairing rule. In DNA, adenine always pairs with thymine, and cytosine always pairs with guanine.

DNA molecules are double stranded. Each strand is made up of nucleotides. The chemical properties of each nucleotide mean it can only bind with one other type of nucleotide. This is called the **base pairing rule** and is explained in the table below. This exercise will help you to learn this rule.

DNA base pairing rule			
Adenine	is always attracted to	**Thymine**	A ⟷ T
Thymine	is always attracted to	**Adenine**	T ⟷ A
Cytosine	is always attracted to	**Guanine**	C ⟷ G
Guanine	is always attracted to	**Cytosine**	G ⟷ C

1. Cut around the nucleotides on page 143 and separate each of the 24 nucleotides by cutting along the columns and rows (see arrows indicating two such cutting points). Although drawn as geometric shapes, these symbols represent chemical structures.

2. Place one of each of the four kinds of nucleotide on their correct spaces below:

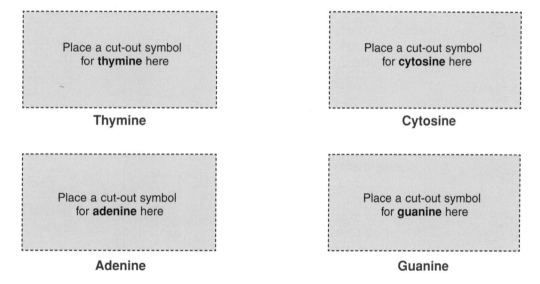

Place a cut-out symbol for **thymine** here	Place a cut-out symbol for **cytosine** here
Thymine	**Cytosine**
Place a cut-out symbol for **adenine** here	Place a cut-out symbol for **guanine** here
Adenine	**Guanine**

3. Identify and **label** each of the following features on the adenine nucleotide immediately above:
   phosphate, **sugar**, **base**, **hydrogen bonds**

4. Create one strand of the DNA molecule by placing the 9 correct 'cut out' nucleotides in the labelled spaces on the following page (DNA molecule). Make sure these are the right way up (with the **P** on the left) and are aligned with the left hand edge of each box. Begin with thymine and end with guanine.

5. Create the complementary strand of DNA by using the base pairing rule above. Note that the nucleotides have to be arranged upside down.

6. Under normal circumstances, it is not possible for adenine to pair up with guanine or cytosine, nor for any other mismatches to occur. Describe the **two factors** that prevent a mismatch from occurring:

   Factor 1: ____

   ____

   Factor 2: ____

   ____

7. Once you have checked that the arrangement is correct, you may glue, paste or tape these nucleotides in place.

> **NOTE**: There may be some value in keeping these pieces loose in order to practise the base pairing rule. For this purpose, *removable tape* would be best.

© 2015 **BIOZONE** International
ISBN: 978-1-927309-31-5
Photocopying Prohibited

DNA molecule

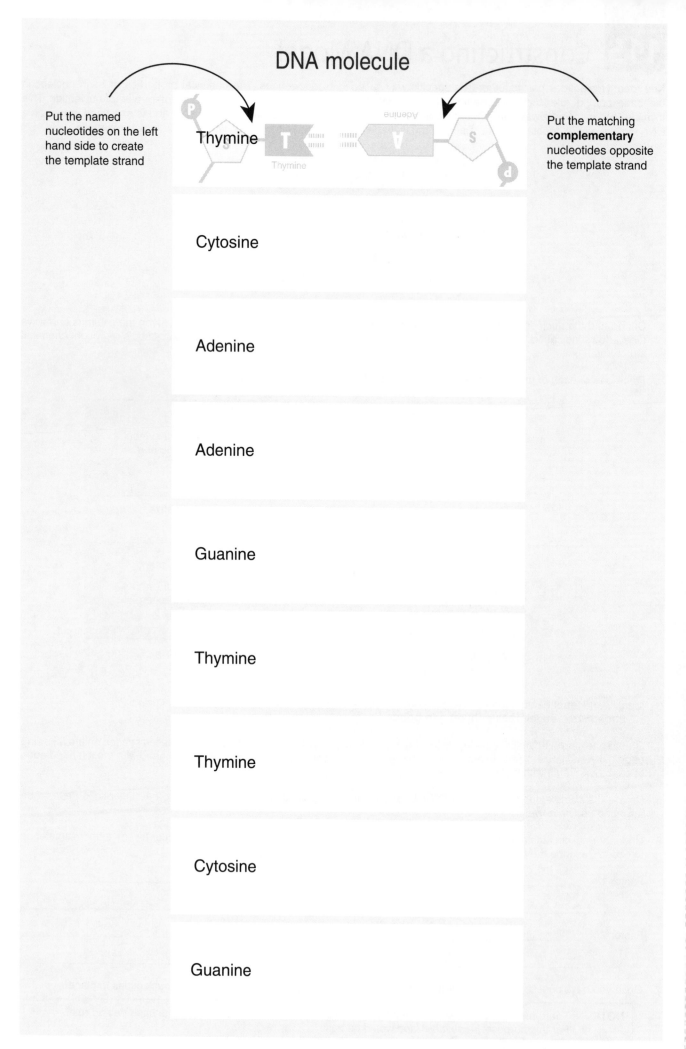

Put the named nucleotides on the left hand side to create the template strand

Put the matching **complementary** nucleotides opposite the template strand

Thymine

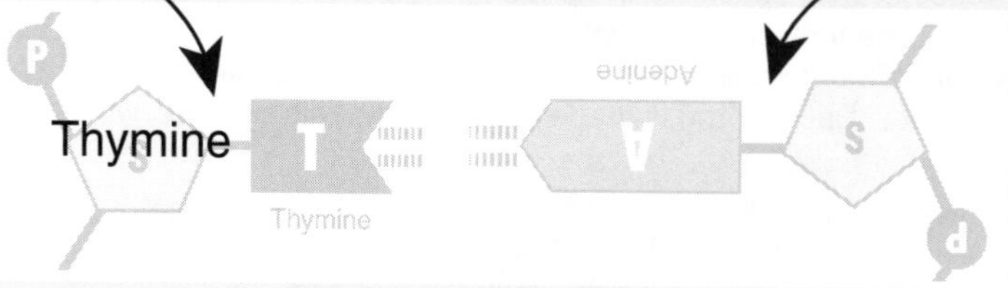
P
S
T
Thymine
A
Adenine
S
P

Cytosine

Adenine

Adenine

Guanine

Thymine

Thymine

Cytosine

Guanine

© 2015 **BIOZONE** International
ISBN:978-1-927309-31-5
Photocopying Prohibited

Nucleotides

Tear out this page along the perforation and separate each of the 24 nucleotides by cutting along the columns and rows (see arrows indicating the cutting points).

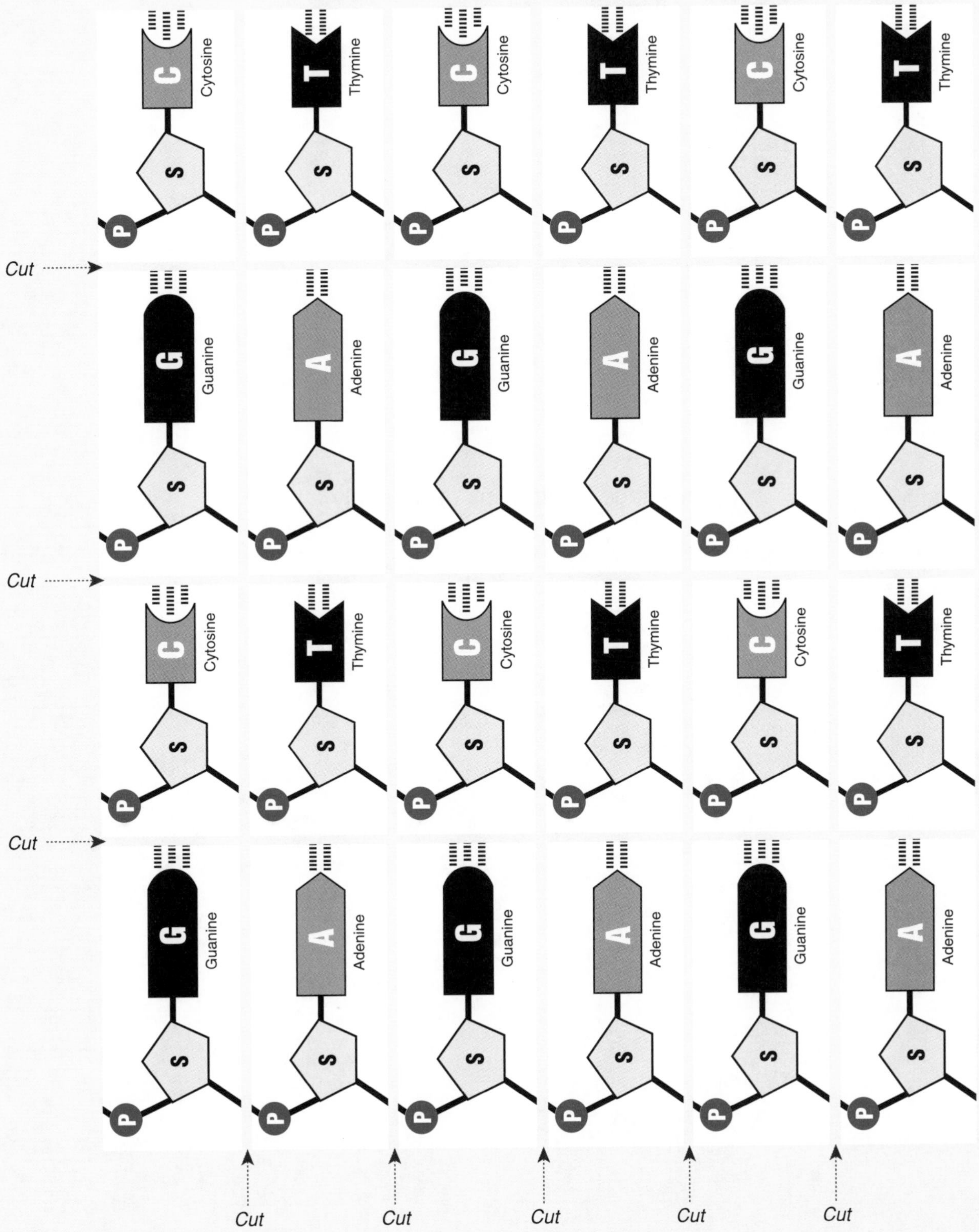
C
Cytosine
S
P
T
Thymine
S
P
C
Cytosine
S
P
T
Thymine
S
P
C
Cytosine
S
P
T
Thymine
S
P
Cut
G
Guanine
S
P
A
Adenine
S
P
G
Guanine
S
P
A
Adenine
S
P
G
Guanine
S
P
A
Adenine
S
P
Cut
C
Cytosine
S
P
T
Thymine
S
P
C
Cytosine
S
P
T
Thymine
S
P
C
Cytosine
S
P
T
Thymine
S
P
Cut
G
Guanine
S
P
A
Adenine
S
P
G
Guanine
S
P
A
Adenine
S
P
G
Guanine
S
P
A
Adenine
S
P
Cut
Cut
Cut
Cut
Cut

© 2015 **BIOZONE** International
ISBN: 978-1-927309-31-5
Photocopying Prohibited

This page is left blank deliberately

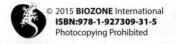

© 2015 **BIOZONE** International
ISBN:978-1-927309-31-5
Photocopying Prohibited

116 DNA Replication

Key Idea: Semi conservative DNA replication produces two identical copies of DNA, each containing half original material and half new material.

Before a cell can divide, it must double its DNA. It does this by a process called DNA replication. This process ensures that each resulting cell receives a complete set of genes from the original cell. After the DNA has replicated, each chromosome is made up of two chromatids, joined at the centromere. The two chromatids will become separated during cell division to form two separate chromosomes. During DNA replication, nucleotides are added at the replication fork. Enzymes are responsible for all of the key events.

Step 1
Unwinding the DNA molecule

A normal chromosome consists of an unreplicated DNA molecule. Before cell division, this long molecule of double stranded DNA must be replicated.

For this to happen, it is first untwisted and separated (unzipped) at high speed at its replication fork by an enzyme called helicase. Another enzyme relieves the strain that this generates by cutting, winding and rejoining the DNA strands.

Step 2
Making new DNA strands

The formation of new DNA is carried out mostly by an enzyme complex called **DNA polymerase**.

DNA polymerase catalyses the condensation reaction that joins adjacent nucleotides. The enzyme works in a 5' to 3' direction, so nucleotides are assembled in a continuous fashion on one strand but in short fragments on the other strand. These fragments are later joined by an enzyme to form one continuous length.

Step 3
Rewinding the DNA molecule

Each of the two new double-helix DNA molecules has one strand of the original DNA (dark grey and white) and one strand that is newly synthesised (blue). The two DNA molecules rewind into their double-helix shape again.

DNA replication is semi-conservative, with each new double helix containing one old (parent) strand and one newly synthesised (daughter) strand. The new chromosome has twice as much DNA as a non-replicated chromosome. The two chromatids will become separated in the cell division process to form two separate chromosomes.

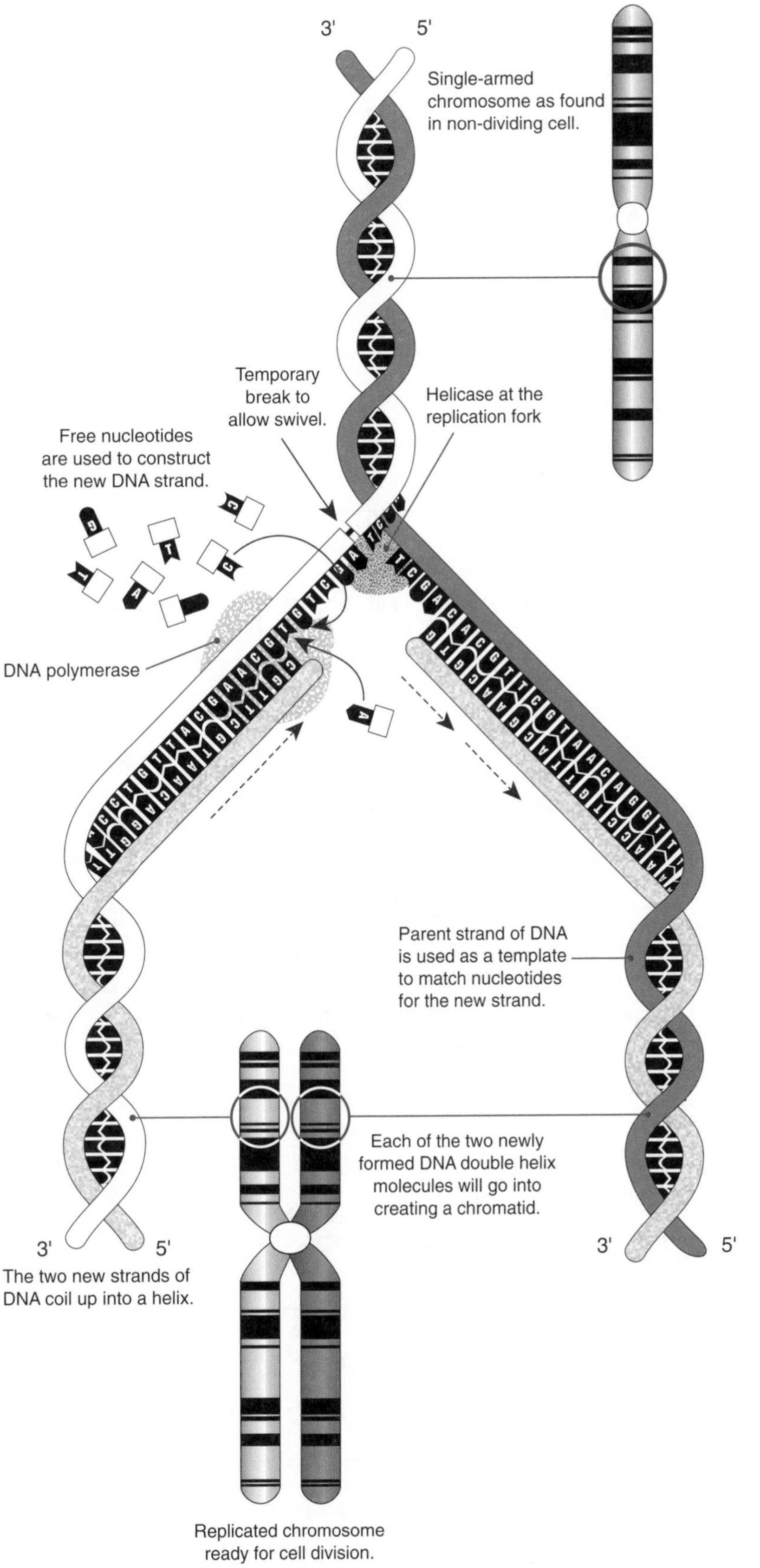
3'
5'
Single-armed chromosome as found in non-dividing cell.
Temporary break to allow swivel.
Helicase at the replication fork
Free nucleotides are used to construct the new DNA strand.
DNA polymerase
Parent strand of DNA is used as a template to match nucleotides for the new strand.
Each of the two newly formed DNA double helix molecules will go into creating a chromatid.
3'
5'
The two new strands of DNA coil up into a helix.
3'
5'
Replicated chromosome ready for cell division.

© 2015 BIOZONE International
ISBN: 978-1-927309-31-5
Photocopying Prohibited

LINK 118 LINK 117 WEB 116 KNOW

1. What is the purpose of DNA replication? ______

2. Summarise the three main steps involved in DNA replication:

   (a) ______

   (b) ______

   (c) ______

3. For a cell with 22 chromosomes, state how many chromatids would exist following DNA replication: ______

4. State the percentage of DNA in each daughter cell that is new and the percentage that is original: ______

5. What does it mean when we say DNA replication is semi-conservative? ______

6. How are the new strands of DNA lengthened during replication: ______

7. What rule ensures that the two new DNA strands are identical to the original strand? ______

8. Why does one strand of DNA need to be copied in short fragments? ______

9. Match the statements in the table below to form complete sentences, then put the sentences in order to make a coherent paragraph about DNA replication and its role:

The enzymes also proofread the DNA during replication...	...is required before mitosis or meiosis can occur.
DNA replication is the process by which the DNA molecule...	...by enzymes.
Replication is tightly controlled...	...to correct any mistakes.
After replication, the chromosome...	...and half new DNA.
DNA replication...	...during mitosis.
The chromatids separate...	...is copied to produce two identical DNA strands.
A chromatid contains half original ...	...is made up of two chromatids.

Write the complete paragraph here: ______

© 2015 **BIOZONE** International
ISBN:978-1-927309-31-5
Photocopying Prohibited

117 Enzyme Control of DNA Replication

Key Idea: DNA replication is a directional process controlled by several different enzymes.

DNA replication involves many enzyme-controlled steps. They are shown below as separate, but many of the enzymes are clustered together as enzyme complexes. As the DNA is replicated, enzymes 'proof-read' it and correct mistakes. The polymerase enzyme can only work in one direction, so that one new strand is constructed as a continuous length (the leading strand) while the other new strand (the lagging strand) is made in short segments to be later joined together.

DNA replication occurs during interphase of the cell cycle at an astounding rate. As many as 4000 nucleotides per second are replicated. This explains how bacterial cells, with as many as 4 million nucleotides, can complete a cell cycle in about 20 minutes. Note that the nucleotides are present as deoxynucleoside triphosphates. When hydrolysed, these provide the energy for incorporating the nucleotide into the strand.

During the replication of the DNA, a mistake is made about once every 100 000 nucleotides replicated. These mistakes are corrected in two ways. A process called proof-reading occurs during replication. A second process called mis-match repair occurs after replication.

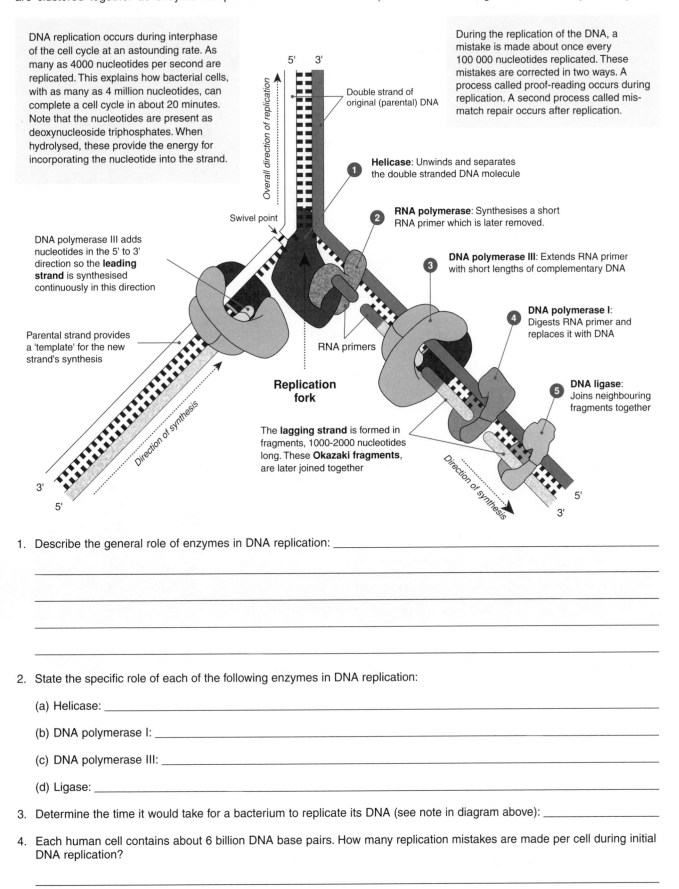

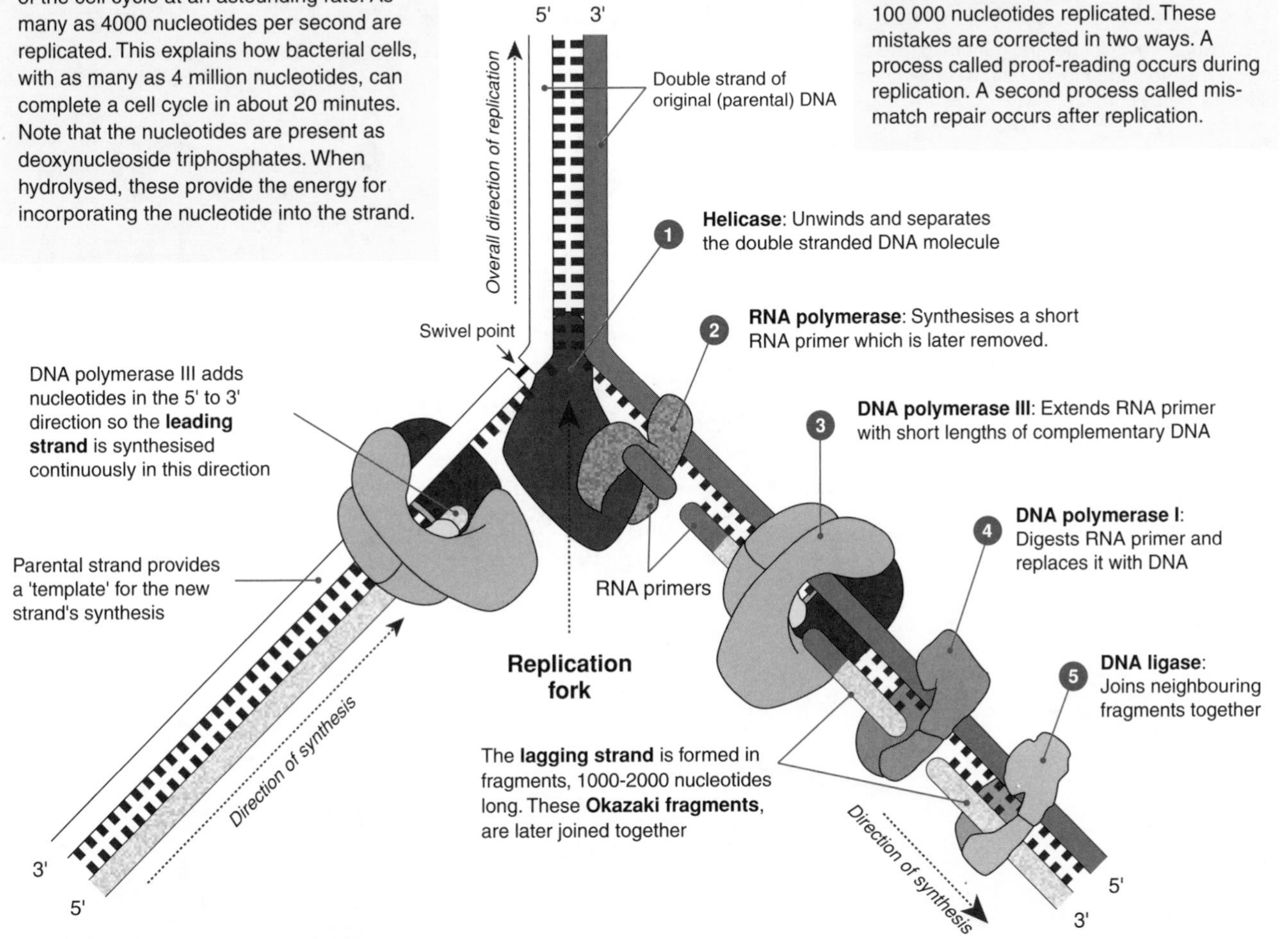
5'
3'
Overall direction of replication
Double strand of original (parental) DNA
1 **Helicase**: Unwinds and separates the double stranded DNA molecule
Swivel point
2 **RNA polymerase**: Synthesises a short RNA primer which is later removed.
DNA polymerase III adds nucleotides in the 5' to 3' direction so the **leading strand** is synthesised continuously in this direction
3 **DNA polymerase III**: Extends RNA primer with short lengths of complementary DNA
4 **DNA polymerase I**: Digests RNA primer and replaces it with DNA
Parental strand provides a 'template' for the new strand's synthesis
RNA primers
Replication fork
5 **DNA ligase**: Joins neighbouring fragments together
Direction of synthesis
The **lagging strand** is formed in fragments, 1000-2000 nucleotides long. These **Okazaki fragments**, are later joined together
Direction of synthesis
3'
5'
5'
3'

1. Describe the general role of enzymes in DNA replication: ______

2. State the specific role of each of the following enzymes in DNA replication:

   (a) Helicase: ______

   (b) DNA polymerase I: ______

   (c) DNA polymerase III: ______

   (d) Ligase: ______

3. Determine the time it would take for a bacterium to replicate its DNA (see note in diagram above): ______

4. Each human cell contains about 6 billion DNA base pairs. How many replication mistakes are made per cell during initial DNA replication?

______

© 2015 **BIOZONE** International
ISBN: 978-1-927309-31-5
Photocopying Prohibited

118 Meselson and Stahl's Experiment

Key Idea: Meselson and Stahl devised an experiment that showed DNA replication is semi-conservative. The anti-parallel, complementary structure of DNA suggested three possible mechanisms for its replication. The **semi-conservative model** proposed that each strand served as a template, forming new DNA molecules that were half old and half new DNA. The **conservative model** proposed that the original DNA served as a complete template so that the new DNA comprised two new strands. The **dispersive model** proposed that the two new DNA molecules had new and old DNA mixed throughout them. **Meselson and Stahl** devised a simple experiment to determine which model was correct.

Meselson and Stahl's experiment

E. coli were grown for several generations in a medium containing a **heavy nitrogen isotope** (^{15}N). Once all the bacterial DNA contained ^{15}N, they were transferred to a medium containing a **light nitrogen isotope** (^{14}N). After the transfer, newly synthesised DNA would contain ^{14}N and old DNA would contain ^{15}N.

1

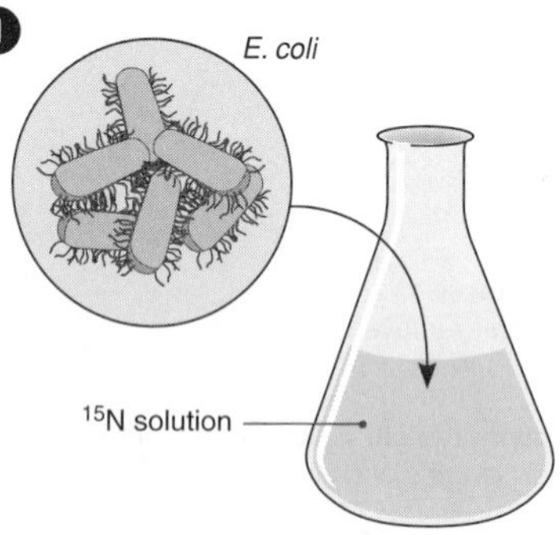
E. coli
15N solution

E. coli were grown in a nutrient solution containing ^{15}N. After 14 generations, all the bacterial DNA contained ^{15}N. A sample is removed. This is **generation 0**.

2

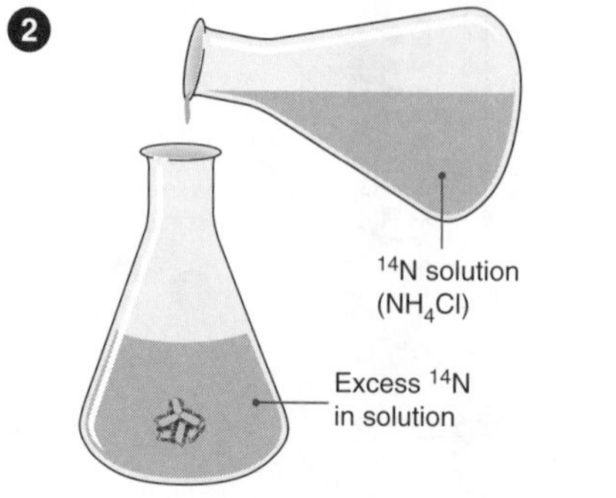
14N solution (NH4Cl)
Excess 14N in solution

Generation 0 is added to a solution containing excess ^{14}N (as NH_4Cl). During replication, new DNA will incorporate ^{14}N and be 'lighter' than the original DNA (which contains only ^{15}N).

3

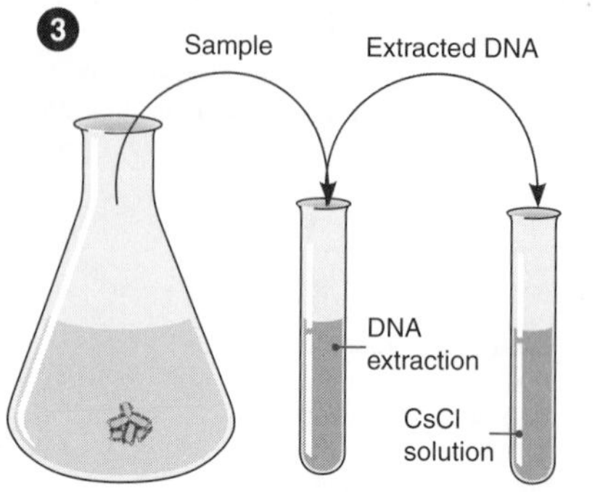
Sample
Extracted DNA
DNA extraction
CsCl solution

Every generation (~ 20 minutes), a sample is taken and treated to release the DNA. The DNA is placed in a CsCl solution which provides a density gradient for separation of the DNA.

4

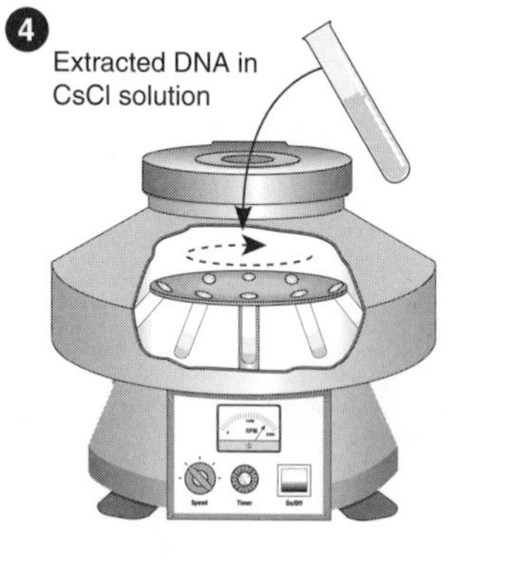
Extracted DNA in CsCl solution

Samples are spun in a high speed ultracentrifuge at 140,000 *g* for 20 hours. Heavier ^{15}N DNA moves closer to the bottom of the test tube than light ^{14}N DNA or intermediate ^{14}N/ ^{15}N DNA.

5

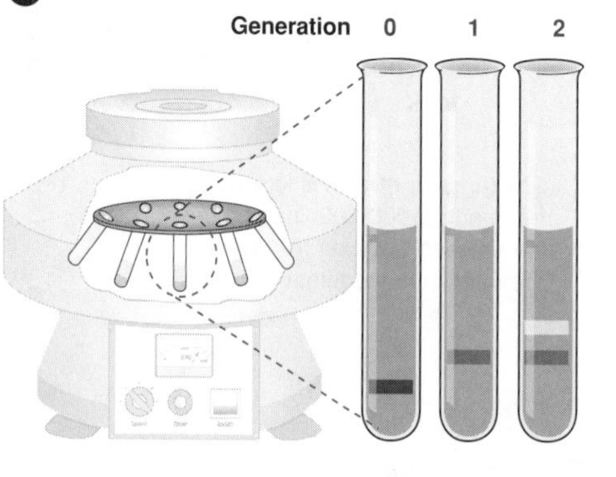
Generation 0 1 2

All the DNA in the generation 0 sample moved to the bottom of the test tube. All the DNA in the generation 1 sample moved to an intermediate position. At generation 2 half the DNA was at the intermediate position and half was near the top of the test tube. In subsequent generations, more DNA was near the top and less was in the intermediate position.

Models for DNA replication

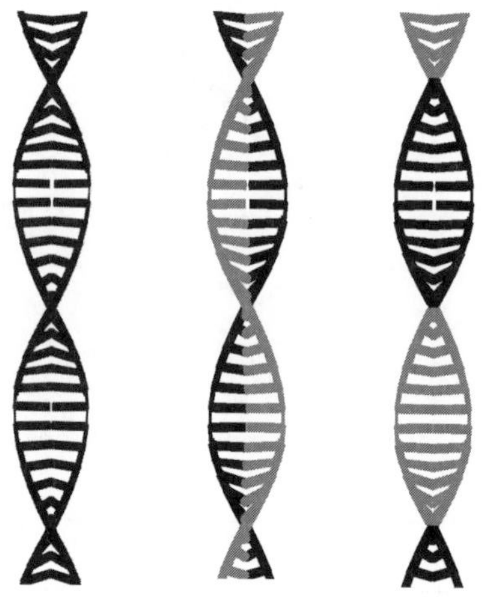
Conservative
Semi-conservative
Dispersive

1. Describe each of the DNA replication models:

   (a) Conservative: ______________________________

   (b) Semi-conservative: ______________________________

   (c) Dispersive: ______________________________

2. Explain why the *E. coli* were grown in an ^{15}N solution before being transferred to an ^{14}N solution: ______________________________

© 2015 BIOZONE International
ISBN:978-1-927309-31-5
Photocopying Prohibited

119 Modelling DNA Replication

Key Idea: Meselson and Stahl's experiment to determine the nature of DNA replication can be modelled.

There were three possible models proposed to explain how DNA replicated. Meselson and Stahl's experiment was able to determine which method was used by starting with parent DNA that was heavier than would normally be expected. They were then able to analyse the relative weight of the replicated DNA to work out the correct replication method.

Instructions:

1. Cut out the DNA shapes provided on this page.
2. Intertwine the first pair (labelled 0) of heavy ^{15}N (black) DNA. This forms Generation 0 (parental DNA).
3. Use the descriptions of the three possible models for DNA replication on the previous page to model DNA replication in semi-conservative, conservative, and dispersive DNA replication.
4. For each replication method, record in the spaces provided on page 105 the percentage of **heavy** ^{15}N-^{15}N (black-black), **intermediate** ^{15}N-^{14}N (black-grey), **light** ^{14}N-^{14}N (grey-grey), or other DNA molecules formed.
5. For the dispersive model you will need to cut the DNA along the dotted lines and then stick them back together in the dispersed sequence with tape. **Construct the dispersive model LAST.**

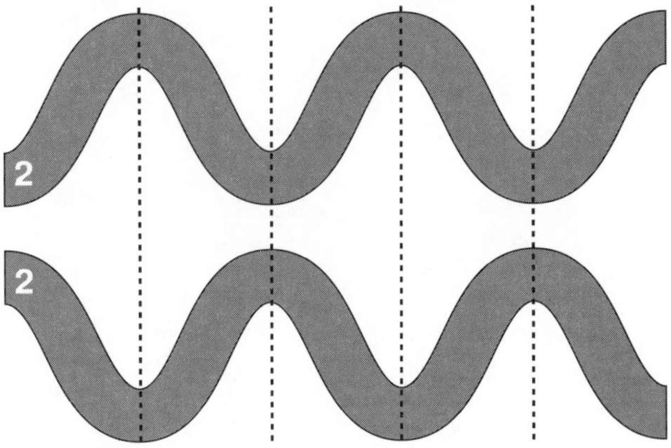
2
2

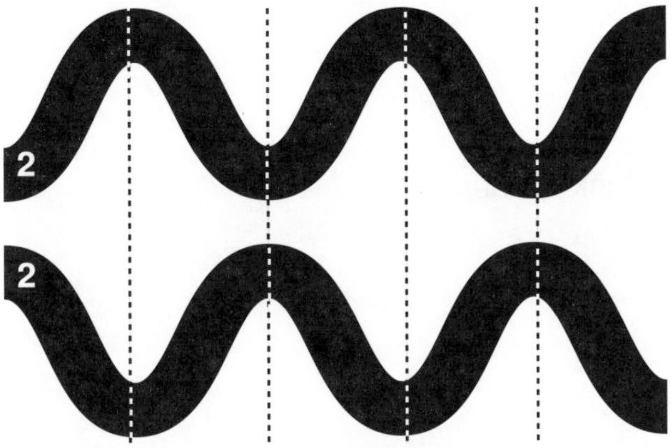
2
2

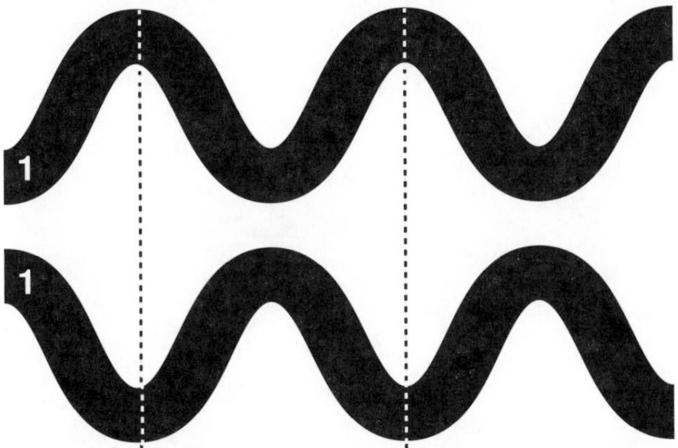
1
1

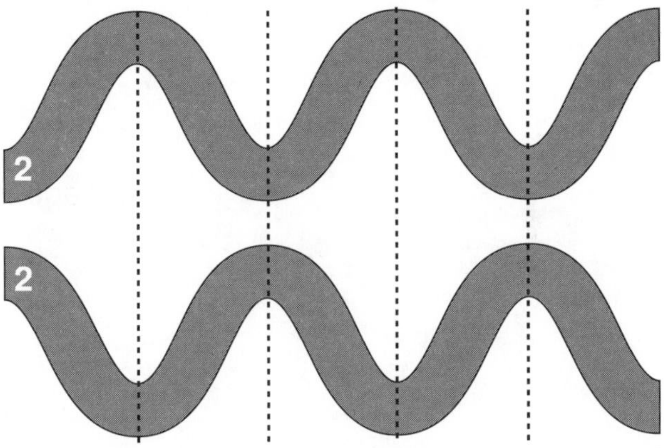
2
2

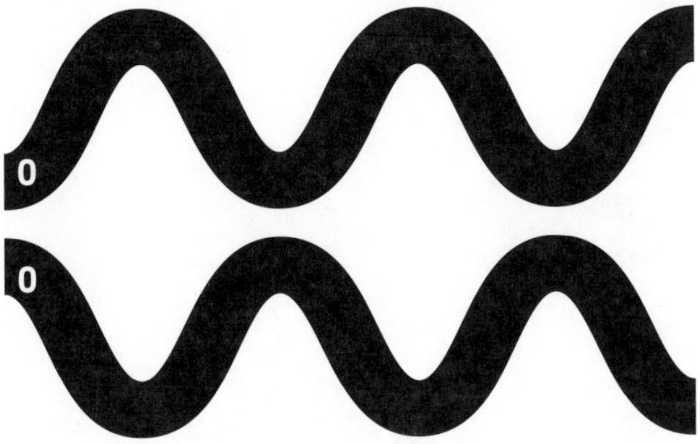
0
0

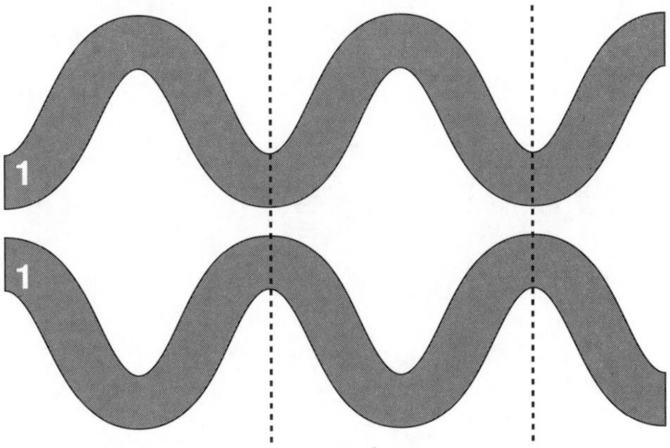
1
1

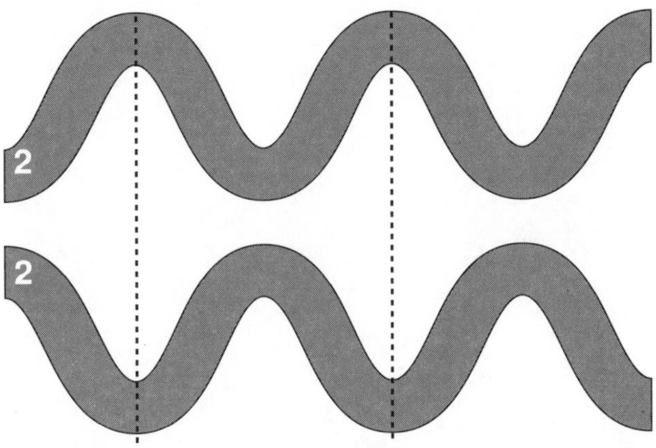
2
2

© 2015 **BIOZONE** International
ISBN: 978-1-927309-31-5
Photocopying Prohibited

LINK 118 PRAC

This page is left blank deliberately

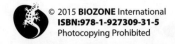

© 2015 **BIOZONE** International
ISBN:978-1-927309-31-5
Photocopying Prohibited

Conservative

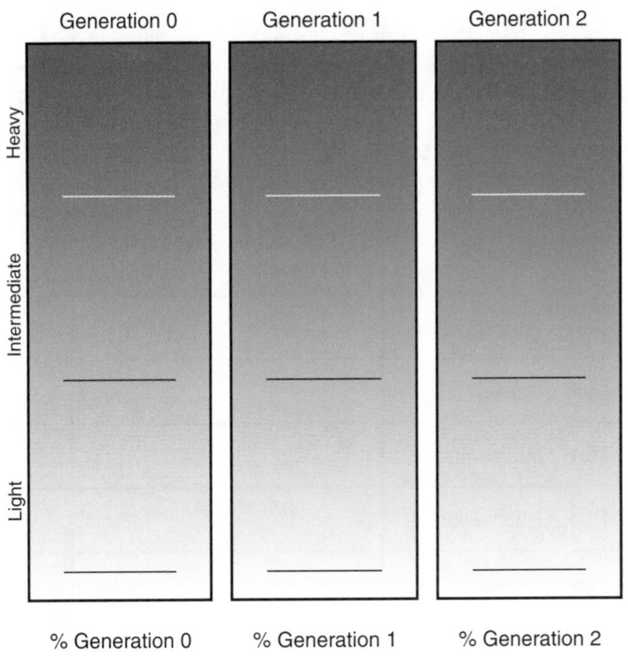
Generation 0
Generation 1
Generation 2
Heavy
Intermediate
Light
% Generation 0
% Generation 1
% Generation 2

Semi-conservative

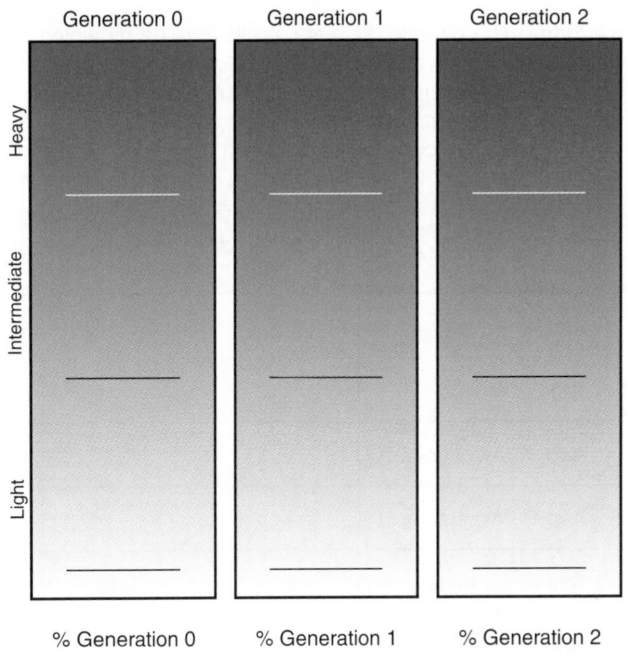
Generation 0
Generation 1
Generation 2
Heavy
Intermediate
Light
% Generation 0
% Generation 1
% Generation 2

Dispersive

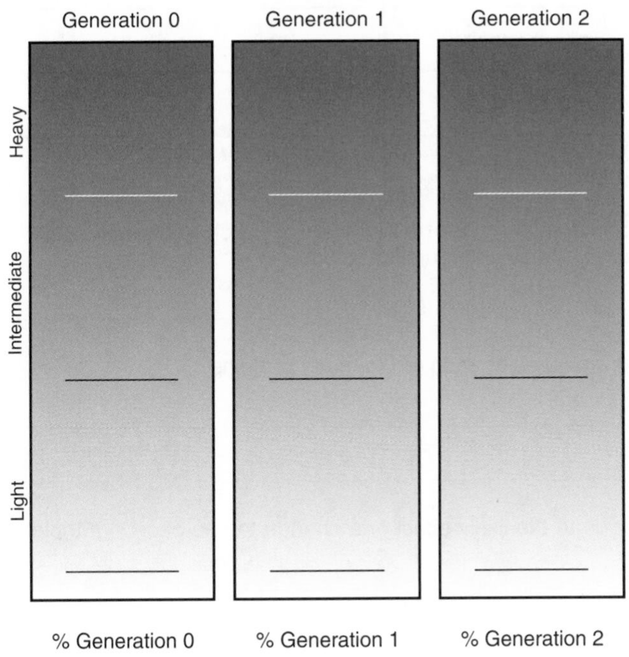
Generation 0
Generation 1
Generation 2
Heavy
Intermediate
Light
% Generation 0
% Generation 1
% Generation 2

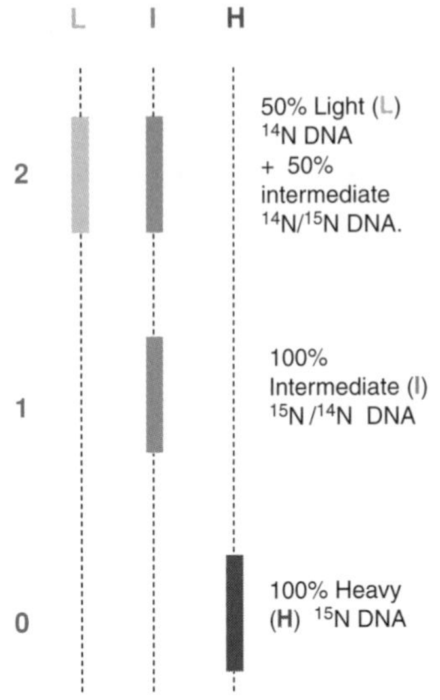
L
I
H
2
50% Light (L) ^{14}N DNA + 50% intermediate $^{14}N/^{15}N$ DNA.
1
100% Intermediate (I) $^{15}N/^{14}N$ DNA
0
100% Heavy (H) ^{15}N DNA

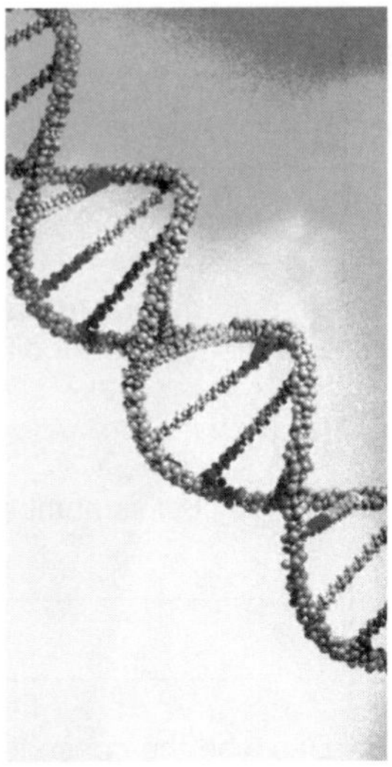

The results from Meselson's and Stahl's are shown graphically above. All the generation 1 DNA contained one light strand (^{14}N) and one heavy strand (^{15}N) to produce an intermediate density. At generation 2, 50% of the DNA was light and 50% was intermediate DNA.

1. (a) Compare your modelling results to the results gained by Meselson and Stahl to decide which of the three DNA replication models is supported by the data:

   ____

   ____

   (b) Was Watson and Crick's proposal correct? ______________________

2. Identify the replication model that fits the following data:

   (a) 100% of generation 0 is "heavy DNA", 50% of generation 1 is "heavy" and 50% is "light", and 25% of generation 2 is "heavy" and 75% is "light":

   ____

   (b) 100% of generation 0 is "heavy DNA", 100% of generation 1 is "intermediate DNA", and 100% generation 2 lies between the "intermediate" and "light" DNA regions:

   ____

© 2015 **BIOZONE** International
ISBN: 978-1-927309-31-5
Photocopying Prohibited

120 The Genetic Code

Key Idea: The genetic code is the set of rules by which the genetic information in DNA or mRNA is translated into proteins. The genetic information for the assembly of amino acids is stored as three-base sequence. These three letter codes on mRNA are called **codons**. Each codon represents one of 20 amino acids used to make proteins. The code is effectively universal, being the same in all living things (with a few minor exceptions). The genetic code is summarised in a mRNA-amino acid table, which identifies the amino acid encoded by each mRNA codon. The code is degenerate, meaning there may be more than one codon for each amino acid. Most of this degeneracy is in the third nucleotide of a codon.

Amino acid	Codons that code for this amino acid	No.	Amino acid	Codons that code for this amino acid	No.
Ala Alanine	GCU, GCC, GCA, GCG	4	**Leu** Leucine		
Arg Arginine			**Lys** Lysine		
Asn Asparagine			**Met** Methionine		
Asp Aspartic acid			**Phe** Phenylalanine		
Cys Cysteine			**Pro** Proline		
Gln Glutamine			**Ser** Serine		
Glu Glutamic acid			**Thr** Threonine		
Gly Glycine			**Trp** Tryptophan		
His Histidine			**Tyr** Tyrosine		
Ile Isoleucine			**Val** Valine		

1. Use the **mRNA-amino acid table** (below) to list in the table above all the **codons** that code for each of the amino acids and the number of different codons that can code for each amino acid (the first amino acid has been done for you).

2. (a) How many amino acids could be coded for if a codon consisted of just two bases? ____________

   (b) Why is this number of bases inadequate to code for the 20 amino acids required to make proteins?

3. Describe the consequence of the degeneracy of the genetic code to the likely effect of a change to one base in a triplet:

mRNA-amino acid table

How to read the table: The table on the right is used to 'decode' the genetic code as a sequence of amino acids in a polypeptide chain, from a given mRNA sequence. To work out which amino acid is coded for by a codon (triplet of bases) look for the first letter of the codon in the row label on the left hand side. Then look for the column that intersects the same row from above that matches the second base. Finally, locate the third base in the codon by looking along the row from the right hand end that matches your codon.

Example: Determine **CAG**

C on the left row,
A on the top column,
G on the right row
CAG is Gln (**glutamine**)

Read second letter here
Read first letter here
Read third letter here

First letter	Second letter: U	Second letter: C	Second letter: A	Second letter: G	Third letter
U	**UUU** Phe **UUC** Phe **UUA** Leu **UUG** Leu	**UCU** Ser **UCC** Ser **UCA** Ser **UCG** Ser	**UAU** Tyr **UAC** Tyr **UAA** STOP **UAG** STOP	**UGU** Cys **UGC** Cys **UGA** STOP **UGG** Trp	U C A G
C	**CUU** Leu **CUC** Leu **CUA** Leu **CUG** Leu	**CCU** Pro **CCC** Pro **CCA** Pro **CCG** Pro	**CAU** His **CAC** His **CAA** Gln **CAG** Gln	**CGU** Arg **CGC** Arg **CGA** Arg **CGG** Arg	U C A G
A	**AUU** Ile **AUC** Ile **AUA** Ile **AUG** Met	**ACU** Thr **ACC** Thr **ACA** Thr **ACG** Thr	**AAU** Asn **AAC** Asn **AAA** Lys **AAG** Lys	**AGU** Ser **AGC** Ser **AGA** Arg **AGG** Arg	U C A G
G	**GUU** Val **GUC** Val **GUA** Val **GUG** Val	**GCU** Ala **GCC** Ala **GCA** Ala **GCG** Ala	**GAU** Asp **GAC** Asp **GAA** Glu **GAG** Glu	**GGU** Gly **GGC** Gly **GGA** Gly **GGG** Gly	U C A G

© 2015 BIOZONE International
ISBN:978-1-927309-31-5
Photocopying Prohibited

121 Genes to Proteins

Key Idea: Genes are sections of DNA that code for proteins. Genes are expressed when they are transcribed into messenger RNA (mRNA) and then translated into a protein. **Gene expression** is the process of rewriting a gene into a protein. It involves **transcription** of the DNA into mRNA and **translation** of the mRNA into protein. A gene is bounded by a start (promoter) region, upstream of the gene, and a terminator region, downstream of the gene. These regions control transcription by telling RNA polymerase where to start and stop transcription of the gene. The information flow for gene to protein is shown below. Nucleotides are read in groups of three called triplets. The equivalent on the mRNA molecule is the codon. Some codons have special control functions (start and stop) in the making of a protein.

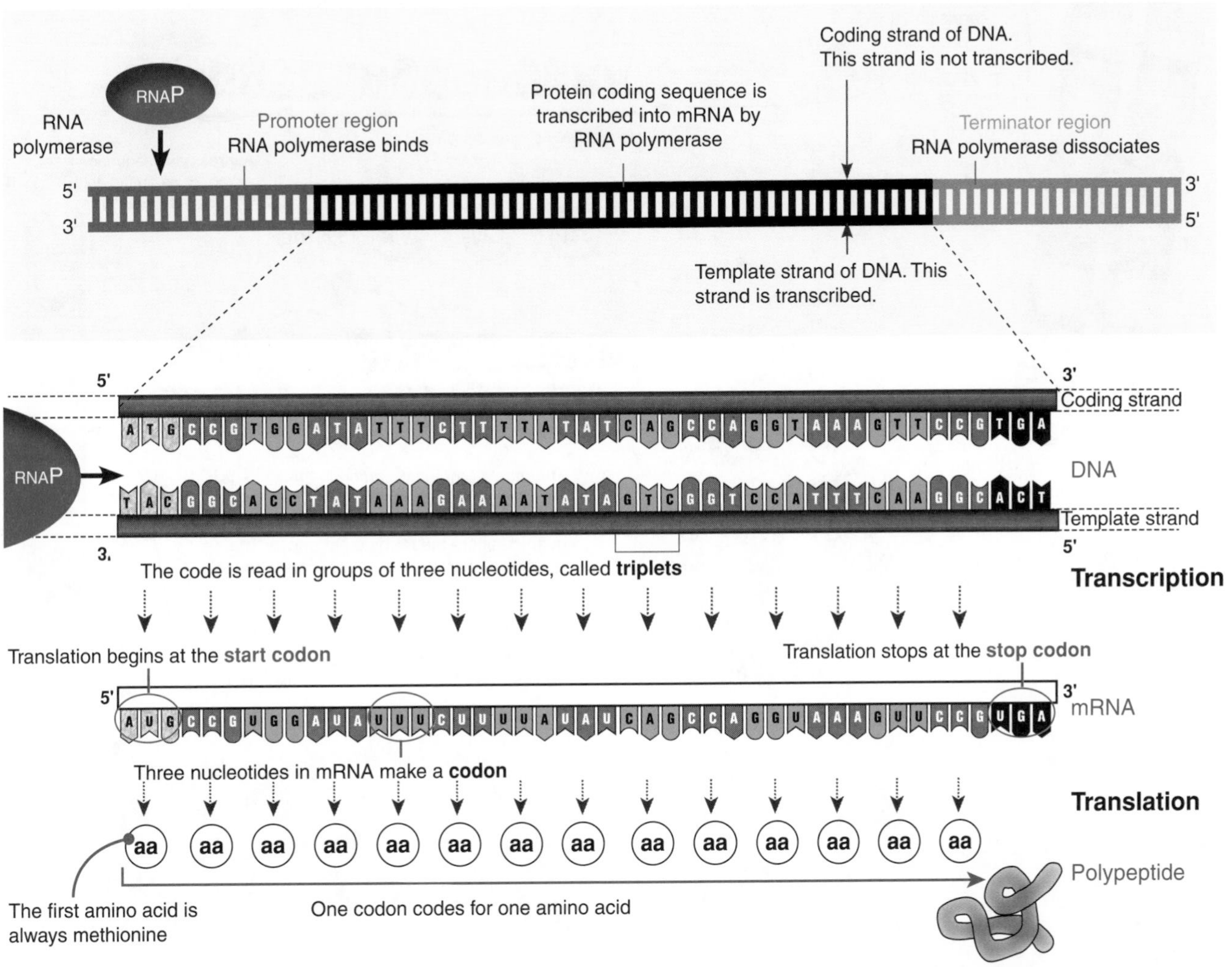
RNAP
RNA polymerase
Promoter region
RNA polymerase binds
Protein coding sequence is transcribed into mRNA by RNA polymerase
Coding strand of DNA. This strand is not transcribed.
Terminator region
RNA polymerase dissociates
5'
3'
3'
5'
Template strand of DNA. This strand is transcribed.
5'
3'
Coding strand
ATGCCGTGGATATTTCTTTTATATCAGCCAGGTAAAGTTCCGTGA
RNAP
DNA
TACGGCACCTATAAAGAAAATATAGTCGGTCCATTTCAAGGCACT
Template strand
3'
5'
The code is read in groups of three nucleotides, called triplets
Transcription
Translation begins at the start codon
Translation stops at the stop codon
5'
3'
AUGCCGUGGAUAUUUCUUUUAUAUCAGCCAGGUAAAGUUCCGUGA
mRNA
Three nucleotides in mRNA make a codon
Translation
aa aa aa aa aa aa aa aa aa aa aa aa aa aa
Polypeptide
The first amino acid is always methionine
One codon codes for one amino acid

1. (a) The three base code on DNA is called: ______________________

   (b) The three base code on mRNA is called: ______________________

2. (a) What is a **gene**? ______________________

   ____

   (b) What molecule transcribes the gene? ______________________

   (c) What is the role of the promoter and terminator regions? ______________________

   ____

3. What does the term **gene expression** mean? ______________________

   ____

4. Recall the anti-parallel nature of DNA, with the strands orientated in opposite directions. Explain its significance:

   ____

   ____

© 2015 **BIOZONE** International
ISBN: 978-1-927309-31-5
Photocopying Prohibited

122 Gene Mutations

Key Idea: Gene mutations are localised changes to the DNA sequence. They can produce new, heritable alleles.

Changes to the DNA base sequence are called **mutations**. These can occur as a result of substances called mutagens or through errors during DNA replication. Mutations affecting a single gene (gene mutation) can occur by deletion, substitution, or insertion of bases into the DNA sequence. Some mutations can create new alleles. Most new alleles will be detrimental. One example, NSRD, a form of genetic hearing loss, accounts for up to 50% of childhood deafness.

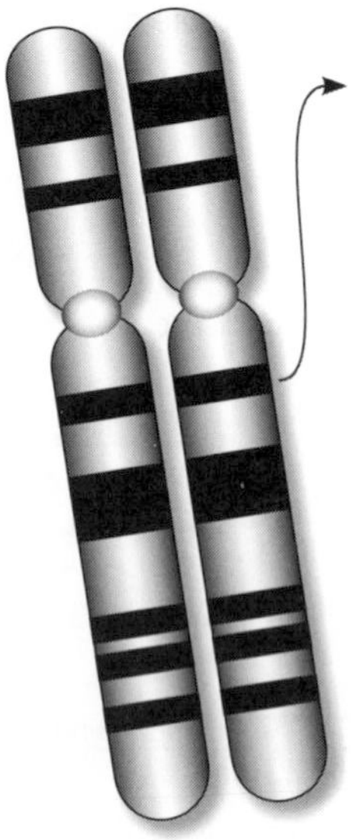

Chromosome 13

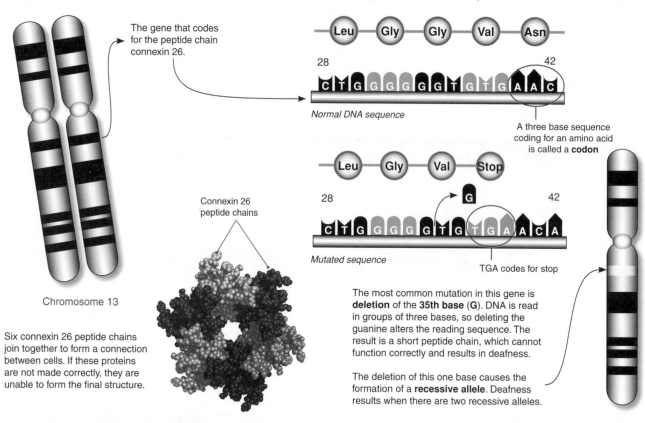

The gene that codes for the peptide chain connexin 26.

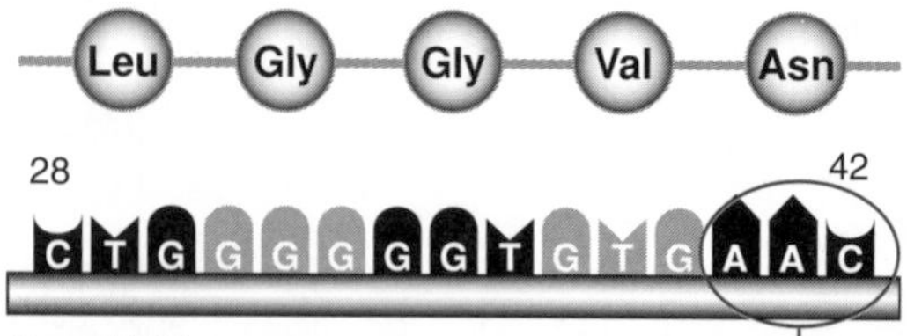

Leu
Gly
Gly
Val
Asn
28
42
C T G G G G G G T G T G A A C

Normal DNA sequence

A three base sequence coding for an amino acid is called a **codon**

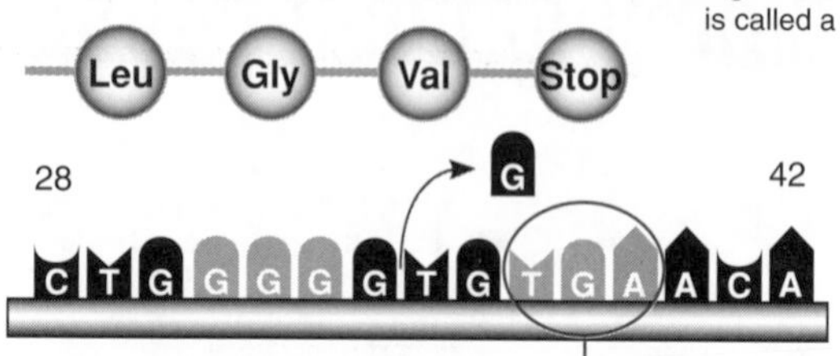

Leu
Gly
Val
Stop
28
G
42
C T G G G G G T G T G A A C A

Mutated sequence

TGA codes for stop

Connexin 26 peptide chains

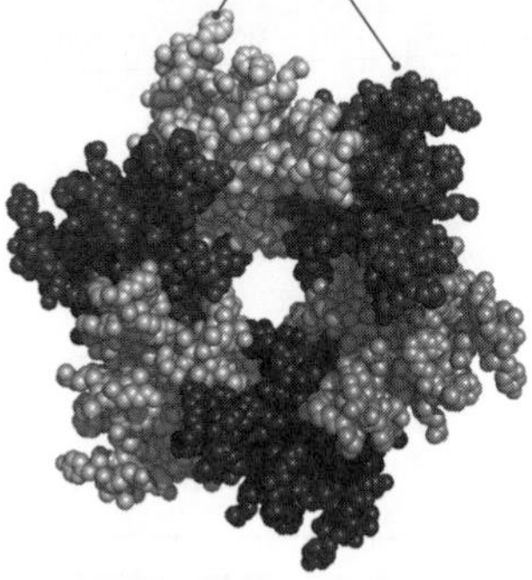

Six connexin 26 peptide chains join together to form a connection between cells. If these proteins are not made correctly, they are unable to form the final structure.

The most common mutation in this gene is **deletion** of the **35th base** (**G**). DNA is read in groups of three bases, so deleting the guanine alters the reading sequence. The result is a short peptide chain, which cannot function correctly and results in deafness.

The deletion of this one base causes the formation of a **recessive allele**. Deafness results when there are two recessive alleles.

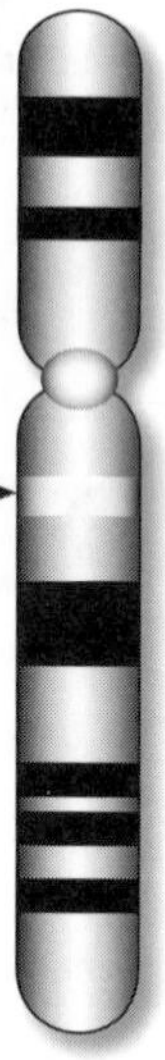

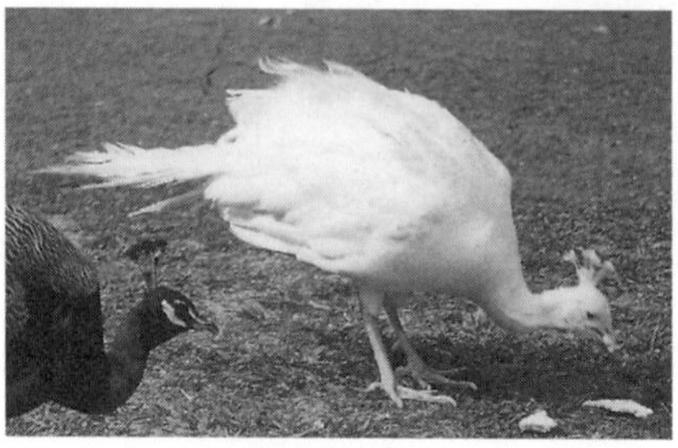

Harmful Mutations

Most mutations cause harmful effects, usually because they stop or alter the production of a protein (often an enzyme). Albinism (above) is one of the more common mutations in nature, and leaves an animal with no pigmentation.

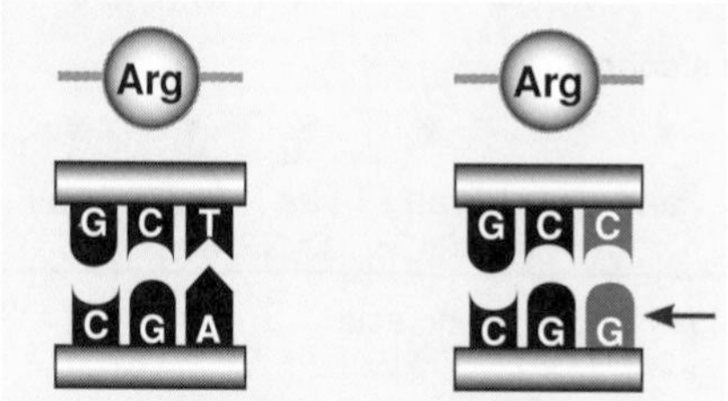

Arg
G C T
C G A
Arg
G C C
C G G

Normal sequence *Mutated sequence*

Silent Mutations

If a mutation does not change the amino acid sequence it is called silent. For example, six different three-base sequences encode arginine. Silent mutations are also **neutral** if they do not alter the fitness of the organism.

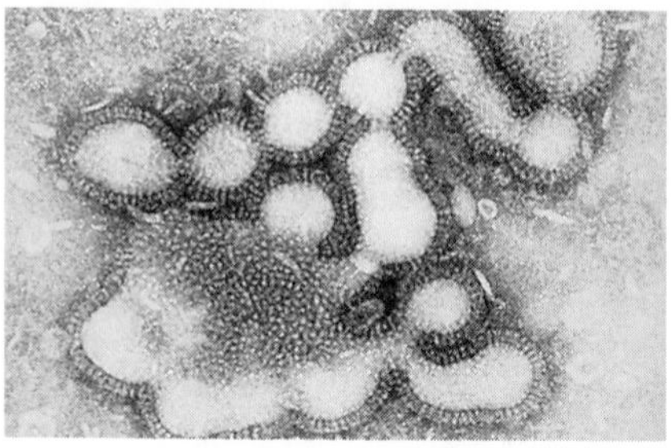

Beneficial Mutations

Sometimes mutations help the survival of an organism. In viruses (e.g. *Influenzavirus* above) genes coding for the glycoprotein coat are constantly mutating, producing new strains that avoid detection by the host's immune system.

1. (a) What is a gene mutation? ___

   (b) How can changes in a DNA sequence occur? ___

   ___

2. Explain how mutation can be harmful or beneficial: ___

   ___

3. (a) What mutation is responsible for NSRD? ___

   (b) What is the immediate effect of this mutation? ___

   (c) How does the mutation cause deafness? ___

   ___

© 2015 BIOZONE International
ISBN:978-1-927309-31-5
Photocopying Prohibited

123 Sickle Cell Mutation

Key Idea: The substitution of one nucleotide from T to A results in sickle cell disease. Heterozygotes are carriers.

Sickle cell disease is an inherited blood disorder caused by a gene mutation (Hb^s), which produces a faulty beta (β) chain haemoglobin (Hb) protein. This in turn produces red blood cells with a deformed sickle appearance and a reduced capacity to carry oxygen. The mutant and the normal allele (gene version) are equally expressed. People heterozygous for the mutation (one mutant allele, one normal allele) are carriers. They have enough functional Hb and suffer only minor effects.

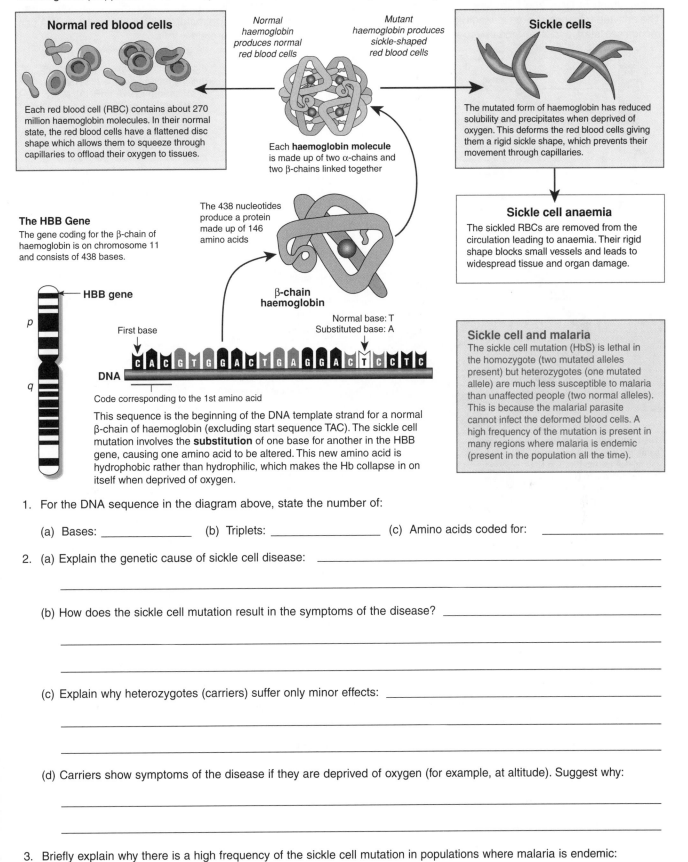

Normal red blood cells

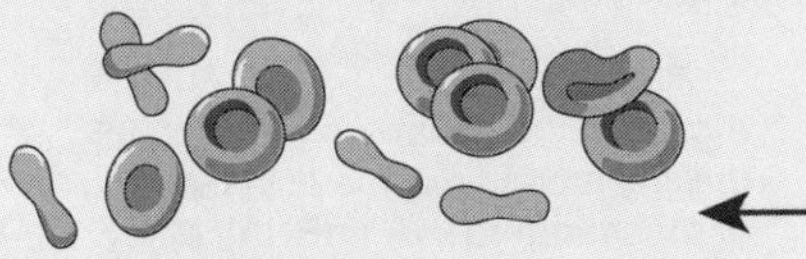

Each red blood cell (RBC) contains about 270 million haemoglobin molecules. In their normal state, the red blood cells have a flattened disc shape which allows them to squeeze through capillaries to offload their oxygen to tissues.

Normal haemoglobin produces normal red blood cells

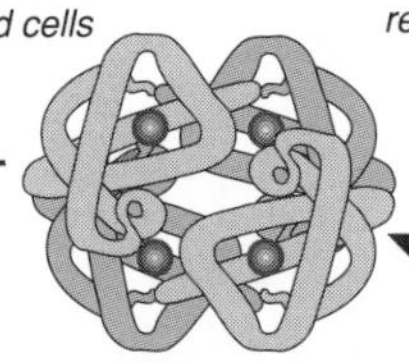

Mutant haemoglobin produces sickle-shaped red blood cells

Each **haemoglobin molecule** is made up of two α-chains and two β-chains linked together

Sickle cells

The mutated form of haemoglobin has reduced solubility and precipitates when deprived of oxygen. This deforms the red blood cells giving them a rigid sickle shape, which prevents their movement through capillaries.

Sickle cell anaemia

The sickled RBCs are removed from the circulation leading to anaemia. Their rigid shape blocks small vessels and leads to widespread tissue and organ damage.

The HBB Gene

The gene coding for the β-chain of haemoglobin is on chromosome 11 and consists of 438 bases.

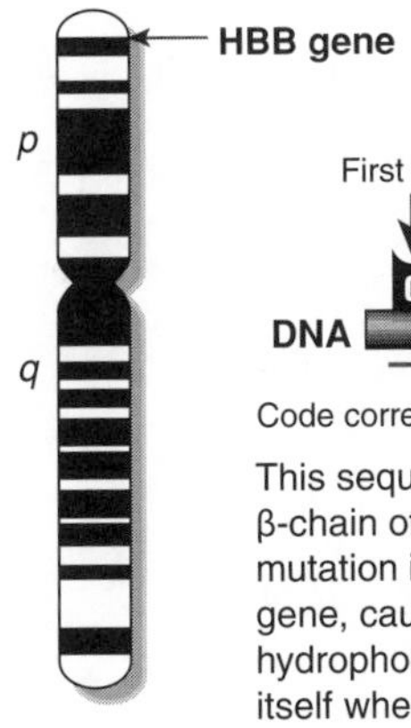
HBB gene
p
q

The 438 nucleotides produce a protein made up of 146 amino acids

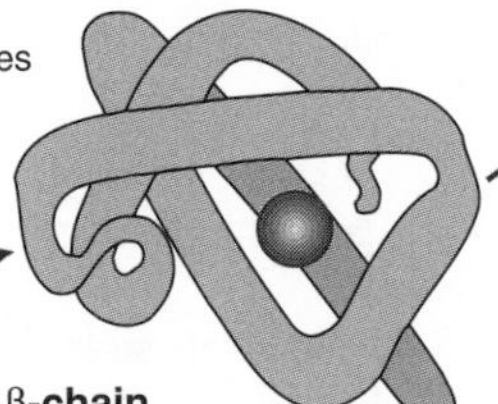

β-chain haemoglobin

First base
Normal base: T
Substituted base: A
C A C G T G G A C T G A G G A C T C C T C
DNA

Code corresponding to the 1st amino acid

This sequence is the beginning of the DNA template strand for a normal β-chain of haemoglobin (excluding start sequence TAC). The sickle cell mutation involves the **substitution** of one base for another in the HBB gene, causing one amino acid to be altered. This new amino acid is hydrophobic rather than hydrophilic, which makes the Hb collapse in on itself when deprived of oxygen.

Sickle cell and malaria

The sickle cell mutation (HbS) is lethal in the homozygote (two mutated alleles present) but heterozygotes (one mutated allele) are much less susceptible to malaria than unaffected people (two normal alleles). This is because the malarial parasite cannot infect the deformed blood cells. A high frequency of the mutation is present in many regions where malaria is endemic (present in the population all the time).

1. For the DNA sequence in the diagram above, state the number of:

   (a) Bases: ______________ (b) Triplets: ______________ (c) Amino acids coded for: ______________

2. (a) Explain the genetic cause of sickle cell disease: ______________

   (b) How does the sickle cell mutation result in the symptoms of the disease? ______________

   (c) Explain why heterozygotes (carriers) suffer only minor effects: ______________

   (d) Carriers show symptoms of the disease if they are deprived of oxygen (for example, at altitude). Suggest why: ______________

3. Briefly explain why there is a high frequency of the sickle cell mutation in populations where malaria is endemic: ______________

© 2015 BIOZONE International
ISBN: 978-1-927309-31-5
Photocopying Prohibited

124 Transcription in Eukaryotes

Key Idea: Transcription is the first step of gene expression. A segment of DNA is transcribed (rewritten) into mRNA. In eukaryotes, transcription takes place in the nucleus.

The enzyme that directly controls transcription is RNA polymerase, which makes a strand of mRNA using the single strand of DNA (the **template strand**) as a template. The enzyme transcribes a gene length of DNA at a time and recognises start and stop signals (codes) at the beginning and end of the gene. Only RNA polymerase is involved in mRNA synthesis as it unwinds the DNA as well. It is common to find several RNA polymerase enzyme molecules on the same gene at any one time, allowing a high rate of mRNA synthesis to occur. In eukaryotes, non-coding sections called **introns** must first be removed and the remaining **exons** spliced together to form mature mRNA before the mRNA can be translated into a protein.

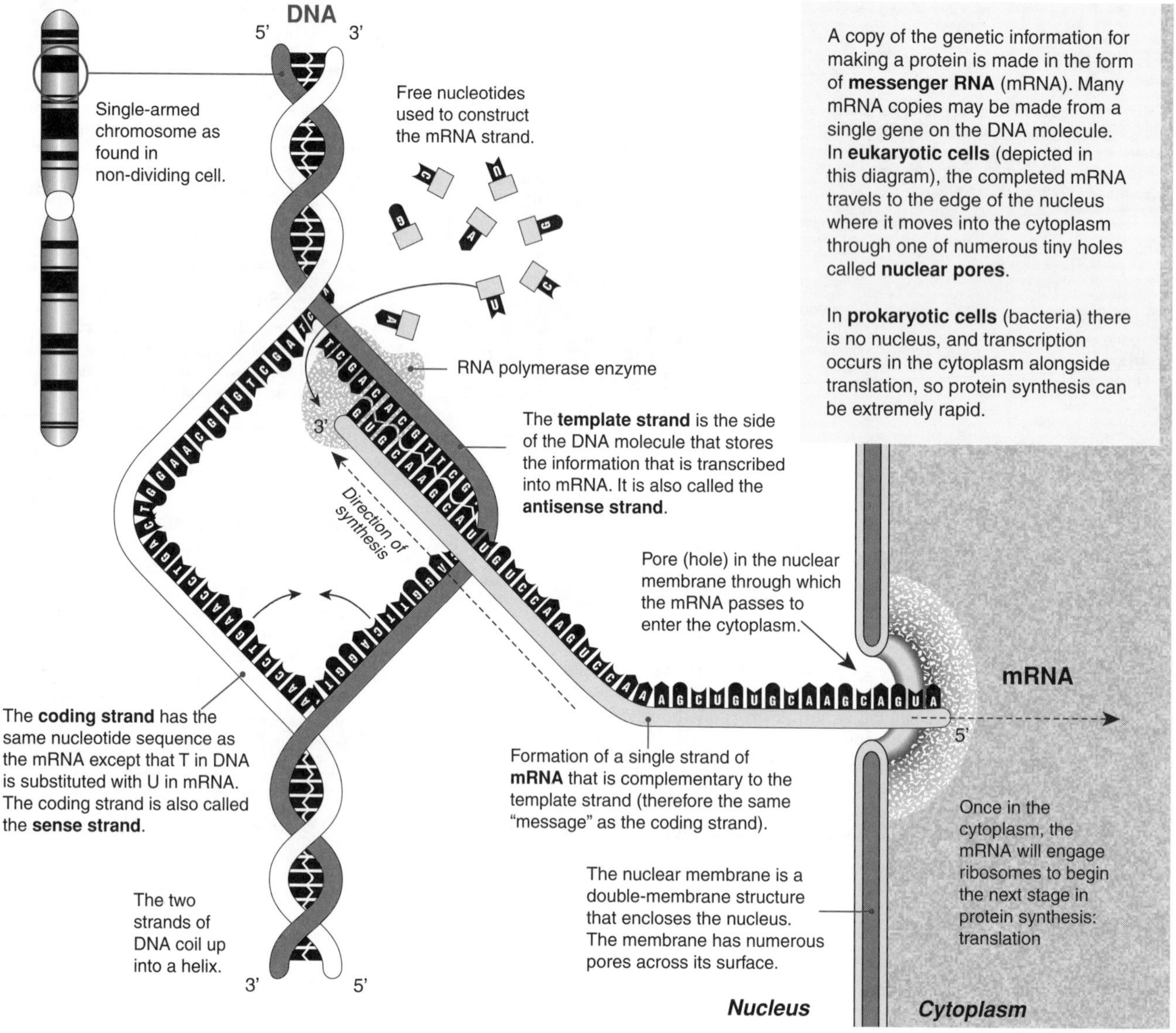

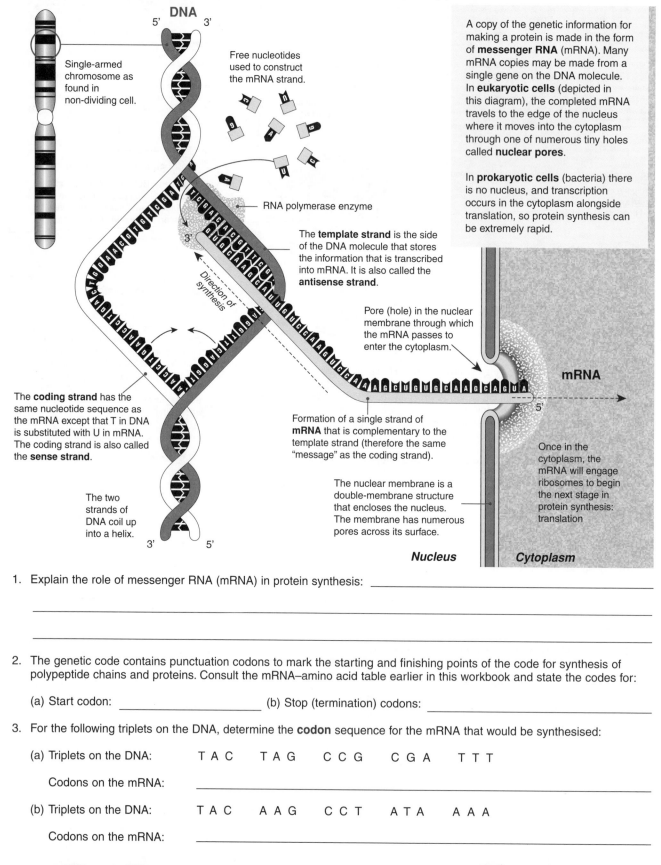

DNA
5'
3'
Single-armed chromosome as found in non-dividing cell.
Free nucleotides used to construct the mRNA strand.
A copy of the genetic information for making a protein is made in the form of **messenger RNA** (mRNA). Many mRNA copies may be made from a single gene on the DNA molecule. In **eukaryotic cells** (depicted in this diagram), the completed mRNA travels to the edge of the nucleus where it moves into the cytoplasm through one of numerous tiny holes called **nuclear pores**.
In **prokaryotic cells** (bacteria) there is no nucleus, and transcription occurs in the cytoplasm alongside translation, so protein synthesis can be extremely rapid.
RNA polymerase enzyme
The **template strand** is the side of the DNA molecule that stores the information that is transcribed into mRNA. It is also called the **antisense strand**.
Direction of synthesis
Pore (hole) in the nuclear membrane through which the mRNA passes to enter the cytoplasm.
mRNA
The **coding strand** has the same nucleotide sequence as the mRNA except that T in DNA is substituted with U in mRNA. The coding strand is also called the **sense strand**.
Formation of a single strand of **mRNA** that is complementary to the template strand (therefore the same "message" as the coding strand).
Once in the cytoplasm, the mRNA will engage ribosomes to begin the next stage in protein synthesis: translation
The two strands of DNA coil up into a helix.
The nuclear membrane is a double-membrane structure that encloses the nucleus. The membrane has numerous pores across its surface.
Nucleus
Cytoplasm

1. Explain the role of messenger RNA (mRNA) in protein synthesis: ______________________________

____

____

2. The genetic code contains punctuation codons to mark the starting and finishing points of the code for synthesis of polypeptide chains and proteins. Consult the mRNA–amino acid table earlier in this workbook and state the codes for:

   (a) Start codon: ______________ (b) Stop (termination) codons: ______________

3. For the following triplets on the DNA, determine the **codon** sequence for the mRNA that would be synthesised:

   (a) Triplets on the DNA: TAC TAG CCG CGA TTT

   Codons on the mRNA: ______________________________

   (b) Triplets on the DNA: TAC AAG CCT ATA AAA

   Codons on the mRNA: ______________________________

© 2015 BIOZONE International
ISBN:978-1-927309-31-5
Photocopying Prohibited

125 Translation

Key Idea: Translation is the second step of gene expression. It occurs in the cytoplasm, where ribosomes read the mRNA code and decode it to synthesise protein.

In eukaryotes, translation occurs in the cytoplasm associated with free ribosomes or ribosomes on the rough endoplasmic reticulum. The diagram below shows how a mRNA molecule can be 'serviced' by many ribosomes at the same time. The role of the tRNA molecules is to bring in the individual amino acids. The anticodon of each tRNA must make a perfect complementary match with the mRNA codon before the amino acid is released. Once released, the amino acid is added to the growing polypeptide chain by enzymes.

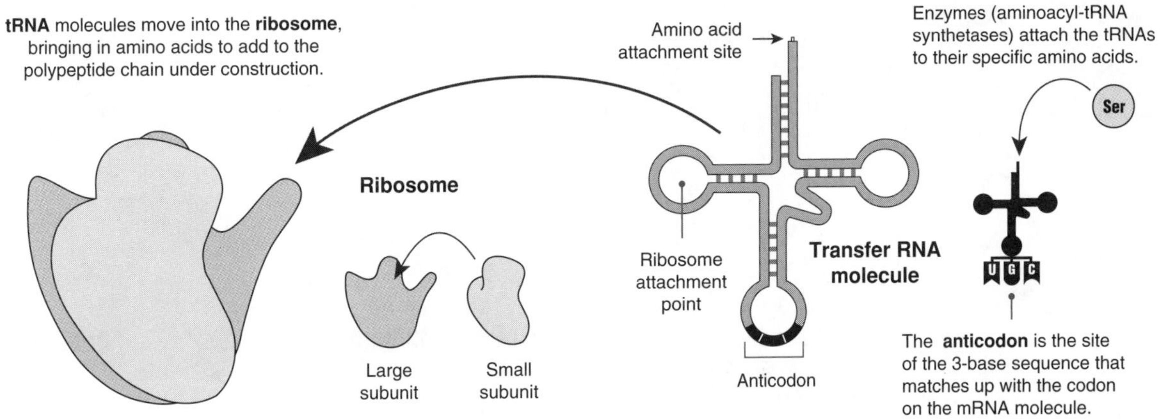
tRNA molecules move into the **ribosome**, bringing in amino acids to add to the polypeptide chain under construction.
Ribosome
Large subunit
Small subunit
Amino acid attachment site
Ribosome attachment point
Transfer RNA molecule
Anticodon
Enzymes (aminoacyl-tRNA synthetases) attach the tRNAs to their specific amino acids.
Ser
UGC
The **anticodon** is the site of the 3-base sequence that matches up with the codon on the mRNA molecule.

Ribosomes are made up of a complex of ribosomal RNA (rRNA) and proteins. They exist as two separate sub-units (above) until they are attracted to a binding site on the mRNA molecule, when they join together. Ribosomes have binding sites that attract transfer RNA (**tRNA**) molecules loaded with amino acids. The tRNA molecules are about 80 nucleotides in length and are made under the direction of genes in the chromosomes. There is a different tRNA molecule for each of the different possible anticodons (see the diagram below) and, because of the degeneracy of the genetic code, there may be up to six different tRNAs carrying the same amino acid.

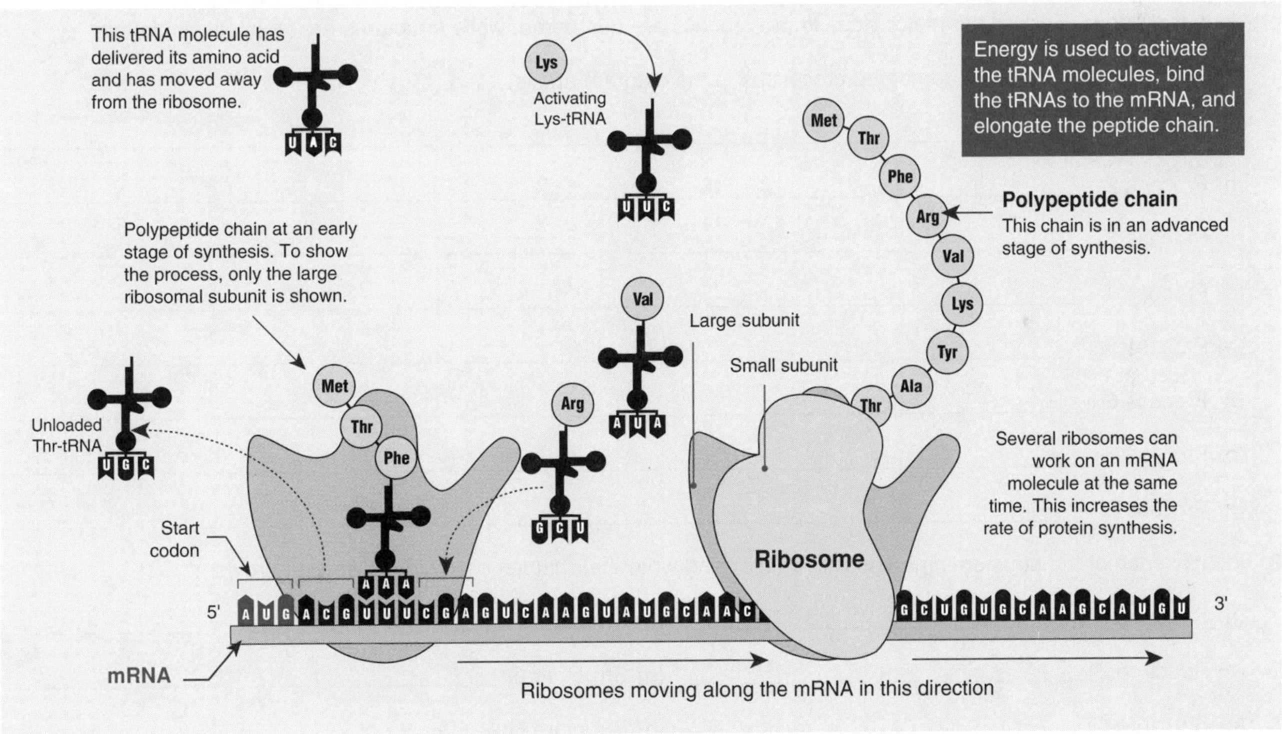
This tRNA molecule has delivered its amino acid and has moved away from the ribosome.
UAC
Lys
Activating Lys-tRNA
UUC
Energy is used to activate the tRNA molecules, bind the tRNAs to the mRNA, and elongate the peptide chain.
Met
Thr
Phe
Arg
Val
Lys
Tyr
Ala
Thr
Polypeptide chain
This chain is in an advanced stage of synthesis.
Polypeptide chain at an early stage of synthesis. To show the process, only the large ribosomal subunit is shown.
Val
AUA
Large subunit
Small subunit
Unloaded Thr-tRNA
UGC
Met
Thr
Phe
Arg
GCU
AAA
Start codon
Several ribosomes can work on an mRNA molecule at the same time. This increases the rate of protein synthesis.
Ribosome
5'
AUGACGUUUCGAGUCAAGUAUGCAAC
GCUGUGCAAGCAUGU
3'
mRNA
Ribosomes moving along the mRNA in this direction

1. For the following codons on the mRNA, determine the **anticodons** for each tRNA that would deliver the amino acids:

   Codons on the mRNA: U A C U A G C C G C G A U U U

   Anticodons on the tRNAs: ______________________________

2. There are many different types of tRNA molecules, each with a different anticodon (HINT: see the mRNA table).

   (a) How many different tRNA types are there, each with a unique anticodon? ______________________________

   (b) Explain your answer: ______________________________

   ____

126 Protein Synthesis Summary

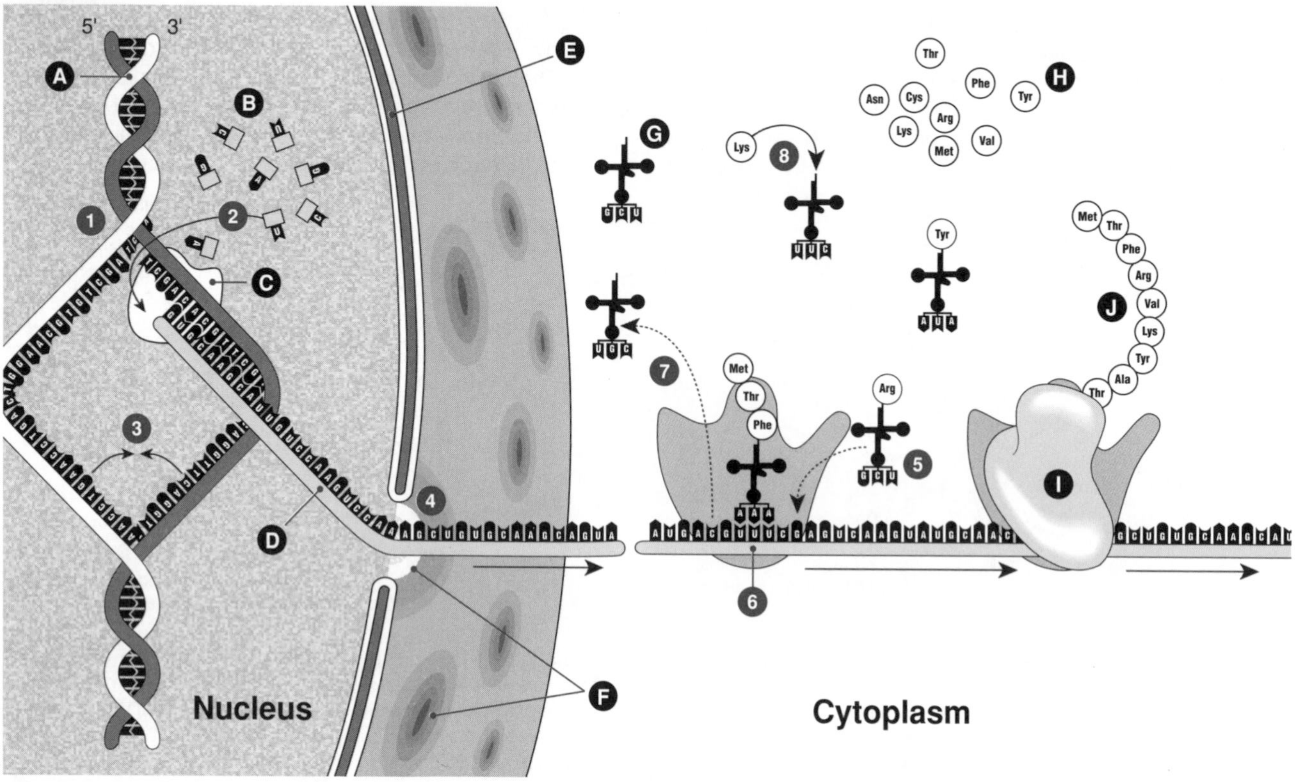

5'
3'
A
B
C
D
E
F
G
H
I
J
1
2
3
4
5
6
7
8
Nucleus
Cytoplasm
Thr
Asn
Cys
Phe
Tyr
Arg
Lys
Met
Val
Lys
Tyr
Met
Thr
Phe
Arg
Val
Lys
Tyr
Ala
Thr
Met
Thr
Phe
Arg

The diagram above shows an overview of the process of protein synthesis. It is a combination of the diagrams from the previous two pages. Each of the major steps in the process are numbered, while structures are labelled with letters.

1. Briefly describe each of the numbered processes in the diagram above:

   (a) Process 1: ____________________

   (b) Process 2: ____________________

   (c) Process 3: ____________________

   (d) Process 4: ____________________

   (e) Process 5: ____________________

   (f) Process 6: ____________________

   (g) Process 7: ____________________

   (h) Process 8: ____________________

2. Identify each of the structures marked with a letter and write their names below in the spaces provided:

   (a) Structure A: ____________________ (f) Structure F: ____________________

   (b) Structure B: ____________________ (g) Structure G: ____________________

   (c) Structure C: ____________________ (h) Structure H: ____________________

   (d) Structure D: ____________________ (i) Structure I: ____________________

   (e) Structure E: ____________________ (j) Structure J: ____________________

3. Describe two factors that would determine whether or not a particular protein is produced in the cell:

   (a) ____________________

   ____

   (b) ____________________

   ____

© 2015 BIOZONE International
ISBN:978-1-927309-31-5
Photocopying Prohibited

127 Chapter Review

Summarise what you know about this topic under the headings provided. You can draw diagrams or mind maps, or write short notes to organise your thoughts. Use the images and hints to help you and refer back to the introduction to check the points covered:

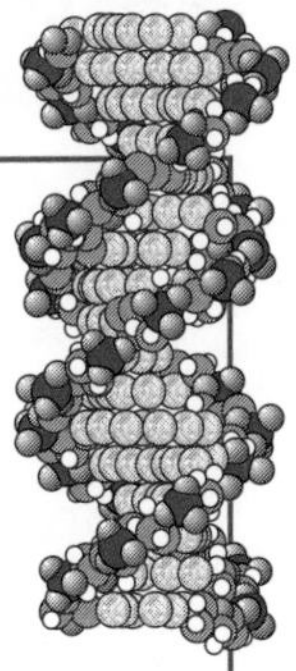

Nucleotides and nucleic acids

HINT: Structure and function of nucleotides, nucleic acids and ATP (a nucleotide derivative).

DNA replication

HINT: How does the structure of DNA relate to its replication.

Gene mutations

HINT: Describe gene mutations. Explain the mutation involved in sickle cell disease.

Genes to proteins

HINT: DNA to mRNA, mRNA to polypeptides. The genetic code.

© 2015 **BIOZONE** International
ISBN: 978-1-927309-31-5
Photocopying Prohibited

128 KEY TERMS AND IDEAS: Did You Get It?

1. Test your vocabulary by matching each term to its correct definition, as identified by its preceding letter code.

base-pairing rule	A	Single stranded nucleic acid that consists of nucleotides containing ribose sugar.
coding strand	B	Macromolecule consisting of many millions of units containing a phosphate group, sugar and a base (A,T, C or G). Stores the genetic information of the cell.
DNA	C	The process of creating an equivalent mRNA copy of a sequence of DNA.
double helix	D	The structural units of nucleic acids, DNA and RNA.
gene	E	The stage of gene expression in which mRNA is decoded to produce a polypeptide..
genetic code	F	The DNA strand with the same base sequence as the mRNA transcript produced (although with thymine replaced by uracil in mRNA).
mutation	G	The sequence of DNA that is read during the synthesis of mRNA.
nucleic acids	H	A single-ringed organic base that forms uracil, cytosine, or thymine in nucleic acids.
nucleotides	I	The rule governing the pairing of complementary bases in DNA
purine	J	A section of DNA that codes for a protein or other functional mRNA product.
pyrimidine	K	Universally found macromolecules composed of chains of nucleotides. These molecules carry genetic information within cells.
RNA	L	A change in the DNA sequence.
template strand	M	A set of rules by which information encoded in DNA or mRNA is translated into proteins
transcription	N	The shape of DNA.
translation	O	A two-ringed organic base that forms adenine and guanine in nucleic acids.

2. An original DNA sequence is shown right: **GCG TGA TTT GTA GGC GCT CTG**

   For each of the following DNA mutations, state the type of mutation that has occurred:

   (a) **GCG TGT TTG TAG GCG CTC TG** ____________________

   (b) **GCG TGA TTT GTA AGG CGC TCT G** ____________________

   (c) **GCG TGA TTT GGA GGC GCT CTG** ____________________

3. For the following DNA sequence, give the mRNA sequence and then Identify the amino acids that are encoded. For this question you may consult the mRNA-amino acid table earlier in the chapter.

   DNA: G A A A C C C T T A C A T A T C G T G C T

   mRNA: ____________________

   Amino acids: ____________________

4. Complete the following paragraph by **deleting** one of the words in the **bracketed () pairs** below:

   In eukaryotes, gene expression begins with (transcription/translation) which occurs in the (cytoplasm/nucleus). (Transcription/Translation) is the copying of the DNA code into (mRNA/tRNA). The (mRNA/tRNA) is then transported to the (cytoplasm/nucleus) where (transcription/translation) occurs. Ribosomes attach to the (mRNA/tRNA) and help match the codons on (mRNA/tRNA) with the anticodons on (mRNA/tRNA). The (mRNA/tRNA) transports the animo acids to the ribosome where they are added to the growing (polypeptide/carbohydrate) chain.

© 2015 **BIOZONE** International
ISBN:978-1-927309-31-5
Photocopying Prohibited

Topic 7 Transport in plants

Key terms

apoplast
cohesion-tension hypothesis
hydrophyte
phloem
potomter
pressure-flow hypothesis
root
sink
solute
source
stem
symplast
translocation
transpiration
transpiration rate
transpiration stream
vascular tissue
water potential
xerophyte
xylem

7.1 Structure of plant transport tissues

Learning outcomes — Activity number

☐ 1 With reference to size and growth form, explain why multicellular plants require a transport system. Describe the general structure of the plant body, identifying the relationship between the support and transport tissues. 129

☐ 2 Describe the structure and function of the vascular system in the roots, stems, and leaves of herbaceous dicotyledonous plants. Describe the composition, arrangement, and role of phloem and xylem tissue. 129-131

☐ 3 PRAC Using prepared slides, draw and label plan diagrams of transverse sections of stems, roots, and leaves of herbaceous dicot plants. Use an eyepiece graticule to show the tissues in the correct proportions. 130-134

☐ 4 PRAC Using prepared slides, draw and label the cells in TS and LS sections of roots, stems, and leaves of herbaceous dicot plants. 130-134

☐ 5 PRAC Using prepared slides, draw and label the structure of xylem vessel elements and phloem sieve tube elements and companion cells. Recognise these cells when viewed with a light microscope. 130 131

☐ 6 Relate the structure of xylem vessel elements, and phloem sieve tube elements and companion cells to their functions. 130 131

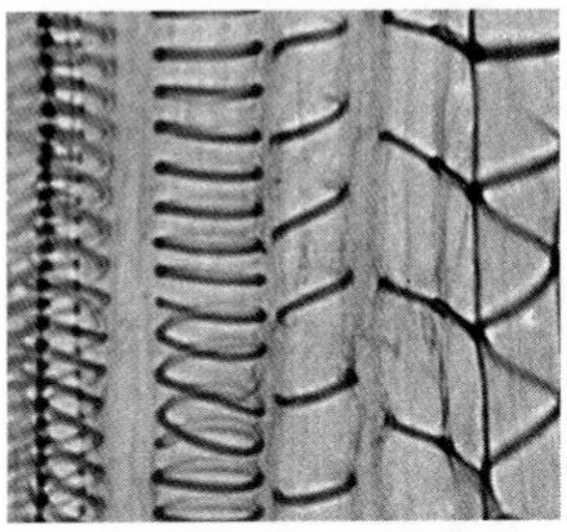

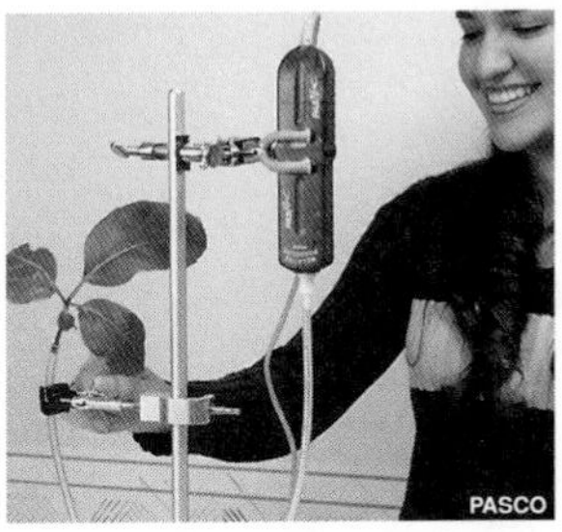
PASCO

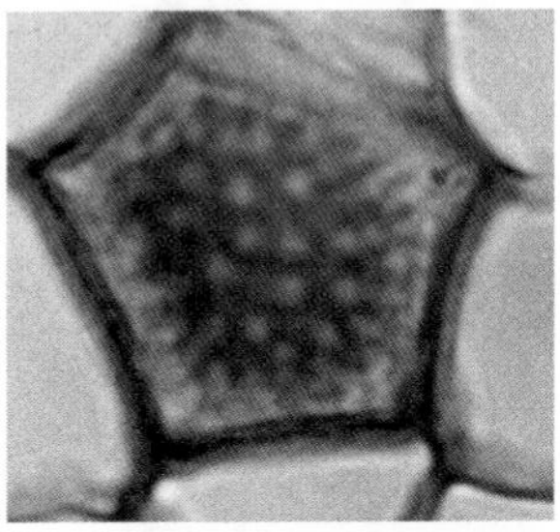

7.2 Transport mechanisms

Learning outcomes — Activity number

☐ 7 Explain the movement of water between plant cells, and between them and their environment in terms of water potential. 135 136

☐ 8 Explain the role of hydrogen bonding of water molecules in the transport of water in the xylem. Define transpiration and explain the transpiration stream in terms of osmosis, gradients in water potential (transpiration pull), cohesion-tension, and capillary action (adhesion to cellulose cell walls). 136

☐ 9 Describe and explain how water and mineral ions are transported from the soil to the xylem and from the roots to the leaves. Include reference to the apoplastic and symplastic pathways and the role of the Casparian strip. 135

☐ 10 Explain why transpiration is a consequence of gas exchange. 136

☐ 11 PRAC Using a simple potometer and grids to determine leaf surface area, investigate and explain factors affecting transpiration rate. 137

☐ 12 Explain and make annotated drawings to show how the leaves of xerophytes are adapted to reduce water loss by transpiration. 138

☐ 13 State that assimilates, e.g. sucrose and amino acids, move between sources and sinks in phloem sieve tubes. 139

☐ 14 Explain translocation in plants as an energy requiring process. Explain how sucrose is transported in the phloem, including reference to the pressure-flow hypothesis and the active loading of sucrose at sources and unloading at sinks. 139

129 Vascular Tissues in Plants

Key Idea: The xylem and phloem form the vascular tissue that moves fluids and minerals about the plant.

The vascular tissues (**xylem** and **phloem**) link all parts of the plant so that water, minerals, and manufactured food can be transported between all regions of the plant. The xylem and phloem are found together in vascular bundles. In dicotyledonous plants (below) the vascular bundles are located in a ring towards the outer edge of the stem. In monocotyledonous plants, the bundles are scattered randomly throughout the stem. The xylem transports water and minerals from the roots to the leaves, while the phloem transports sugars through the plant to where they are needed.

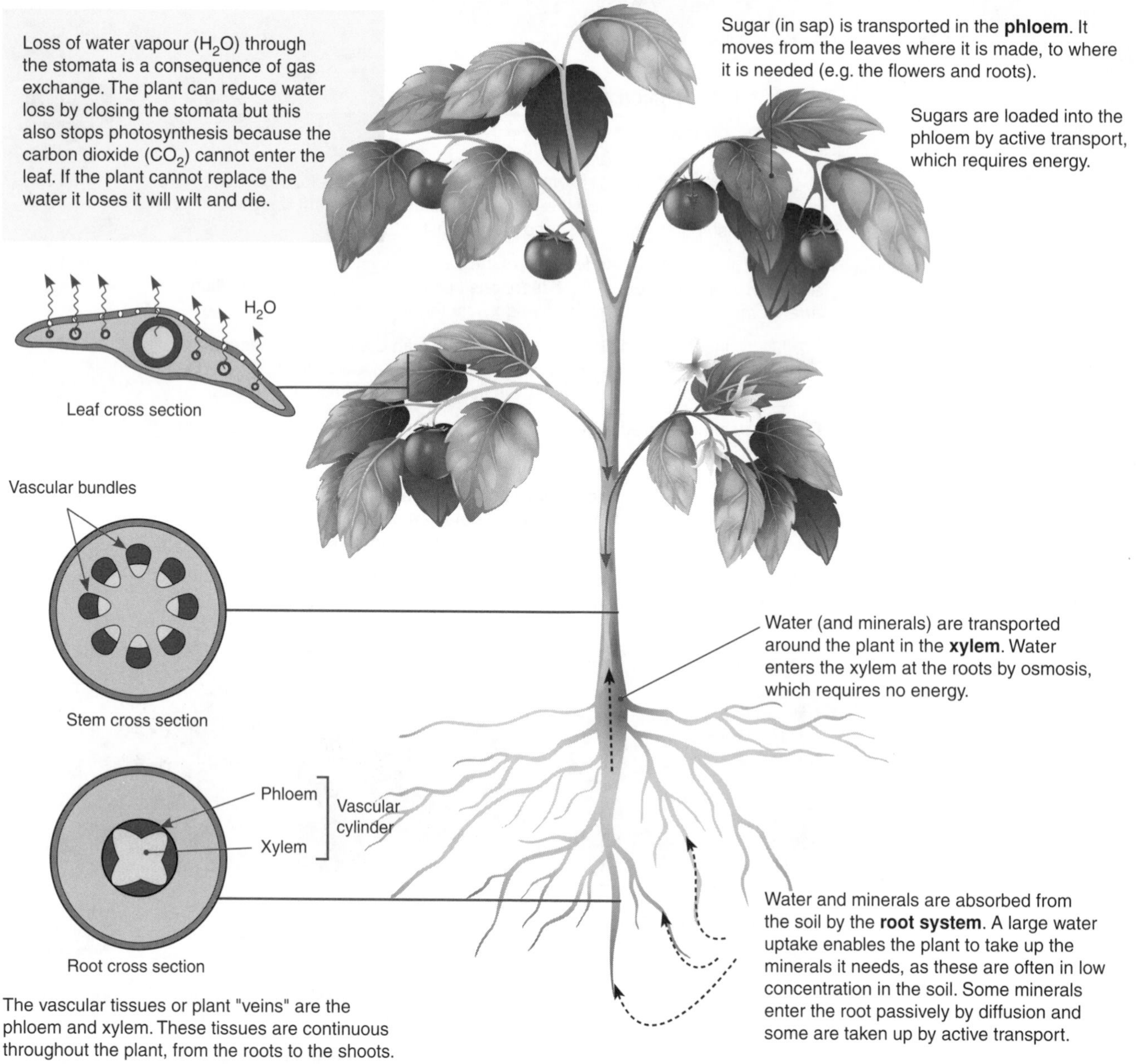

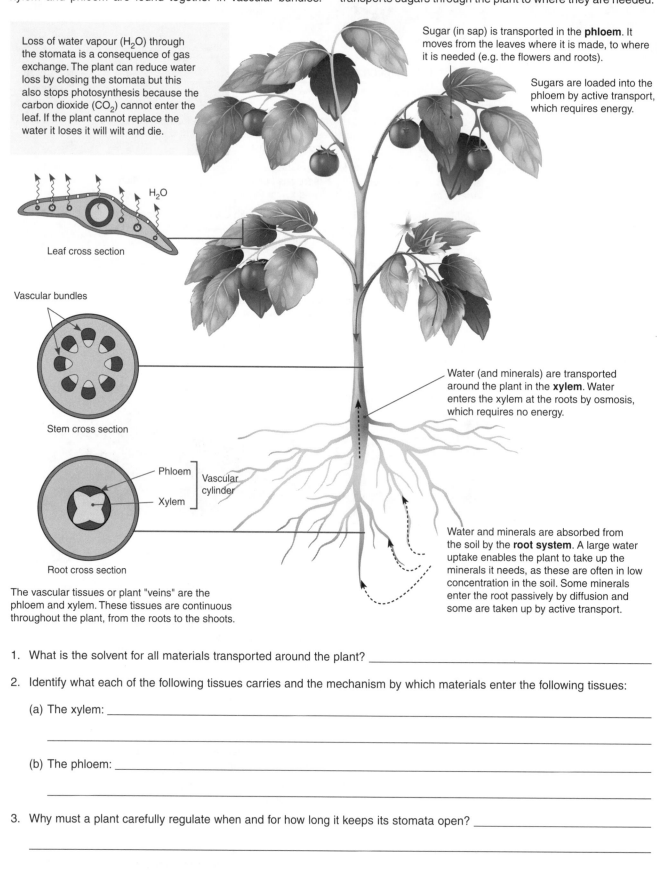

Loss of water vapour (H_2O) through the stomata is a consequence of gas exchange. The plant can reduce water loss by closing the stomata but this also stops photosynthesis because the carbon dioxide (CO_2) cannot enter the leaf. If the plant cannot replace the water it loses it will wilt and die.
Sugar (in sap) is transported in the **phloem**. It moves from the leaves where it is made, to where it is needed (e.g. the flowers and roots).
Sugars are loaded into the phloem by active transport, which requires energy.
H_2O
Leaf cross section
Vascular bundles
Stem cross section
Water (and minerals) are transported around the plant in the **xylem**. Water enters the xylem at the roots by osmosis, which requires no energy.
Phloem
Xylem
Vascular cylinder
Root cross section
Water and minerals are absorbed from the soil by the **root system**. A large water uptake enables the plant to take up the minerals it needs, as these are often in low concentration in the soil. Some minerals enter the root passively by diffusion and some are taken up by active transport.
The vascular tissues or plant "veins" are the phloem and xylem. These tissues are continuous throughout the plant, from the roots to the shoots.

1. What is the solvent for all materials transported around the plant? ______________________

2. Identify what each of the following tissues carries and the mechanism by which materials enter the following tissues:

   (a) The xylem: ______________________

   ____

   (b) The phloem: ______________________

   ____

3. Why must a plant carefully regulate when and for how long it keeps its stomata open? ______________________

____

____

© 2015 BIOZONE International
ISBN:978-1-927309-31-5
Photocopying Prohibited

130 Xylem

Key Idea: The xylem is involved in water and mineral transport in vascular plants.

Xylem is the principal water conducting tissue in vascular plants. It is also involved in conducting dissolved minerals, in food storage, and in supporting the plant body. As in animals, tissues in plants are groupings of different cell types that work together for a common function. In angiosperms, it is composed of five cell types: tracheids, vessels, xylem parenchyma, sclereids (short sclerenchyma cells), and fibres. The tracheids and vessel elements form the bulk of the tissue. They are heavily strengthened and are the conducting cells of the xylem. Parenchyma cells are involved in storage, while fibres and sclereids provide support. When mature, xylem is dead.

1. (a) What cells conduct the water in xylem?

(b) What other cells are present in xylem tissue and what are their roles?

2. (a) How does water pass between vessels?

(b) How does water pass between tracheids:

(c) Which cell type do you think provides the most rapid transport of water and why?

(d) Why do you think the tracheids and vessel elements have/need secondary thickening?

3. How can xylem vessels and tracheids be dead when mature and functional?

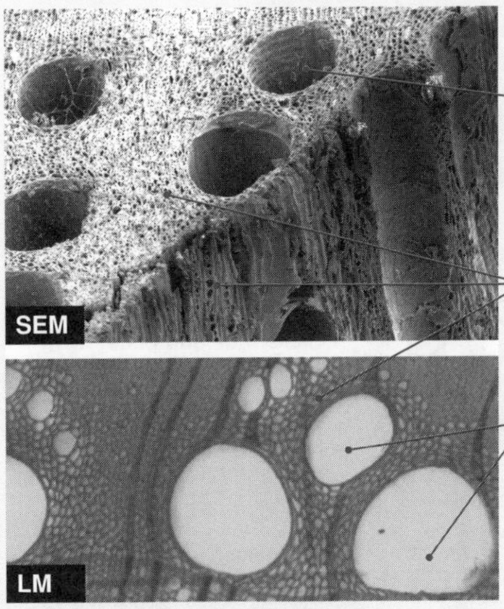
SEM
LM
Water moves through the continuous tubes made by the vessel elements of the xylem.
Smaller tracheids are connected by pits in the walls but do not have end wall perforations
Vessels
Xylem is dead when mature. Note how the cells have lost their cytoplasm.
McKDandy cc 2.5

As shown in these SEM and light micrographs of xylem, the **tracheids** and **vessel elements** form the bulk of the xylem tissue. They are heavily strengthened and are involved in moving water through the plant. The transporting elements are supported by parenchyma (packing and storage cells) and sclerenchyma cells (fibres and sclereids), which provide mechanical support to the xylem.

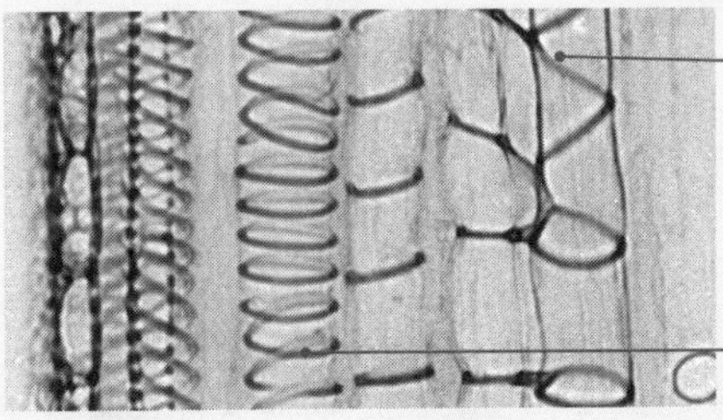
RCN
The xylem cells form continuous tubes through which water is conducted.
Spiral thickening of **lignin** around the walls of the vessel elements give extra strength and rigidity.

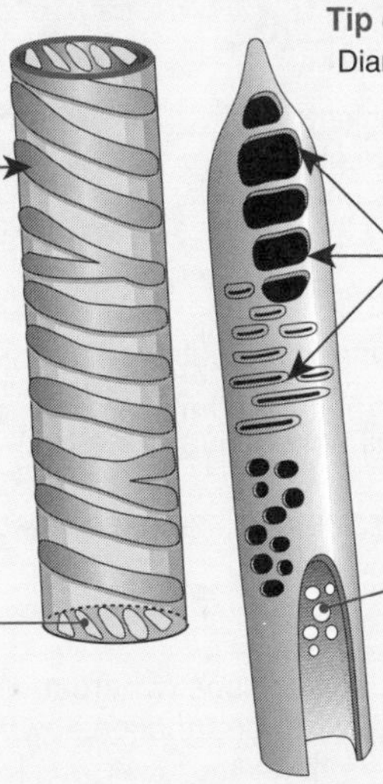
Vessel element
Diameter up to 500 µm
Secondary walls of cellulose are laid down after the cell has elongated or enlarged and lignin is deposited to add strength. This thickening is a feature of tracheids and vessels.
Vessels connect end to end. The end walls of the vessels are perforated to allow rapid water transport.
Tip of tracheid
Diameter ~80 µm
Pits and bordered pits allow transfer of water between cells but there are no end wall perforations.
No cytoplasm or nucleus in mature cell.
Tracheids are longer and thinner than vessels.

Vessel elements and tracheids are the two water conducting cell types in the xylem of flowering plants. Tracheids are long, tapering hollow cells. Water passes from one tracheid to another through thin regions in the wall called pits. Vessel elements are much larger cells with secondary thickening in different patterns (e.g. spirals). Vessel end walls are perforated to allow efficient conduction of water.

© 2015 **BIOZONE** International
ISBN: 978-1-927309-31-5
Photocopying Prohibited

131 Phloem

Key Idea: Phloem is the principal food (sugar) conducting tissue in vascular plants, transporting dissolved sugars around the plant.

Like xylem, **phloem** is a complex tissue, comprising a variable number of cell types. The bulk of phloem tissue comprises the **sieve tubes** (sieve tube members and sieve cells) and their companion cells. The sieve tubes are the principal conducting cells in phloem and are closely associated with the **companion cells** (modified parenchyma cells) with which they share a mutually dependent relationship. Other parenchyma cells, concerned with storage, occur in phloem, and strengthening fibres and sclereids (short sclerenchyma cells) may also be present. Unlike xylem, phloem is alive when mature.

LS through a sieve tube end plate

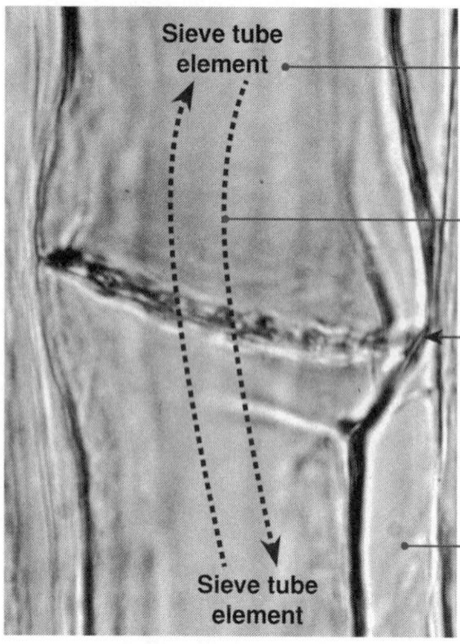
Sieve tube element
Sieve tube element
RCN

The sieve tube elements (also called sieve tube members) lose most of their organelles but are still alive when mature.

Sugar solution flows in both directions

Sieve tube end plate
Tiny holes (arrowed in the photograph below) perforate the sieve tube elements allowing the sugar solution to pass through.

Companion cell
A cell adjacent to the sieve tube member, responsible for keeping it alive.

TS through a sieve tube end plate

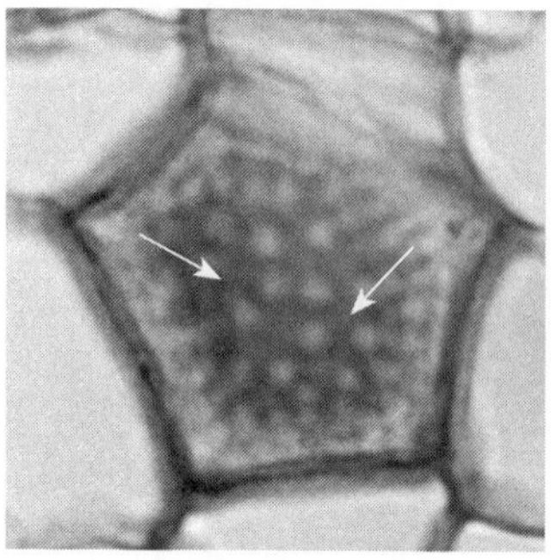
RCN

Adjacent sieve tube elements are connected through **sieve plates** through which phloem sap flows.

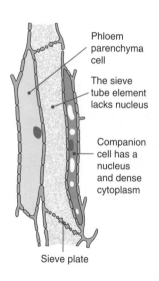

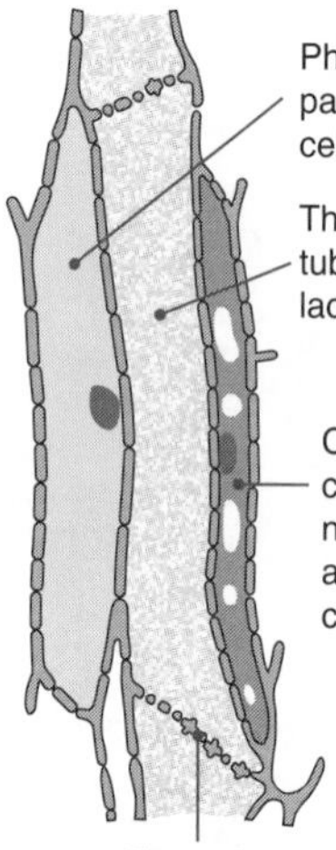
Phloem parenchyma cell
The sieve tube element lacks nucleus
Companion cell has a nucleus and dense cytoplasm
Sieve plate

The structure of phloem tissue

Phloem is alive at maturity and functions in the transport of sugars and minerals around the plant. Like xylem, it forms part of the structural vascular tissue of plants.

Fibres are associated with phloem as they are in xylem. Here they are seen in cross section where you can see the extremely thick cell walls and the way the fibres are clustered in groups. See the previous page for a view of fibres in longitudinal section.

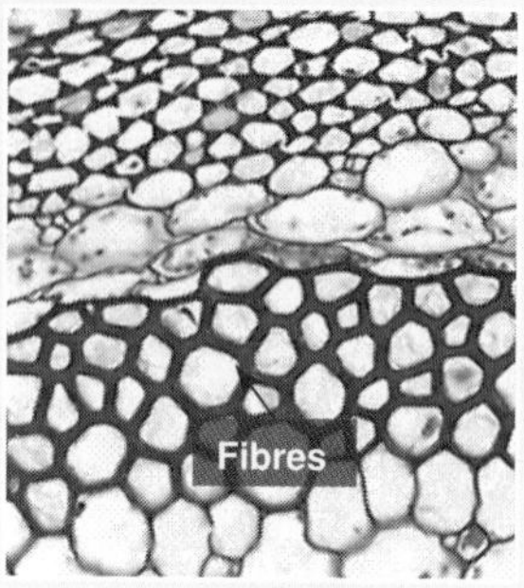
Fibres
WBS

In this cross section through a buttercup root, the smaller companion cells can be seen lying alongside the sieve tube members. It is the sieve tube elements that, end on end, produce the **sieve tubes**. They are the conducting tissue of phloem.

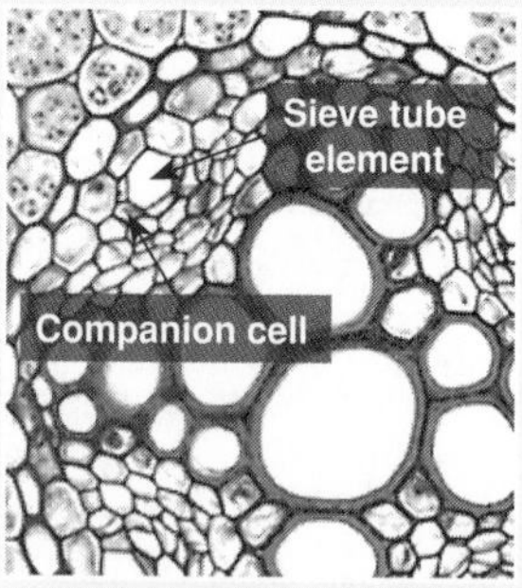
Sieve tube element
Companion cell
WBS

In this longitudinal section of a buttercup root, each sieve tube element has a thin **companion cell** associated with it. Companion cells retain their nucleus and control the metabolism of the sieve tube member next to them. They also have a role in the loading and unloading of sugar into the phloem.

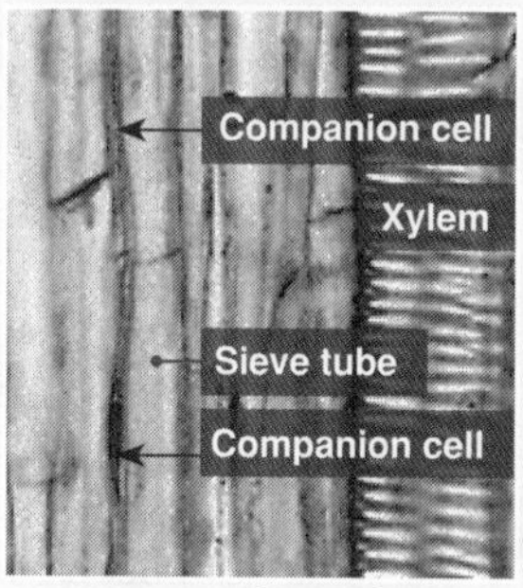
Companion cell
Xylem
Sieve tube
Companion cell
WBS

1. (a) What is the conducting cell type in phloem? ______

   (b) What other cell type is associated with these conducting cells? ______

   (c) Describe two roles of these associated cells: ______

   ______

2. Mature phloem is a live tissue, whereas xylem (the water transporting tissue) is dead when mature. Why is it necessary for phloem to be alive to be functional, whereas xylem can function as a dead tissue?

   ______

3. What is the role of fibres and sclereids in phloem? ______

   ______

4. What are the large open cells next to the phloem in the centre photo above right? ______

© 2015 **BIOZONE** International
ISBN:978-1-927309-31-5
Photocopying Prohibited

132 Stems

Key Idea: The vascular tissue in dicots can be identified by its appearance in sections viewed with a light microscope.

The vascular tissue (xylem and phloem) in the stems of dicotyledonous plants (dicots) is organised in bundles, which are distributed in a regular fashion around the outer edge of the stem. Each vascular bundle contains xylem tissue to the inside and phloem to the outside, separated by a ring of vascular cambium (actively dividing cells).

Dicot stem structure

In dicots, the vascular bundles are arranged in an orderly fashion around the periphery of the stem. Each vascular bundle contains **xylem** (to the inside) and **phloem** (to the outside). Between the phloem and the xylem is the **vascular cambium**. The cambium is a layer of cells that divide to produce the thickening of the stem, secondary xylem to the inside and secondary phloem to the outside.

Between the vascular bundles and the epidermis is the cortex of thick-walled collenchyma cells, which provide support and structure to the stem. The centre of the stem, called the **pith**, is filled with thin-walled parenchyma cells.

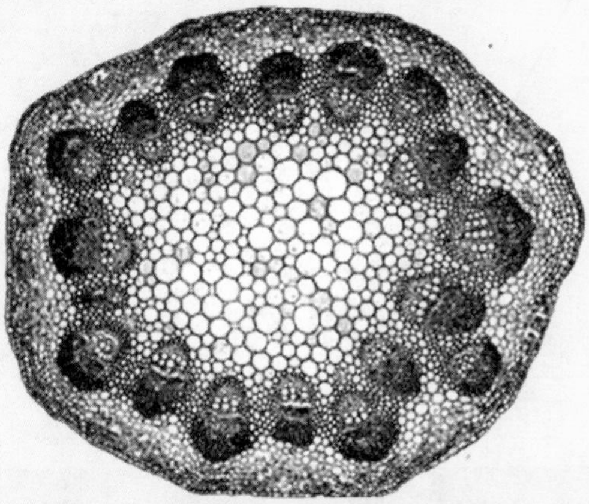

WBS

The image above shows a transverse section through the stem of a typical dicot stem (sunflower) as viewed with a light microscope. A plan diagram, illustrating the distribution and arrangement of the tissues, is shown below.

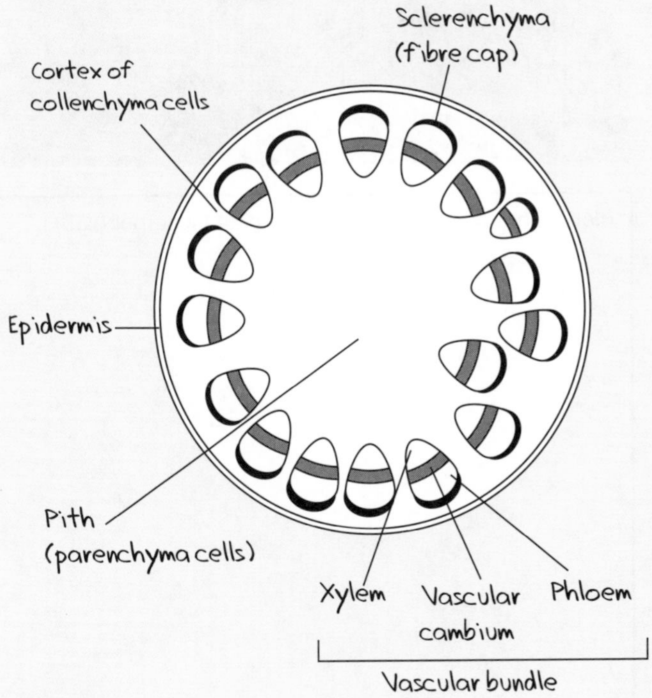
Sclerenchyma (fibre cap)
Cortex of collenchyma cells
Epidermis
Pith (parenchyma cells)
Xylem
Vascular cambium
Phloem
Vascular bundle

1. Describe how the vascular tissue in the stem of a dicot is arranged:

____

____

2. Identify the phloem (P) and xylem (X) tissue In the micrograph of a dicot stem below:

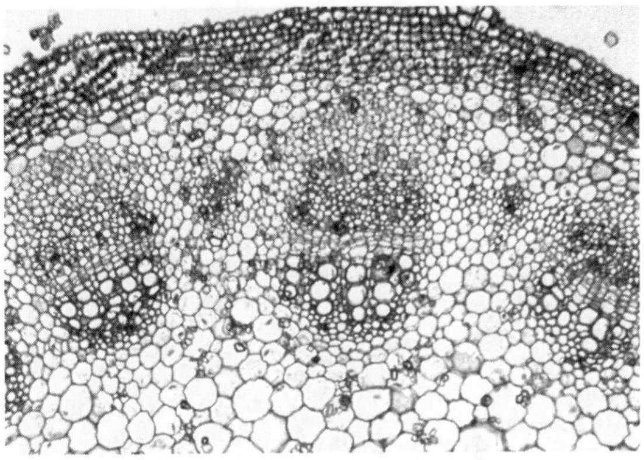

3. The diagram below shows a cross section of a typical dicot stem. identify the labels A - F:

A. ____

B. ____

C. ____

D. ____

E. ____

F. ____

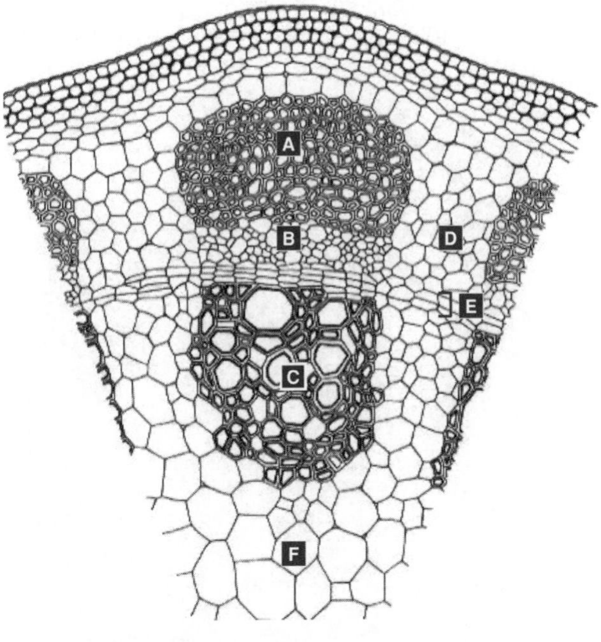
A
B
C
D
E
F

John main, PLU

Cross section through a typical dicot stem

© 2015 BIOZONE International
ISBN: 978-1-927309-31-5
Photocopying Prohibited

133 Roots

Key Idea: The xylem and phloem in dicot roots are arranged together forming a central cylinder called the stele.

The vascular tissue in dicot roots forms a central cylinder called the stele. Outside the stele is a cortex of large packing cells, which store starch and other substances. Roots absorb water and minerals from the soil so they can be transported to the rest of the plant. The root epidermis has a thin cuticle that presents no barrier to water entry. The surface area for water absorption is increased by the presence of root hairs, single cell extensions of the epidermal cells.

Dicot root structure

The primary tissues of a dicot root are structurally simple. The vascular tissue (xylem and phloem) forms a central cylinder through the root called the **stele**. The vascular tissue is surrounded by the pericycle, a ring of cells from which lateral roots arise. The large cortex is made up of parenchyma (packing) cells, which store starch and other substances. The air spaces between the cells are essential for aeration of the root tissue, which is non-photosynthetic.

The primary xylem (X) of dicot roots forms a star shape in the centre of the vascular cylinder with usually 3 or 4 points (below). The phloem (P) is located between the regions of xylem tissue.

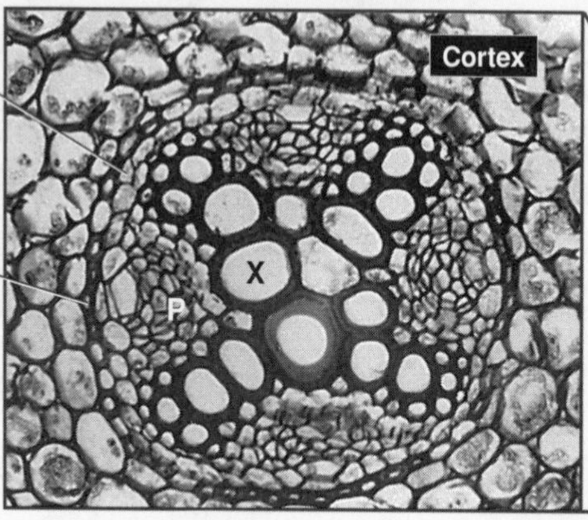
Pericycle: outermost part of the stele
Endodermis: innermost layer of the cortex. The cells of the endodermis have a waterproof band, called the Casparian strip, which forces water to enter the cells.
Cortex
X
P

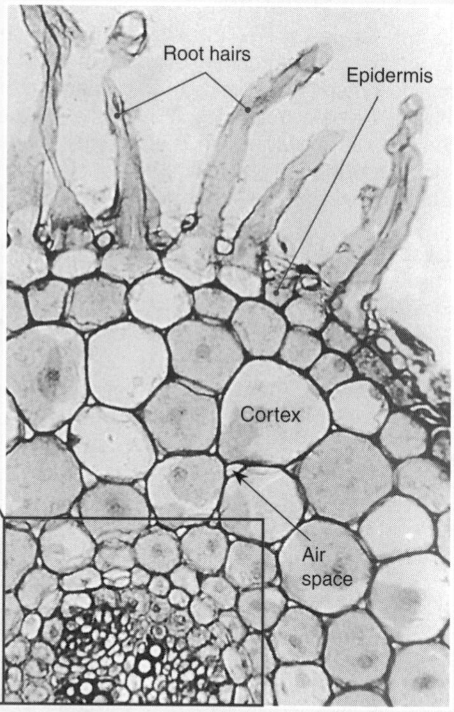
Root hairs
Epidermis
Cortex
Air space

1. The image on the right is an electron micrograph showing xylem vessels in a toothpick. Calculate the magnification of the image:

____

____

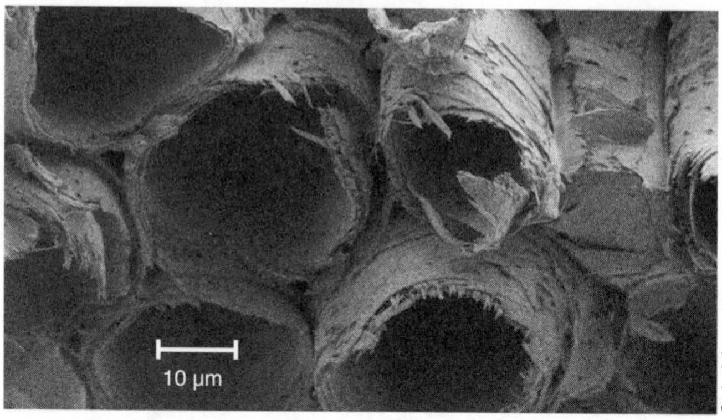
10 µm

Capkuckokos cc 4.0

2. The image below is a photomicrograph (x50) showing a partial section through a dicot root. Use this image and the information above to construct a plan diagram:

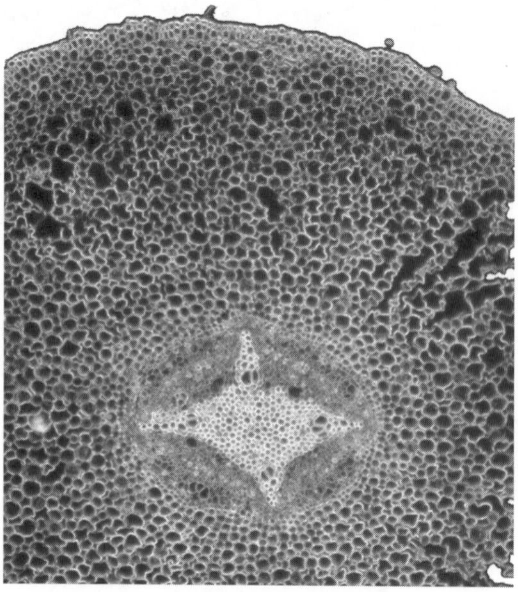

Plan diagram, partial section through a dicot root (x50)

© 2015 BIOZONE International
ISBN:978-1-927309-31-5
Photocopying Prohibited

134 Leaves

Key Idea: The vascular tissue in dicot leaves forms the leaf veins. The veins are supported and protected by a ring of parenchyma cells called the bundle sheath.

In dicot leaves, the vascular tissue is called the **leaf vein**, and is located in the spongy mesophyll layer (below). The vein is surrounded by a bundle sheath, layers of parenchyma cells that form a protective layer around the vein. The leaf is the site of photosynthesis in the plant, so the phloem transfers sugars from the source (where they are made) to where they are used (sink).

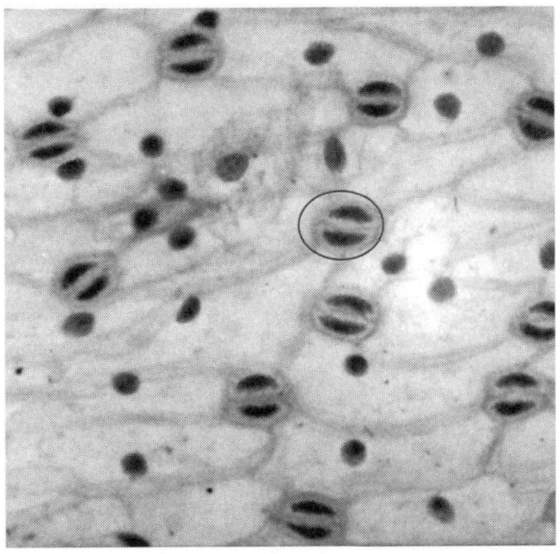

Light micrograph (x90) of the lower epidermis of a dicot plant with stomata (pores) flanked by dark, sausage shaped guard cells (example circled).

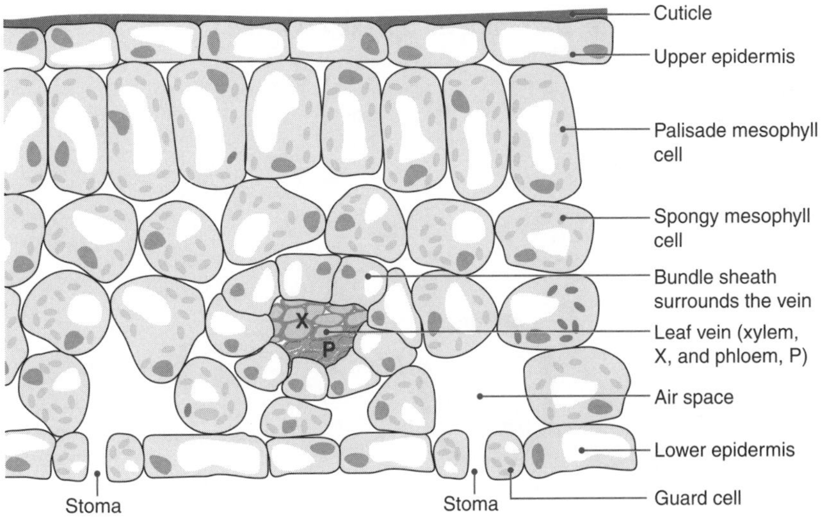
Cuticle
Upper epidermis
Palisade mesophyll cell
Spongy mesophyll cell
Bundle sheath surrounds the vein
Leaf vein (xylem, X, and phloem, P)
X
P
Air space
Lower epidermis
Guard cell
Stoma
Stoma

1. Aphids feed on phloem sap. Suggest why aphids are most abundant on the underside of a dicot leaf:

___

2. The image below shows a cross section through a dicot leaf (light microscope x 30). Use the word list to label the photograph and circle the leaf vein. Construct a plan diagram to show the arrangement of the tissues:

Word list:
xylem, phoem,
air space,
guard cells,
upper epidermis,
palisade mesophyll,
spongy mesophyll,
bundle sheath,
collenchyma,
lower epidermis

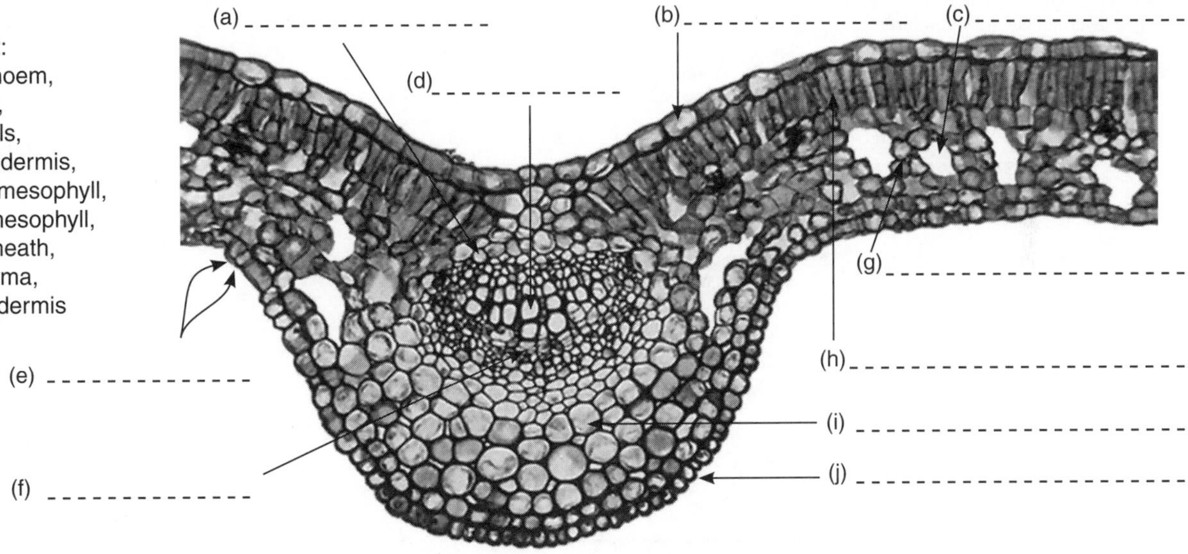
(a) ________________
(b) ________________
(c) ________________
(d) ________________
(e) ________________
(f) ________________
(g) ________________
(h) ________________
(i) ________________
(j) ________________

Plan diagram, cross section through a dicot leaf (x 30)

© 2015 **BIOZONE** International
ISBN: 978-1-927309-31-5
Photocopying Prohibited

135 Uptake at the Root

Key Idea: Water uptake by the root is a passive process. Mineral uptake can be passive or active.

Plants need to take up water and minerals constantly. They must compensate for the continuous loss of water from the leaves and provide the materials the plant needs to make food. The uptake of water and minerals is mostly restricted to the younger, most recently formed cells of the roots and the root hairs. Water uptake occurs by osmosis, whereas mineral ions enter the root by diffusion and active transport. Pathways for water movements through the plant are outlined below.

Water and mineral uptake by roots

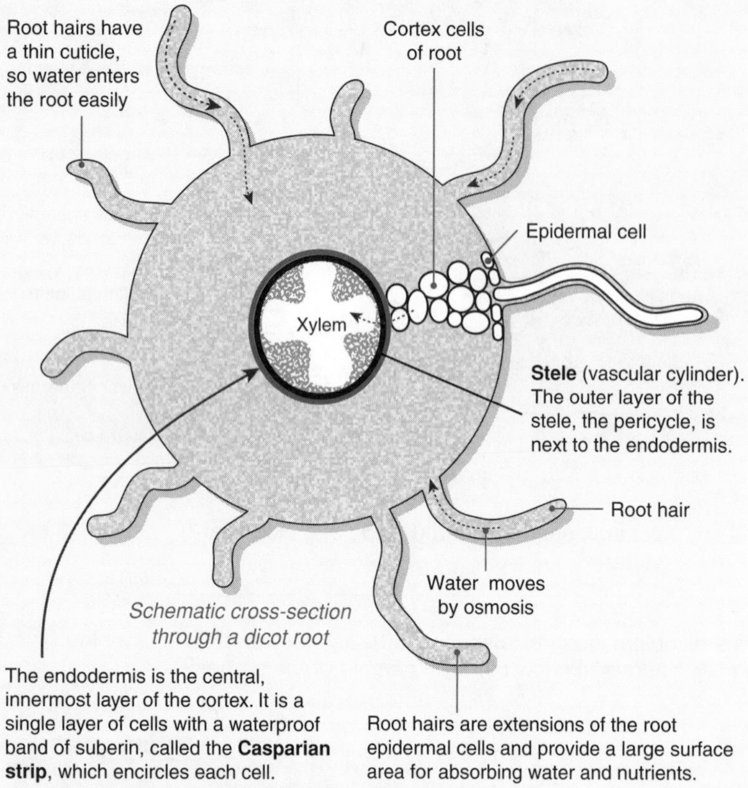
Root hairs have a thin cuticle, so water enters the root easily
Cortex cells of root
Epidermal cell
Xylem
Stele (vascular cylinder). The outer layer of the stele, the pericycle, is next to the endodermis.
Root hair
Water moves by osmosis
Schematic cross-section through a dicot root
The endodermis is the central, innermost layer of the cortex. It is a single layer of cells with a waterproof band of suberin, called the **Casparian strip**, which encircles each cell.
Root hairs are extensions of the root epidermal cells and provide a large surface area for absorbing water and nutrients.

Paths for water movement through the plant

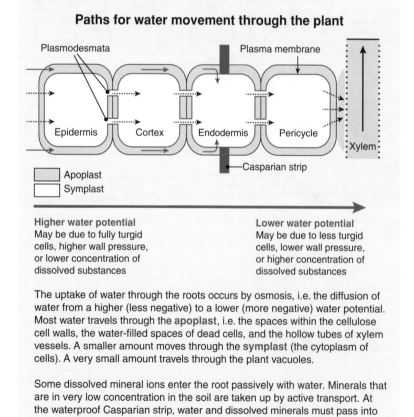

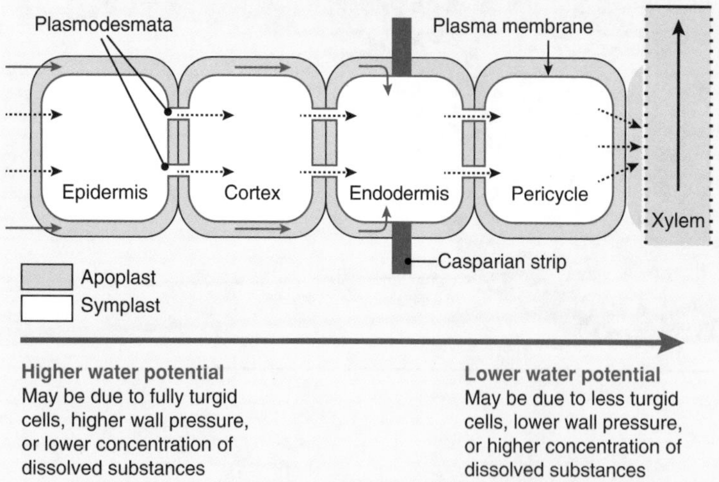
Plasmodesmata
Plasma membrane
Epidermis
Cortex
Endodermis
Pericycle
Xylem
Casparian strip
Apoplast
Symplast
Higher water potential
May be due to fully turgid cells, higher wall pressure, or lower concentration of dissolved substances
Lower water potential
May be due to less turgid cells, lower wall pressure, or higher concentration of dissolved substances

The uptake of water through the roots occurs by osmosis, i.e. the diffusion of water from a higher (less negative) to a lower (more negative) water potential. Most water travels through the **apoplast**, i.e. the spaces within the cellulose cell walls, the water-filled spaces of dead cells, and the hollow tubes of xylem vessels. A smaller amount moves through the **symplast** (the cytoplasm of cells). A very small amount travels through the plant vacuoles.

Some dissolved mineral ions enter the root passively with water. Minerals that are in very low concentration in the soil are taken up by active transport. At the waterproof Casparian strip, water and dissolved minerals must pass into the symplast, so the flow of materials into the stele can be regulated.

1. (a) What two mechanisms do plants use to absorb nutrients?

(b) Describe the two main pathways by which water moves through a plant:

2. Plants take up water constantly to compensate for losses due to transpiration. Describe a benefit of a large water uptake:

3. (a) How does the Casparian strip affect the route water takes into the stele?

(b) Why might this feature be an advantage in terms of selective mineral uptake?

© 2015 BIOZONE International
ISBN:978-1-927309-31-5
Photocopying Prohibited

136 Transpiration

Key Idea: Water moves through the xylem primarily as a result of evaporation from the leaves and the cohesive and adhesive properties of water molecules.

Plants lose water all the time through their stomata as a consequence of gas exchange. Approximately 99% of the water a plant absorbs from the soil is lost by evaporation from the leaves and stem. This loss is called **transpiration** and the flow of water through the plant is called the **transpiration stream**. Plants rely on a gradient in water potential (ψ) from the roots to the air to move water through their cells. Water flows passively from soil to air along a gradient of decreasing water potential. The gradient is the driving force for the movement of water up a plant. Transpiration has benefits to the plant because evaporative water loss is cooling and the transpiration stream helps the plant to take up minerals. Factors contributing to water movement are described below.

Air
Evaporative loss of water from the leaves as water vapour
ψ = –30 000 kPa

Leaves
Highest solute concentration
Lowest free water concentration
ψ = –1200 kPa

Water flows passively from a high water potential to areas where there is a lower (more negative) water potential. This gradient is the driving force in the transport of water up a plant.

The continuous flow of water is called the **transpiration stream**. It is primarily responsible for water moving up the plant.

Soil
Highest free water concentration
Lowest solute concentration
ψ = –10 kPa

Water
Water
Solute particle
Xylem
Water

The role of stomata

Water loss occurs mainly through stomata (pores in the leaf). The rate of water loss can be regulated by specialised guard cells (G) each side of the stoma (S), which open or close the pore.

- Stomata open: gas exchange and transpiration rate increase.
- Stomata closed: gas exchange and transpiration rates decrease.

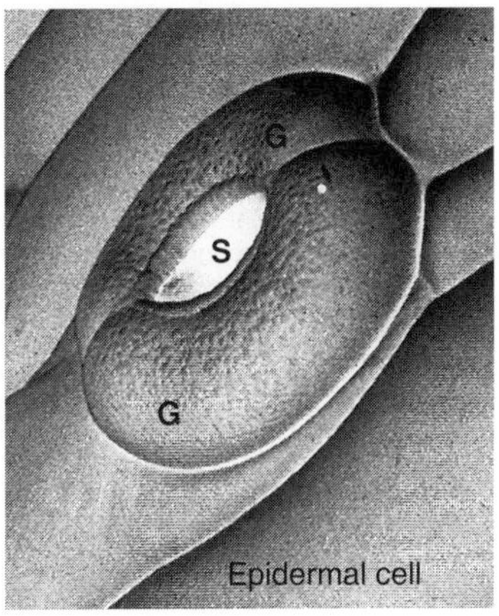
G
S
G
Epidermal cell
EII

1. (a) What is transpiration? ______________________________

____

(b) Describe one benefit of the transpiration stream for a plant: ______________________________

____

____

____

2. Why is transpiration an inevitable consequence of gas exchange? ______________________________

____

© 2015 BIOZONE International
ISBN: 978-1-927309-31-5
Photocopying Prohibited

Processes involved in moving water through the xylem

1 Transpiration pull
Water is lost from the air spaces by evaporation through stomata and is replaced by water from the mesophyll cells. The constant loss of water to the air (and production of sugars) creates a lower (more negative) water potential in the leaves than in the cells further from the evaporation site. Water is pulled through the plant down a **decreasing gradient in water potential**.

2 Cohesion-tension
The transpiration pull is assisted by the special **cohesive** properties of water. Water molecules cling together as they are pulled through the plant. They also **adhere** to the walls of the xylem (**adhesion**). This creates one **unbroken column of water** through the plant. The upward pull on the cohesive sap creates a tension (a negative pressure). This helps water uptake and movement up the plant.

3 Root pressure
Water entering the stele from the soil creates a **root pressure**; a weak 'push' effect for the water's upward movement through the plant. Root pressure can force water droplets from some small plants under certain conditions (**guttation**), but generally it plays a minor part in the ascent of water.

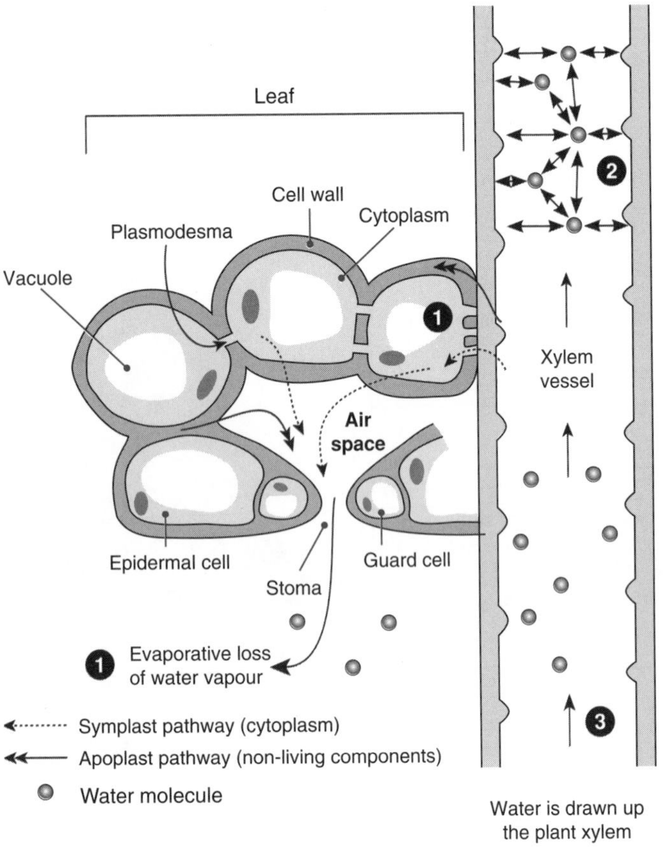
Leaf
Cell wall
Cytoplasm
Plasmodesma
Vacuole
1
2
Xylem vessel
Air space
Epidermal cell
Guard cell
Stoma
1 Evaporative loss of water vapour
Symplast pathway (cytoplasm)
Apoplast pathway (non-living components)
Water molecule
3
Water is drawn up the plant xylem

3. How does the plant regulate the amount of water lost from the leaves? ______________________

____

4. (a) What would happen if too much water was lost from the leaves? ______________________

____

(b) When might this happen? ______________________

5. Describe the three processes that assist the transport of water from the roots of the plant upward:

(a) ______________________

____

____

(b) ______________________

____

____

(c) ______________________

____

____

6. The maximum height water can move up the xylem by cohesion-tension alone is about 10 m. How then does water move up the height of a 40 m tall tree?

____

____

____

© 2015 **BIOZONE** International
ISBN:978-1-927309-31-5
Photocopying Prohibited

137 Investigating Plant Transpiration

Key Idea: The relationship between the rate of transpiration and the environment can be investigated using a potometer. This activity describes a typical experiment to investigate the effect of different environmental conditions on transpiration rate using a potometer. You will present and analyse the results provided.

The potometer

A potometer is a simple instrument for investigating transpiration rate (water loss per unit time). The equipment is simple to use and easy to obtain. A basic potometer, such as the one shown right, can easily be moved around so that transpiration rate can be measured under different environmental conditions.

Some physical conditions investigated are:

- Humidity or vapour pressure (high or low)
- Temperature (high or low)
- Air movement (still or windy)
- Light level (high or low)
- Water supply

It is also possible to compare the transpiration rates of plants with different adaptations e.g. comparing transpiration rates in plants with rolled leaves vs rates in plants with broad leaves. If possible, experiments like these should be conducted simultaneously using replicate equipment. If conducted sequentially, care should be taken to keep the environmental conditions the same for all plants used.

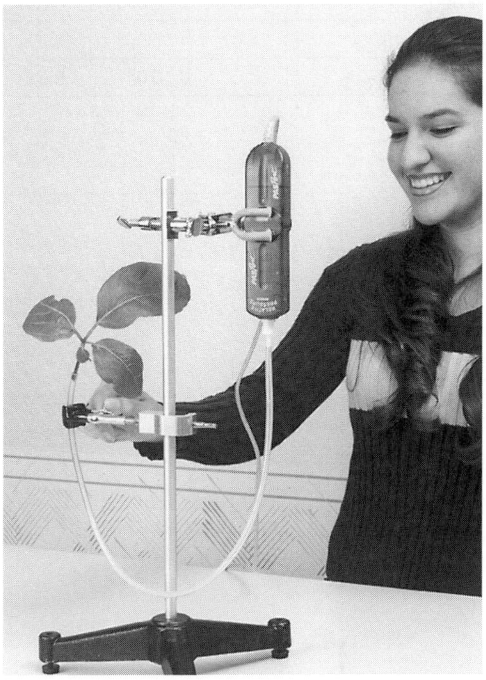

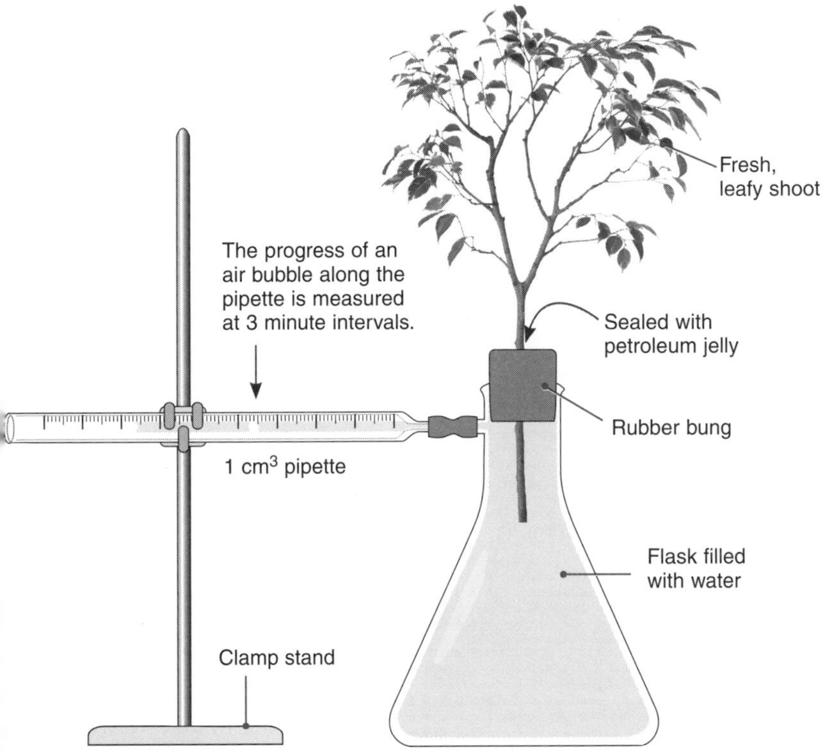
Fresh, leafy shoot
The progress of an air bubble along the pipette is measured at 3 minute intervals.
Sealed with petroleum jelly
Rubber bung
1 cm³ pipette
Flask filled with water
Clamp stand

The apparatus

This experiment investigated the influence of environmental conditions on plant transpiration rate. The experiment examined four conditions: room conditions (ambient), wind, bright light, and high humidity. After setting up the potometer, the apparatus was equilibrated for 10 minutes, and then the position of the air bubble in the pipette was recorded. This is the time 0 reading. The plant was then exposed to one of the environmental conditions. Students recorded the location of the air bubble every three minutes over a 30 minute period. The potometer readings for each environmental condition are presented in Table 1 (next page).

The aim

To investigate the effect of environmental conditions on the transpiration rate of plants.

Background

Plants lose water all the time by evaporation from the leaves and stem. This loss, mostly through pores in the leaf surfaces, is called **transpiration**. Despite the adaptations of plants to reduce water loss (e.g. waxy leaf cuticle), 99% of the water a plant absorbs from the soil is lost by evaporation. Environmental conditions affect transpiration rate by increasing or decreasing the gradient for diffusion of water molecules between the plant and its external environment.

Hypothesis

All the plants will lose water, but the greatest losses will be in hot or windy conditions.

A class was divided into four groups to study how four different environmental conditions (ambient, wind, bright light, and high humidity) affected transpiration rate. A **potometer** was used to measure transpiration rate (water loss per unit time). A basic potometer, such as the one shown left, can easily be moved around so that transpiration rate can be measured under different environmental conditions.

© 2015 **BIOZONE** International
ISBN: 978-1-927309-31-5
Photocopying Prohibited

LINK 136 LINK 18 LINK 11 WEB 137 DATA

Table 1. Potometer readings in cm^3 water loss

Treatment \ Time / min	0	3	6	9	12	15	18	21	24	27	30
Ambient	0	0.002	0.005	0.008	0.012	0.017	0.022	0.028	0.032	0.036	0.042
Wind	0	0.025	0.054	0.088	0.112	0.142	0.175	0.208	0.246	0.283	0.325
High humidity	0	0.002	0.004	0.006	0.008	0.011	0.014	0.018	0.019	0.021	0.024
Bright light	0	0.021	0.042	0.070	0.091	0.112	0.141	0.158	0.183	0.218	0.239

1. (a) Plot the potometer data from Table 1 on the grid provided:

   (b) Identify the independent variable: ______

2. (a) Identify the control: ______

   (b) Explain the purpose of including an experimental control in an experiment: ______

   (c) Which factors increased water loss? ______

   (d) How does each environmental factor influence water loss? ______

   (e) Explain why the plant lost less water in humid conditions: ______

© 2015 BIOZONE International
ISBN:978-1-927309-31-5
Photocopying Prohibited

138 Adaptations of Xerophytes

Key Idea: Xerophytes are plants adapted for conserving water in dry (arid) conditions.

Plants adapted to dry conditions are called **xerophytes** and they show structural (xeromorphic) and physiological adaptations for water conservation. These include small, hard leaves, an epidermis with a thick cuticle, sunken stomata, succulence (ability to store water), and absence of leaves. Salt tolerant plants (halophytes) and alpine plants may also show xeromorphic features due to the lack of free water and high evaporative losses in these environments.

Adaptations in cacti

Desert plants, such as cacti (below), must cope with low or sporadic rainfall and high transpiration rates.

Leaves modified into spines or hairs to reduce water loss. Light coloured spines reflect solar radiation.
Rounded shape reduces surface area.
Stem becomes the major photosynthetic organ, plus a reservoir for water storage.
The surface tissues of many cacti are tolerant of temperatures in excess of 50°C.
Cacti have a shallow, but extensive fibrous root system. When in the ground the roots are spread out around the plant.

Aciaia tree

Hairs

Other xeromorphic plants reduce water loss by covering their surface with fine hairs, reducing air movement, and trapping moisture near the leaf. Some, such as acacias (above left), have deep root systems that enable them to access water from lower water tables. Adaptations such as waxy leaves also reduce water loss and, in many desert plants, germination is triggered only by a certain quantity of rainfall.

Leaf adaptations

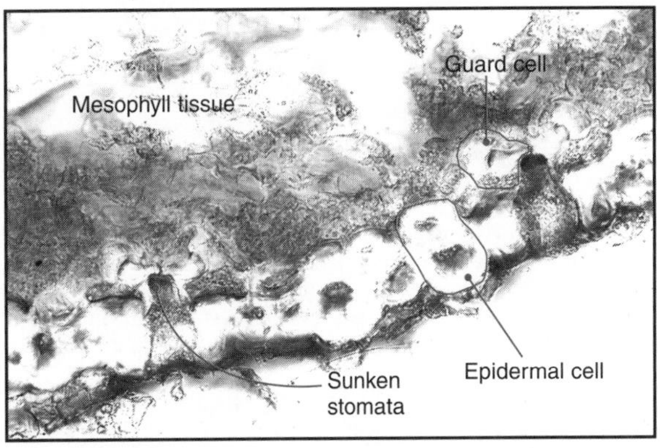

Mesophyll tissue
Guard cell
Sunken stomata
Epidermal cell

Western New Mexico University Department of Natural Sciences / Dale A. Zimmerman Herbarium

Above is a section through the edge of a pine needle at 400X magnification. Pines show xeromorphic characteristics in their leaves including sunken stomata. The stomata are often found in grooves along the needle which helps to reduce water loss.

1. Redraw the image from a slide (top) in the box above. Include labels and draw the mesophyll tissue in plan view. Use the magnification to produce a scale.

Methods of water conservation

Adaptation for water conservation	Effect of adaptation	Example
Thick, waxy cuticle to stems and leaves	Reduces water loss through the cuticle.	*Pinus* sp. ivy (*Hedera*), sea holly (*Eryngium*), prickly pear (*Opuntia*).
Reduced number of stomata	Fewer pores through which water is lost.	Prickly pear (*Opuntia*), *Nerium* sp.
Stomata sunken in pits, grooves, or depressions. Leaf surface covered with fine hairs. Massing of leaves into a rosette at ground level.	Moist air is trapped close to the area of water loss, reducing the diffusion gradient and therefore the rate of water loss.	**Sunken stomata**: *Pinus* sp., *Hakea* sp. **Hairy leaves**: lamb's ear. **Leaf rosettes**: dandelion (*Taraxacum*), daisy.
Stomata closed during the light, open at night	CAM metabolism: CO_2 is fixed during the night, water loss in the day is minimised.	**CAM plants**, e.g. American aloe, pineapple, *Kalanchoe, Yucca*.
Leaves reduced to scales, stem photosynthetic Leaves curled, rolled, or folded when flaccid	Reduction in surface area from which transpiration can occur.	**Leaf scales**: broom (*Cytisus*). **Rolled leaf**: marram (*Ammophila*), *Erica* sp.
Fleshy or succulent stems Fleshy or succulent leaves	When readily available, water is stored in the tissues for times of low availability.	**Fleshy stems**: *Opuntia*, candle plant (*Kleinia*). **Fleshy leaves**: *Bryophyllum*.
Deep root system below the water table	Roots tap into the lower water table.	Acacias, oleander.
Shallow root system absorbing surface moisture	Roots absorb overnight condensation.	Most cacti.

© 2015 **BIOZONE** International
ISBN: 978-1-927309-31-5
Photocopying Prohibited

LINK 136 LINK 134 WEB 138 KNOW

Adaptations in halophytes and drought tolerant plants

RA

Ice plant (*Carpobrotus*): The leaves of many desert and beach dwelling plants are fleshy or succulent. The leaves are triangular in cross section and crammed with water storage cells. The water is stored after rain for use in dry periods. The shallow root system is able to take up water from the soil surface, taking advantage of any overnight condensation.

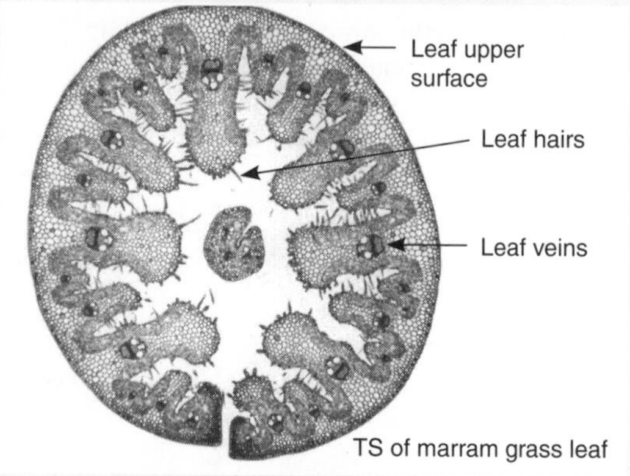
Leaf upper surface
Leaf hairs
Leaf veins
TS of marram grass leaf
RCN

Marram grass (*Ammophila*): The long, wiry leaf blades of this beach grass are curled downwards with the stomata on the inside. This protects them against drying out by providing a moist microclimate around the stomata. Plants adapted to high altitude often have similar adaptations.

RA

Ball cactus (*Echinocactus grusonii*): In many cacti, the leaves are modified into long, thin spines which project outward from the thick fleshy stem. This reduces the surface area over which water loss can occur. The stem stores water and takes over as the photosynthetic organ. As in succulents, a shallow root system enables rapid uptake of surface water.

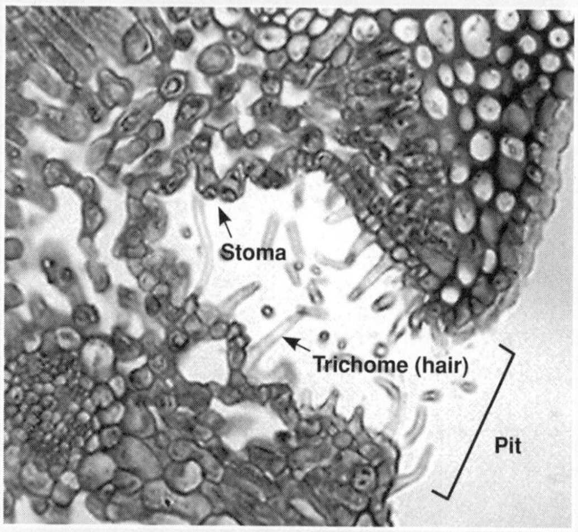
Stoma
Trichome (hair)
Pit
WBS

Oleander is a xerophyte from the Mediterranean region with many water conserving features. It has a thick multi-layered epidermis and the stomata are sunken in trichome-filled pits on the leaf underside. The pits restrict water loss to a greater extent than they reduce uptake of carbon dioxide.

2. Explain the purpose of **xeromorphic** adaptations: ______________________

____

3. Describe three xeromorphic adaptations of plants:

(a) ______________________

(b) ______________________

(c) ______________________

4. Describe a physiological mechanism by which plants can reduce water loss during the daylight hours: ______________________

____

____

5. Explain why creating a moist microenvironment around the areas of water loss reduces transpiration rate: ______________________

____

6. Explain why seashore plants (halophytes) exhibit many desert-dwelling adaptations: ______________________

____

____

© 2015 **BIOZONE** International
ISBN:978-1-927309-31-5
Photocopying Prohibited

139 Translocation

Key Idea: Phloem transports the organic products of photosynthesis (sugars) through the plant in an active, energy-requiring process called translocation.

In angiosperms, the sugar moves through the sieve-tube members, which are arranged end-to-end and perforated with sieve plates. Apart from water, phloem sap comprises mainly sucrose. It may also contain minerals, hormones, and amino acids, in transit around the plant. Movement of sap in the phloem is from a **source** (a plant organ where sugar is made or mobilised) to a **sink** (a plant organ where sugar is stored or used). Loading sucrose into the phloem at a source involves energy expenditure; it is slowed or stopped by high temperatures or respiratory inhibitors. In some plants, unloading the sucrose at the sinks also requires energy, although in others, diffusion alone is sufficient to move sucrose from the phloem into the cells of the sink organ.

Phloem transport

Phloem sap moves from source to sink at rates as great as 100 m h^{-1}, which is too fast to be accounted for by cytoplasmic streaming. The most acceptable model for phloem movement is the **mass flow hypothesis** (also know as the pressure flow hypothesis). Phloem sap moves by bulk flow, which creates a pressure (hence the term "pressure-flow"). The key elements in this model are outlined below and right. For simplicity, the cells that lie between the source (and sink) cells and the phloem sieve-tube have been omitted.

1. Loading sugar into the phloem from a source (e.g. leaf cell) increases the solute concentration (decreases the water potential, ψ) inside the sieve-tube cells. This causes the sieve-tubes to take up water from the surrounding tissues by osmosis.
2. The water uptake creates a hydrostatic pressure that forces the sap to move along the tube, just as pressure pushes water through a hose.
3. The pressure gradient in the sieve tube is reinforced by the active unloading of sugar and consequent loss of water by osmosis at the sink (e.g. root cell).
4. Xylem recycles the water from sink to source.

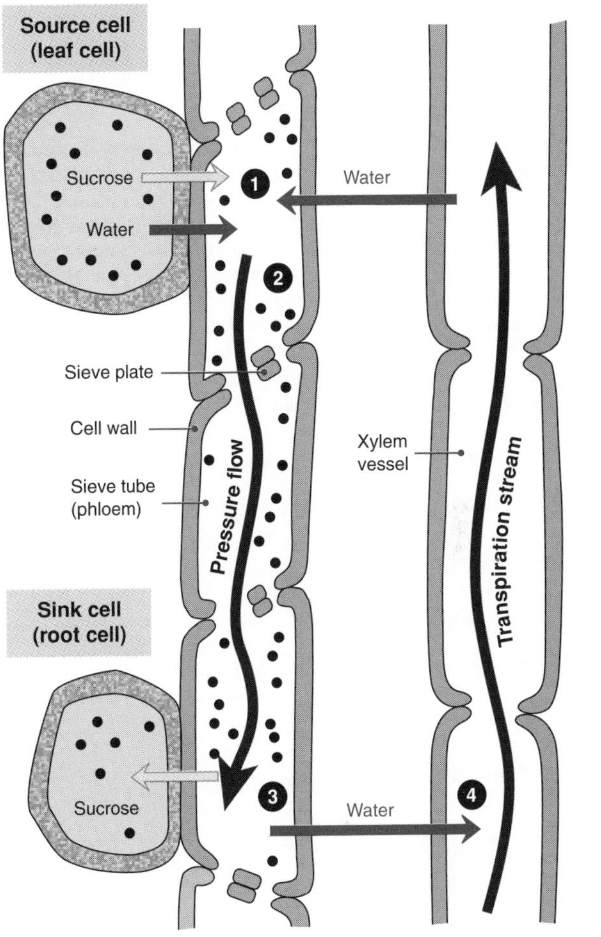
Source cell (leaf cell)
Sucrose
Water
1
Water
2
Sieve plate
Cell wall
Sieve tube (phloem)
Pressure flow
Xylem vessel
Transpiration stream
Sink cell (root cell)
Sucrose
3
Water
4

Source: Modified after Campbell *Biology* 1993

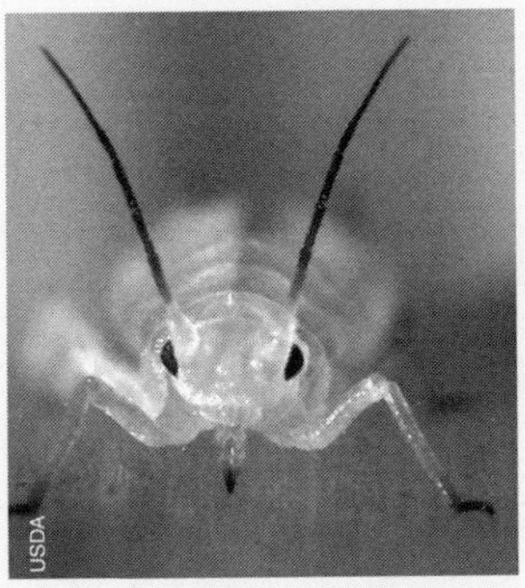
USDA

Measuring phloem flow

Aphids can act as natural phloem probes to measure phloem flow. The sucking mouthparts (stylet) of the insect penetrates the phloem sieve-tube cell. While the aphid feeds, it can be severed from its stylet, which remains in place and continues to exude sap. Using different aphids, the rate of flow of this sap can be measured at different locations on the plant.

1. (a) From what you know about osmosis, explain why water follows the sugar as it moves through the phloem:

(b) What is meant by '**source to sink**' flow in phloem transport?

2. Why does a plant need to move food around, particularly from the leaves to other regions?

© 2015 **BIOZONE** International
ISBN: 978-1-927309-31-5
Photocopying Prohibited

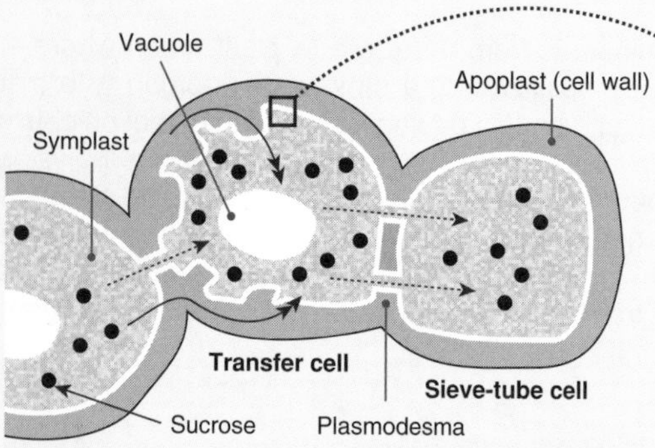
Vacuole
Apoplast (cell wall)
Symplast
Transfer cell
Sieve-tube cell
Sucrose
Plasmodesma
Phloem parenchyma cell
Apoplast pathway (cell wall)
Symplast pathway (cytoplasm)

Loading sucrose into the phloem

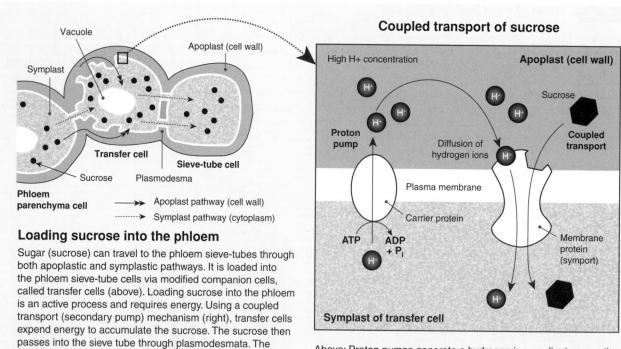

Sugar (sucrose) can travel to the phloem sieve-tubes through both apoplastic and symplastic pathways. It is loaded into the phloem sieve-tube cells via modified companion cells, called transfer cells (above). Loading sucrose into the phloem is an active process and requires energy. Using a coupled transport (secondary pump) mechanism (right), transfer cells expend energy to accumulate the sucrose. The sucrose then passes into the sieve tube through plasmodesmata. The transfer cells have wall ingrowths that increase surface area for the transport of solutes. Using this mechanism, some plants can accumulate sucrose in the phloem to 2-3 times the concentration in the mesophyll.

Coupled transport of sucrose

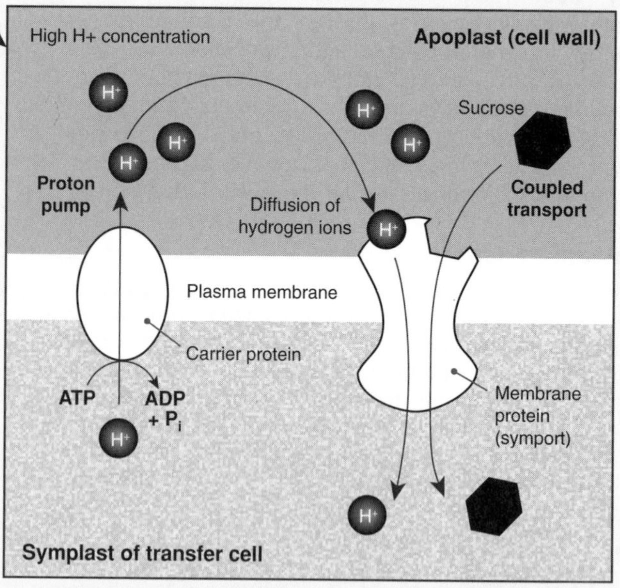
High H+ concentration
Apoplast (cell wall)
Sucrose
Proton pump
Diffusion of hydrogen ions
Coupled transport
Plasma membrane
Carrier protein
ATP
ADP + P_i
Membrane protein (symport)
Symplast of transfer cell

Above: Proton pumps generate a hydrogen ion gradient across the membrane of the transfer cell. This process requires expenditure of energy. The gradient is then used to drive the transport of sucrose, by coupling the sucrose transport to the diffusion of hydrogen ions back into the cell.

3. In your own words, describe what is meant by the following:

   (a) Translocation:

   (b) Pressure-flow movement of phloem:

   (c) Coupled transport of sucrose:

4. Briefly explain how sucrose is transported into the phloem:

5. Explain the role of the companion (transfer) cell in the loading of sucrose into the phloem:

6. (a) What does the flow of phloem sap from a severed aphid stylet indicate?

   (b) Where would you expect the flow rate to be greatest and why?

   (c) Why do you think aphid stylets are particularly useful for studying the rate of flow in phloem?

© 2015 BIOZONE International
ISBN:978-1-927309-31-5
Photocopying Prohibited

140 Chapter Review

Summarise what you know about this topic under the headings provided. You can draw diagrams or mind maps, or write short notes. Use the images and hints to help you and refer back to the introduction to check the points covered:

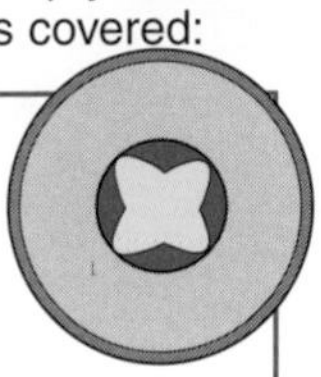

Plant transport tissues:
HINT: Describe the arrangement of vascular tissue in dicot stems, roots, and leaves.

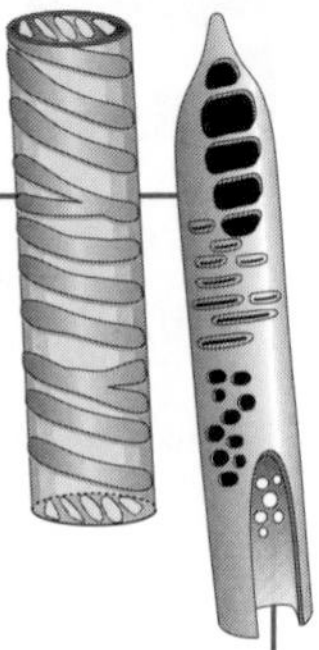

Xylem and phloem:
HINT: Describe the cells that make up xylem and phloem.

Transpiration:
HINT: Describe and explain transpiration and the factors affecting it.

Translocation:
HINT: How is sugar transported around plants?

© 2015 **BIOZONE** International
ISBN: 978-1-927309-31-5
Photocopying Prohibited

141 KEY TERMS AND IDEAS: Did You Get It?

1. (a) What is the name given to the loss of water vapour from plant leaves and stems? ____________________

   (b) What plant tissue is involved in this process? ____________________

   (c) Is this tissue alive or dead? ____________________

   (d) Does this process require energy? ____________________

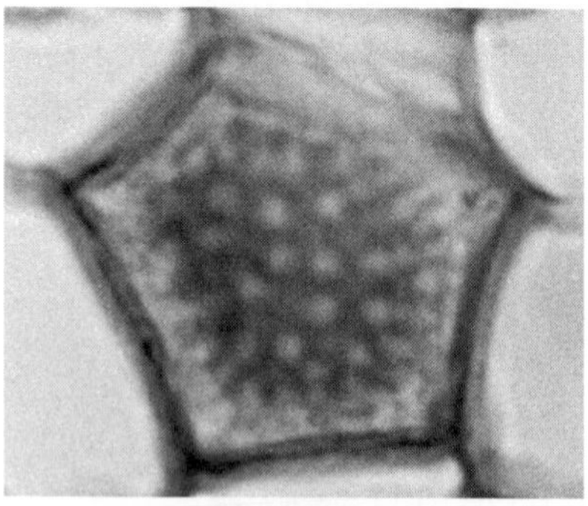

RCN

2. (a) What does the image (right) show: ____________________

   (b) In what tissue would you find it? ____________________

   (c) Is this tissue alive or dead? ____________________

   (d) What transport process is it associated with? ____________________

   (e) What is being moved in this process? ____________________

3. The image on the right shows tissues from a dicot plant.

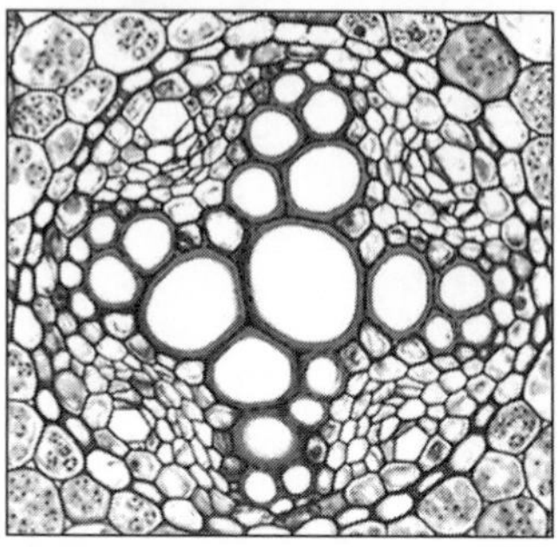

WBS

   (a) This image depicts part of a stem / root / leaf (circle one).

   (b) Give a reason for the answer you gave in (a): ____________________

   ____

   ____

   (c) Label the xylem (X) and phloem (P) on the diagram.

4. An experiment was performed to investigate transpiration from a hydrangea shoot in a potometer. The experiment was set up and the plant left to stabilise (environmental conditions: still air, light shade, 20°C). The plant was then placed in different environmental conditions and the water loss was measured each hour. Finally, the plant was returned to original conditions, allowed to stabilise and transpiration rate measured again. The data are presented below:

Experimental conditions	Temperature /°C	Humidity / %	Transpiration rate / g h^{-1}
(a) Still air, light shade, room temperature	20°C	70	1.20
(b) Moving air, light shade	20°C	70	1.60
(c) Still air, bright sunlight	23°C	70	3.75
(d) Still air and dark, moist chamber	19.5°C	100	0.05

   (a) What conditions acted as the control in this experiment? ____________________

   (b) Which factors increased transpiration rate and why? ____________________

   ____

   ____

   (c) Why did the plant have such a low transpiration rate in humid, dark conditions? ____________________

   ____

   ____

5. Match each term to its definition, as identified by its preceding letter code.

cohesion-tension	**A** Pores in the leaf surface through which gases and water vapour can pass.
potometer	**B** Partial explanation for the movement of water up the plant in the transpiration stream.
stomata	**C** The loss of water vapour by plants, mainly from leaves via the stomata.
transpiration	**D** Device used for investigating the rate of transpiration.

TEST

© 2015 **BIOZONE** International
ISBN:978-1-927309-31-5
Photocopying Prohibited

Topic 8 Transport in mammals

Key terms

artery (pl. arteries)
atrioventricular node
atrium (pl. atria)
blood
Bohr effect
capillary (pl. capillaries)
carbamino-haemoglobin
carbonic anhydrase
cardiac cycle
closed circulatory system
diastole
double circulatory system
haemoglobin
haemoglobinic acid
heart
lymph
lymphocyte
monocyte
neutrophil
open circulatory system
oxygen dissociation curve
Purkyne tissue
red blood cell (=erythrocyte)
respiratory gas
single circulatory system
sinoatrial node
systole
tissue fluid
vein
ventricle
white blood cell (=leucocyte)

8.1 The circulatory system

Learning outcomes — Activity number

- ☐ 1 With reference to size, metabolic rate, and surface area and volume ratios, explain why multicellular animals require an internal transport system. Understand that the mammalian circulatory system is a closed, double circulation and identify its components and their functions. **142**
- ☐ 2 **PRAC** Using prepared slides, observe and make plan diagrams of the structure of arteries, veins, and capillaries. Use the features of these vessels to recognise them in prepared slides using light microscopy. **145-147**
- ☐ 3 Explain the relationship between structure and function of blood vessels in mammals, to include arteries, veins, and capillaries. **145-147**
- ☐ 4 **PRAC** Using prepared slides and photomicrographs, observe and draw the structure of blood cells to include red blood cells, monocytes, neutrophils, and lymphocytes. **143 144**
- ☐ 5 Describe and distinguish between blood, tissue fluid, and lymph. If required, explain how tissue fluid is formed from plasma with reference to differences in hydrostatic pressure and oncotic pressure at either end of a capillary bed. **147 149**
- ☐ 6 Describe the role of haemoglobin in transporting oxygen and carbon dioxide. Include reference to the role of carbonic anhydrase, and the formation of haemoglobinic acid and carbaminohaemoglobin. **150**
- ☐ 7 Describe and explain the significance of the oxygen dissociation curves for adult oxyhaemoglobin at different carbon dioxide concentrations (the Bohr effect). **150**
- ☐ 8 Describe and explain the effect of high altitude on red blood cell count. **151**

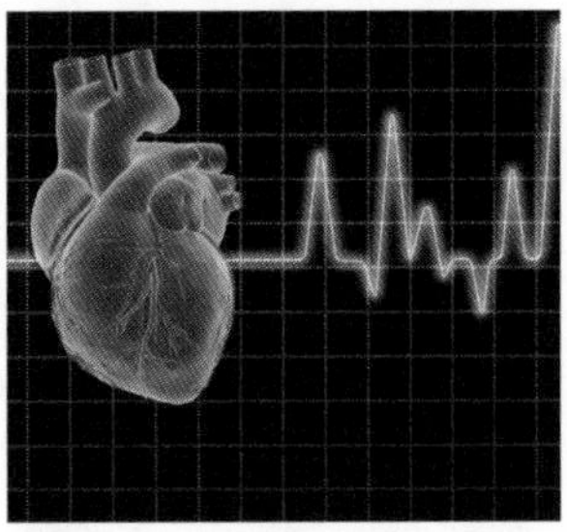

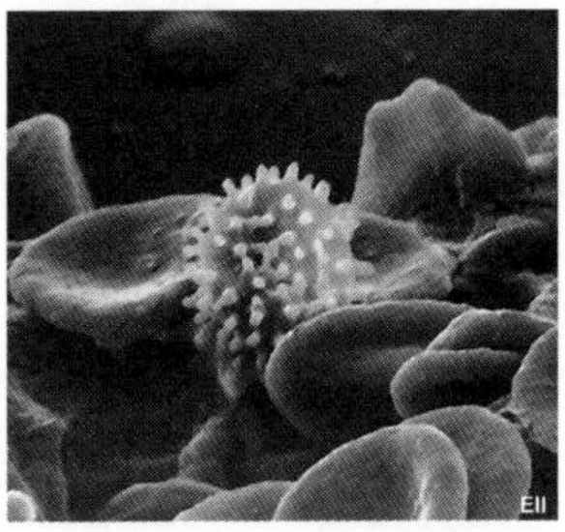
EII

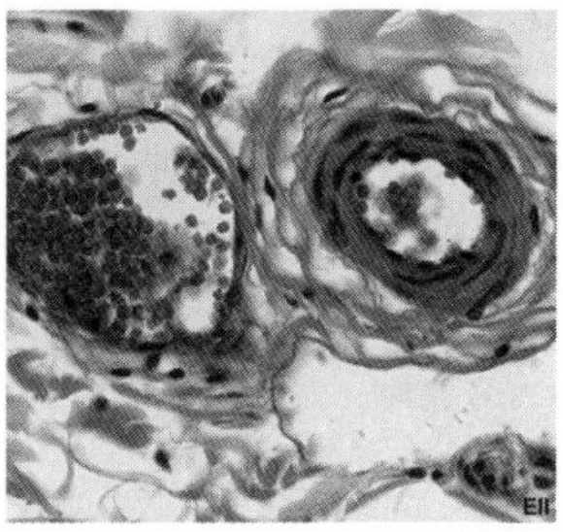
EII

8.2 The heart

Learning outcomes — Activity number

- ☐ 9 Describe the external and internal structure of the mammalian heart. Identify pulmonary and systemic circuits and the vessels entering and leaving the heart. **152**
- ☐ 10 **PRAC** Dissect, examine, and draw a mammalian heart to demonstrate your understanding of its external and internal structure. **153**
- ☐ 11 Explain the differences in the thickness of the walls of the different heart chambers in terms of their functions and with reference to resistance to flow. **152**
- ☐ 12 Describe the cardiac cycle, including the role of the heart valves and the blood pressure changes during systole and diastole. **154**
- ☐ 13 Explain how the heartbeat is initiated and regulated, including reference to the myogenic nature of the beat, and the role of the sinoatrial node or pacemaker, atrioventricular node, and Purkyne tissue. **155**

142 The Mammalian Transport System

Key Idea: The mammalian circulatory system is a double circuit made up of a pulmonary circuit and a systemic circuit. As animals increase in size and complexity, an internal transport system is required to supply nutrients and oxygen to cells and remove metabolic wastes. The mammalian circulatory system is a closed network of blood vessels that carry blood away from the heart, transport it to the tissues of the body, and then return it to the heart. Mammals have a double circulatory system: a **pulmonary system**, which carries blood between the heart and lungs, and a **systemic system**, which carries blood between the heart and the rest of the body. Two important subdivisions are the coronary circulation, which supplies the heart muscle, and the hepatic portal circulation, which runs from the gut to the liver.

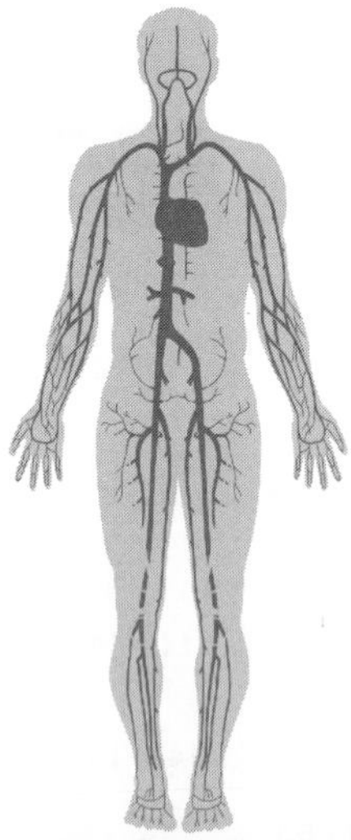

Schematic overview of the human circulatory system

Deoxygenated blood (coloured blue below) travels to the right side of the heart via the vena cavae. The heart pumps the deoxygenated blood to the lungs where it releases carbon dioxide and receives oxygen. The oxygenated blood (coloured white below) travels via the pulmonary vein back to the heart from where it is pumped to all parts of the body. The **venous system** (figure, left) returns blood from the capillaries to the heart. The **arterial system** (figure right) carries blood from the heart to the capillaries. **Portal systems** carry blood between two capillary beds.

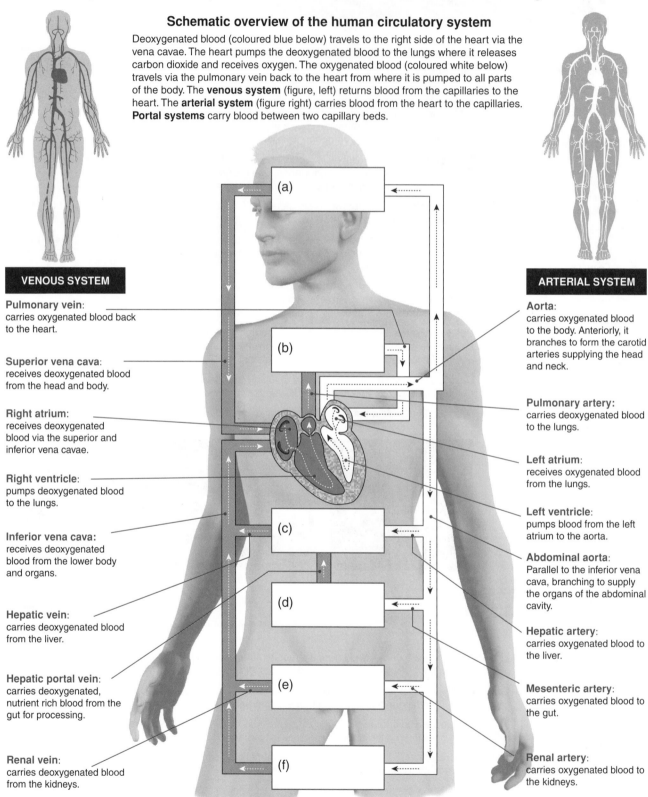

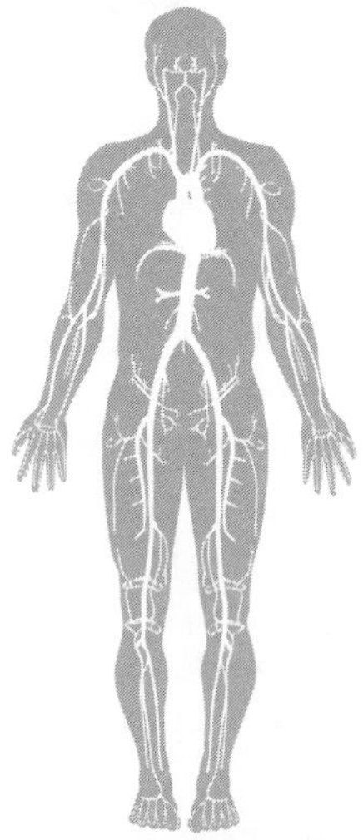

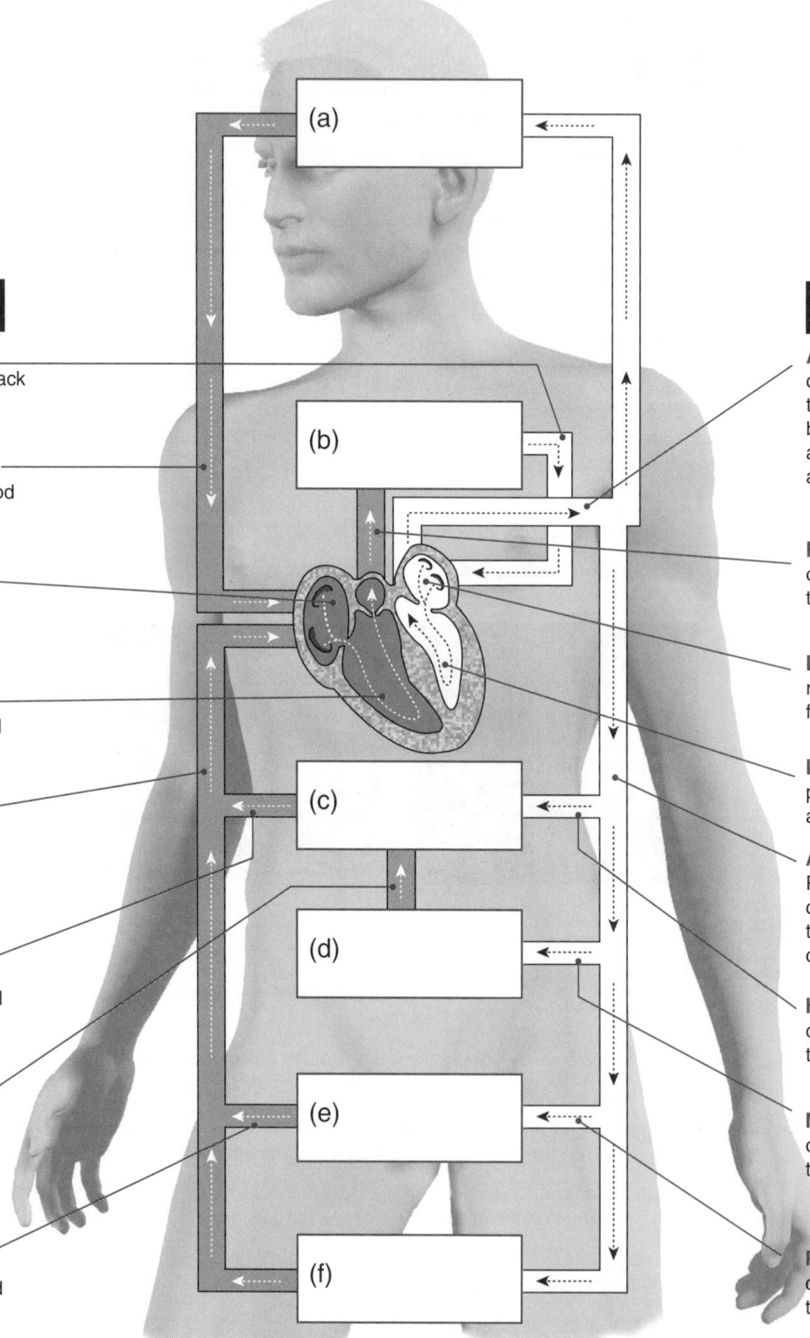

VENOUS SYSTEM
Pulmonary vein: carries oxygenated blood back to the heart.
Superior vena cava: receives deoxygenated blood from the head and body.
Right atrium: receives deoxygenated blood via the superior and inferior vena cavae.
Right ventricle: pumps deoxygenated blood to the lungs.
Inferior vena cava: receives deoxygenated blood from the lower body and organs.
Hepatic vein: carries deoxygenated blood from the liver.
Hepatic portal vein: carries deoxygenated, nutrient rich blood from the gut for processing.
Renal vein: carries deoxygenated blood from the kidneys.
(a)
(b)
(c)
(d)
(e)
(f)
ARTERIAL SYSTEM
Aorta: carries oxygenated blood to the body. Anteriorly, it branches to form the carotid arteries supplying the head and neck.
Pulmonary artery: carries deoxygenated blood to the lungs.
Left atrium: receives oxygenated blood from the lungs.
Left ventricle: pumps blood from the left atrium to the aorta.
Abdominal aorta: Parallel to the inferior vena cava, branching to supply the organs of the abdominal cavity.
Hepatic artery: carries oxygenated blood to the liver.
Mesenteric artery: carries oxygenated blood to the gut.
Renal artery: carries oxygenated blood to the kidneys.

1. Complete the diagram above by labelling the boxes with the correct organs: *lungs, liver, head, intestines, genitals/lower body, kidneys.*

2. Circle the two blood vessels involved in the pulmonary circuit.

© 2015 **BIOZONE** International
ISBN:978-1-927309-31-5
Photocopying Prohibited

143 Blood

Key Idea: Blood transports nutrients, wastes, hormones, and respiratory gases around the body.

Blood is a complex connective tissue made up of cellular components suspended in matrix of liquid plasma. It makes up about 8% of body weight. If a blood sample is taken, the cells can be separated from the plasma by centrifugation. The cells (formed elements) settle as a dense red pellet below the transparent, straw-coloured plasma. Blood performs many functions. It transports nutrients, respiratory gases, hormones, and wastes and has a role in thermoregulation through the distribution of heat. Blood also defends against infection and its ability to clot protects against blood loss. The examination of blood is also useful in diagnosing disease because the cellular components of blood are normally present in specified ratios. Deviations from these ratios may indicate disease.

Mammalian blood

CELLULAR COMPONENTS
The cellular (or formed) elements of blood float in the plasma and make up 40-50% of the total blood volume.

White blood cells and platelets make up 2-3% of the total blood volume.

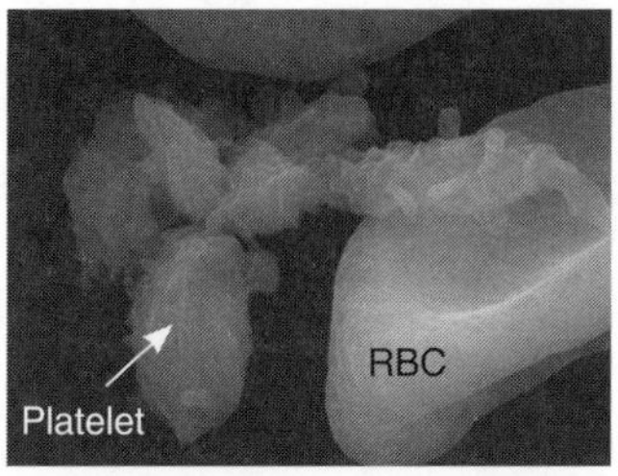
Platelet
RBC

White blood cells (leucocytes) are involved in internal defence. Lymphocytes are a type of leucocyte important in immunity. They make up 24% of the white cell count.

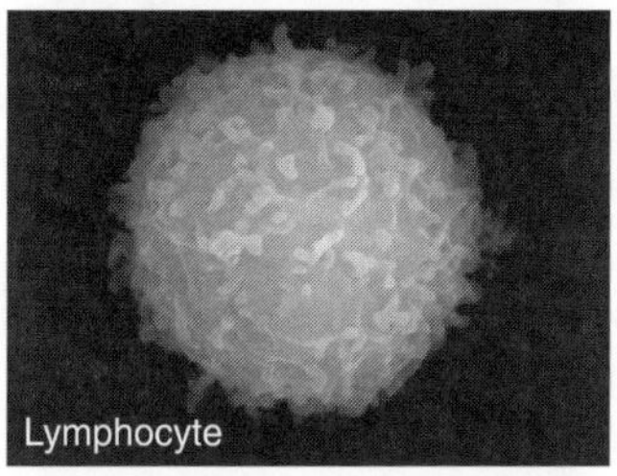
Lymphocyte

Platelets are small, membrane-bound cell fragments with a role in blood clotting.

Red blood cells (RBCs) account for 38-48% of total blood volume. RBCs transport oxygen (carried bound to haemoglobin) and a small amount of carbon dioxide. Unlike other blood cells, RBCs have no nucleus and lack most organelles. They are packed full of haemoglobin protein.

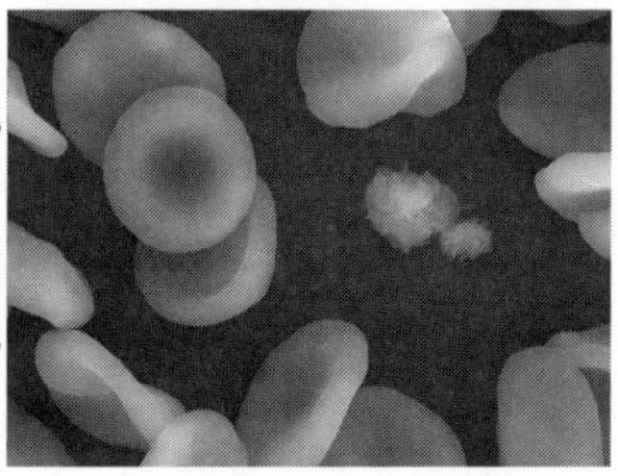

All EM iamges: Dartmouth College

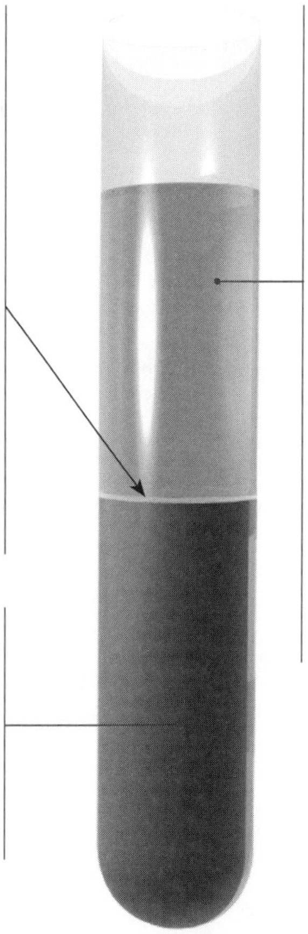

NON-CELLULAR COMPONENTS
The non-cellular part of the blood is the plasma, a watery matrix making up 50-60% of blood volume.
Most of the blood is water. It transports dissolved substances, provides cells with water, distributes heat, and maintains blood volume.
Most of the plasma is water, but it also contains dissolved proteins, glucose, amino acids, vitamins, minerals, urea, uric acid, CO_2, hormones, and antibodies.

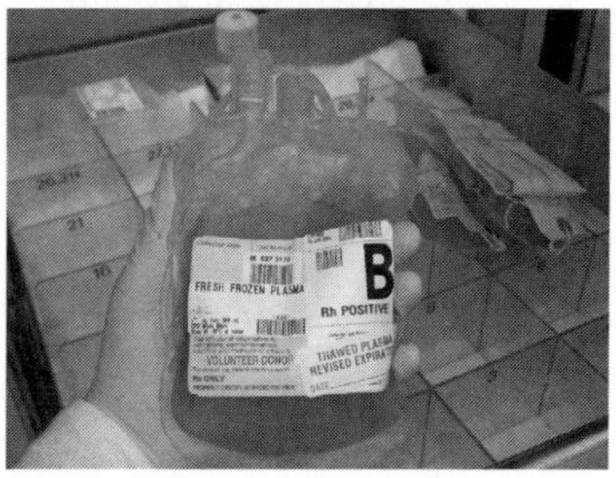
B

Blood plasma

1. Describe one feature distinguishing red and white blood cells in mammalian blood: ______________________________

____

2. Describe two functions of the blood plasma: ______________________________

____

____

____

3. What is the function of platelets in the blood? ______________________________

____

4. Explain why the blood can be called a "liquid tissue": ______________________________

____

____

____

____

© 2015 **BIOZONE** International
ISBN: 978-1-927309-31-5
Photocopying Prohibited

144 Drawing Blood Cells

Key Idea: Blood cells can be distinguished by their shape and size. For leucocytes, features of the nuclei are also diagnostic. Determining the type and number of blood cells present in a sample is a common technique in diagnosing disease. Blood is taken from a patient and prepared for viewing under a light microscope. Wright's stain is applied to differentiate the cells. It contains eosin, which stain cytoplasms orange-pink, and methylene blue, which stains the nuclei of the leucocytes blue-purple. The shape and size of the nucleus is an important factor in differentiating the leucocytes from each other.

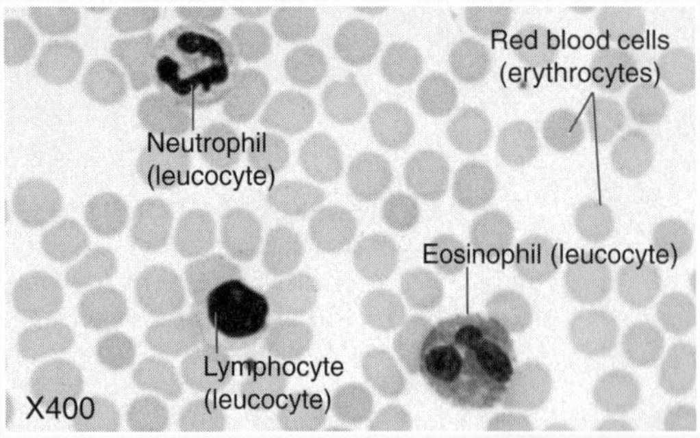
Red blood cells (erythrocytes)
Neutrophil (leucocyte)
Eosinophil (leucocyte)
Lymphocyte (leucocyte)
X400
Ell

During your practical work, you will be required to identify and draw cells in a prepared blood smear viewed with a light microscope. It can be difficult to distinguish between the types of white blood cells (leucocytes) in prepared smears, even at X400. An example of what you are likely to see in a well prepared blood smear is shown above.

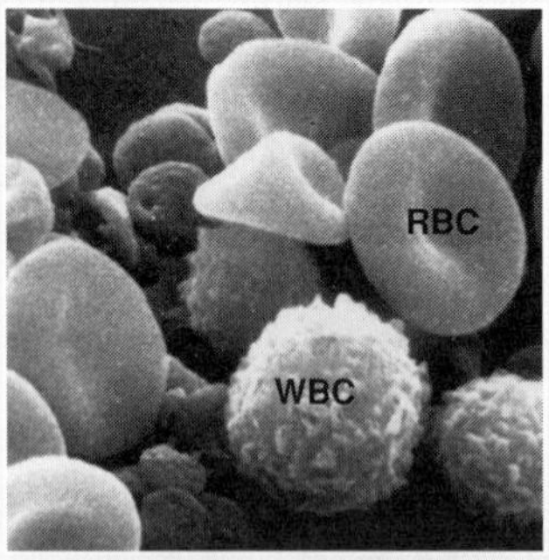
RBC
WBC

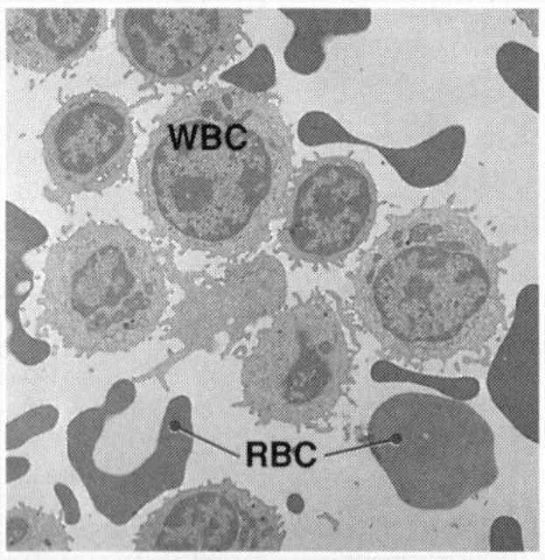
WBC
RBC
RBC
Ell

Electron microscopes can achieve higher resolution than light microscopes, so more detail can be observed. The left image, is a scanning electron micrograph showing the surface detail of human red and white blood cells. The image above right has been taken with a transmission electron microscope. It shows the details of red blood cells (RBC) and white blood cells (WBC) in section. RBC appear featureless because they lack nuclei and organelles.

1. (a) Would red blood cells take up the methylene blue in Wright's stain? ______________________

   (b) Why/why not? ______________________

   ____

2. The images below show four different types of blood cells commonly seen in blood smears viewed under a light microscope. Draw the images and make notes about their distinguishing features:

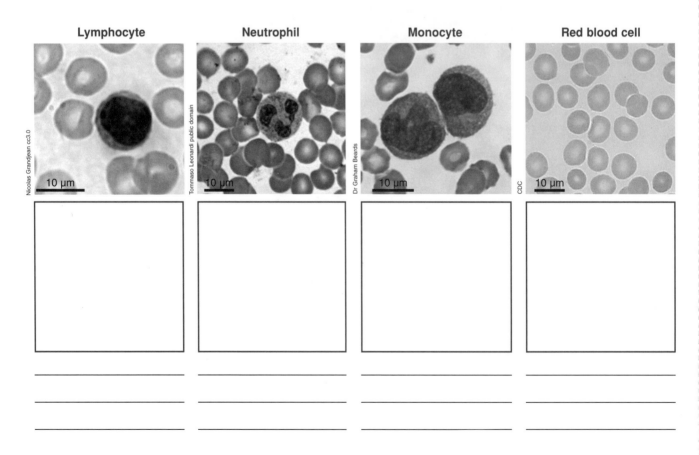

Lymphocyte

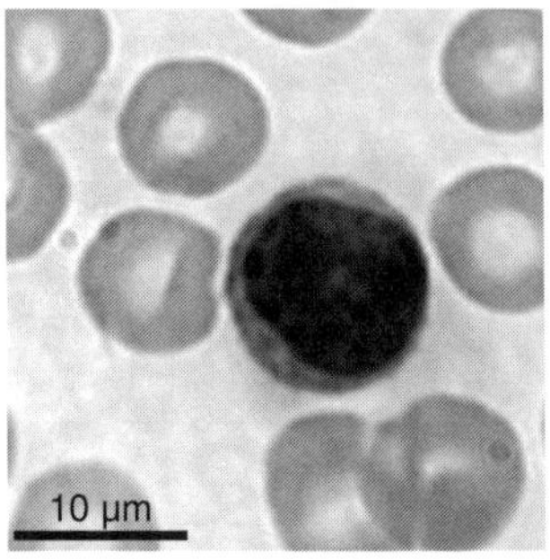
10 µm

Nicolas Grandjean cc3.0

Neutrophil

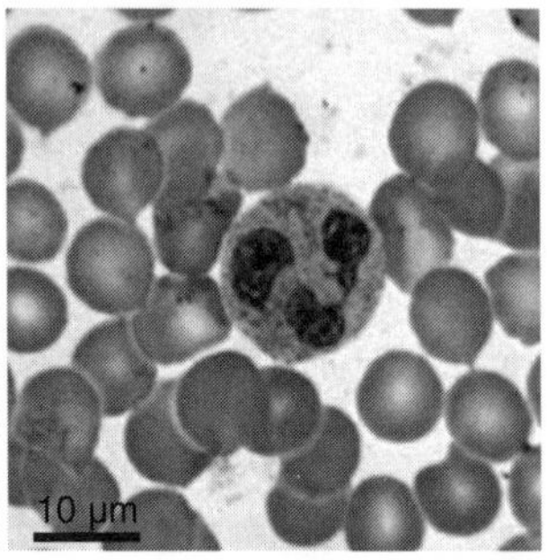
10 µm

Tommaso Leonardi public domain

Monocyte

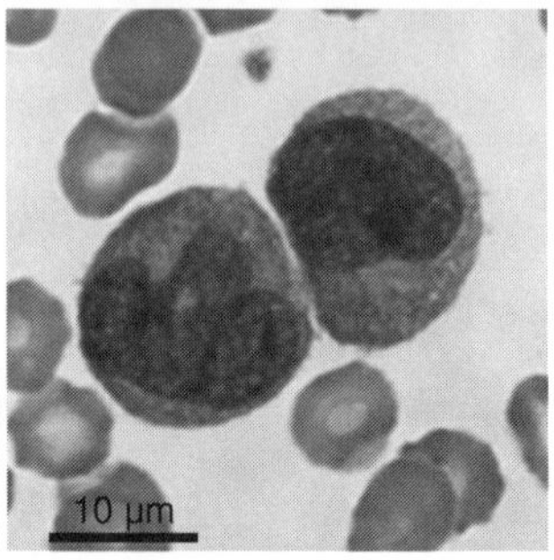
10 µm

Dr Graham Beards

Red blood cell

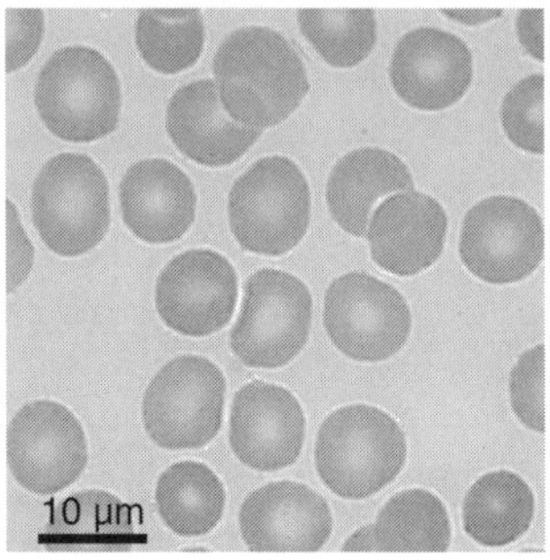
10 µm

CDC

SKILL LINK 22 LINK 23 LINK 143 LINK 181

© 2015 **BIOZONE** International
ISBN:978-1-927309-31-5
Photocopying Prohibited

145 Arteries

Key Idea: Arteries are thick-walled blood vessels that carry blood away from the heart to the capillaries within the tissues. In vertebrates, **arteries** are the blood vessels that carry blood away from the heart to the capillaries within the tissues. The large arteries that leave the heart divide into medium-sized (distributing) arteries. Within the tissues and organs, these distributing arteries branch to form **arterioles**, which deliver blood to capillaries. Arterioles lack the thick layers of arteries and consist only of an endothelial layer wrapped by a few smooth muscle fibres at intervals along their length. Blood flow to the tissues is altered by contraction (**vasoconstriction**) or relaxation (**vasodilation**) of the blood vessel walls. Vasoconstriction increases blood pressure whereas vasodilation has the opposite effect.

Arteries

Arteries, regardless of size, can be recognised by their well-defined rounded **lumen** (internal space) and the muscularity of the vessel wall. Arteries have an elastic, stretchy structure that gives them the ability to withstand the high pressure of blood being pumped from the heart. At the same time, they help to maintain pressure by having some contractile ability themselves (a feature of the central muscle layer). Arteries nearer the heart have more elastic tissue, giving greater resistance to the higher blood pressures of the blood leaving the left ventricle. Arteries further from the heart have more muscle to help them maintain blood pressure. Between heartbeats, the arteries undergo elastic recoil and contract. This tends to smooth out the flow of blood through the vessel.

Arteries comprise three main regions (right):

1. A thin inner layer of epithelial cells called the **tunica intima** (endothelium) lines the artery.
2. A thick central layer (the **tunica media**) of elastic tissue and smooth muscle that can both stretch and contract.
3. An outer connective tissue layer (the **tunica externa**) has a lot of elastic tissue.

Structure of an artery

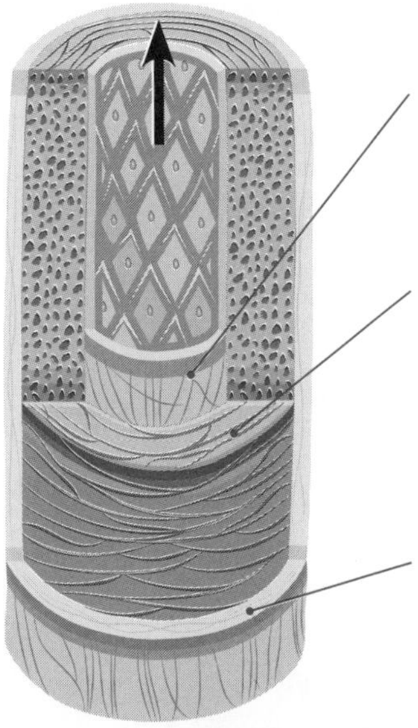
Tunica intima (endothelium)
Thin endothelial layer of squamous epithelium is in contact with the blood. Arrow indicates direction of blood flow.
Tunica media
Thick layer of elastic tissue and smooth muscle tissue allows for both stretch and contraction, maintaining blood flow without loss of pressure.
Tunica externa
Layer of elastic connective tissue (collagen and elastin) anchors the artery to other tissues and allows it to resist overexpansion. Relatively thinner in larger elastic arteries and thicker in muscular, distributing arteries.

Cross section through a large artery

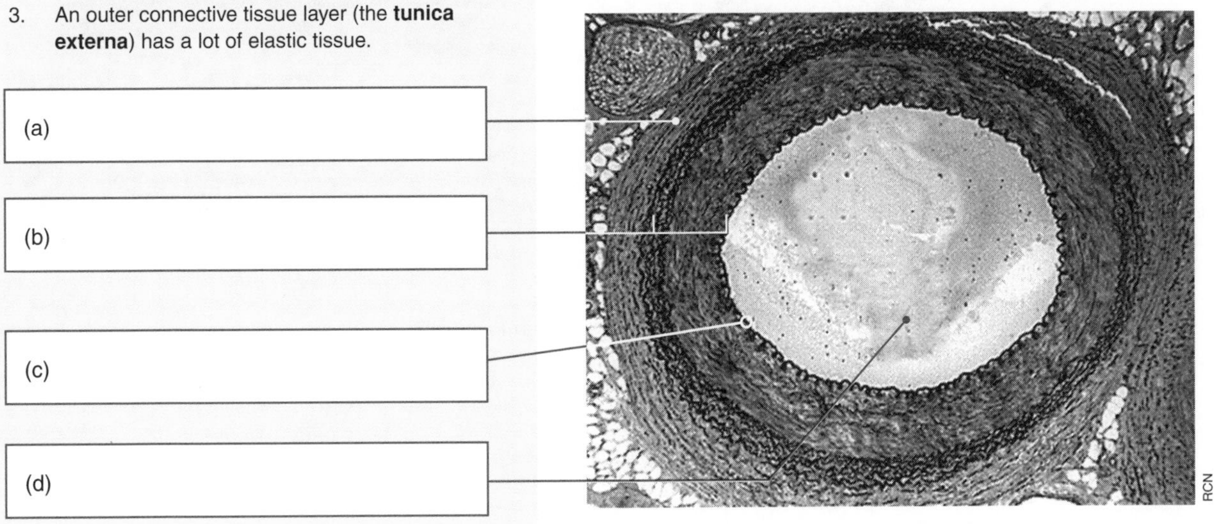
(a)
(b)
(c)
(d)
RCN

1. Using the information above to help you, label the photograph (a)-(d) of the cross section through an artery (above).
2. Why do the walls of arteries need to be thick with a lot of elastic tissue? ______________________________

____

3. What is the purpose of the smooth muscle in the artery walls? ______________________________

____

4. How to arteries contribute to the regulation of blood pressure? ______________________________

____

____

____

© 2015 **BIOZONE** International
ISBN: 978-1-927309-31-5
Photocopying Prohibited

146 Veins

Key Idea: Veins are blood vessels that return the blood from the tissues to the heart. Veins have a large lumen.

Veins are the blood vessels that return blood to the heart from the tissues. The smallest veins (**venules**) return blood from the capillaries to the veins. Veins and their branches contain about 59% of the blood in the body. The structural differences between veins and arteries are mainly associated with differences in the relative thickness of the vessel layers and the diameter of the lumen (space within the vessel). These, in turn, are related to the vessel's functional role.

Veins

When several capillaries unite, they form small veins called **venules**. The venules collect the blood from capillaries and drain it into **veins**. Veins are made up of the same three layers as arteries but they have less elastic and muscle tissue, a relatively thicker tunica externa, and a larger, less defined **lumen**. The venules closest to the capillaries consist of an **endothelium** and a tunica externa of connective tissue. As the venules approach the veins, they also contain the tunica media characteristic of veins (right). Although veins are less elastic than arteries, they can still expand enough to adapt to changes in the pressure and volume of the blood passing through them. Blood flowing in the veins has lost a lot of pressure because it has passed through the narrow capillary vessels. The low pressure in veins means that many veins, especially those in the limbs, need to have valves to prevent backflow of the blood as it returns to the heart.

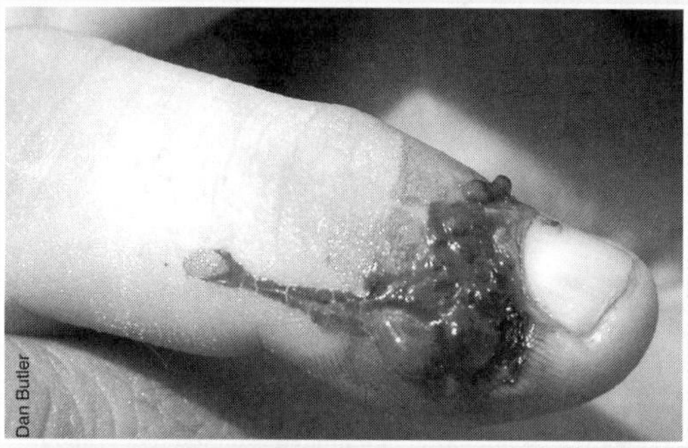
Dan Butler

If a vein is cut, as is shown in this severed finger wound, the blood oozes out slowly in an even flow, and usually clots quickly as it leaves. In contrast, arterial blood spurts rapidly and requires pressure to staunch the flow.

Structure of a vein

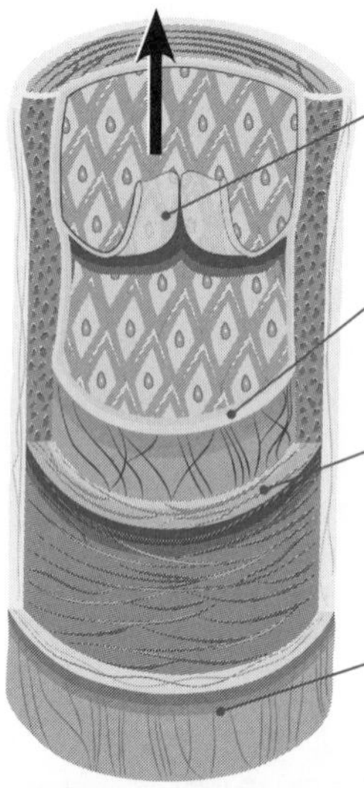
One-way valves
Valves located along the length of veins keep the blood moving towards the heart (prevent back-flow). Arrow indicates direction of blood flow.
Tunica intima (endothelium)
Thin endothelial layer of squamous epithelium lines the vein.
Tunica media
Layer of smooth muscle tissue with collagen fibres (connective tissue). The tunica media is much thinner relative to that of an artery and the smaller venules may lack this layer.
Tunica externa
Layer of connective tissue (mostly collagen). Relatively thicker than in arteries and thicker than the tunica media.

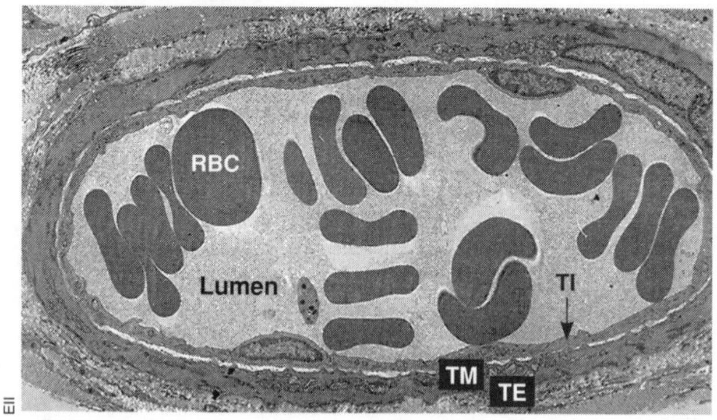
RBC
Lumen
TI
TM
TE
EII

Above: TEM of a vein showing red blood cells (RBC) in the lumen, and the tunica intima (TI), tunica media (TM), and tunica externa (TE).

1. Contrast the structure of veins and arteries for each of the following properties:

   (a) Thickness of muscle and elastic tissue: ________________

   (b) Size of the lumen (inside of the vessel): ________________

2. With respect to their functional roles, explain the differences you have described above: ________________

3. What is the role of the valves in assisting the veins to return blood back to the heart? ________________

4. Why does blood ooze from a venous wound, rather than spurting as it does from an arterial wound? ________________

© 2015 BIOZONE International
ISBN:978-1-927309-31-5
Photocopying Prohibited

147 Capillaries

Key Idea: Capillaries are small, thin-walled vessels that allow the exchange of material between the blood and the tissues. In vertebrates, **capillaries** are very small vessels that connect arterial and venous circulation and allow efficient exchange of nutrients and wastes between the blood and tissues. Capillaries form networks or beds and are abundant where metabolic rates are high. Fluid that leaks out of the capillaries has an essential role in bathing the tissues.

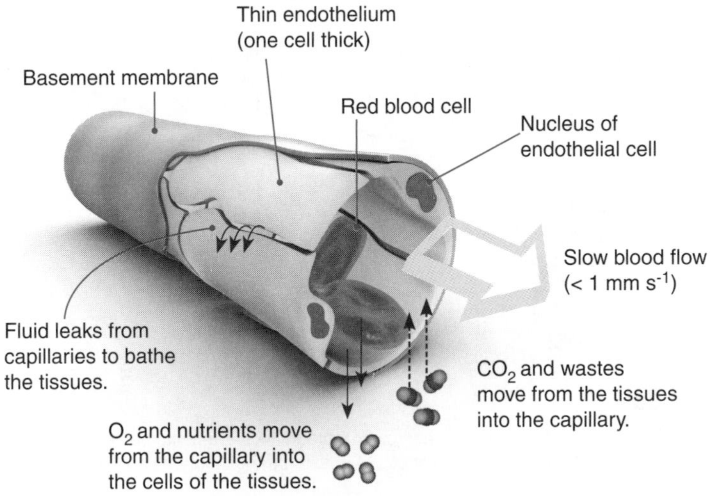

Thin endothelium (one cell thick)
Basement membrane
Red blood cell
Nucleus of endothelial cell
Slow blood flow (< 1 mm s^{-1})
Fluid leaks from capillaries to bathe the tissues.
CO_2 and wastes move from the tissues into the capillary.
O_2 and nutrients move from the capillary into the cells of the tissues.

Exchanges in capillaries

Blood passes from the arterioles into the capillaries where the exchange of materials between the body cells and the blood takes place. Capillaries are small blood vessels with a diameter of just 4-10 µm. The only tissue present is an **endothelium** of squamous epithelial cells. Capillaries are so numerous that no cell is more than 25 µm from any capillary.

Blood pressure causes fluid to leak from capillaries through small gaps where the endothelial cells join. This fluid bathes the tissues, supplying nutrients and oxygen, and removing wastes (left). The density of capillaries in a tissue is an indication of that tissue's metabolic activity. For example, cardiac muscle relies heavily on oxidative metabolism. It has a high demand for blood flow and is well supplied with capillaries. Smooth muscle is far less active than cardiac muscle, relies more on anaerobic metabolism, and does not require such an extensive blood supply.

Comparing blood, tissue fluid, and lymph

	Blood	Tissue fluid	Lymph
Cells	Erythrocytes, leucocytes, platelets	Some leucocytes	Lymphocytes
Proteins	Hormones and plasma proteins	Some hormones and proteins	Few
Glucose	High	None	Low
Amino acids	High	Used by body cells	Low
Oxygen	High	Used by body cells	Low
Carbon dioxide	Low	Produced by body cells	High

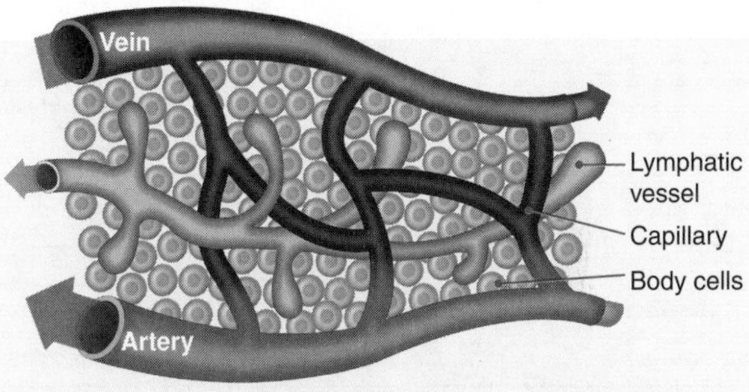

Vein
Artery
Lymphatic vessel
Capillary
Body cells

The pressure at the arterial end of a capillary forces fluid from the blood through gaps between the capillary endothelial cells. This **tissue fluid** contains nutrients and oxygen. Some of it returns to the blood at the venous end of the capillary bed, but some is drained by lymph vessels to form **lymph**. Blood transports nutrients, wastes, and respiratory gases to and from the tissues. Tissue fluid helps transport these between the blood and the tissues. Lymph drains excess tissue fluid and returns it to the general circulation and it has a role in the immune system.

1. What is the role of capillaries? ______________________________

____

2. Describe the structure of a capillary, contrasting it with the structure of a vein and an artery:

____

____

____

____

____

3. Distinguish between blood, tissue fluid, and lymph: ______________________________

____

____

____

____

© 2015 **BIOZONE** International
ISBN: 978-1-927309-31-5
Photocopying Prohibited

LINK 149 LINK 148 WEB 147 KNOW

148 Capillary Networks

Key Idea: Capillaries form branching networks where exchanges between the blood and tissues take place.

The flow of blood through a capillary bed is called microcirculation. In most parts of the body, there are two types of vessels in a capillary bed: the true capillaries, where exchanges take place, and a vessel called a vascular shunt, which connects the arteriole and venule at either end of the bed. The shunt diverts blood past the true capillaries when the metabolic demands of the tissue are low. When tissue activity increases, the entire network fills with blood.

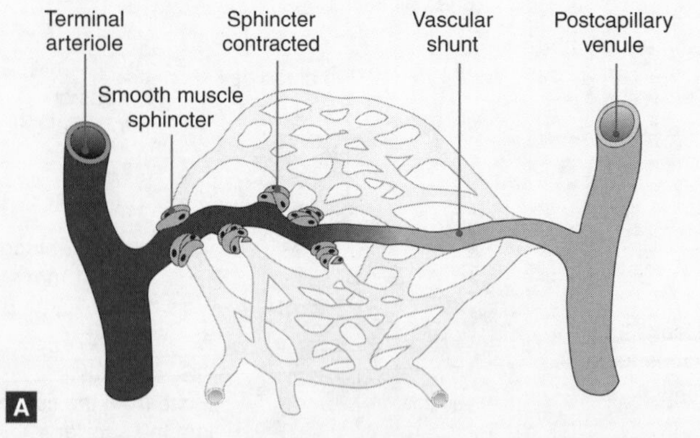
Terminal arteriole
Sphincter contracted
Vascular shunt
Postcapillary venule
Smooth muscle sphincter
A

When the sphincters contract (close), blood is diverted via the vascular shunt to the postcapillary venule, bypassing the exchange capillaries.

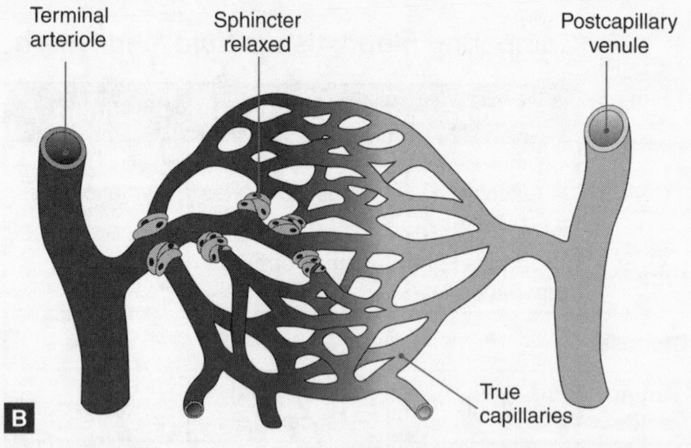
Terminal arteriole
Sphincter relaxed
Postcapillary venule
True capillaries
B

When the sphincters are relaxed (open), blood flows through the entire capillary bed allowing exchanges with the cells of the surrounding tissue.

Connecting capillary beds

The role of portal venous systems

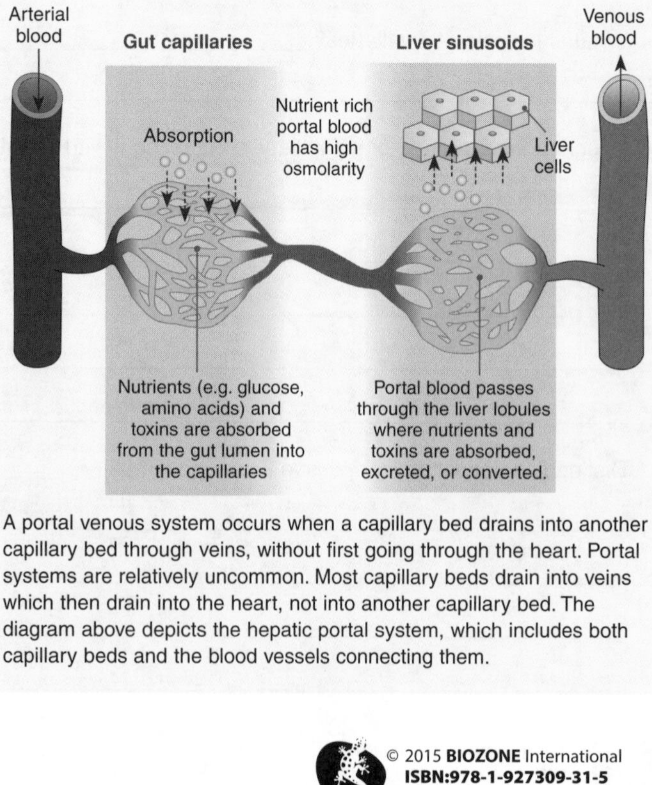
Arterial blood
Gut capillaries
Liver sinusoids
Venous blood
Absorption
Nutrient rich portal blood has high osmolarity
Liver cells
Nutrients (e.g. glucose, amino acids) and toxins are absorbed from the gut lumen into the capillaries
Portal blood passes through the liver lobules where nutrients and toxins are absorbed, excreted, or converted.

A portal venous system occurs when a capillary bed drains into another capillary bed through veins, without first going through the heart. Portal systems are relatively uncommon. Most capillary beds drain into veins which then drain into the heart, not into another capillary bed. The diagram above depicts the hepatic portal system, which includes both capillary beds and the blood vessels connecting them.

1. Describe the structure of a capillary network:

____

____

____

____

____

____

2. Explain the role of the smooth muscle sphincters and the vascular shunt in a capillary network:

____

____

____

____

____

____

3. (a) Describe a situation where the capillary bed would be in the condition labelled **A**:

____

____

____

____

(b) Describe a situation where the capillary bed would be in the condition labelled **B**:

____

____

____

____

4. How does a portal venous system differ from other capillary systems?

____

____

____

____

____

____

© 2015 BIOZONE International
ISBN:978-1-927309-31-5
Photocopying Prohibited

149 The Formation of Tissue Fluid

Key Idea: Tissue fluid is formed by leakage from capillaries. It provides oxygen and nutrients to tissues and removes wastes. The network of capillaries supplying the body's tissues ensures that no cell is far from a supply of nutrients and oxygen. Substances reach the cells through the tissue fluid, moving into and out of the capillaries by diffusion, by cytosis, and through gaps where the membranes are not tightly joined. Specialised capillaries, such as those in the intestine and kidney, where absorption or filtration is important, are relatively more leaky. Fluid moves across the leaky capillary membranes in a direction that depends on the balance between the blood pressure and the oncotic pressure at each end of a capillary bed. Oncotic pressure (also called colloid osmotic pressure) tends to pull water into the capillaries.

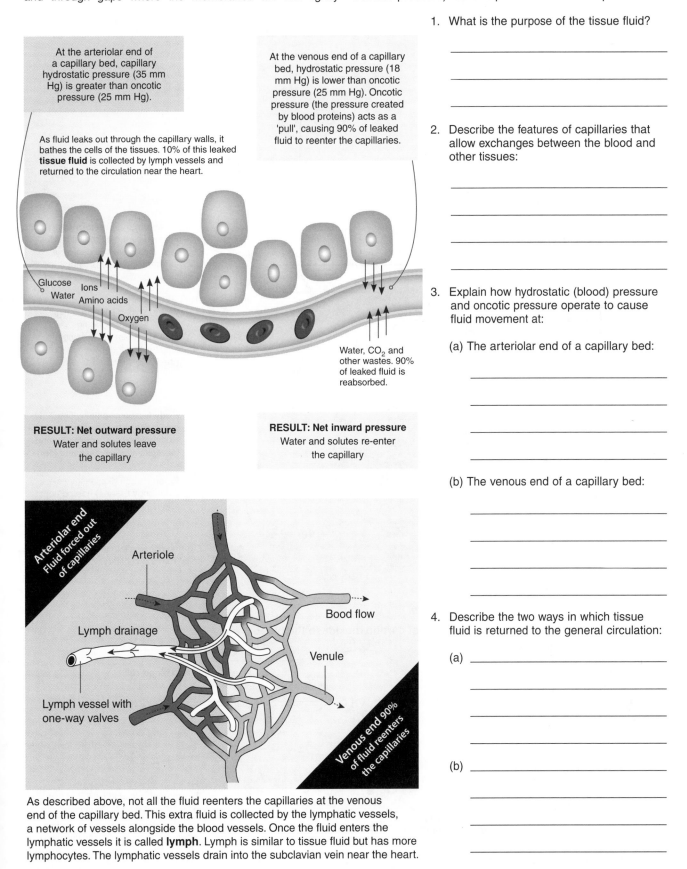

At the arteriolar end of a capillary bed, capillary hydrostatic pressure (35 mm Hg) is greater than oncotic pressure (25 mm Hg).

At the venous end of a capillary bed, hydrostatic pressure (18 mm Hg) is lower than oncotic pressure (25 mm Hg). Oncotic pressure (the pressure created by blood proteins) acts as a 'pull', causing 90% of leaked fluid to reenter the capillaries.

As fluid leaks out through the capillary walls, it bathes the cells of the tissues. 10% of this leaked **tissue fluid** is collected by lymph vessels and returned to the circulation near the heart.

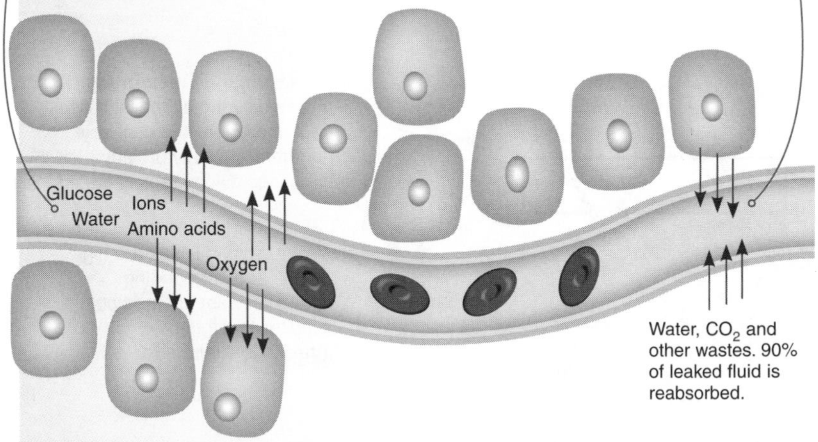
Glucose
Water
Ions
Amino acids
Oxygen
Water, CO_2 and other wastes. 90% of leaked fluid is reabsorbed.

RESULT: Net outward pressure
Water and solutes leave the capillary

RESULT: Net inward pressure
Water and solutes re-enter the capillary

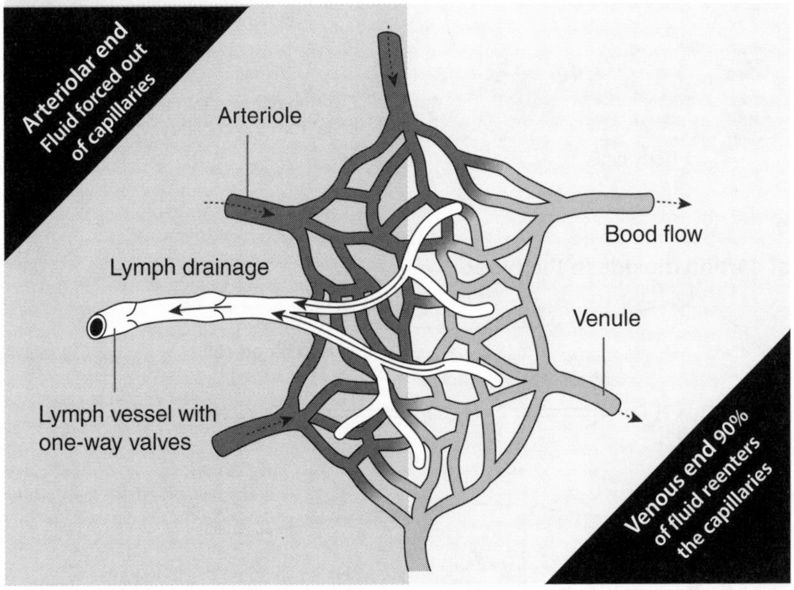
Arteriolar end
Fluid forced out of capillaries
Arteriole
Bood flow
Lymph drainage
Venule
Lymph vessel with one-way valves
Venous end 90% of fluid reenters the capillaries

As described above, not all the fluid reenters the capillaries at the venous end of the capillary bed. This extra fluid is collected by the lymphatic vessels, a network of vessels alongside the blood vessels. Once the fluid enters the lymphatic vessels it is called **lymph**. Lymph is similar to tissue fluid but has more lymphocytes. The lymphatic vessels drain into the subclavian vein near the heart.

1. What is the purpose of the tissue fluid?

2. Describe the features of capillaries that allow exchanges between the blood and other tissues:

3. Explain how hydrostatic (blood) pressure and oncotic pressure operate to cause fluid movement at:

(a) The arteriolar end of a capillary bed:

(b) The venous end of a capillary bed:

4. Describe the two ways in which tissue fluid is returned to the general circulation:

(a)

(b)

© 2015 **BIOZONE** International
ISBN: 978-1-927309-31-5
Photocopying Prohibited

150 Gas Transport in Mammals

Key Idea: Haemoglobin is a respiratory pigment in red blood cells, which binds oxygen and increases the efficiency of its transport and delivery to tissues throughout the body.

The transport of respiratory gases around the body is the role of the blood and its respiratory pigment. In vertebrates, e.g humans, oxygen is transported throughout the body chemically bound to the respiratory pigment **haemoglobin** inside the red blood cells. In the muscles, oxygen from haemoglobin is transferred to and retained by **myoglobin**, a molecule that is chemically similar to haemoglobin except that it consists of only one haem-globin unit. Myoglobin has a greater affinity for oxygen than haemoglobin and acts as an oxygen store within muscles, releasing the oxygen during periods of prolonged or extreme muscular activity.

Gas exchange and transport

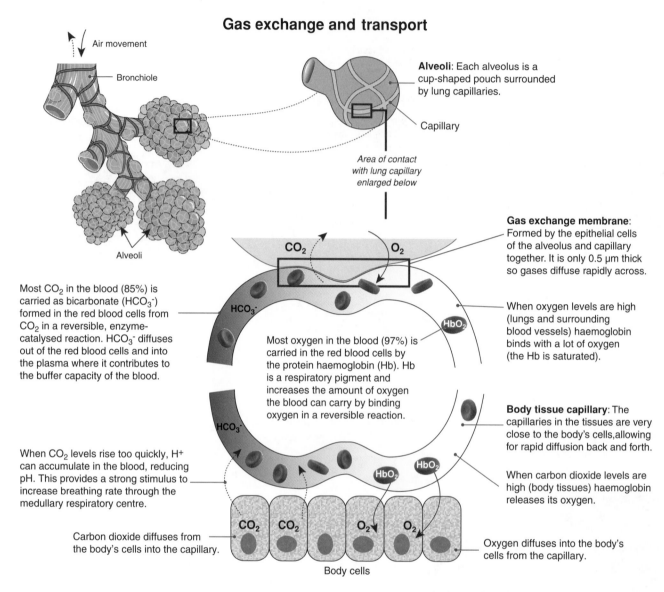

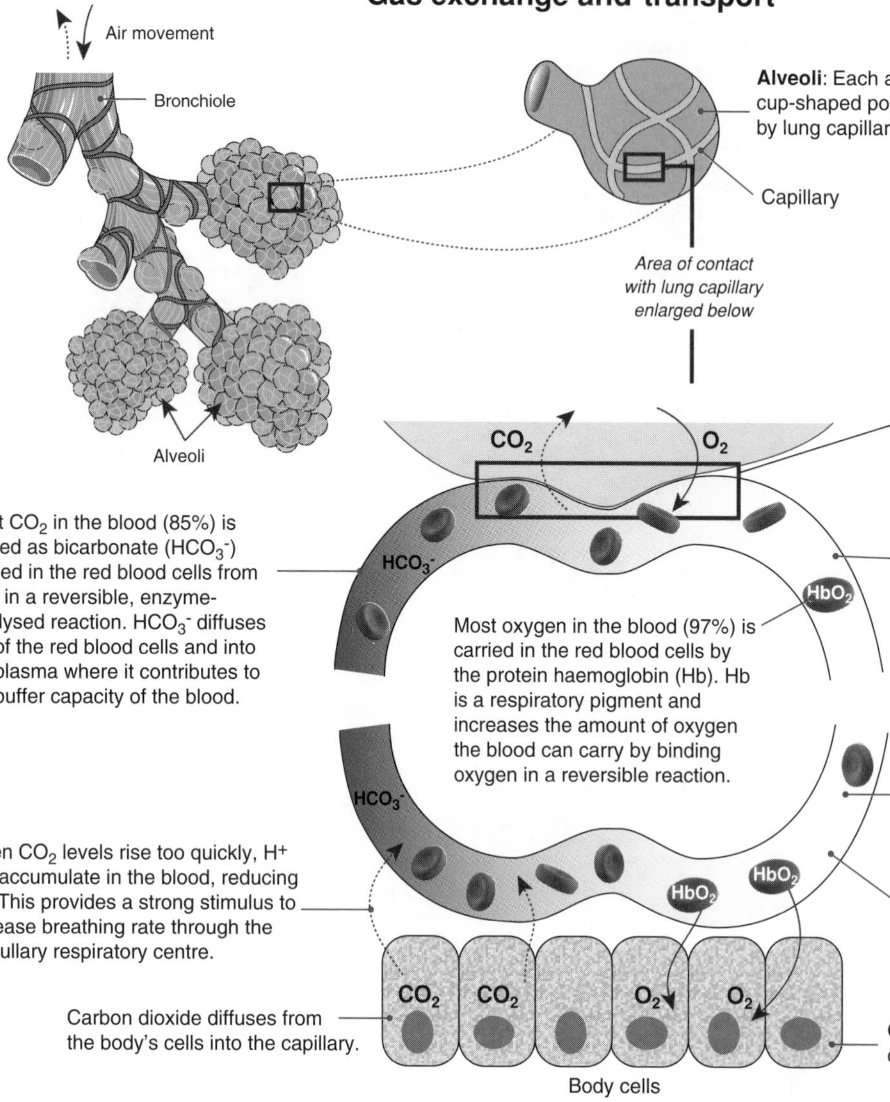
Air movement
Bronchiole
Alveoli
Alveoli: Each alveolus is a cup-shaped pouch surrounded by lung capillaries.
Capillary
Area of contact with lung capillary enlarged below
Gas exchange membrane: Formed by the epithelial cells of the alveolus and capillary together. It is only 0.5 µm thick so gases diffuse rapidly across.
CO_2
O_2
HCO_3^-
HbO_2
Most CO_2 in the blood (85%) is carried as bicarbonate (HCO_3^-) formed in the red blood cells from CO_2 in a reversible, enzyme-catalysed reaction. HCO_3^- diffuses out of the red blood cells and into the plasma where it contributes to the buffer capacity of the blood.
When oxygen levels are high (lungs and surrounding blood vessels) haemoglobin binds with a lot of oxygen (the Hb is saturated).
Most oxygen in the blood (97%) is carried in the red blood cells by the protein haemoglobin (Hb). Hb is a respiratory pigment and increases the amount of oxygen the blood can carry by binding oxygen in a reversible reaction.
Body tissue capillary: The capillaries in the tissues are very close to the body's cells,allowing for rapid diffusion back and forth.
When CO_2 levels rise too quickly, H^+ can accumulate in the blood, reducing pH. This provides a strong stimulus to increase breathing rate through the medullary respiratory centre.
When carbon dioxide levels are high (body tissues) haemoglobin releases its oxygen.
Carbon dioxide diffuses from the body's cells into the capillary.
Oxygen diffuses into the body's cells from the capillary.
Body cells

Transport of carbon dioxide in the blood

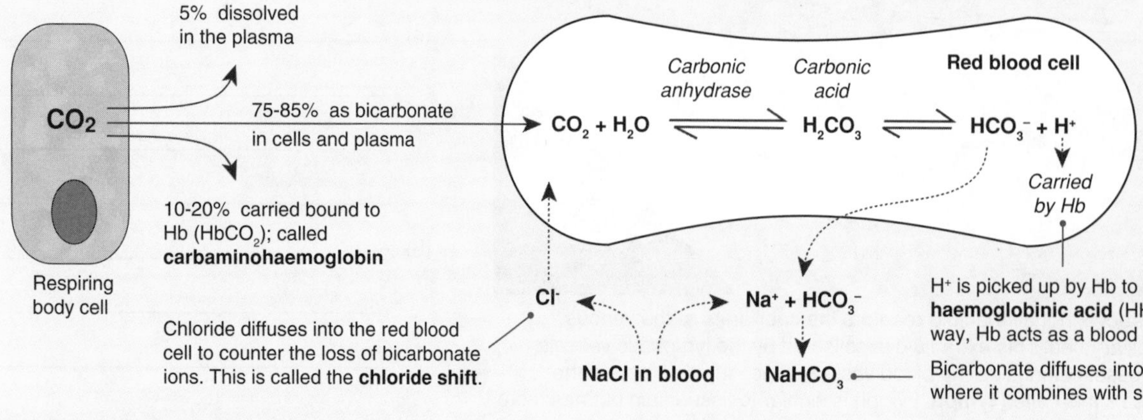
CO_2
Respiring body cell
5% dissolved in the plasma
75-85% as bicarbonate in cells and plasma
10-20% carried bound to Hb ($HbCO_2$); called **carbaminohaemoglobin**
Red blood cell
Carbonic anhydrase
Carbonic acid
$CO_2 + H_2O \rightleftharpoons H_2CO_3 \rightleftharpoons HCO_3^- + H^+$
Carried by Hb
Cl^-
$Na^+ + HCO_3^-$
NaCl in blood
$NaHCO_3$
Chloride diffuses into the red blood cell to counter the loss of bicarbonate ions. This is called the **chloride shift**.
H^+ is picked up by Hb to form **haemoglobinic acid** (HHb). In this way, Hb acts as a blood buffer.
Bicarbonate diffuses into the plasma where it combines with sodium.

© 2015 BIOZONE International
ISBN:978-1-927309-31-5
Photocopying Prohibited

Oxygen does not easily dissolve in blood, but is carried in chemical combination with haemoglobin (Hb) in red blood cells. The most important factor determining how much oxygen is carried by Hb is the level of oxygen in the blood. The greater the oxygen tension, the more oxygen will combine with Hb. This relationship can be illustrated with an oxygen-haemoglobin dissociation curve as shown below (Fig. 1). In the lung capillaries, (high O_2), a lot of oxygen is picked up and bound by Hb. In the tissues, (low O_2), oxygen is released. In skeletal muscle, myoglobin picks up oxygen from haemoglobin and therefore serves as an oxygen store when oxygen tensions begin to fall. The release of oxygen is enhanced by the **Bohr effect** (Fig. 2).

Respiratory pigments and the transport of oxygen

Fig.1: Dissociation curves for haemoglobin and myoglobin at normal body temperature for fetal and adult human blood.

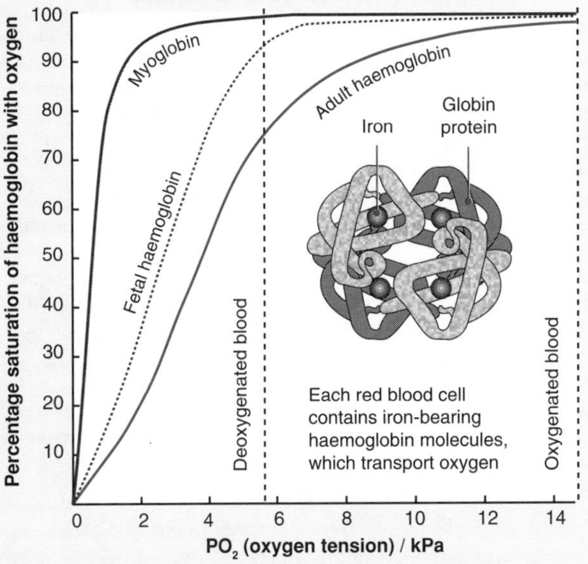
Percentage saturation of haemoglobin with oxygen
100
90
80
70
60
50
40
30
20
10
0
2
4
6
8
10
12
14
PO2 (oxygen tension) / kPa
Myoglobin
Fetal haemoglobin
Adult haemoglobin
Iron
Globin protein
Deoxygenated blood
Oxygenated blood
Each red blood cell contains iron-bearing haemoglobin molecules, which transport oxygen

As oxygen level increases, more oxygen combines with haemoglobin (Hb). Hb saturation remains high, even at low oxygen tensions. Fetal Hb has a high affinity for oxygen and carries 20-30% more than maternal Hb. Myoglobin in skeletal muscle has a very high affinity for oxygen and will take up oxygen from haemoglobin in the blood.

Fig.2: Oxyhaemoglobin dissociation curves for human blood at normal body temperature at different blood pH.

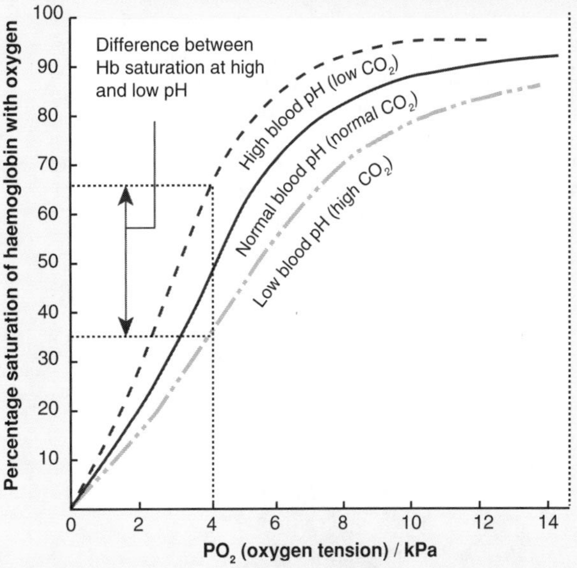
Percentage saturation of haemoglobin with oxygen
100
90
80
70
60
50
40
30
20
10
0
2
4
6
8
10
12
14
PO2 (oxygen tension) / kPa
Difference between Hb saturation at high and low pH
High blood pH (low CO2)
Normal blood pH (normal CO2)
Low blood pH (high CO2)

As pH increases (lower CO_2), more oxygen combines with Hb. As the blood pH decreases (higher CO_2), Hb binds less oxygen and releases more to the tissues (the **Bohr effect**). The difference between Hb saturation at high and low pH represents the amount of oxygen released to the tissues.

1. (a) Identify two regions in the body where oxygen levels are very high: __________

   (b) Identify two regions where carbon dioxide levels are very high: __________

2. Explain the significance of the **reversible binding** reaction of haemoglobin (Hb) to oxygen: __________

3. (a) Haemoglobin saturation is affected by the oxygen level in the blood. Describe the nature of this relationship:

   (b) Comment on the significance of this relationship to oxygen delivery to the tissues: __________

4. (a) Describe how fetal Hb is different to adult Hb: __________

   (b) Explain the significance of this difference to oxygen delivery to the fetus: __________

5. At low blood pH, less oxygen is bound by haemoglobin and more is released to the tissues:

   (a) Name this effect: __________

   (b) Comment on its significance to oxygen delivery to respiring tissue: __________

6. Explain the significance of the very high affinity of myoglobin for oxygen: __________

7. Identify the two main contributors to the buffer capacity of the blood: __________

© 2015 **BIOZONE** International
ISBN: 978-1-927309-31-5
Photocopying Prohibited

151 The Effects of High Altitude

Key Idea: An increase in the number of red blood cells and haemoglobin, together with an increase in heart rate, help the body adjust to the low oxygen tensions of high altitude.

Air pressure decreases with altitude so the pressure (therefore amount) of oxygen in the air also decreases. Many of the physiological effects of high altitude arise from the low oxygen pressure, not the low air pressure in itself. Humans can make both short and long term physiological adjustments (acclimatisation) to altitude. Some of these involve long and short term responses of the cardiovascular system.

Physiological adjustments to altitude

The body makes several physiological adjustments to compensate for the low oxygen pressure at altitude. However, sudden exposure to an altitude of 2000 m causes breathlessness, and ascending above 4500 m too rapidly results in mountain sickness. The symptoms include breathlessness and nausea. Continuing to ascend with mountain sickness can result in fatal accumulation of fluid on the lungs and brain.

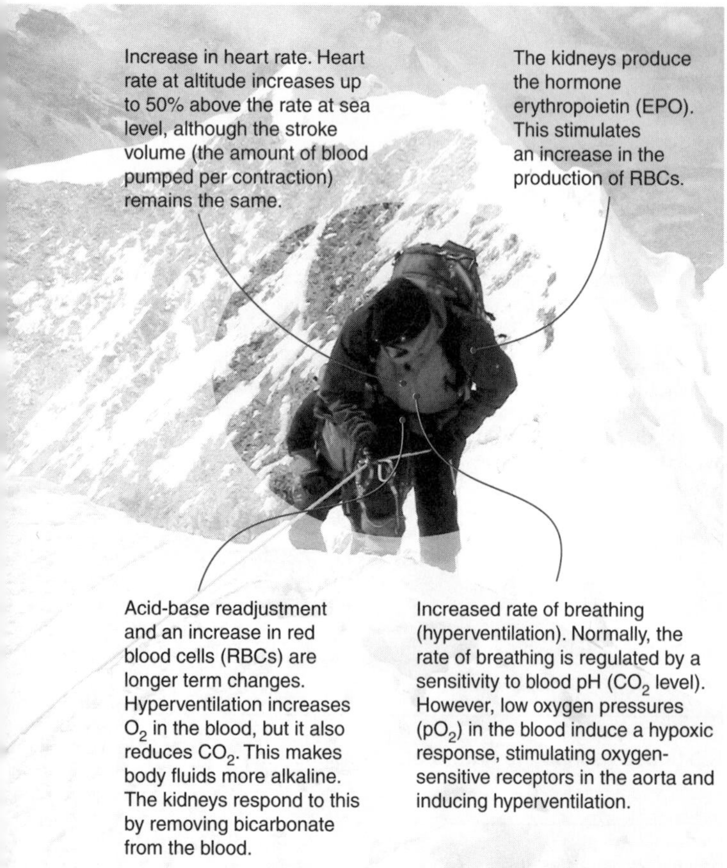
Increase in heart rate. Heart rate at altitude increases up to 50% above the rate at sea level, although the stroke volume (the amount of blood pumped per contraction) remains the same.
The kidneys produce the hormone erythropoietin (EPO). This stimulates an increase in the production of RBCs.
Acid-base readjustment and an increase in red blood cells (RBCs) are longer term changes. Hyperventilation increases O_2 in the blood, but it also reduces CO_2. This makes body fluids more alkaline. The kidneys respond to this by removing bicarbonate from the blood.
Increased rate of breathing (hyperventilation). Normally, the rate of breathing is regulated by a sensitivity to blood pH (CO_2 level). However, low oxygen pressures (pO_2) in the blood induce a hypoxic response, stimulating oxygen-sensitive receptors in the aorta and inducing hyperventilation.

Red blood cell count increases at altitude

Some physiological adjustments to altitude take place almost immediately (e.g. increased breathing and heart rates). Other adjustments, such as increasing the number of red blood cells (RBCs) and associated haemoglobin level, may take weeks. These responses all improve the rate oxygen is supplied to the body's tissues. When more permanent adjustments to physiology are made (increased blood cells and capillaries), heart and breathing rates return to normal.

After only a few days at high altitude, the RBC count begins to increase. This is due to an increase in the production of a hormone called erythropoietin (EPO). EPO stimulates the bone marrow to produce more RBCs. As the RBC count increases, the level of the oxygen-transporting protein haemoglobin also increases and more oxygen can be transported around the body to supply working cells. After only a few weeks at high altitude, the proportion of RBCs in blood increases from about 45% to 60% (which also increases blood viscosity, i.e. makes the blood thicker).

Effects of altitude on haemoglobin levels

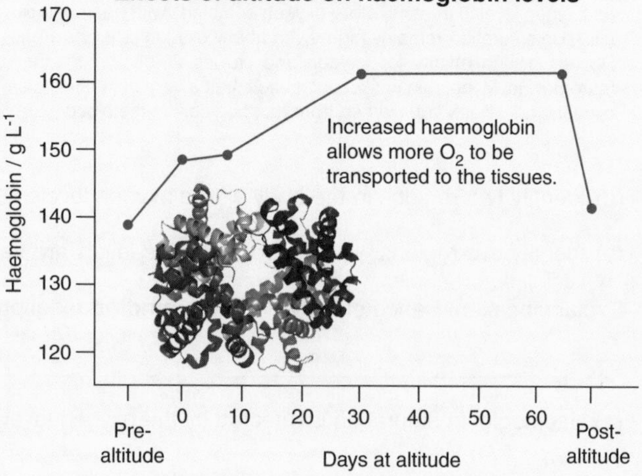
170
160
150
140
130
120
Haemoglobin / g L^-1
Increased haemoglobin allows more O_2 to be transported to the tissues.
Pre-altitude
0
10
20
30
40
50
60
Post-altitude
Days at altitude

1. (a) Describe the initial effects of high altitude on the body in people who have not acclimatised: ______

   (b) What name is given to describe these effects? ______

2. (a) How is RBC production increased? ______

   (b) How is an increase in RBCs an advantage at altitude? ______

3. Some athletes use synthetic EPO to boost their RBC count. Suggest why this practice is banned? ______

4. Why might use of synthetic EPO pose a health hazard? ______

© 2015 BIOZONE International
ISBN:978-1-927309-31-5
Photocopying Prohibited

152 The Human Heart

Key Idea: Humans have a four chambered heart divided into left and right halves. It acts as a double pump.

The heart is the centre of the human cardiovascular system. It is a hollow, muscular organ made up of four chambers (two **atria** and two **ventricles**) that alternately fill and empty of blood, acting as a double pump. The left side (systemic circuit) pumps blood to the body tissues and the right side (pulmonary circuit) pumps blood to the lungs. The heart lies between the lungs, to the left of the midline, and is surrounded by a double layered pericardium of connective tissue, which prevents over distension of the heart and anchors it within the central compartment of the thoracic cavity.

Human heart structure

(sectioned, anterior view)

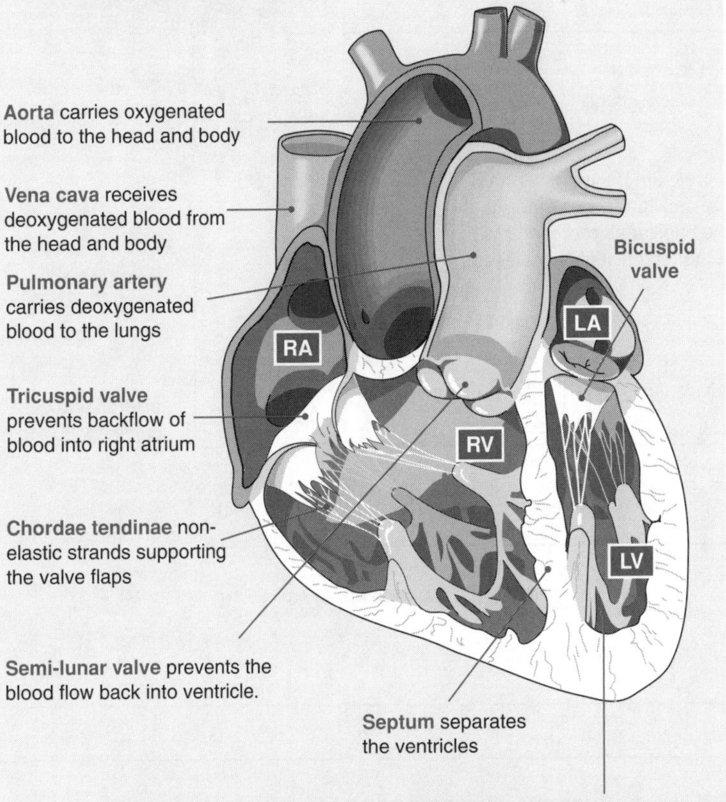

Aorta carries oxygenated blood to the head and body
Vena cava receives deoxygenated blood from the head and body
Pulmonary artery carries deoxygenated blood to the lungs
Tricuspid valve prevents backflow of blood into right atrium
Chordae tendinae non-elastic strands supporting the valve flaps
Semi-lunar valve prevents the blood flow back into ventricle.
Septum separates the ventricles
Bicuspid valve
RA
LA
RV
LV

The heart is not a symmetrical organ. Although the quantity of blood pumped by each side of the heart is the same, the walls of the left ventricle are thicker and more muscular than those of the right ventricle. The difference affects the shape of the ventricular cavities, so the right ventricle is twisted over the left.

Key to abbreviations

- **RA** Right atrium: receives deoxygenated blood via the vena cavae
- **RV** Right ventricle: pumps deoxygenated blood to the lungs via the pulmonary artery
- **LA** Left atrium: receives blood from the lungs via the pulmonary veins
- **LV** Left ventricle: pumps oxygenated blood to the head and body via the aorta

Top view of a heart in section to show valves

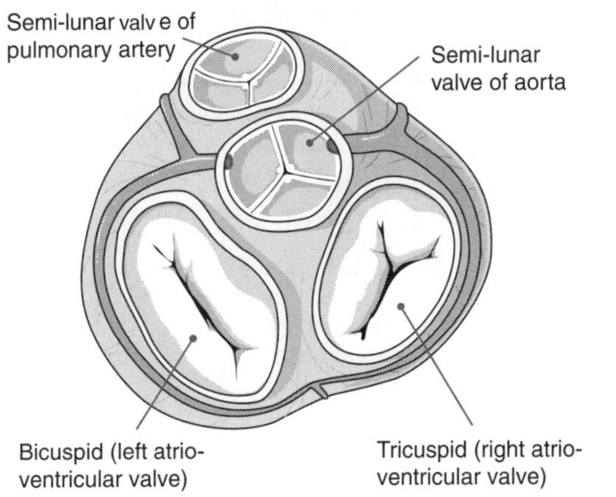

Semi-lunar valv e of pulmonary artery
Semi-lunar valve of aorta
Bicuspid (left atrio-ventricular valve)
Tricuspid (right atrio-ventricular valve)

Anterior view of heart to show coronary arteries

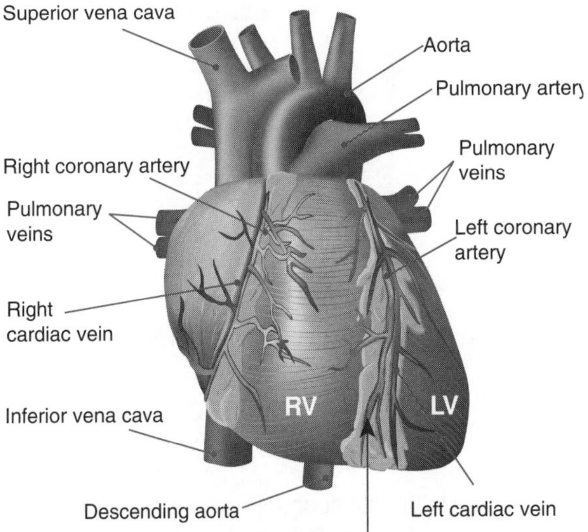

Superior vena cava
Aorta
Pulmonary artery
Pulmonary veins
Right coronary artery
Pulmonary veins
Left coronary artery
Right cardiac vein
Inferior vena cava
RV
LV
Descending aorta
Left cardiac vein

The high oxygen demands of the heart muscle are met by a dense capillary network branching from the coronary arteries. The coronary arteries (left and right) arise from the aorta and spread over the surface of the heart supplying the cardiac muscle with oxygenated blood. The left carries 70% of the coronary blood supply and the right the remaining 30%. Deoxygenated blood is collected by the cardiac veins and returned to the right atrium via a large coronary sinus.

1. In the schematic diagram of the heart, below, label the four chambers and the main vessels entering and leaving them. The arrows indicate the direction of blood flow. Use large coloured circles to mark the position of each of the four valves.

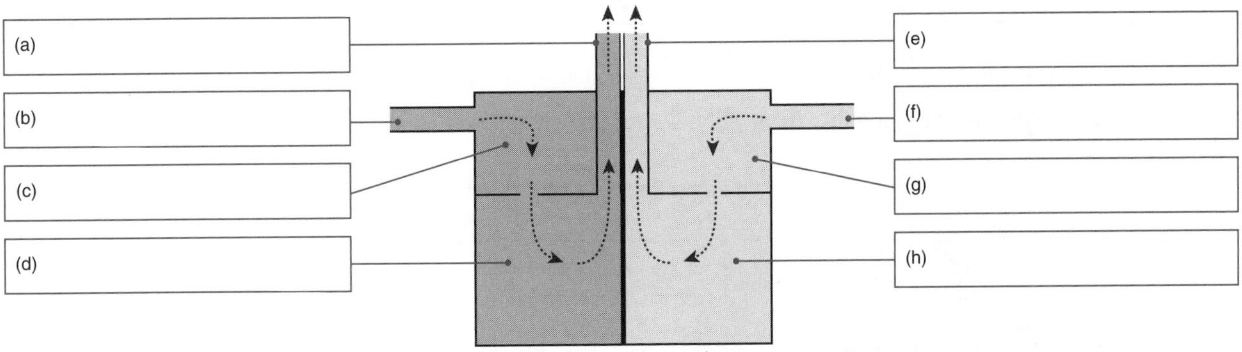

(a)
(b)
(c)
(d)
(e)
(f)
(g)
(h)

© 2015 BIOZONE International
ISBN: 978-1-927309-31-5
Photocopying Prohibited

Pressure changes and the asymmetry of the heart

The heart is not a symmetrical organ. The left ventricle and its associated arteries are thicker and more muscular than the corresponding structures on the right side. This asymmetry is related to the necessary pressure differences between the pulmonary (lung) and systemic (body) circulations (not to the distance over which the blood is pumped *per se*). The graph below shows changes in blood pressure in each of the major blood vessel types in the systemic and pulmonary circuits (the horizontal distance not to scale). The pulmonary circuit must operate at a much lower pressure than the systemic circuit to prevent fluid from accumulating in the alveoli of the lungs. The left side of the heart must develop enough "spare" pressure to enable increased blood flow to the muscles of the body and maintain kidney filtration rates without decreasing the blood supply to the brain.

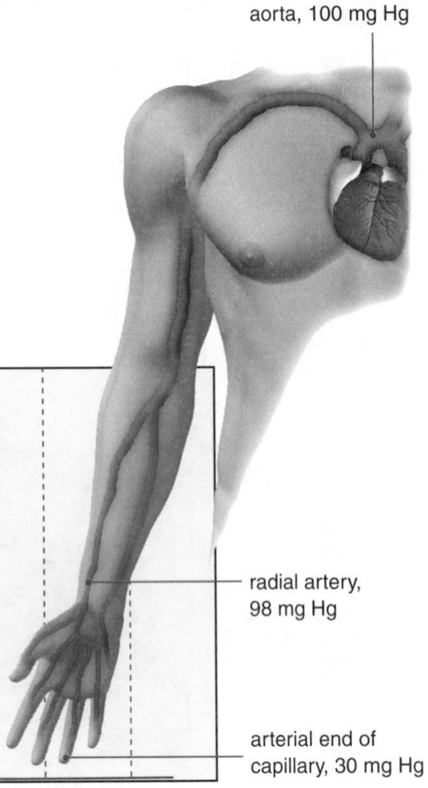
aorta, 100 mg Hg
radial artery, 98 mg Hg
arterial end of capillary, 30 mg Hg

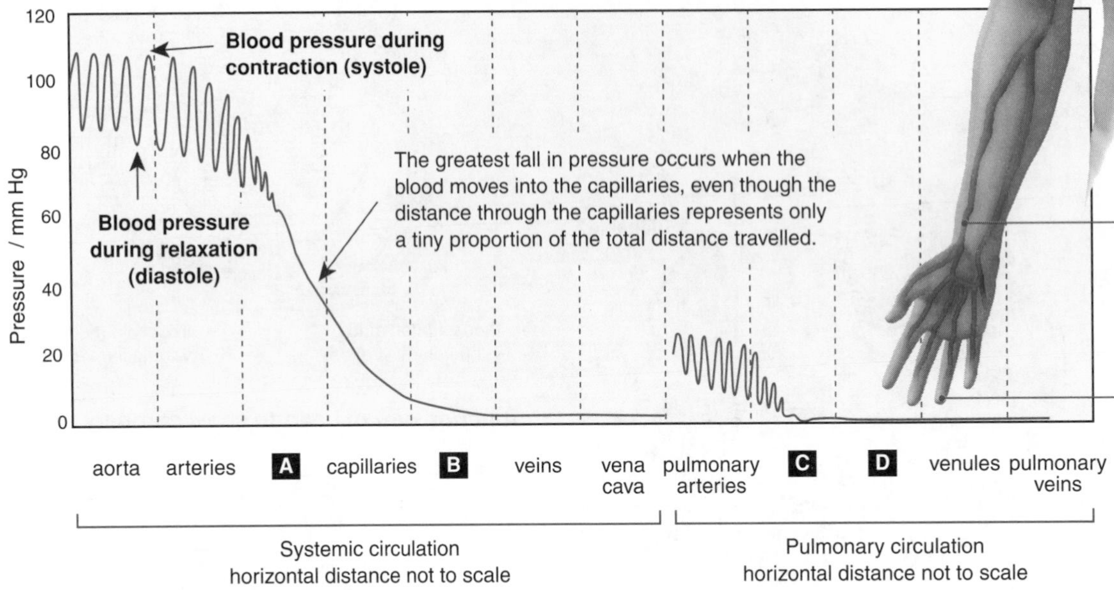
120
100
80
60
40
20
0
Pressure / mm Hg
Blood pressure during contraction (systole)
Blood pressure during relaxation (diastole)
The greatest fall in pressure occurs when the blood moves into the capillaries, even though the distance through the capillaries represents only a tiny proportion of the total distance travelled.
aorta
arteries
A
capillaries
B
veins
vena cava
pulmonary arteries
C
D
venules
pulmonary veins
Systemic circulation
horizontal distance not to scale
Pulmonary circulation
horizontal distance not to scale

2. What is the purpose of the valves in the heart? ______________________________

____

3. The heart is full of blood, yet it requires its own blood supply. Suggest two reasons why this is the case:

(a) ______________________________

(b) ______________________________

4. Predict the effect on the heart if blood flow through a coronary artery is restricted or blocked: ______________________________

____

____

5. Identify the vessels corresponding to the letters **A-D** on the graph above:

A: ______________ B: ______________ C: ______________ D: ______________

6. (a) Why must the pulmonary circuit operate at a lower pressure than the systemic system? ______________________________

____

____

(b) Relate this to differences in the thickness of the wall of the left and right ventricles of the heart: ______________________________

____

____

7. What are you recording when you take a pulse? ______________________________

____

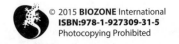

© 2015 **BIOZONE** International
ISBN:978-1-927309-31-5
Photocopying Prohibited

153 Dissecting a Mammalian Heart

Key Idea: Dissecting a sheep's heart allows hands-on exploration of a mammalian heart.

The dissection of a sheep's heart is a common practical activity and allows hands-on exploration of the appearance and structure of a mammalian heart. A diagram of a heart is an idealised representation of an organ that may look quite different in reality. You must learn to transfer what you know from a diagram to the interpretation of the real organ.

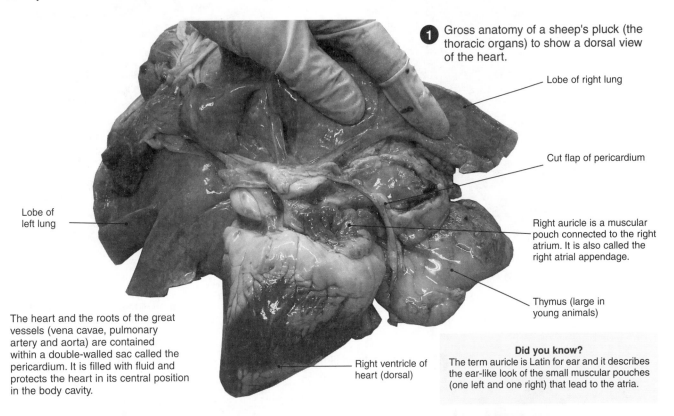

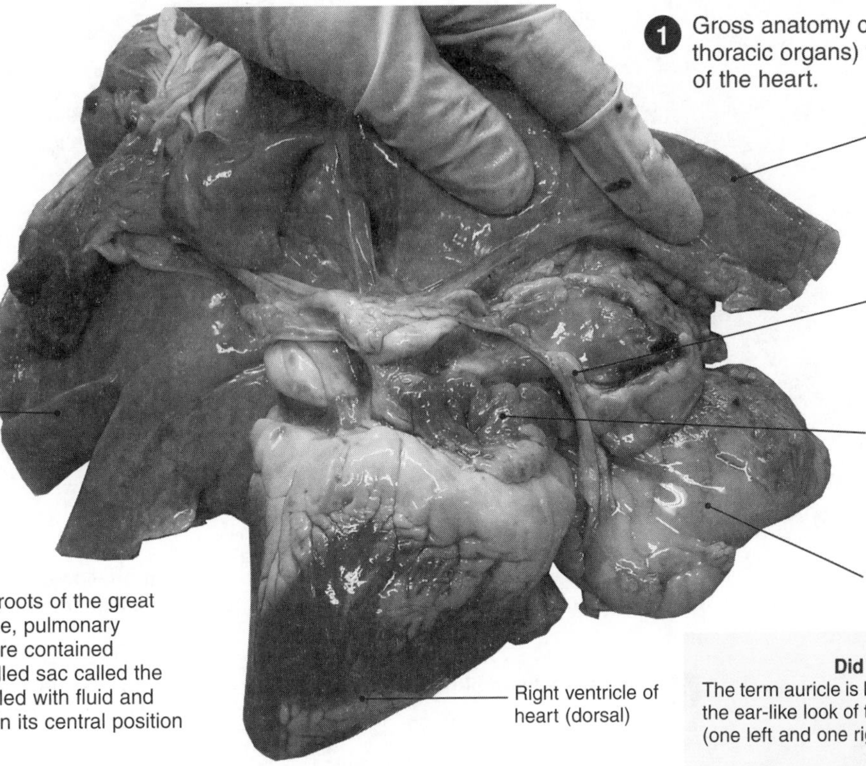
1
Gross anatomy of a sheep's pluck (the thoracic organs) to show a dorsal view of the heart.
Lobe of right lung
Cut flap of pericardium
Lobe of left lung
Right auricle is a muscular pouch connected to the right atrium. It is also called the right atrial appendage.
Thymus (large in young animals)
Right ventricle of heart (dorsal)

The heart and the roots of the great vessels (vena cavae, pulmonary artery and aorta) are contained within a double-walled sac called the pericardium. It is filled with fluid and protects the heart in its central position in the body cavity.

Did you know?
The term auricle is Latin for ear and it describes the ear-like look of the small muscular pouches (one left and one right) that lead to the atria.

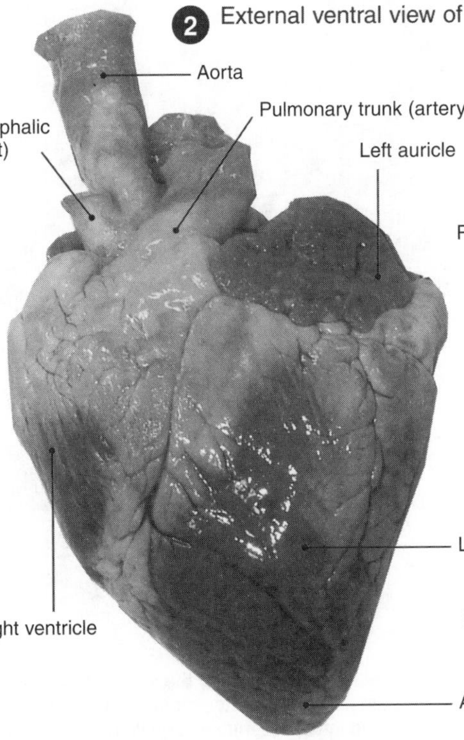
2
External ventral view of heart
Aorta
Pulmonary trunk (artery)
Brachiocephalic artery (cut)
Left auricle
Left ventricle
Right ventricle
Apex

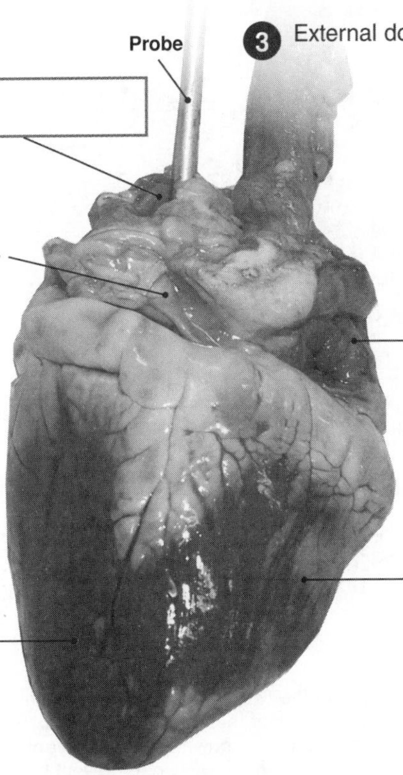
Probe
3
External dorsal view of heart
Pulmonary veins
Right auricle
Right ventricle
Left ventricle

Note the main surface features of an isolated heart. The narrow pointed end forms the **apex** of the heart, while the wider end, where the blood vessels enter is the **base**. The ventral surface of the heart (above) is identified by a groove, the **interventricular sulcus**, which marks the division between the left and right ventricles.

1. Use coloured lines to indicate the interventricular sulcus and the base of the heart. Label the coronary arteries.

On the dorsal surface of the heart, above, locate the large thin-walled **vena cavae** and **pulmonary veins**. You may be able to distinguish between the anterior and posterior vessels. On the right side of the dorsal surface (as you look at the heart) at the base of the heart is the **right atrium**, with the **right ventricle** below it.

2. On this photograph, label the vessel indicated by the probe.

© 2015 **BIOZONE** International
ISBN: 978-1-927309-31-5
Photocopying Prohibited

4 Dorsal view of heart

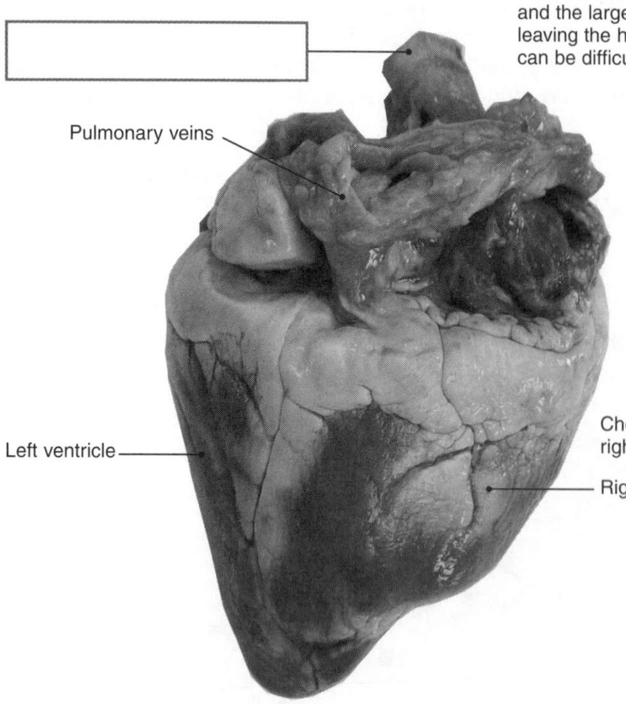
Pulmonary veins
Left ventricle
Right ventricle

5 Shallow section, ventral view of heart

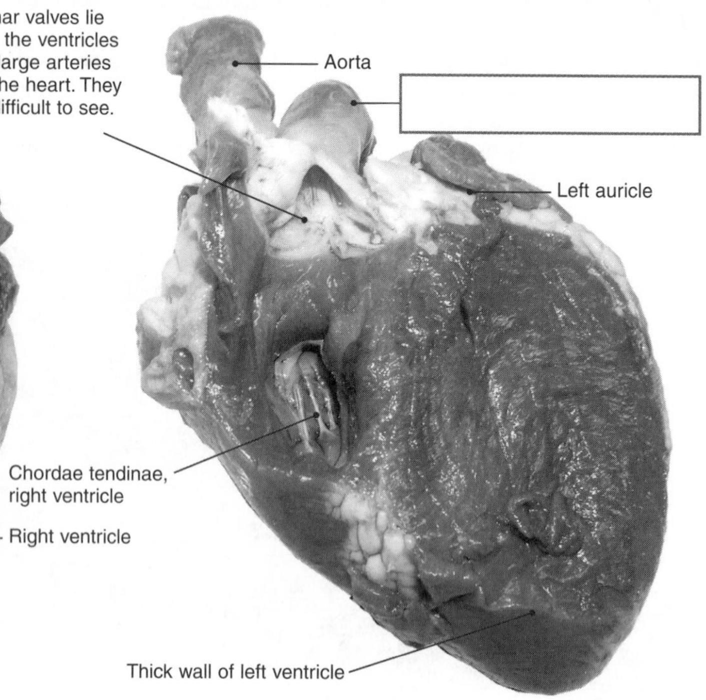
Semi-lunar valves lie between the ventricles and the large arteries leaving the heart. They can be difficult to see.
Aorta
Left auricle
Chordae tendinae, right ventricle
Thick wall of left ventricle

3. On this **dorsal view**, label the vessel indicated. Palpate the heart and feel the difference in the thickness of the left and right ventricle walls.

4. This photograph shows a shallow section to expose the right ventricle. Label the vessel in the box indicated.

6 Frontal sections of heart to show chambers

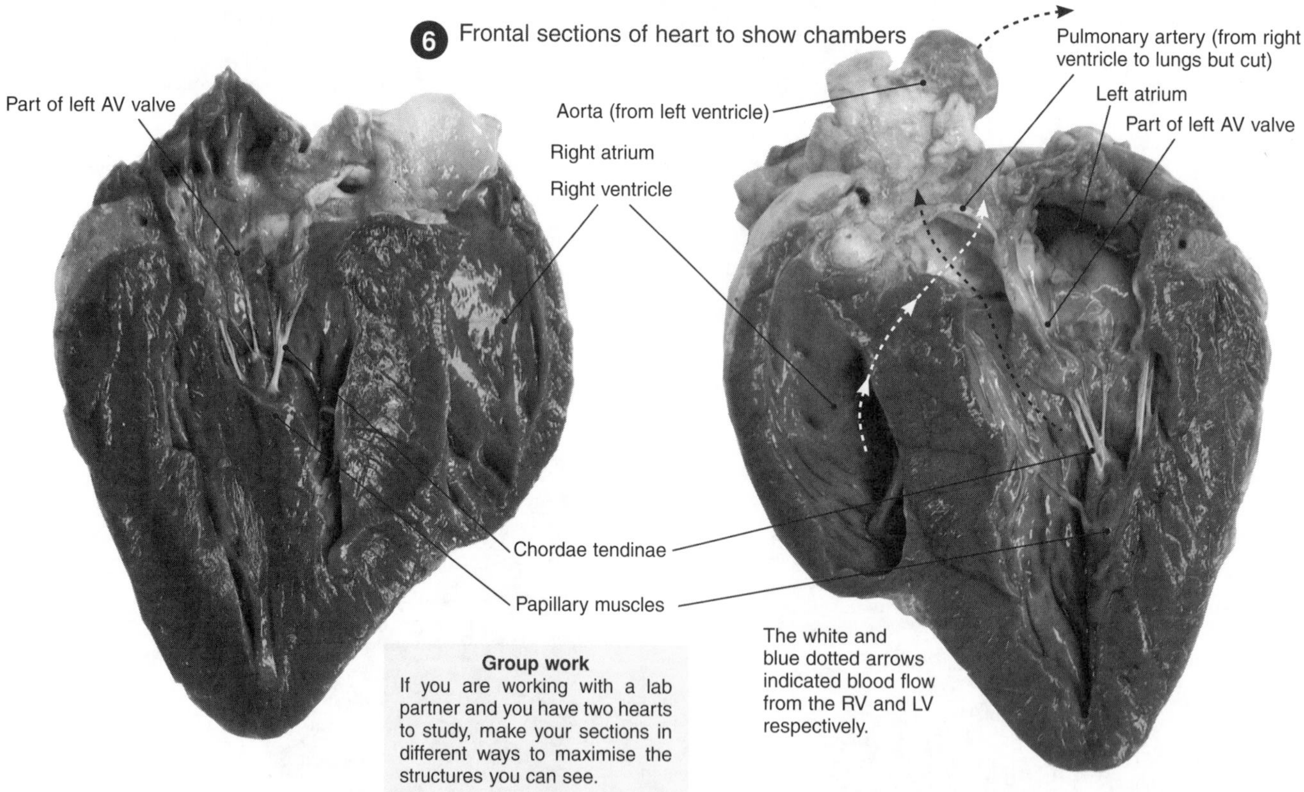
Part of left AV valve
Aorta (from left ventricle)
Right atrium
Right ventricle
Pulmonary artery (from right ventricle to lungs but cut)
Left atrium
Part of left AV valve
Chordae tendinae
Papillary muscles
The white and blue dotted arrows indicated blood flow from the RV and LV respectively.

Group work
If you are working with a lab partner and you have two hearts to study, make your sections in different ways to maximise the structures you can see.

If the heart is sectioned and the two halves opened, the valves of the heart can be seen. Each side of the heart has a one-way valve between the atrium and the ventricle known as the **atrioventricular valve**. They close during ventricular contraction to prevent back flow of the blood into the lower pressure atria.

5. Judging by their position and structure, what do you suppose is the function of the chordae tendinae?

____

____

The atrioventricular (AV) valves of the two sides of the heart are similar in structure except that the right AV valve has three cusps (tricuspid) while the left atrioventricular valve has two cusps (bicuspid or mitral valve). Connective tissue (**chordae tendineae**) run from the cusps to **papillary muscles** on the ventricular wall.

6. What feature shown here most clearly distinguishes the left and right ventricles?.

____

____

© 2015 **BIOZONE** International
ISBN:978-1-927309-31-5
Photocopying Prohibited

154 The Cardiac Cycle

Key Idea: The cardiac cycle refers to the sequence of events of a heartbeat and involves three main stages: atrial systole, ventricular systole, and complete cardiac diastole.

The heart pumps with alternate contractions (**systole**) and relaxations (**diastole**). Heartbeat occurs in a cycle involving three stages: atrial systole, ventricular systole, and complete cardiac diastole. Pressure changes in the heart's chambers generated by the cycle of contraction and relaxation are responsible for blood movement and cause the heart valves to open and close, preventing backflow of blood. The heartbeat occurs in response to electrical impulses, which can be recorded as a trace called an electrocardiogram.

The cardiac cycle

The **pulse** results from the rhythmic expansion of the arteries as the blood spurts from the left ventricle. Pulse rate therefore corresponds to heart rate.

Stage 1: Atrial contraction and ventricular filling
The ventricles relax and blood flows into them from the atria. Note that 70% of the blood from the atria flows passively into the ventricles. It is during the last third of ventricular filling that the atria contract.

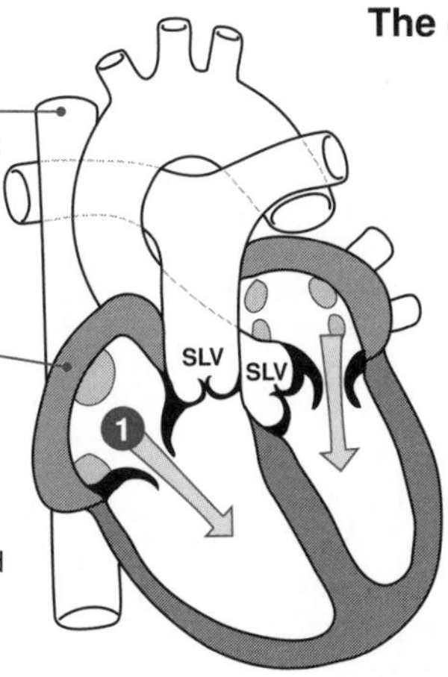
SLV
SLV
1

Heart during ventricular filling

Stage 2: Ventricular contraction
The atria relax, the ventricles contract, and blood is pumped from the ventricles into the aorta and the pulmonary artery. The start of ventricular contraction coincides with the first heart sound.

Stage 3: (not shown) There is a short period of atrial and ventricular relaxation. Semilunar valves (**SLV**) close to prevent backflow into the ventricles (see diagram, left). The cycle begins again. For a heart beating at 75 beats per minute, one cardiac cycle lasts about 0.8 seconds.

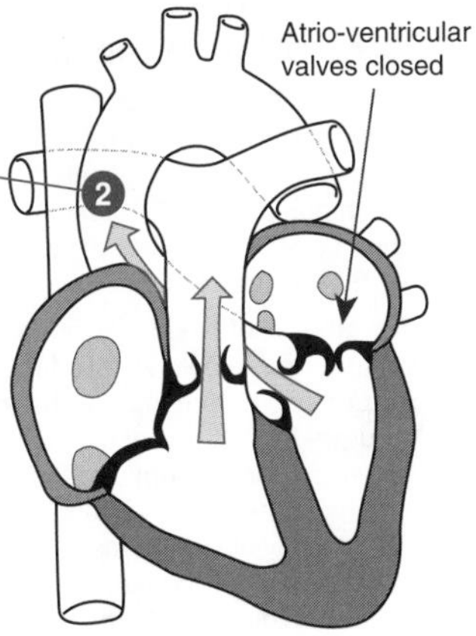
Atrio-ventricular valves closed
2

Heart during ventricular contraction

Cardiac cycle events and the electrocardiogram (ECG)

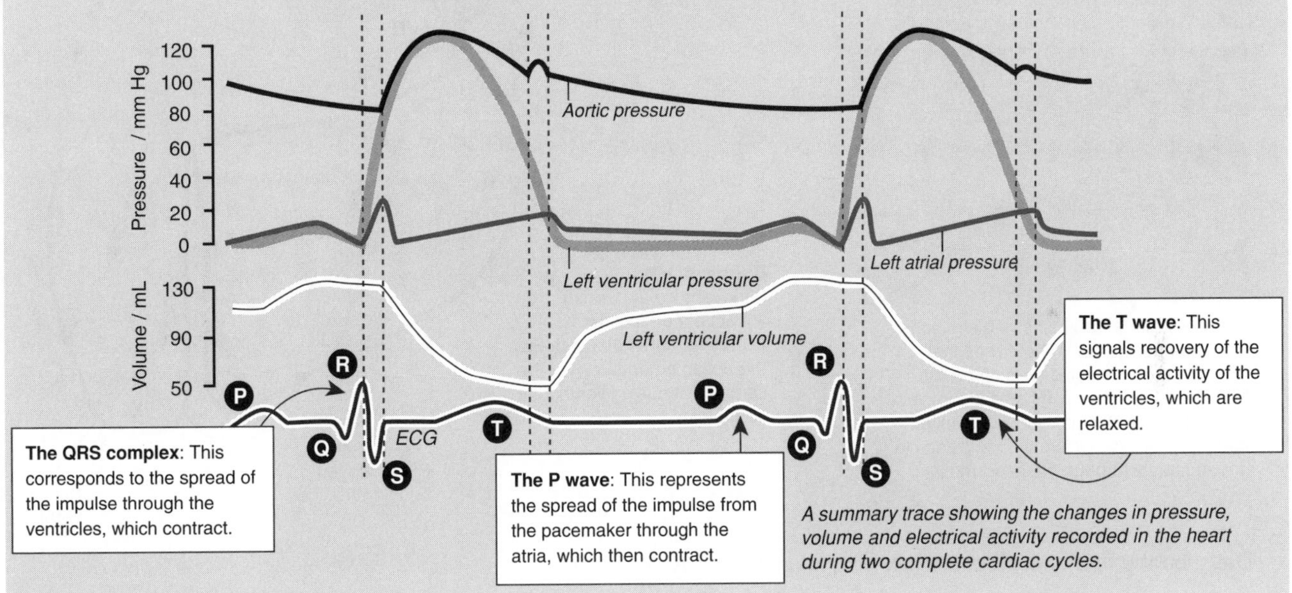
Pressure / mm Hg
120
100
80
60
40
20
0
Aortic pressure
Left ventricular pressure
Left atrial pressure
Volume / mL
130
90
50
Left ventricular volume
P
Q
R
S
T
ECG
The QRS complex: This corresponds to the spread of the impulse through the ventricles, which contract.
The P wave: This represents the spread of the impulse from the pacemaker through the atria, which then contract.
The T wave: This signals recovery of the electrical activity of the ventricles, which are relaxed.

A summary trace showing the changes in pressure, volume and electrical activity recorded in the heart during two complete cardiac cycles.

1. On the ECG trace above:

   (a) When is the aortic pressure highest? ____________________

   (b) Which electrical event immediately precedes the increase in ventricular pressure? ____________________

   (c) What is happening when the pressure of the left ventricle is lowest? ____________________

2. Suggest the physiological reason for the period of electrical recovery experienced each cycle (the T wave):

   ____

3. Using the letters indicated, mark the points on trace above corresponding to each of the following:

   (a) E: Ejection of blood from the ventricle

   (b) BVC: Closing of the bicuspid valve

   (c) FV: Filling of the ventricle

   (d) BVO: Opening of the bicuspid valve

© 2015 BIOZONE International
ISBN: 978-1-927309-31-5
Photocopying Prohibited

155 Control of Heart Activity

Key Idea: Heartbeat is initiated by the sinoatrial node which acts as a pacemaker by setting the basic heart rhythm.

The heartbeat is myogenic, meaning it originates within the cardiac muscle itself. The heartbeat is regulated by a conduction system consisting of the pacemaker (**sinoatrial node**) and a specialised conduction system of Purkyne tissue. The pacemaker sets the basic heart rhythm, but this rate can be influenced by hormones and by the cardiovascular control centre. Changing the rate and force of heart contraction is the main mechanism for controlling cardiac output.

Generation of the heartbeat

The basic rhythmic heartbeat is **myogenic**. The nodal cells (SAN and atrioventricular node) spontaneously generate rhythmic action potentials without neural stimulation. The normal resting rate of self-excitation of the SAN is about 50 beats per minute.

The amount of blood ejected from the left ventricle per minute is called the **cardiac output**. It is determined by the **stroke volume** (the volume of blood ejected with each contraction) and the **heart rate** (number of heart beats per minute). Cardiac muscle responds to stretching by contracting more strongly. The greater the blood volume entering the ventricle, the greater the force of contraction. This relationship is important in regulating stroke volume in response to demand.

The hormone **epinephrine** also influences cardiac output, increasing heart rate in preparation for vigorous activity. Changing the rate and force of heart contraction is the main mechanism for controlling cardiac output in order to meet changing demands.

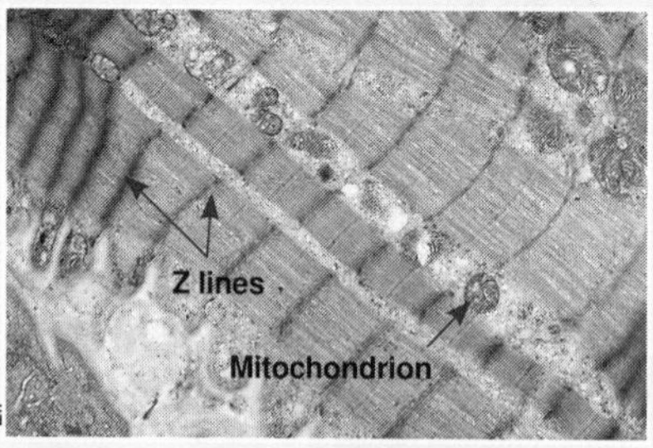
Z lines
Mitochondrion
EII

TEM of cardiac muscle showing striations in a fibre (muscle cell). The Z lines that delineate the contractile units of the rod-like units of the fibre. The fibres are joined by specialised electrical junctions called Intercalated discs, which allow impulses to spread rapidly through the heart muscle.

Sinoatrial node (SAN) is also called the **pacemaker**. It is a small mass of specialised muscle cells on the wall of the right atrium, near the entry point of the superior vena cava. The pacemaker initiates the cardiac cycle, spontaneously generating **action potentials** that cause the atria to contract. The SAN sets the basic heart rate, but this rate is influenced by hormones, such as adrenaline (epinephrine) and impulses from the autonomic nervous system.

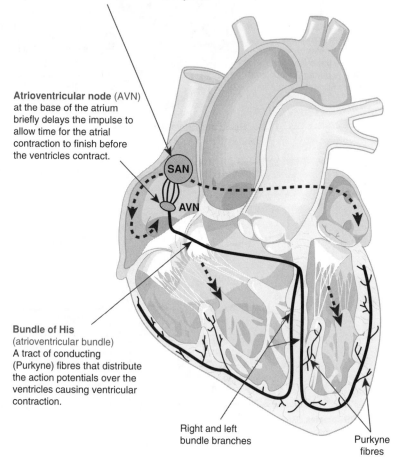

Atrioventricular node (AVN) at the base of the atrium briefly delays the impulse to allow time for the atrial contraction to finish before the ventricles contract.

Bundle of His (atrioventricular bundle) A tract of conducting (Purkyne) fibres that distribute the action potentials over the ventricles causing ventricular contraction.

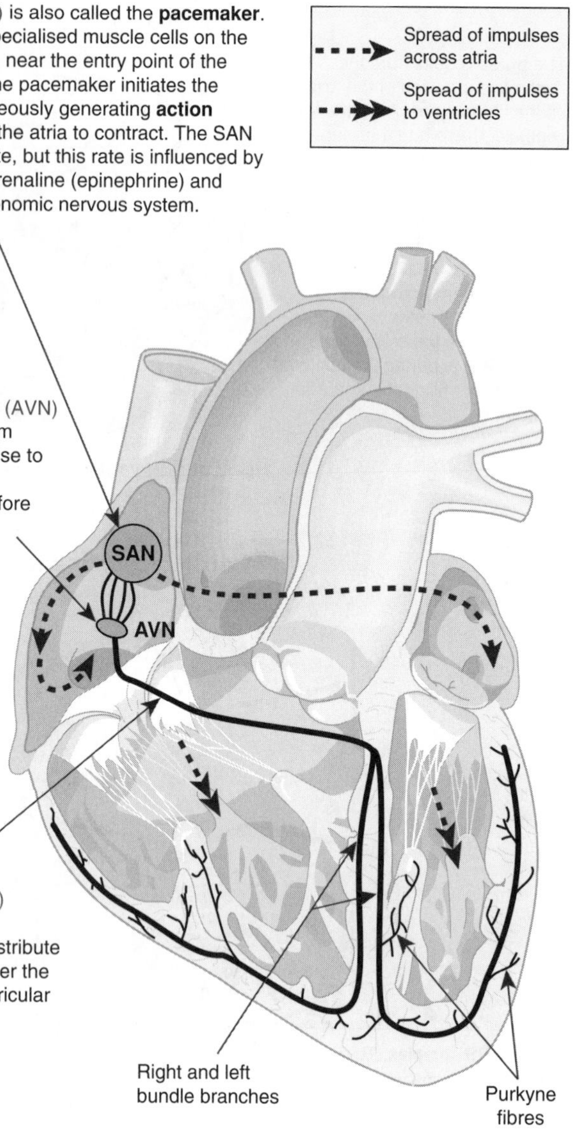
Spread of impulses across atria
Spread of impulses to ventricles
SAN
AVN
Right and left bundle branches
Purkyne fibres

1. Describe the role of each of the following in heart activity:

   (a) The sinoatrial node: ______

   (b) The atrioventricular node: ______

   (c) The bundle of His: ______

   (d) Intercalated discs: ______

2. What is the significance of delaying the impulse at the AVN? ______

3. What is the advantage of the physiological response of cardiac muscle to stretching? ______

4. The heart-beat is intrinsic. Why is it important to be able to influence the basic rhythm via the central nervous system?

© 2015 BIOZONE International
ISBN:978-1-927309-31-5
Photocopying Prohibited

156 Review of the Human Heart

Key Idea: The human heart comprises four chambers, which act as a double pump. Its contraction is myogenic, but can be influenced by other factors.

This activity summarises features of heart structure and function. Use it as a self-test, but see the earlier activities in this chapter if you need help.

1. On the diagram below, label the identified components of heart structure and intrinsic control (**a-n**).

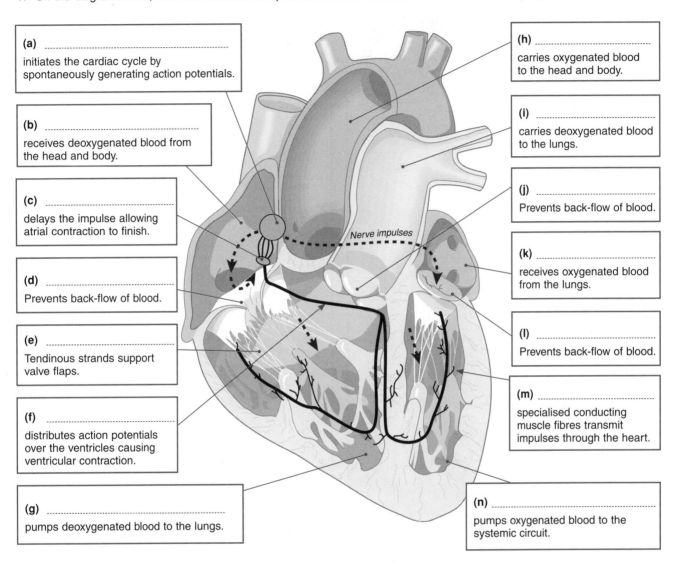

(a) ....
initiates the cardiac cycle by spontaneously generating action potentials.

(b) ....
receives deoxygenated blood from the head and body.

(c) ....
delays the impulse allowing atrial contraction to finish.

(d) ....
Prevents back-flow of blood.

(e) ....
Tendinous strands support valve flaps.

(f) ....
distributes action potentials over the ventricles causing ventricular contraction.

(g) ....
pumps deoxygenated blood to the lungs.

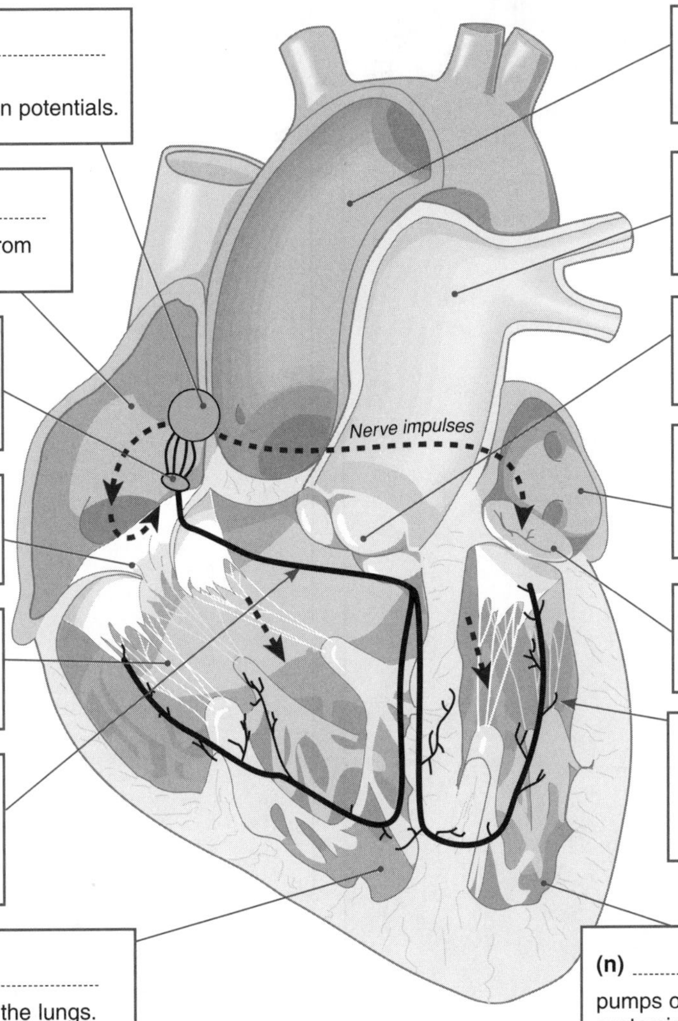
Nerve impulses

(h) ....
carries oxygenated blood to the head and body.

(i) ....
carries deoxygenated blood to the lungs.

(j) ....
Prevents back-flow of blood.

(k) ....
receives oxygenated blood from the lungs.

(l) ....
Prevents back-flow of blood.

(m) ....
specialised conducting muscle fibres transmit impulses through the heart.

(n) ....
pumps oxygenated blood to the systemic circuit.

2. An **ECG** is the result of different impulses produced at each phase of the **cardiac cycle** (the sequence of events in a heartbeat). For each electrical event indicated in the ECG below, describe the corresponding event in the cardiac cycle:

A ....
The spread of the impulse from the pacemaker (sinoatrial node) through the atria.

B ....
The spread of the impulse through the ventricles.

C ....
Recovery of the electrical activity of the ventricles.

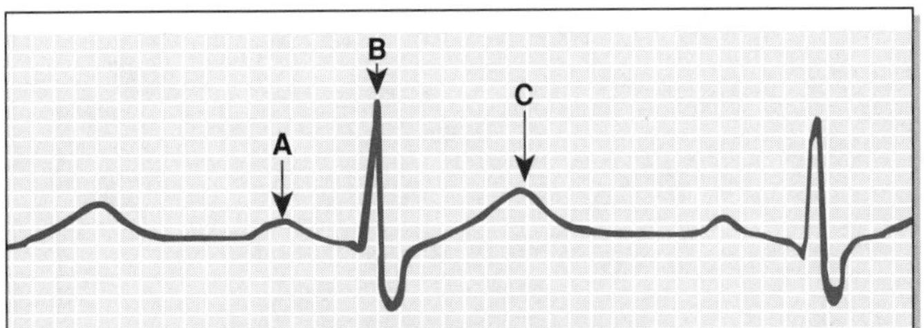
A
B
C

Electrical activity in the heart

3. (a) On the trace above, mark the region where the ventricular pressure is highest.

(b) What is happening to the ventricular volume at this time? ....

....

© 2015 **BIOZONE** International
ISBN: 978-1-927309-31-5
Photocopying Prohibited

LINK 155 LINK 154 LINK 152 TEST

157 Chapter Review

Summarise what you know about this topic under the headings provided. You can draw diagrams or mind maps, or write short notes to organise your thoughts. Use the images and hints to help you and refer back to the introduction to check the points covered:

The mammalian circulatory system

HINT: Describe the structure and function of the circulatory system, including the blood vessels.

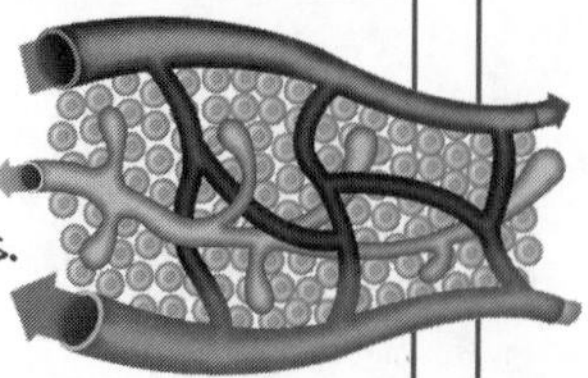

The heart

HINT: Describe the structure of the heart and the intrinsic control of heart activity.

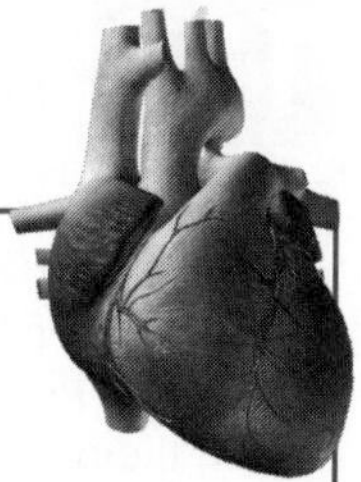

Oxygen transport

HINT: Describe how oxygen is transported around the body and the Bohr effect.

© 2015 BIOZONE International
ISBN:978-1-927309-31-5
Photocopying Prohibited

158 KEY TERMS AND IDEAS: Did You Get It?

1. (a) What type of blood vessel transports blood away from the heart? ____________

   (b) What type of blood vessel transports blood to the heart? ____________

   (c) What type of blood vessel enables exchanges between the blood and tissues? ____________

2. (a) What is the circulatory fluid in vertebrates called? ____________

   (b) Which cell type in this fluid transports oxygen? ____________

   (c) Which cell type in this fluid fights disease? ____________

   (d) Which components of this fluid are involved in clotting? ____________

3. (a) What is the name given to the contraction phase of the cardiac cycle? ____________

   (b) What is the name given to the relaxation phase of the cardiac cycle? ____________

4. 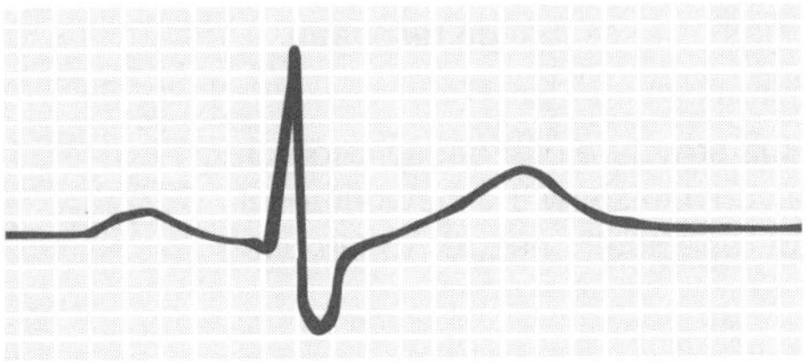

   (a) What does the image (left) show: ____________

   (b) Circle the QRS complex.

   (c) Circle the region corresponding to lowest ventricular pressure.

   (d) Ventricular volume at this time is increasing/decreasing (delete one).

5. Identify the blood vessels labelled **A** and **B** on the photo (right). Give reasons for your answer:

   A: ____________

   ____

   B: ____________

   ____

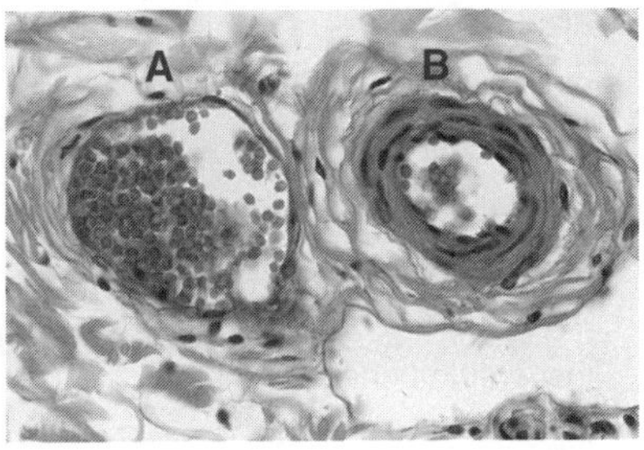

A
B

EII

6. Match the following words with their definitions:

atrium ....

blood ....

Bohr effect ....

closed circulatory system ....

double circulatory system ....

haemoglobin ....

heart ....

leucocytes ....

lymph ....

red blood cells ....

tissue fluid ....

ventricle ....

A A chamber of the mammalian heart that pumps blood into arteries.

B Circulatory system in which the blood is fully contained within vessels.

C These cells lack a nucleus, but contain large amounts of haemoglobin.

D Muscular chambered organ of the vertebrate circulatory system.

E A large iron-containing protein, which transports oxygen in the blood of vertebrates.

F A chamber of the mammalian heart that receives blood directly from the body or lung.

G A fluid derived from the blood plasma by leakage through capillaries. It bathes the tissues and is also called interstitial fluid.

H Clear fluid contained within the lymphatic system. It is similar in composition to the interstitial fluid.

I Circulatory system in which blood travels from the heart to lungs and back (via the pulmonary circuit) before being pumped to the rest of the body.

J The effect that occurs as haemoglobin binds less oxygen and releases more to the tissues (due to pH decrease as a result of elevated CO_2).

K Name given to a group of blood cells involved in internal defence.

L Circulatory fluid of vertebrates containing numerous cell types. It transports respiratory gases, nutrients, and wastes.

© 2015 **BIOZONE** International
ISBN: 978-1-927309-31-5
Photocopying Prohibited

Topic 9 Gas exchange and smoking

Key terms

alveoli
breathing
bronchi
bronchioles
carbon dioxide
carbon monoxide
carcinogen
cartilage
cellular respiration
ciliated epithelium
COPD
diaphragm
expiration (exhalation)
gas exchange
gas exchange membrane
goblet cells
inspiration (inhalation)
lung cancer
lungs
mucous glands
nicotine
oxygen
pneumocytes
respiratory gas
smooth muscle
squamous epithelium
surfactant
tar
trachea

9.1 Principles of gas exchange

Learning outcomes

Activity number

☐ 1 Distinguish between cellular respiration and gas exchange and explain why organisms must exchange respiratory gases with their environment and why they need specialised gas exchange surfaces. 159

☐ 2 Describe the gross structure of the human gas exchange system, explaining how the cells, tissues, and organs function together to exchange respiratory gases between the blood and the environment. 160

☐ 3 **PRAC** Observe and draw plan diagrams of the structure of the respiratory tract (trachea, bronchi, bronchioles, and alveoli) to show the distribution of cartilage, ciliated epithelium, goblet cells, smooth muscle, squamous epithelium, and blood vessels. 160

☐ 4 Describe the functions of cartilage, cilia, goblet cells, mucous glands, smooth muscle, and elastic fibres, and recognise these cells and tissues in prepared slides, photomicrographs, and electron micrographs of the gas exchange system. 160

☐ 5 Describe how gases are exchanged between air in the alveoli and the blood across the gas exchange membrane. Include the role of breathing and how it is achieved, with reference to changes in pressure and volume in the thorax as a result of the muscular activity of the intercostal muscles and diaphragm. 160 161

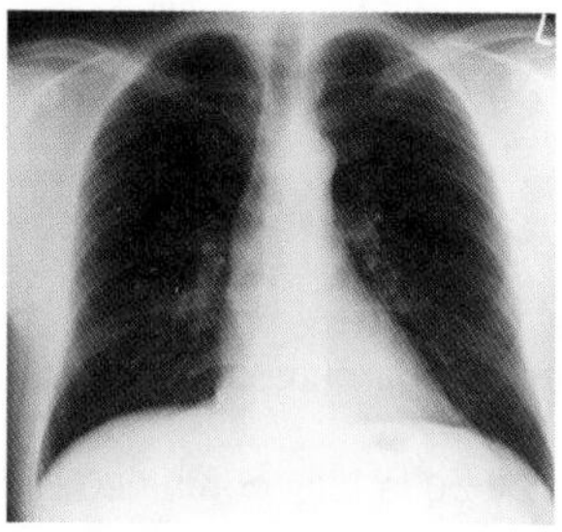

istock

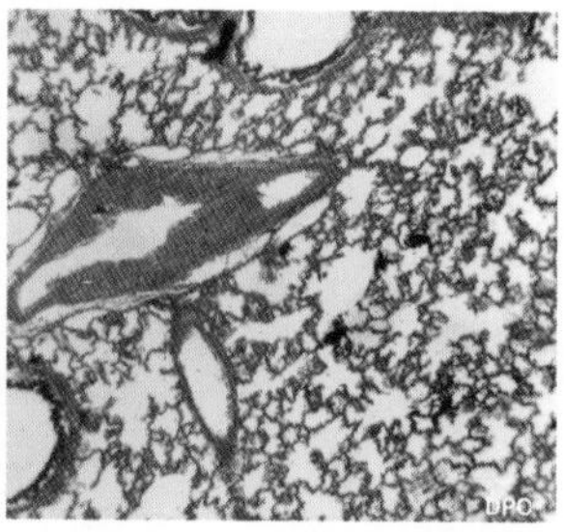

9.2 Smoking

Learning outcomes

Activity number

☐ 6 Recognise smoking as one the major controllable risk factors in chronic life-threatening diseases affecting the gas exchange and circulatory systems. 162

☐ 7 Describe the effects of tar and carcinogens in tobacco smoke on the gas exchange system with reference to lung cancer and chronic obstructive pulmonary disease (COPD). 163

☐ 8 Describe the short term effects of nicotine and carbon monoxide on the cardiovascular system. 163

159 The Gas Exchange System

Key Idea: The respiratory system is made up of specialised cells and tissues, which work together to enable the exchange of gases between the body's cells and the environment.

The respiratory (or gas exchange) system consists of the passages in the mouth and nose, the tubes and epithelial tissues of the lungs, and the muscles of the diaphragm and ribcage. Each of these regions is specialised to perform a particular role in the organ system's overall function, which is to exchange respiratory gases (oxygen and carbon dioxide) between the body's cells and the environment.

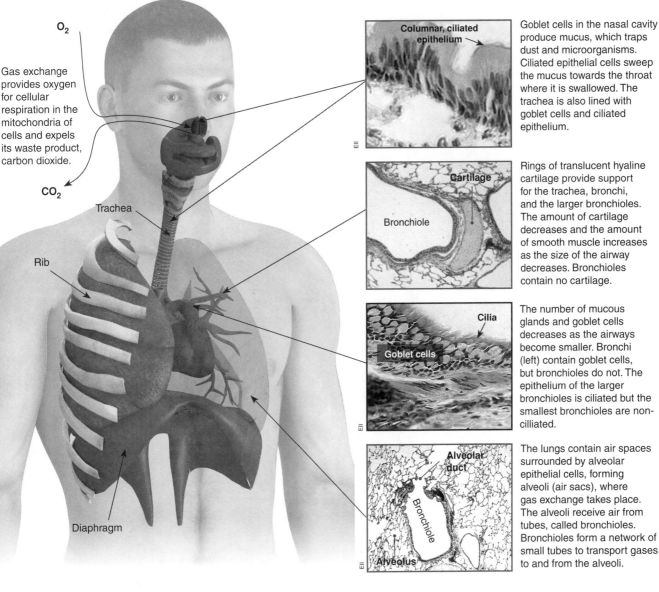

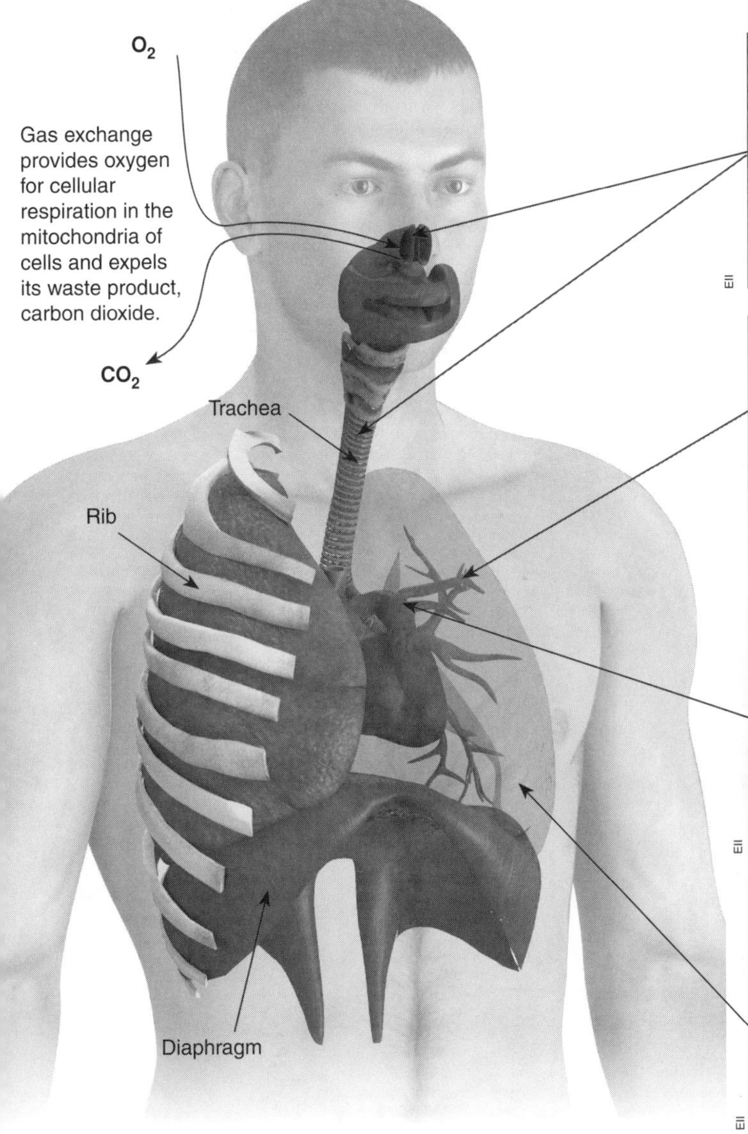
O_2
Gas exchange provides oxygen for cellular respiration in the mitochondria of cells and expels its waste product, carbon dioxide.
CO_2
Trachea
Rib
Diaphragm

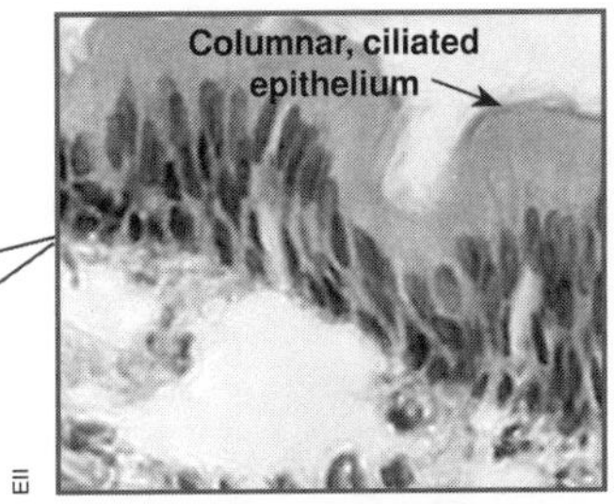
Columnar, ciliated epithelium
EII

Goblet cells in the nasal cavity produce mucus, which traps dust and microorganisms. Ciliated epithelial cells sweep the mucus towards the throat where it is swallowed. The trachea is also lined with goblet cells and ciliated epithelium.

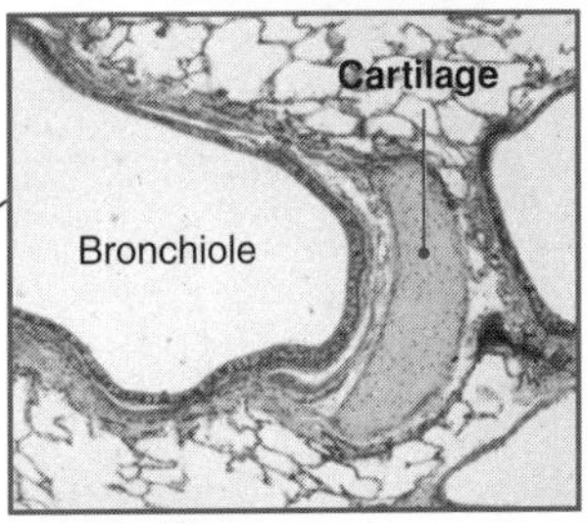
Cartilage
Bronchiole

Rings of translucent hyaline cartilage provide support for the trachea, bronchi, and the larger bronchioles. The amount of cartilage decreases and the amount of smooth muscle increases as the size of the airway decreases. Bronchioles contain no cartilage.

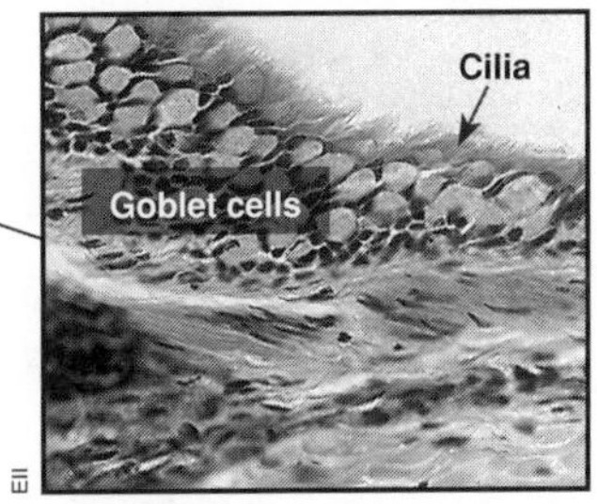
Cilia
Goblet cells
EII

The number of mucous glands and goblet cells decreases as the airways become smaller. Bronchi (left) contain goblet cells, but bronchioles do not. The epithelium of the larger bronchioles is ciliated but the smallest bronchioles are non-cilliated.

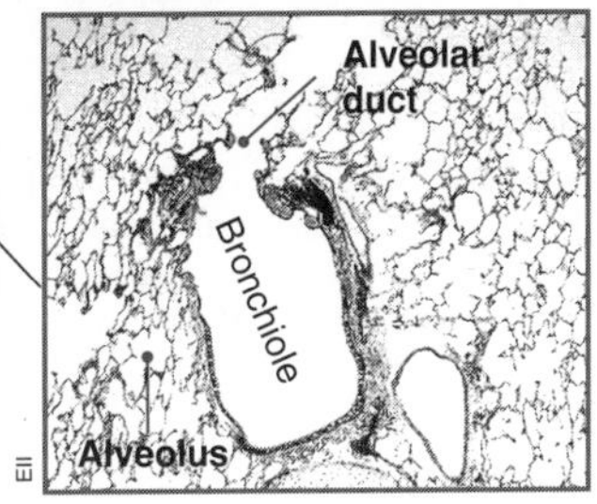
Alveolar duct
Bronchiole
Alveolus
EII

The lungs contain air spaces surrounded by alveolar epithelial cells, forming alveoli (air sacs), where gas exchange takes place. The alveoli receive air from tubes, called bronchioles. Bronchioles form a network of small tubes to transport gases to and from the alveoli.

1. Name three types of cells in the respiratory system and their function:

   (a) ____

   ____

   (b) ____

   ____

   (c) ____

   ____

2. Which cells form the alveoli? ____

3. What is the purpose of the hyaline cartilage in the respiratory system? ____

   ____

4. Where does gas exchange take place in the lungs? ____

© 2015 **BIOZONE** International
ISBN: 978-1-927309-31-5
Photocopying Prohibited

160 The Lungs

Key Idea: Lungs are internal sac-like organs connected to the outside by a system of airways. The smallest airways end in thin-walled alveoli, where gas exchange occurs.

The respiratory system includes all the structures associated with exchanging respiratory gases with the environment. In mammals, the gas exchange organs are paired lungs connected to the outside air by way of a system of tubular passageways: the trachea, bronchi, and bronchioles.

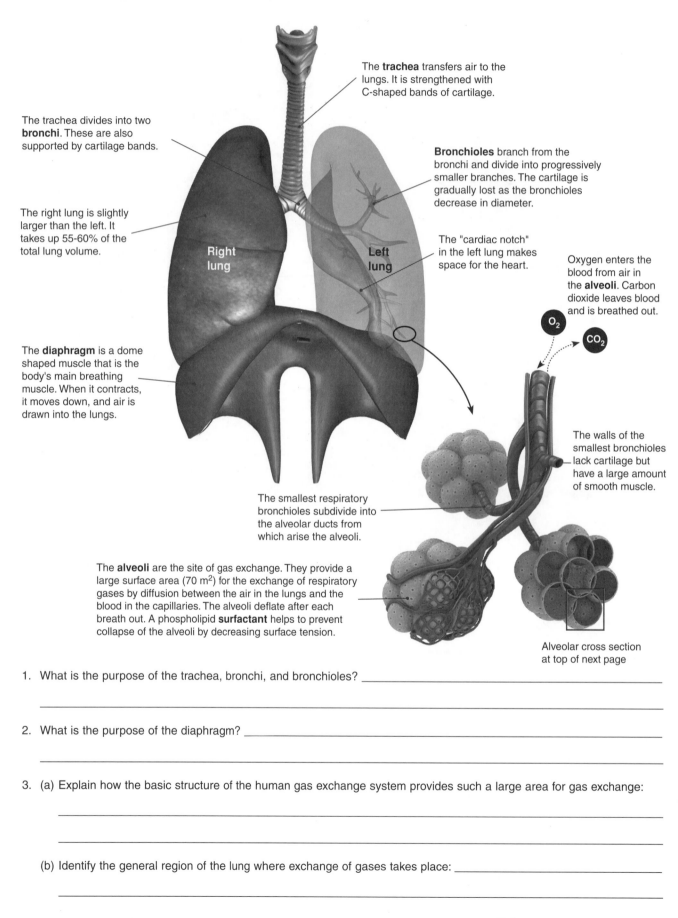

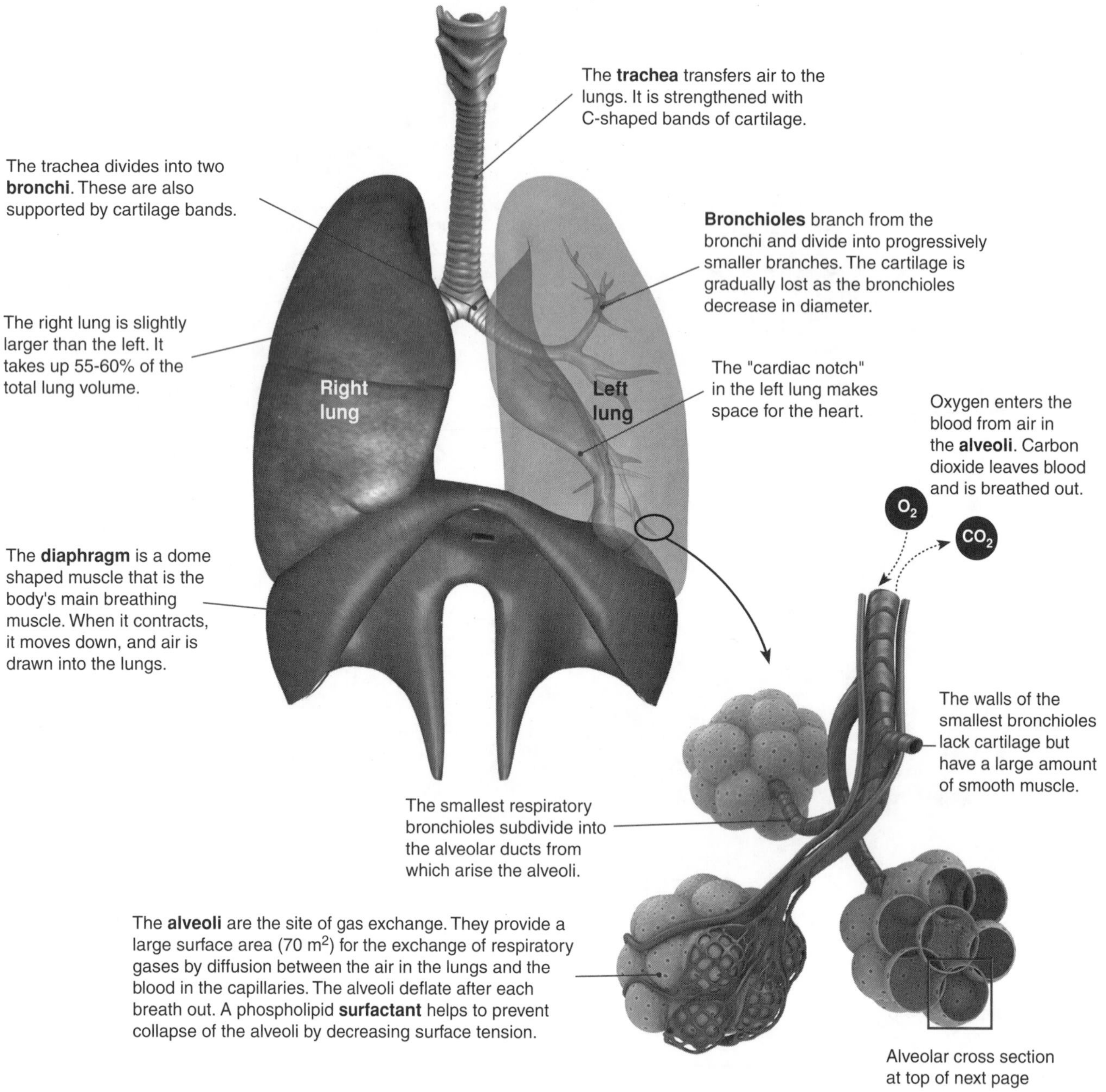
The **trachea** transfers air to the lungs. It is strengthened with C-shaped bands of cartilage.
The trachea divides into two **bronchi**. These are also supported by cartilage bands.
Bronchioles branch from the bronchi and divide into progressively smaller branches. The cartilage is gradually lost as the bronchioles decrease in diameter.
The right lung is slightly larger than the left. It takes up 55-60% of the total lung volume.
Right lung
Left lung
The "cardiac notch" in the left lung makes space for the heart.
Oxygen enters the blood from air in the **alveoli**. Carbon dioxide leaves blood and is breathed out.
O_2
CO_2
The **diaphragm** is a dome shaped muscle that is the body's main breathing muscle. When it contracts, it moves down, and air is drawn into the lungs.
The walls of the smallest bronchioles lack cartilage but have a large amount of smooth muscle.
The smallest respiratory bronchioles subdivide into the alveolar ducts from which arise the alveoli.
The **alveoli** are the site of gas exchange. They provide a large surface area (70 m^2) for the exchange of respiratory gases by diffusion between the air in the lungs and the blood in the capillaries. The alveoli deflate after each breath out. A phospholipid **surfactant** helps to prevent collapse of the alveoli by decreasing surface tension.
Alveolar cross section at top of next page

1. What is the purpose of the trachea, bronchi, and bronchioles? ______________________________

____

2. What is the purpose of the diaphragm? ______________________________

____

3. (a) Explain how the basic structure of the human gas exchange system provides such a large area for gas exchange:

____

____

(b) Identify the general region of the lung where exchange of gases takes place: ______________________________

____

© 2015 **BIOZONE** International
ISBN:978-1-927309-31-5
Photocopying Prohibited

Cross section through an alveolus

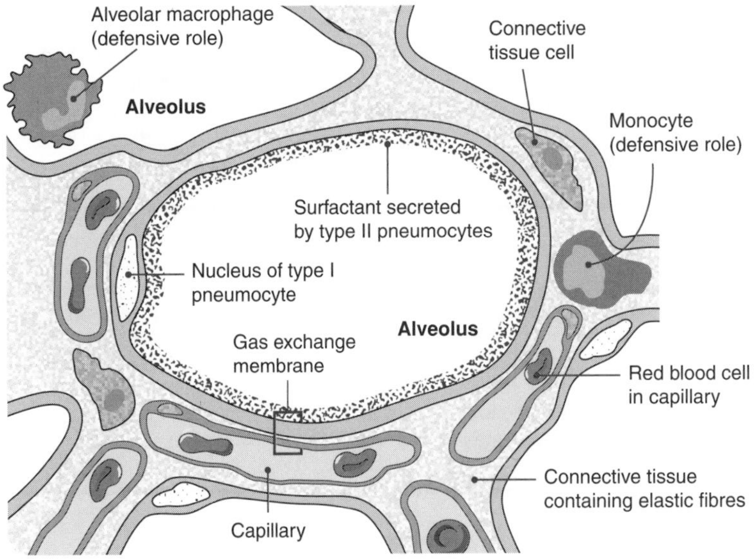
Alveolar macrophage
(defensive role)
Alveolus
Connective
tissue cell
Monocyte
(defensive role)
Surfactant secreted
by type II pneumocytes
Nucleus of type I
pneumocyte
Gas exchange
membrane
Alveolus
Red blood cell
in capillary
Connective tissue
containing elastic fibres
Capillary

The gas exchange membrane

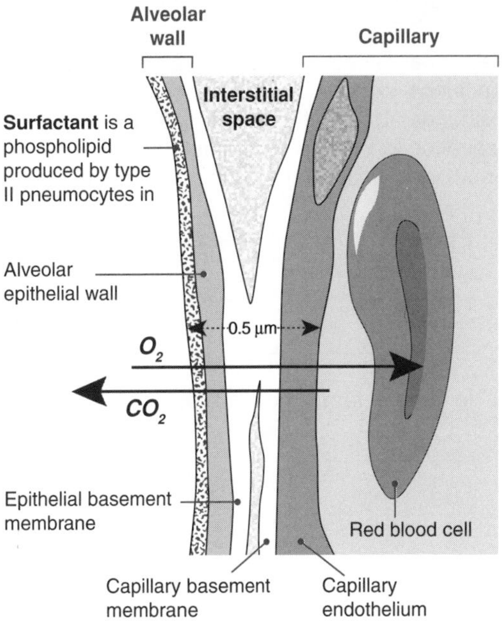
Alveolar
wall
Capillary
Interstitial
space
Surfactant is a
phospholipid
produced by type
II pneumocytes in
Alveolar
epithelial wall
0.5 µm
O_2
CO_2
Epithelial basement
membrane
Red blood cell
Capillary basement
membrane
Capillary
endothelium

The diagram above illustrates the physical arrangement of the alveoli to the capillaries through which the blood moves. The alveolus is lined with alveolar epithelial cells called pneumocytes. Phagocytes (monocytes and macrophages) are also present to protect the lung tissue. Elastic connective tissue gives the alveoli their ability to expand and recoil.

The gas exchange membrane is the layered junction between the alveolar epithelial cells, the endothelial cells of the capillary, and their associated basement membranes (thin connective tissue layers under the epithelia). Gases move freely across this membrane.

4. Describe the structure and purpose of the gas exchange membrane: ___________________________

____

____

5. The diagram below shows the different types of cells and their positions and occurrence in the lungs. Use it to answer the following questions:

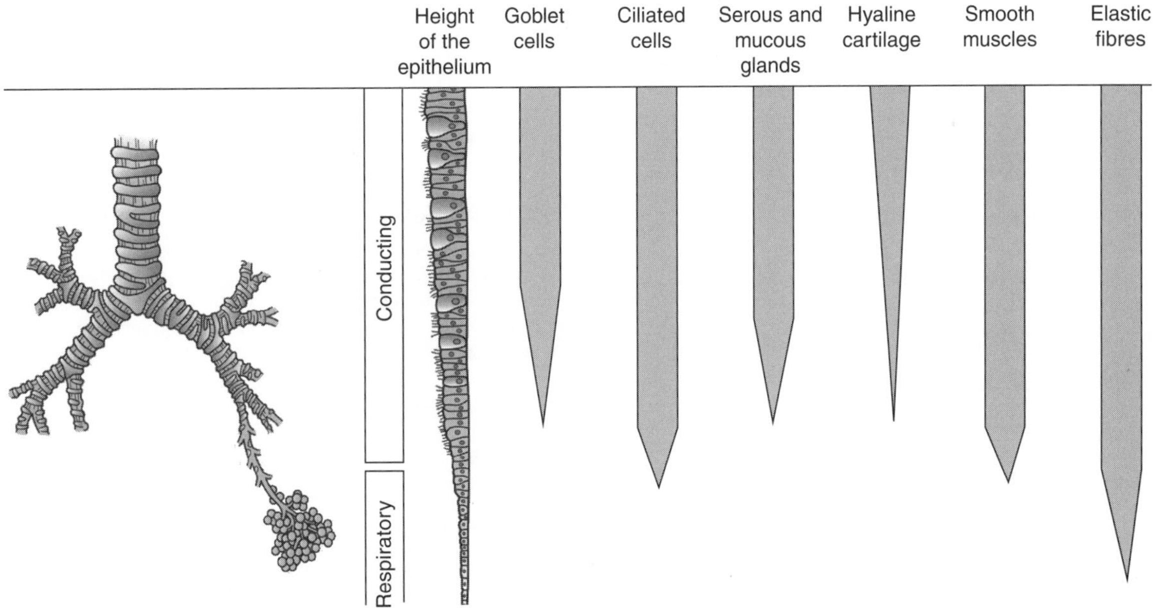
Height
of the
epithelium
Goblet
cells
Ciliated
cells
Serous and
mucous
glands
Hyaline
cartilage
Smooth
muscles
Elastic
fibres
Conducting
Respiratory

(a) Why does the epithelium become very thin in the respiratory zone? ___________________________

____

____

(b) Why would elastic fibres be present in the respiratory zone, while hyaline cartilage is not? ___________________________

____

____

© 2015 **BIOZONE** International
ISBN: 978-1-927309-31-5
Photocopying Prohibited

161 Breathing

Key Idea: Breathing provides a continual supply of air to the lungs to maintain the concentration gradients for gas exchange. Different muscles are used in inspiration and expiration to force air in and out of the lungs.

Breathing (ventilation) provides a continual supply of oxygen-rich air to the lungs and expels air high in carbon dioxide. Together with the cardiovascular system, which transports respiratory gases between the alveolar and the cells of the body, breathing maintains concentration gradients for gas exchange. Breathing is achieved by the action of muscles.

Breathing and muscle action

Muscles can only do work by contracting, so they can only perform movement in one direction. To achieve motion in two directions, muscles work as antagonistic pairs. Antagonistic pairs of muscles have opposing actions and create movement when one contracts and the other relaxes. Breathing in humans involves two sets of antagonistic muscles. The external and internal intercostal muscles of the ribcage, and the diaphragm and abdominal muscles.

Inspiration (inhalation or breathing in)

During quiet breathing, inspiration is achieved by increasing the thoracic volume (therefore decreasing the pressure inside the lungs). Air then flows into the lungs in response to the decreased pressure inside the lung. Inspiration is always an active process involving muscle contraction.

1. External intercostal muscles contract causing the ribcage to expand and move up. Diaphragm contracts and moves down.
2. Thoracic volume increases, lungs expand, and the pressure inside the lungs decreases.
3. Air flows into the lungs in response to the pressure gradient.

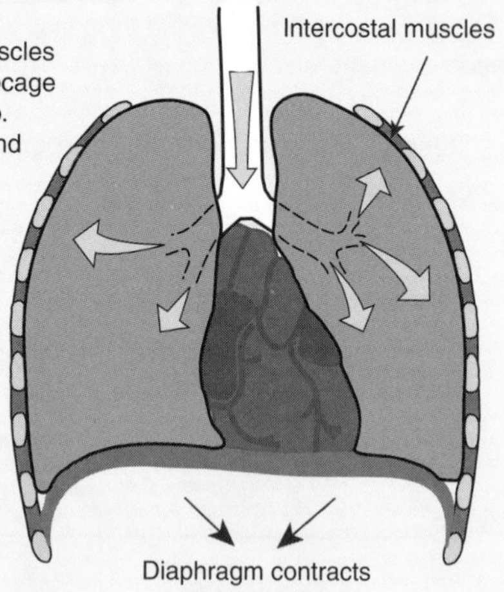
Intercostal muscles
Diaphragm contracts and moves down

Expiration (exhalation or breathing out)

In quiet breathing, expiration is a passive process, achieved when the external intercostals and diaphragm relax and thoracic volume decreases. Air flows passively out of the lungs to equalise with the air pressure. In active breathing, muscle contraction is involved in bringing about both inspiration and expiration.

1. In **quiet breathing**, external intercostals and diaphragm relax. The elasticity of the lung tissue causes recoil.

   In **forced breathing**, the internal intercostals and abdominal muscles contract to compress the thoracic cavity and increase the force of the expiration.
2. Thoracic volume decreases and the pressure inside the lungs increases.
3. Air flows passively out of the lungs in response to the pressure gradient.

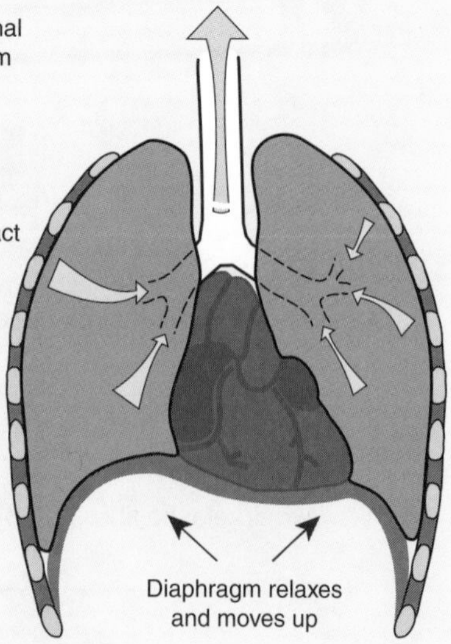
Diaphragm relaxes and moves up

1. Explain the purpose of breathing: ______________

____

____

2. In general terms, how is breathing achieved?

____

____

____

____

3. (a) Describe the sequence of events involved in quiet breathing:

____

____

____

____

____

(b) What is the essential difference between this and the situation during forced breathing:

____

____

____

4. During inspiration, which muscles are:

(a) Contracting: ______________________________

____

(b) Relaxed: ______________________________

____

5. During forced expiration, which muscles are:

(a) Contracting: ______________________________

____

(b) Relaxed: ______________________________

____

6. Explain the role of antagonistic muscles in breathing:

____

____

____

© 2015 BIOZONE International
ISBN:978-1-927309-31-5
Photocopying Prohibited

162 Living With Chronic Lung Disease

Activity limitation in people with and without COPD

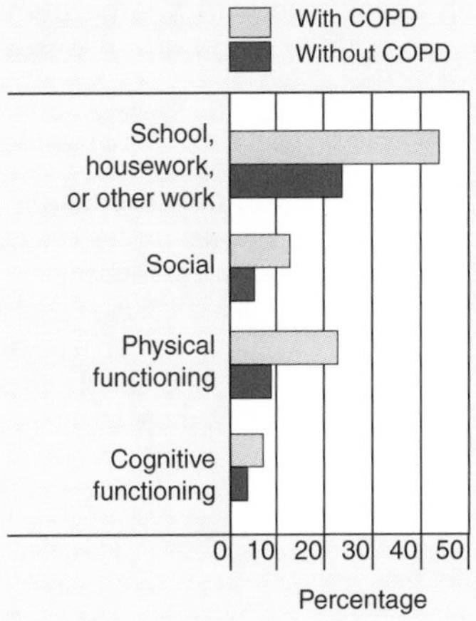
With COPD
Without COPD
School, housework, or other work
Social
Physical functioning
Cognitive functioning
0
10
20
30
40
50
Percentage

Cognitive, physical, social and activity-related limitations are more common among people with chronic obstructive pulmonary disease.

The impact of COPD in the UK

Chronic obstructive pulmonary disease (or COPD) includes **chronic bronchitis** and **emphysema**, which often occur together. COPD affects about one million people in the UK. Most of those affected are over the age 40 and smoking is the cause in the vast majority of cases. This relationship is clear; people who have never smoked rarely develop COPD. The symptoms of COPD and asthma are similar, but COPD causes permanent damage to the airways, and so symptoms are chronic (persistent) and treatment is limited.

COPD severely limits the capacity of sufferers to carry out even a normal daily level of activity. A survey by the American Lung Association of hundreds of people living with COPD found that nearly half became short of breath while washing, dressing, or doing light housework (left). Over 25% reported difficulty in breathing while sitting or lying still. Lack of oxygen also places those with COPD at high risk of heart failure. As the disease becomes more severe, sufferers usually require long-term oxygen therapy, in which they are more or less permanently attached to an oxygen supply.

In the UK, COPD accounts for more time off work than any other illness. The indirect costs of this chronic condition have been estimated at 24 million lost working days per annum. A 'flare-up' of COPD, during which the symptoms worsen, is one of the commonest reasons for admission to hospital and the disease places a substantial burden on health services. The number of primary care consultations for COPD is four times higher than for angina, and 30% of those admitted to hospital with COPD for the first time will be readmitted within 3 months (*NHS-UK*). At least 25,000 people die each year in the UK from the end stages of COPD, but the actual number may be higher as COPD is often present in patients who die from heart failure and stroke. Many of these people have several years of ill health before they die. Being able to breathe is something we don't often think about. What must it be like to struggle for each breath, every minute of every day for years?

A personal story

Deborah Ripley's message from her mother Jenny (used with permission).

"Fear, anxiety, depression, and carbon monoxide are ruining whatever life my mother has left. I posted this portrait of my Mum on the photo website Flickr because she wants to send a warning to anyone who's still smoking. I've just returned from visiting her in a nursing home where she's virtually shackled to the bed. Getting up to go to the bathroom practically kills her. She was admitted to hospital after a bout of pneumonia, which required intensive antibiotic therapy and left her hardly able to breathe. She has moderate dementia caused by a series of mini-strokes, which is aggravated by the pneumonia. She has no recollection of who has visited her or when, so consequently thinks she's alone most of the time, which is upsetting and disturbing for her.

This is all caused by damage to her brain and lungs as a result of 65 years of smoking. In those moments when she is lucid, she asks me who she can warn that this could happen to them. She said 'if people could see me lying here like this it would put them off...' None of her other known blood relatives suffered this sort of decline in their old age and, as far as I know, none of them smoked".

Thankfully, Jenny's pneumonia subsequently subsided and her COPD is well managed. However, constant vigilance is important because flare-ups are common with COPD and recovery from lung infections is difficult when breathing is already compromised.

Used with permission ©deborahripley.com

1. Describe the economic impact of smoking-related diseases, such as emphysema and chronic bronchitis: ____________

2. Discuss the personal costs of a smoking-related disease and comment on the value of personal testimonials such as those from Deborah's mother:

© 2015 **BIOZONE** International
ISBN: 978-1-927309-31-5
Photocopying Prohibited

163 Smoking and the Gas Exchange System

Key Idea: Tobacco smoking is a major health hazard associated with nicotine addiction, cancer, and chronic diseases of the cardiovascular and gas exchange systems.

Tobacco smoking has been accepted as a major health hazard only relatively recently in historical terms, despite its practice in Western countries for more than 400 years, and much longer elsewhere. Cigarettes became popular at the end of World War I because they were cheap, convenient, and easy to smoke. The mild smoke is readily inhaled, allowing nicotine (an addictive poison) to be quickly absorbed into the bloodstream. Cigarette smoke also contains poisonous gases, such as carbon monoxide, and the tar contains many carcinogens. Smoking is associated with a large number of diseases, including cancers, COPD, and heart disease.

The effects of tobacco smoking on the gas exchange system

All forms of tobacco-smoking increase the risk of mouth cancer, lip cancer, and cancer of the throat (pharynx).

Smoking and the carcinogens in tobacco smoke is strongly linked to lung cancer. Most cancers that start in the lung derive from uncontrolled growth of epithelial cells. The vast majority of lung cancer cases occur in smokers.

Lung capacity is reduced.

Smoking is also linked to chronic obstructive pulmonary, disease (COPD). COPD is a persistent inflammatory lung disease that causes obstructed airflow from the lungs. It causes symptoms, such as shortness of breath and chronic bronchitis, and changes to the lung tissue itself, such as emphysema.

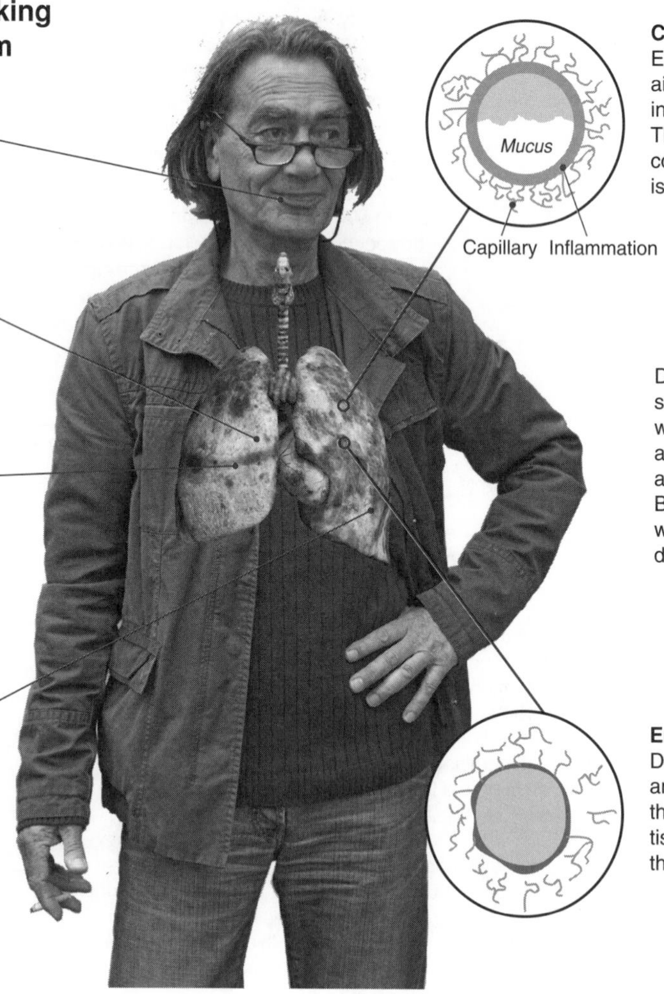
Mucus
Capillary
Inflammation

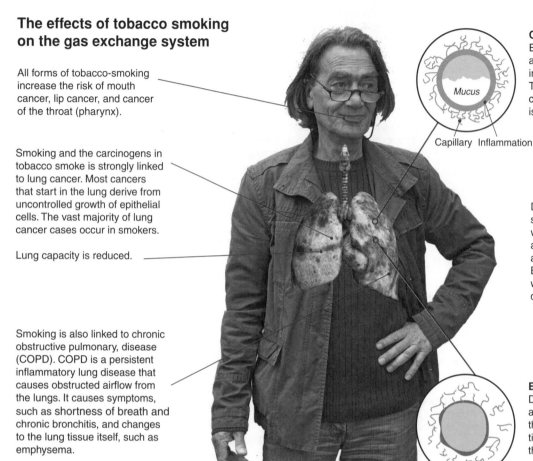

Chronic bronchitis: Excess mucus blocks airways, causing inflammation and infection. There is often a persistent cough. Cigarette smoking is the most common cause.

Diagrams show cross sections through a bronchiole with chronic bronchitis (upper) and emphysema (lower). Both are associated with COPD. Bronchitis is a symptom, whereas emphysema is a description of lung changes.

Emphysema: Destruction of capillaries and structures supporting the small airways and lung tissue. Cigarette smoking is the most common cause.

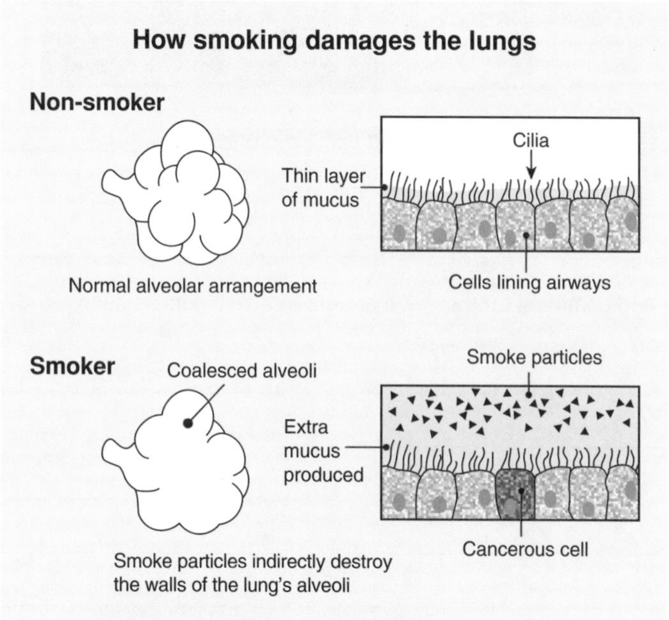
How smoking damages the lungs
Non-smoker
Cilia
Thin layer of mucus
Normal alveolar arrangement
Cells lining airways
Smoker
Coalesced alveoli
Smoke particles
Extra mucus produced
Cancerous cell
Smoke particles indirectly destroy the walls of the lung's alveoli

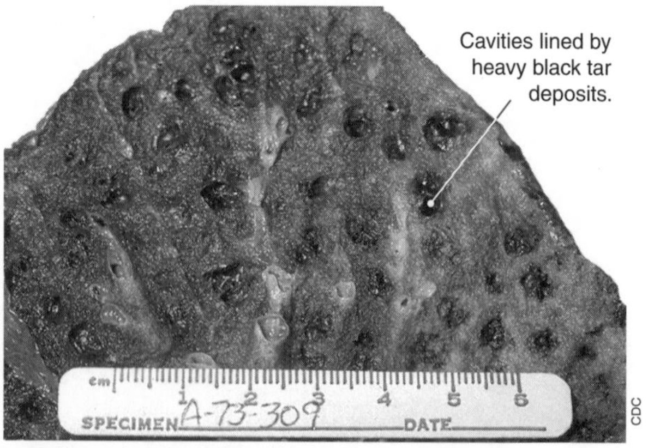
Cavities lined by heavy black tar deposits.
SPECIMEN A-73-309
DATE
CDC

Lung tissue from a patient with emphysema. Tobacco tar deposits can be seen. Tar is a toxic resinous, residue of tobacco smoke and contains at least 17 known carcinogens (cancer-causing agents) including benzene, acrylamide and acrylonitrile. Tar damages the teeth and gums, desensitises taste buds, and accumulates in the lung tissue (above). The carcinogenic components of tar cause DNA mutations in the delicate epithelial cells of the lung, leading to lung cancer.

© 2015 BIOZONE International
ISBN:978-1-927309-31-5
Photocopying Prohibited

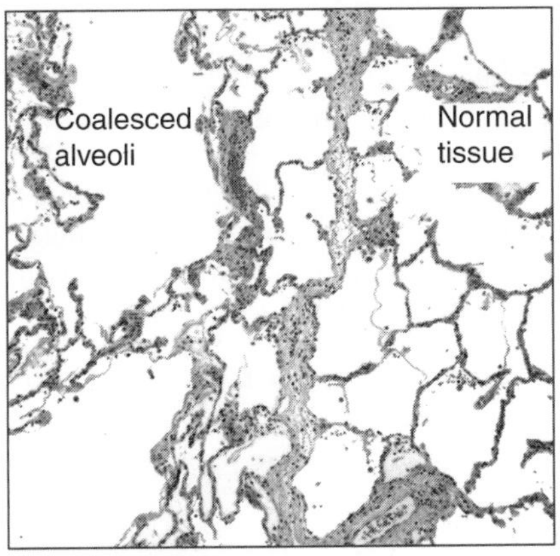
Coalesced
alveoli
Normal
tissue

Emphysema, which is characterised by narrowing of the small airways and breakdown of lung tissue, is typical of COPD. The breakdown of the lung tissue causes the formation of large air pockets (left) and airflow and gas exchange rates are poor.

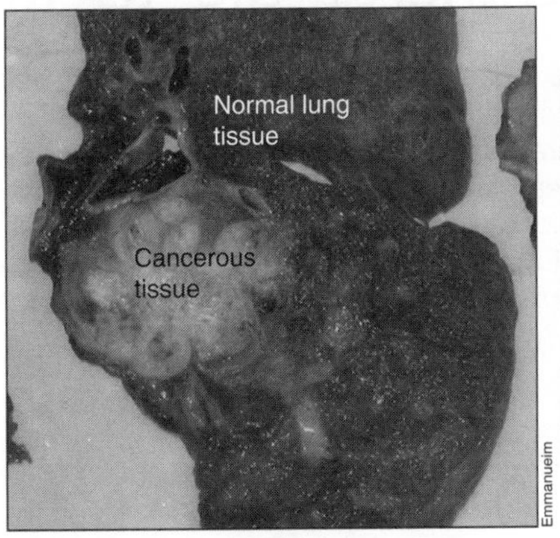
Normal lung
tissue
Cancerous
tissue
Emmanueim

Most lung cancers begin in the epithelial cells of the lung. DNA damage from exposure to the carcinogens in tar leads to cell proliferation and tumour formation. Lung cancer is the second most common form of cancer in the UK and the vast majority of cases are associated with cigarette smoking.

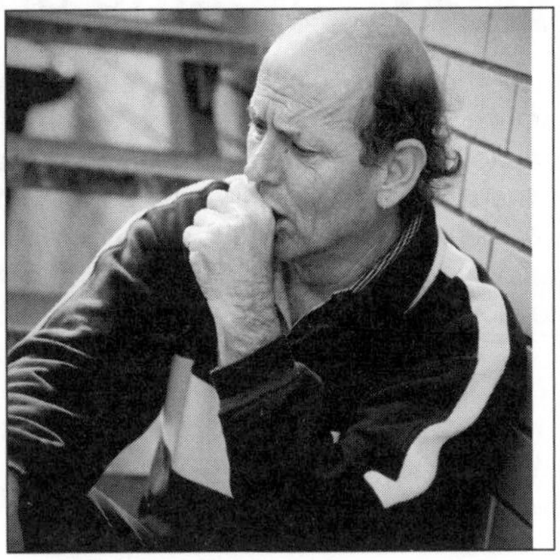

Chronic bronchitis is associated with COPD although there are other causes. It is accompanied by a persistent, productive cough, where sufferers attempt to cough up the mucus that accumulates in the airways and leads to inflammation. The poor airflow is not improved with bronchodilator therapy.

1. Discuss the physical changes to the lung that result from long-term smoking: ______

2. COPD is a chronic inflammatory disease associated with smoking:

   (a) What does chronic mean? ______

   (b) What symptoms are associated with COPD: ______

   (c) How are these related to the changes in the lung tissue itself: ______

3. Describe how the inhalation of the particulates, such as tar, in tobacco smoke can lead to lung cancer:

4. A long term study showed the correlation between smoking and lung cancer, providing supporting evidence for the adverse effects of smoking (right):

   (a) Explain why a long term study was important:

   (b) The study made a link between cigarette consumption and mortality from lung cancer. What else did it show?

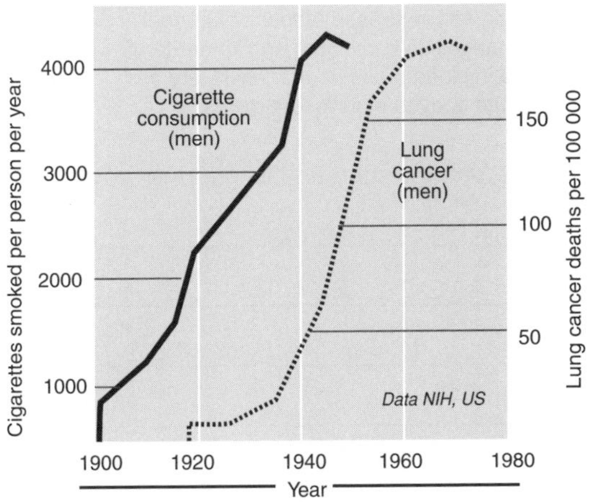
Cigarettes smoked per person per year
4000
3000
2000
1000
Cigarette
consumption
(men)
Lung
cancer
(men)
150
100
50
Lung cancer deaths per 100 000
Data NIH, US
1900
1920
1940
1960
1980
Year

© 2015 **BIOZONE** International
ISBN: 978-1-927309-31-5
Photocopying Prohibited

164 Smoking and the Cardiovascular System

Key Idea: The nicotine and carbon monoxide in tobacco smoke have immediate and long term effects on the cardiovascular system. These effects are associated with increased blood pressure and elevated heart rate.

Together with the carcinogens in tar, nicotine and carbon monoxide are among the most harmful components of tobacco smoke. Nicotine is an addictive poison acting quickly to constrict arteries, increase blood pressure and heart rate, mobilise fat stores, and increase metabolic rate. Carbon monoxide is also toxic, displacing oxygen from haemoglobin and reducing the oxygen content of the blood. The effects of nicotine and carbon monoxide increase the workload of the heart and increase the risk of heart disease, peripheral vascular disease, and stroke.

Short term effects of smoking

After inhaling, nicotine enters the bloodstream rapidly and reaches the brain within 8 s where it increases the release of many chemical messengers including acetylcholine and dopamine and stimulates the brain's reward centres.

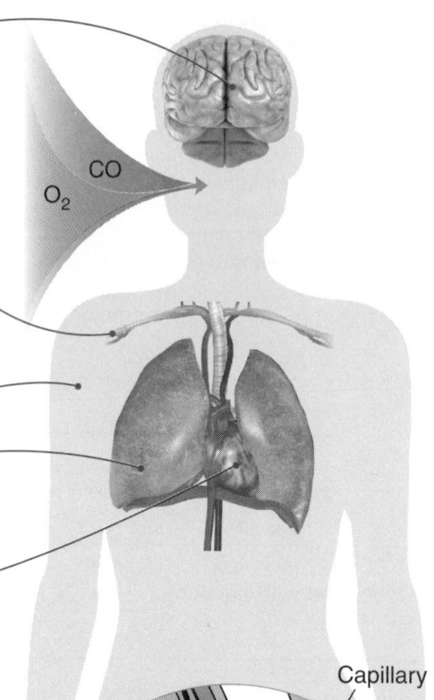
CO
O_2

Nicotine raises blood pressure (10-30 points). Chronic high blood pressure is the single most important risk factor for stroke (cell death in the brain as a result of impaired blood flow).

Surface blood vessel constriction drops skin temperature by up to 5°C.

Very sharp rise in carbon monoxide levels in the lungs contributing to breathlessness.

Nicotine causes a rapid increase in heart rate by up to 20 beats per minute.

Long term effects of smoking

The nicotine and carbon monoxide in tobacco smoke increase the viscosity of the blood, which increases the risk of fatty plaques forming in the coronary and carotid arteries. These plaques increase the risk of heart attack and stroke.

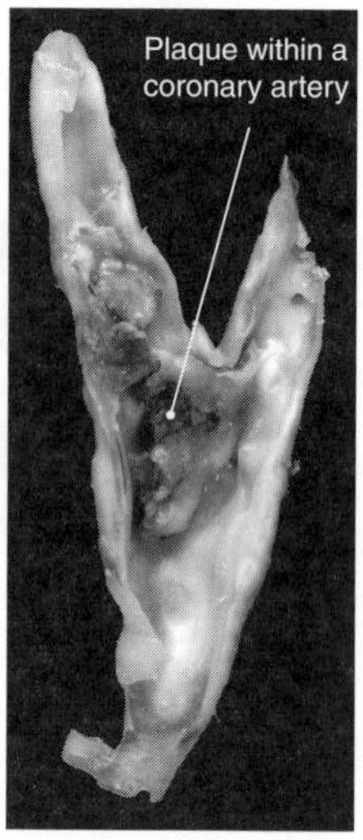
Plaque within a coronary artery

Heart attacks usually result when blood flow to the heart muscle is interrupted, often following rupture of a plaque. The muscle becomes starved of oxygen and dies.

Chronic high blood pressure and elevated heart rate, coupled with high levels of CO make the heart work harder to deliver the oxygen needed by the cells and tissues of the body.

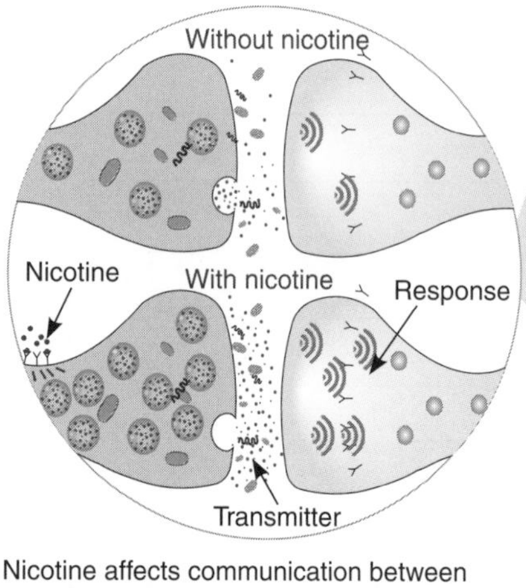
Without nicotine
Nicotine
With nicotine
Response
Transmitter

Nicotine affects communication between nerve cells and between nerve cells and muscles. It interacts with cell receptors, stimulating greater release of transmitter substance and increased response in target cells. It causes an immediate and longer term increase in blood pressure and heart rate and causes the body to mobilise fat stores.

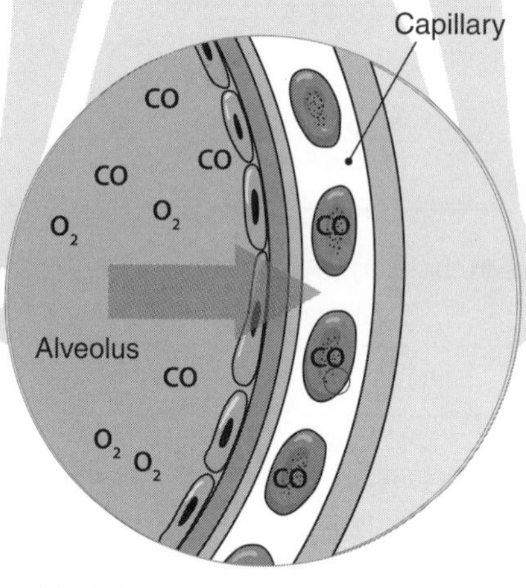
Capillary
CO
CO
CO
O_2
O_2
Alveolus
CO
O_2 O_2
CO
CO
CO

Inhaled smoke contains high levels of carbon monoxide, which crosses the gas exchange membrane along with oxygen to enter the blood with the capillaries of the lung. Here, the carbon monoxide (CO) is preferentially picked up by the haemoglobin in the red blood cells, which normally transport oxygen.

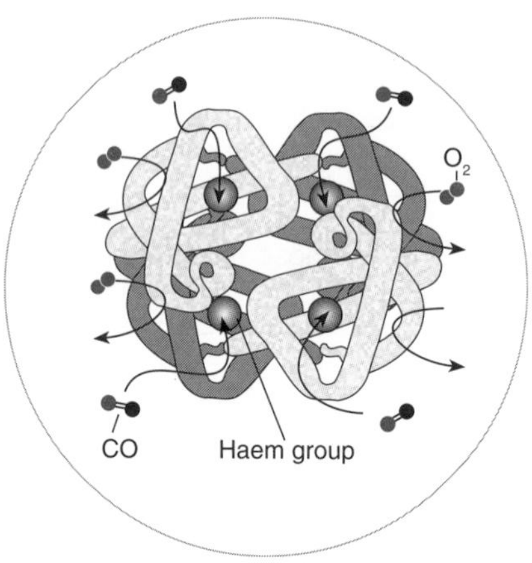
O_2
CO
Haem group

The blood protein haemoglobin (Hb) binds and carries oxygen within the red blood cells to supply the cells and tissues of the body. However, CO has a much higher affinity for Hb than oxygen, so when CO is inhaled, it displaces oxygen from Hb. As a result, less oxygen is supplied to the tissues. High levels of CO are fatal.

1. Describe the short and long term effects of nicotine and carbon monoxide on the cardiovascular system: ______________

____

____

____

____

____

© 2015 BIOZONE International
ISBN:978-1-927309-31-5
Photocopying Prohibited

165 Chapter Review

Summarise what you know about this topic under the headings provided. You can draw diagrams or mind maps, or write short notes to organise your thoughts. Use the images and hints to help you and refer back to the introduction to check the points covered:

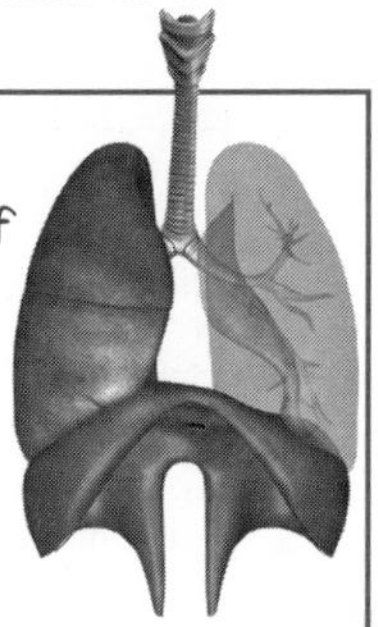

The gas exchange system
HINT: Describe the gross structure of the human gas exchange system.

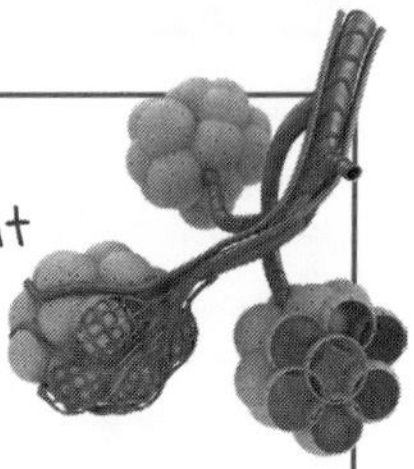

Gas exchange
HINT: How does gas exchange occur at the alveoli?

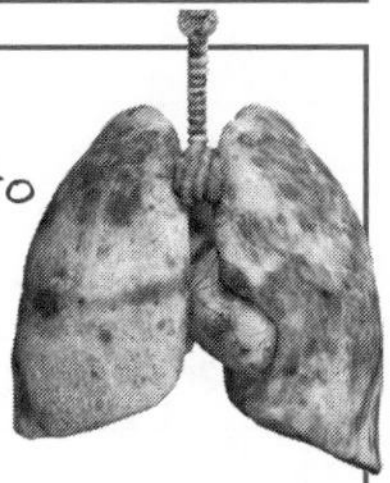

Smoking
HINT: How does smoking contribute to lung cancer and COPD?

Nicotine and carbon monoxide
HINT: What short term effects do nicotine and CO have on the cardiovascular system?

© 2015 **BIOZONE** International
ISBN: 978-1-927309-31-5
Photocopying Prohibited

166 KEY TERMS AND IDEAS: Did You Get It?

1. The diagrams below show sections through the respiratory tract at three different locations.
   (a) Identify the part of the respiratory tract represented by each of the three cross sections:

   A: ______________________________

   B: ______________________________

   C: ______________________________

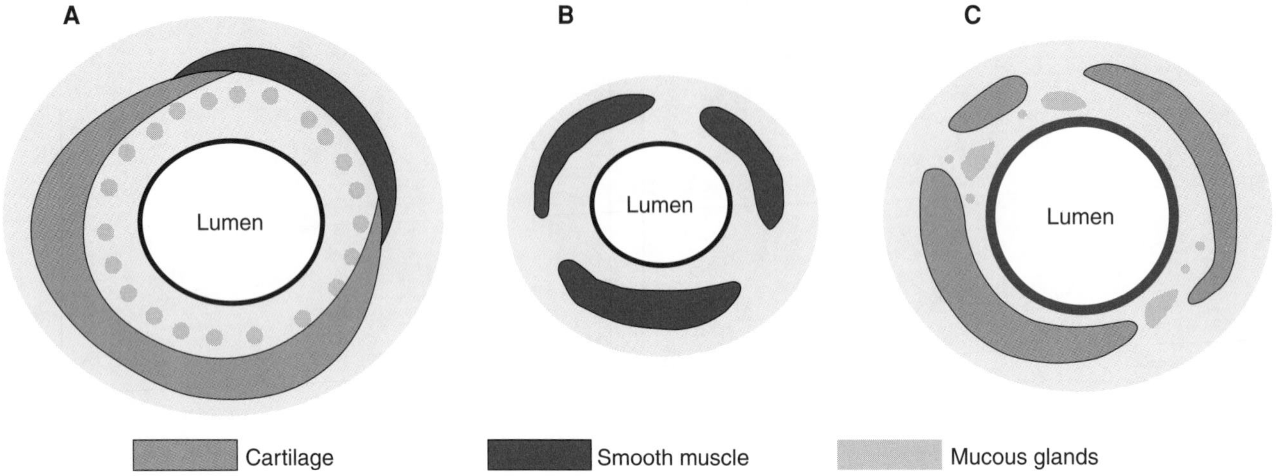
A
B
C
Lumen
Lumen
Lumen
Cartilage
Smooth muscle
Mucous glands

   (b) With reference to the amount and distribution of cartilage, smooth muscle, and mucus glands, explain how you identified each section:

   ____

2. Based on the graph, right, what evidence is there to link COPD and smoking:

   ____

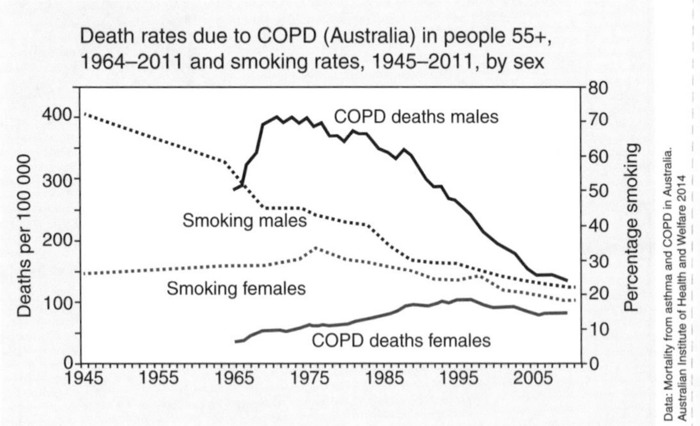
Death rates due to COPD (Australia) in people 55+, 1964–2011 and smoking rates, 1945–2011, by sex
Deaths per 100 000
Percentage smoking
COPD deaths males
Smoking males
Smoking females
COPD deaths females
0
100
200
300
400
0
10
20
30
40
50
60
70
80
1945
1955
1965
1975
1985
1995
2005
Data: Mortality from asthma and COPD in Australia. Australian Institute of Health and Welfare 2014

3. What causes restrictive lung disease and how does it affect the lungs?

   ____

4. (a) What is the function of the goblet cells? ______________________________

   (b) What is the function of the ciliated epithelium in the respiratory tract? ______________________________

   (c) What is the purpose of cartilage around the trachea? ______________________________

© 2015 BIOZONE International
ISBN:978-1-927309-31-5
Photocopying Prohibited

Topic 10

Infectious disease

Key terms

antibiotic
antibiotic resistance
bacteria
cholera
disease
fungi
HIV/AIDS
horizontal gene transfer
infectious disease
lung cancer
malaria
measles
mutation
non-infectious disease
pathogen
penicillin
protistans
sickle cell disease
smallpox
transmission
tuberculosis (TB)
viruses

10.1 Infectious diseases

Learning outcomes

		Activity number
☐	1 Define the term disease. Distinguish between an infectious disease (e.g. tuberculosis) and a non-infectious disease (e.g. sickle cell disease, lung cancer).	167
☐	2 Identify the causative organism (pathogen) of the following infectious diseases: cholera, malaria, tuberculosis (TB), HIV/AIDS, smallpox, and measles.	168-173
☐	3 Explain how cholera is transmitted and discuss the biological, social and economic factors important in its control and prevention.	169
☐	4 Explain how measles is transmitted and discuss the biological, social, and economic factors important in its control and prevention.	170
☐	5 Explain how malaria is transmitted and discuss the biological, social, and economic factors important in its control and prevention. Discuss the factors that influence malaria's distribution and assess the global importance of this disease.	171
☐	6 Explain how TB is transmitted and discuss the biological, social, and economic factors important in its control and prevention. Discuss the factors that influence TB's distribution and assess the global importance of this disease.	172
☐	7 Explain how HIV/AIDS is transmitted and discuss the biological, social, and economic factors important in its control and prevention. Discuss the factors that influence the global distribution of HIV/AIDS and assess its global importance.	173 174

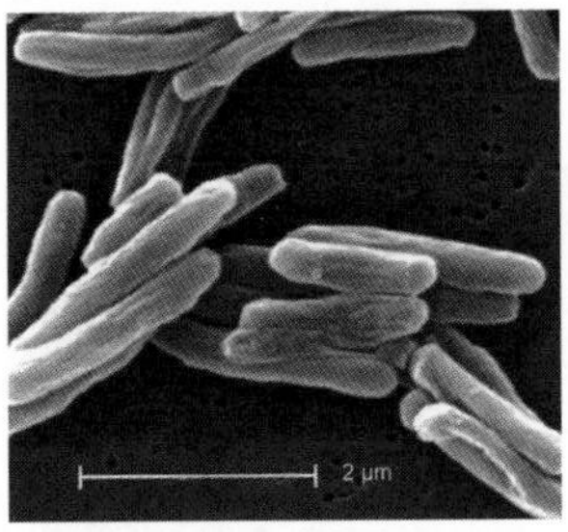
2 µm

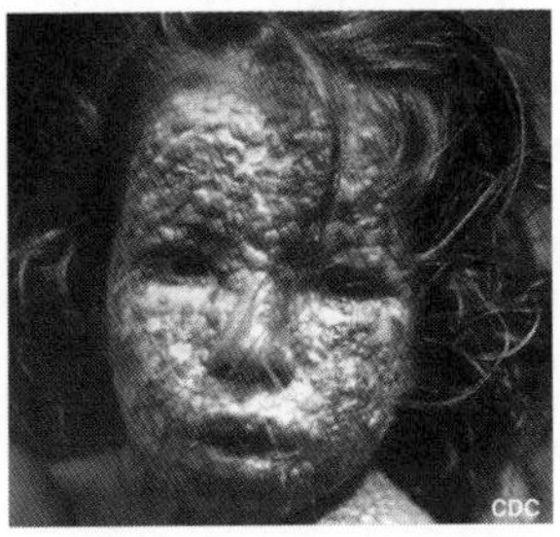
CDC

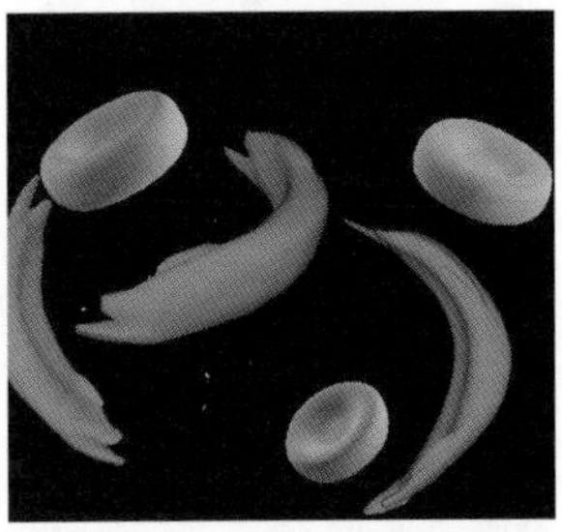

10.2 Antibiotics

Learning outcomes

		Activity number
☐	8 Explain what is meant by an antibiotic and describe how antibiotics are able to control bacterial growth and why they are not effective against viruses.	175
☐	9 Explain how penicillin acts on bacteria and why the discovery of penicillin was so important to the control of bacterial infections.	175
☐	10 Explain how bacteria become resistant to antibiotics with reference to mutation and to (natural) selection. Outline the role of horizontal gene transfer between different bacteria in the spread of resistance.	176
☐	11 Discuss the consequences of antibiotic resistance and the steps that can be taken to reduce its impact.	177

167 Types of Disease

Key Idea: Infectious diseases are caused by pathogens and can be spread (transmitted) from one person to another. Non-infectious diseases are caused by environmental or genetic factors and are not transmitted between people.

The term **disease** refers to an abnormal condition affecting some aspect of an organism's physiology and functioning. Many factors can cause disease, and each disease usually has a characteristic set of signs and symptoms. Disease can be subdivided into two broad categories, infectious and non-infectious diseases. **Infectious diseases** are caused by a pathogen, i.e. a disease causing agent and can be transmitted (passed on) to other people. **Non-infectious diseases** are not caused by pathogens and cannot be transmitted to other people.

Infectious disease

Infectious diseases are caused by pathogenic microorganisms, such as bacteria, viruses, protoctistan parasites, or fungi. Infectious diseases spread from one person to another, either directly or indirectly. Those that are easily spread, such as measles, are said to be highly contagious. Such diseases are a threat to public health and must be notified to health authorities. Many of the serious contagious bacterial and viral diseases of the past are now controlled through vaccination programmes.

Human cities can contain millions of people, often living very closely together. In these congested conditions, infectious diseases can spread rapidly, especially if sanitation or personal hygiene is poor, or if seasonal weather produces conditions favourable to spread of the pathogen. High speed transport, e.g. by air, can spread a pathogen around a region very quickly.

CDC: James Gathany

The mode of transmission affects how quickly a pathogen spreads. Direct person to person contact (i.e. touching) is a slower method of transmission, whereas spreading via mucus droplets coughed into the air (left) or by animal vectors can help a pathogen spread widely, very quickly (e.g. malaria).

Non-infectious disease

Non-infectious diseases, such as chronic lung disease and sickle cell disease, are not spread between people and pose a much lower risk to public health than infectious disease. Non-infectious diseases can be caused by lifestyle and environmental factors (e.g. poor diet, smoking, pollution, or too much sun exposure). They can also be caused by genetic (inherited) factors.

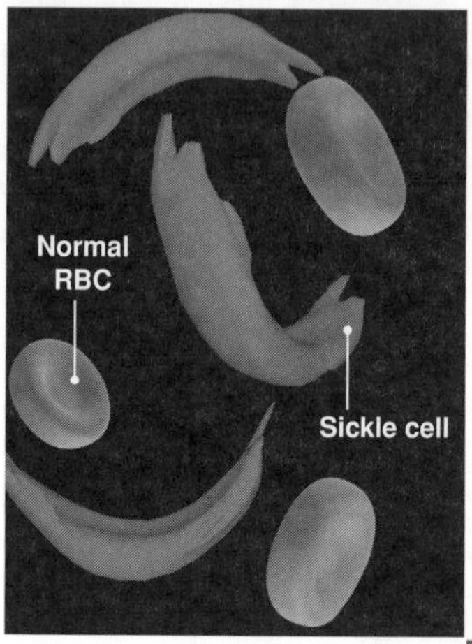
Normal RBC
Sickle cell

Sickle cell disease is an inherited non-infectious disease affecting red blood cells. A mutation (change in DNA) produces a faulty haemoglobin protein. This in turn produces red blood cells with a deformed sickle appearance and a reduced capacity to carry oxygen. The deformed cells adhere to the walls of blood vessels, slowing or stopping the flow of blood. When this happens, oxygen cannot adequately supply the tissues. There is no cure.

Lung cancer (uncontrolled cell growth in the lungs) is a non-infectious disease primarily caused by lifestyle factors. Cigarette smoking (right) is the major cause of lung cancer. People with lung cancer may have difficulty breathing, and oxygen supply to the body becomes limited as lung function is increasingly impaired by tumour growth. Although lung cancer can be treated, it is most often fatal because it is often not detected until it is quite advanced and has spread to other areas of the body.

1. Explain the difference between an infectious and a non-infectious disease: ______

2. Using examples, describe the factors that contribute to a non-infectious disease? ______

3. What causes sickle cell disease and what are its effects? ______

© 2015 BIOZONE International
ISBN:978-1-927309-31-5
Photocopying Prohibited

168 Types of Pathogens

Key Idea: Pathogens are organisms that cause infectious disease. Bacteria, viruses, and protozoa can be pathogens.

Pathogens are disease causing organisms. They can be transmitted between hosts and are the cause of many infectious diseases. The goal of a pathogen is to multiply and spread between hosts before being detected by the host's immune system. To achieve this pathogens have highly effective modes of transmission to maximise their distribution to suitable hosts. Viruses, some bacteria, and some protozoans are example of pathogens.

Types of Pathogen

USDA

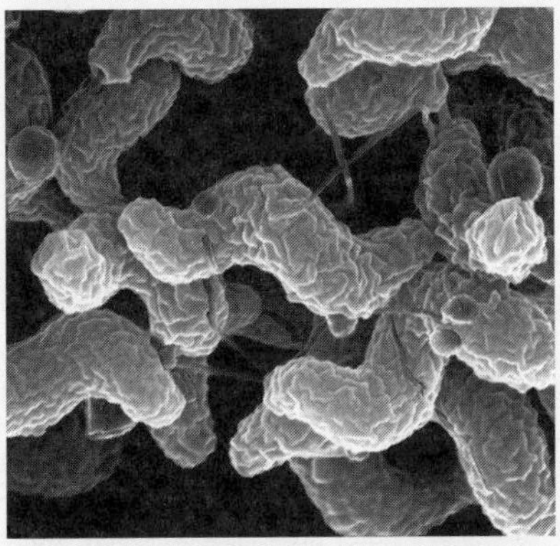

Campylobacter jejuni causes food poisoning and is often caused by eating under-cooked poultry.

Pathogenic **bacteria** cause many different types of diseases, many which can be fatal if left untreated. Examples of bacterial disease include tuberculosis, cholera, and food poisoning. Bacterial diseases are commonly transmitted through food, water, air, or by direct contact. Bacterial diseases can be treated with antibiotics or prevented through vaccination. Other preventative mechanisms include improved water treatment (cholera) and food handling.

CDC

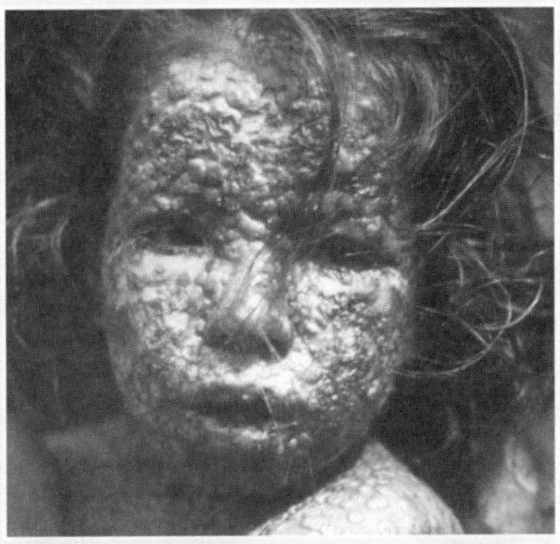

Photo: Bangladeshi girl with smallpox (1973). Smallpox was eradicated from the country in 1977.

Viruses cause many diseases such as measles and HIV/AIDS. Antibiotics are ineffective against viral diseases but they can be controlled through vaccination programmes. Smallpox is an example of a highly infectious viral disease spread by aerosol droplets and direct contact. It is caused by the *Variola* virus and killed 300 million people in the 20th century. It has now been eradicated as a the result of a rigorous global vaccination programme.

Photo: Ute Frevert

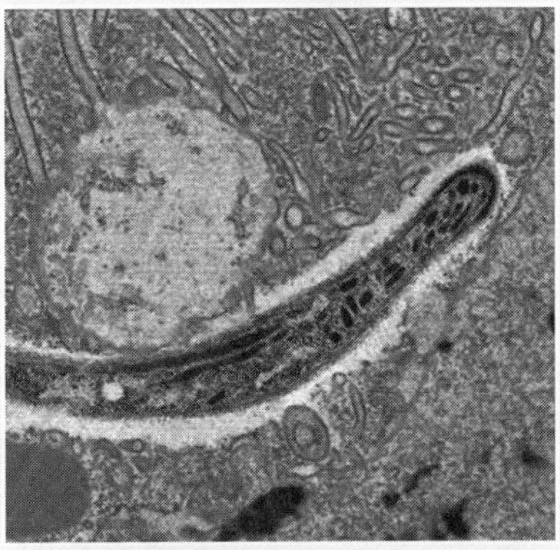

Malaria sporozoite moving through gut epithelia. The parasite is carried by a mosquito vector.

Eukaryotic pathogens include fungi, algae, protozoa, and parasitic worms. Most are highly specialised parasites with a number of hosts, e.g. the malaria parasite (*Plasmodium* species) has a mosquito and a human host. Certain stages in its life cycle reside within the host's cells, making it a difficult disease to treat. Like many other pathogens, the parasite causing malaria shows resistance to the drugs used to treat it.

Pathogen success and failure

In general, a host's immune system quickly recognises an invading pathogen as foreign, usually on the basis of its surface proteins (antigens) or the toxins it produces. This recognition triggers an immune (defensive) response in the host that destroys the pathogen. To be successful, a pathogen must avoid the host's immune system for long enough to infect a new host.

Different pathogens use different strategies to avoid detection and infect other hosts. They may multiply rapidly and spread before the immune system can react (e.g. common cold, right) or they may produce a slower chronic infection that is more difficult for the immune system to overcome (e.g. HIV/AIDS).

Pathogens that kill the host before being able to spread are not successful. In high density populations, diseases with a high mortality (death rate) such as Bubonic plague, Ebola, and smallpox, can spread successfully (witness the 2014 Ebola outbreaks in western African countries). However, in low density areas, pathogens that kill their host quickly have poor transmission, as too few hosts can be infected during the infectious period.

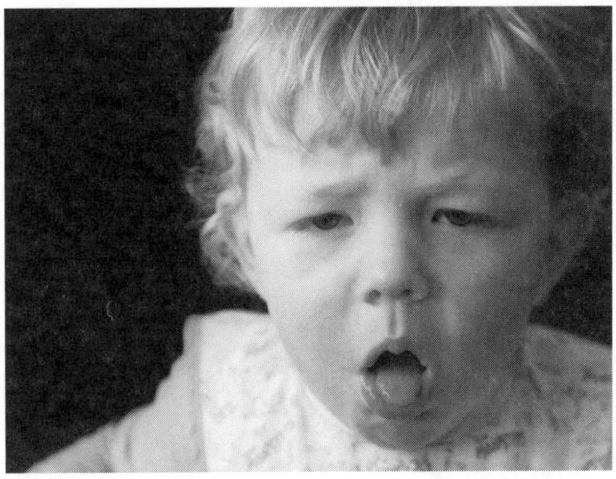

One method a pathogen can use to spread between hosts is to cause an irritation in the throat that produces a cough. The cough spreads infected droplets to other hosts.

1. (a) What must a pathogen do to be successful? ______________________

____

(b) What social conditions might influence spread of a pathogen? ______________________

____

2. Why is a killing the host too quickly a disadvantage to the pathogen? ______________________

____

3. Describe two common methods by which pathogens are spread between hosts: ______________________

____

© 2015 BIOZONE International
ISBN: 978-1-927309-31-5
Photocopying Prohibited

169 Cholera

Key Idea: Cholera is a bacterial disease that causes severe diarrhoea and is spread by drinking contaminated water.

Cholera is an intestinal infection caused by the bacterium *Vibrio cholerae.* Infection results in severe diarrhoea, which may be fatal if left untreated. Cholera is spread by consuming water or food contaminated with the cholera bacterium. The disease can be prevented by hygienic disposal of human faeces, providing an adequate supply of safe drinking water, safe food handling and preparation, and effective general hygiene (e.g. hand washing with soap).

Cholera causes severe diarrhoea

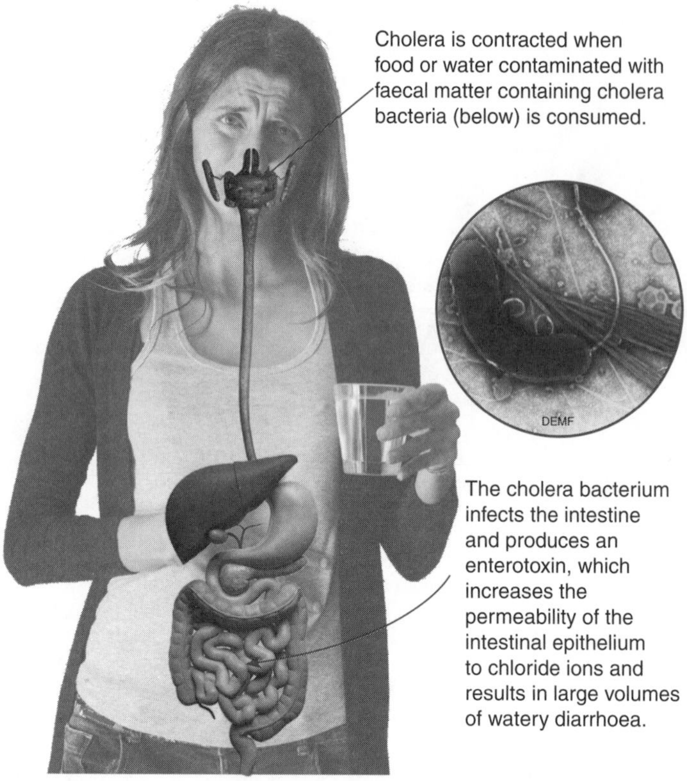
Cholera is contracted when food or water contaminated with faecal matter containing cholera bacteria (below) is consumed.
DEMF
The cholera bacterium infects the intestine and produces an enterotoxin, which increases the permeability of the intestinal epithelium to chloride ions and results in large volumes of watery diarrhoea.

The diarrhoea can lead to severe dehydration, electrolyte imbalance, kidney failure, and death within hours if untreated. Cholera is treated with oral rehydration salts (ORS) containing glucose and electrolytes, which are taken up by active transport by the intestinal cells. This reverses the osmotic gradient and allows blood volume to be restored. Up to 80% of cases can be successfully treated with ORS.

Control and prevention of cholera

Cholera is transmitted between people when the water supply is contaminated with human faeces containing cholera bacteria. Outbreaks are most likely in overcrowded regions where safe disposal of human sewage is lacking, allowing human waste to contaminate drinking water. Such areas include developing nations, countries with civil disputes, refugee camps and slums, and regions hit with natural disasters, such as cyclones or tsunamis.

Doreen Mbalo cc2.0

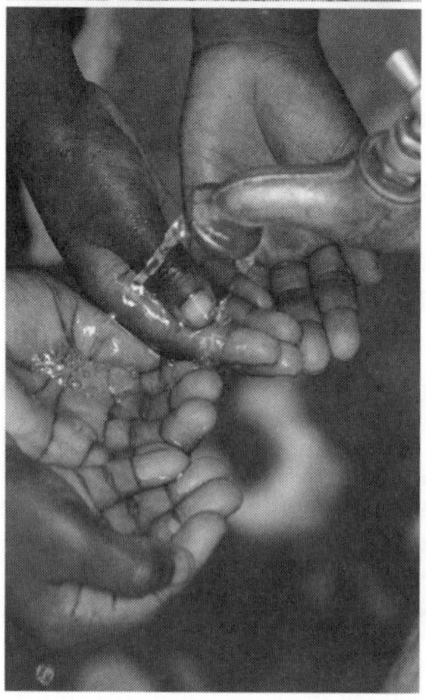

Photo left: Fecal sludge is being dumped into the local river at a slum near Nairobi, Kenya.

Drinking water can also become contaminated with faeces when pit latrines (holes in the ground) and wells supplying drinking water are located closely together. The human waste seeps into the drinking water.

Having the infrastructure to provide clean drinking water and safe disposal of human waste is the most effective way to prevent cholera. However, in many of the regions commonly affected, there is no money to provide even the most basic services, so cholera outbreaks are common.

Basic hygienic food handling and hand washing reduce the risk of transmission. The World Health Organisation (WHO) monitors outbreaks of cholera so resources can be distributed where they are most needed. An oral cholera vaccine is used to help control outbreaks. It works most effectively alongside other preventative mechanisms described above.

1. (a) Name the cholera pathogen: ______________________

   (b) State what type of pathogen it is: ______________________

2. How is the cholera pathogen transmitted? ______________________

____

____

3. (a) Why are cholera outbreaks more common in poorer, developing nations or after natural disasters? ______________________

   ____

   ____

   (b) Discuss the ways that cholera can be prevented and controlled: ______________________

   ____

   ____

   ____

© 2015 BIOZONE International
ISBN:978-1-927309-31-5
Photocopying Prohibited

170 Measles

Key Idea: The measles virus is highly contagious. Vaccination is the best means to prevent the disease.

Measles is a highly contagious disease affecting the respiratory system. It is caused by the measles virus, a virus belonging to the *Morbillivirus* genus. The measles virus is spread very easily. This is because the virus can remain infectious outside the body for up to two hours and because a person is contagious four days before the characteristic rash appears. Measles is a serious disease and can be fatal if there are respiratory complications such as pneumonia.

Transmission of the measles virus

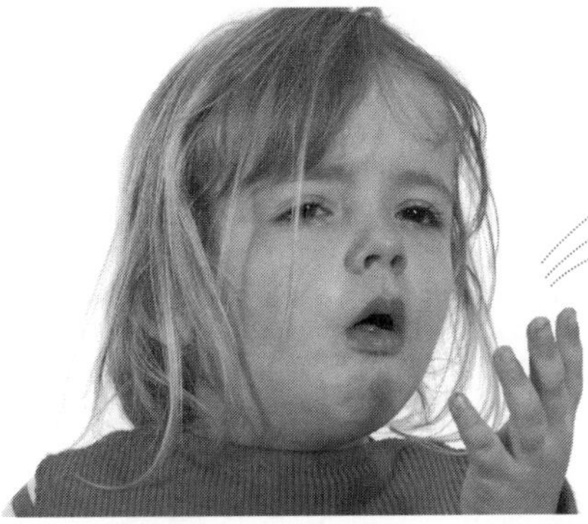

People who have the measles are contagious from 4 days before to 4-5 days after the rash appears. This means an infected person can spread the virus before they know they are sick.

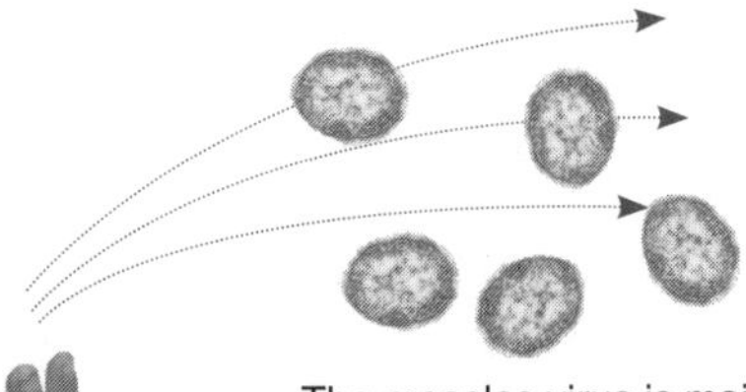

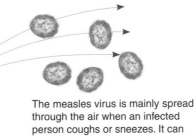

The measles virus is mainly spread through the air when an infected person coughs or sneezes. It can also be spread through contact with saliva or nasal secretions.

The measles virus is highly contagious. Nine out of ten people who are not immune will catch it after being in close contact with an infected person. Both children and adults can catch measles if they don't have immunity.

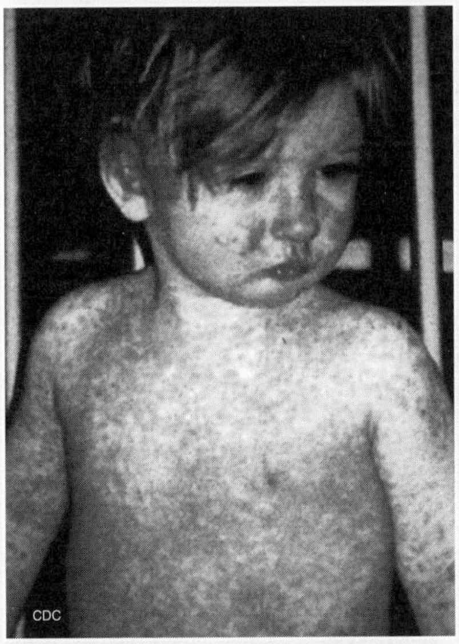
CDC

Child with a typical measles rash, which starts on the face and moves down the body. Measles begins with symptoms similar to the common cold, e.g. coughing, fever, sore eyes. These symptoms spread the virus before the rash appears.

Prevention and control of measles

Immunisation is the most effective way to prevent measles. The measles vaccine is given in combination as the measles-mumps-rubella (MMR) vaccine. A single dose of the MMR vaccine is 93% effective at preventing measles. Two doses are 97% effective. However, despite being proven effective, some people do not vaccinate their children against measles. Often this is because they believe they are putting their child's health at risk by doing so. If too many people fail to vaccinate, then a measles outbreak is more ikely.

Annual number of notified measles cases (UK, 1940-2008)

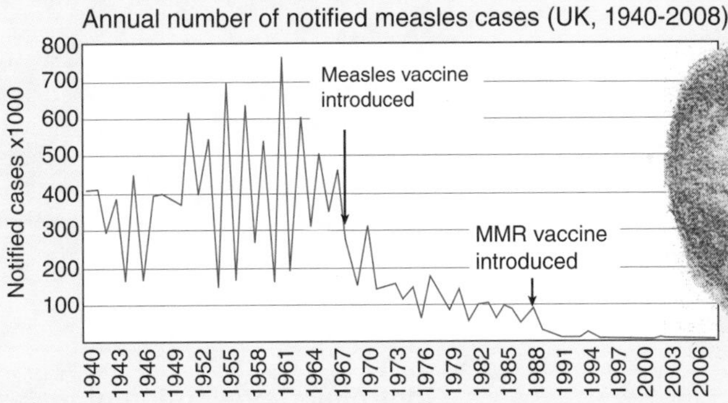
Notified cases x1000
800
700
600
500
400
300
200
100
Measles vaccine introduced
MMR vaccine introduced
1940
1943
1946
1949
1952
1955
1958
1961
1964
1967
1970
1973
1976
1979
1982
1985
1988
1991
1994
1997
2000
2003
2006

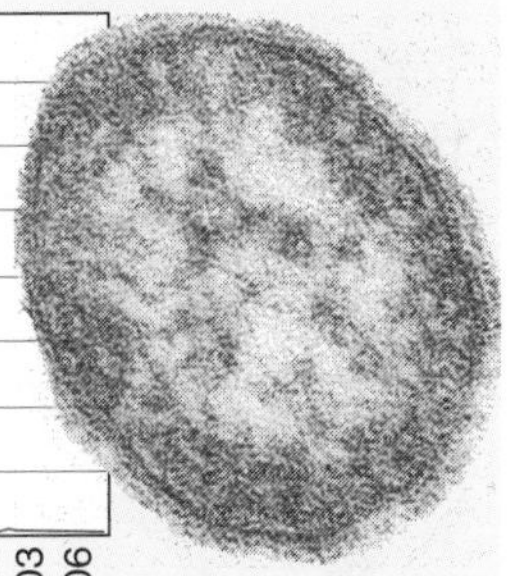

More than 95% of measles deaths occur in developing countries, especially in parts of Africa and Asia, where there are insufficient resources to vaccinate the population and the disease is still common. Disruptions to routine immunisation schedules (e.g. after a natural disaster or during conflict) can cause a spike in measles cases. The measles virus is also more easily spread when people are living in overcrowded conditions.

1. (a) Name the measles pathogen: ______________________

   (b) State what type of pathogen it is: ______________________

2. Measles is very contagious. Explain why: ______________________

3. Vaccination is the best method for preventing measles. Why are two doses recommended? ______________________

© 2015 **BIOZONE** International
ISBN: 978-1-927309-31-5
Photocopying Prohibited

171 Malaria

Key Idea: Malaria is caused by parasitic protozoa. The protozoa are carried by the *Anopheles* mosquito and are transmitted to humans when they are bitten by the mosquito. Malaria is a disease caused by protozoan parasites of the genus *Plasmodium*. The plasmodia have a life cycle involving two hosts, *Anopheles* mosquitoes and humans. Humans become infected when bitten by mosquitoes infected with the protozoans. In their human host, the plasmodia infect red blood cells (RBCs) and multiply inside the cells by asexual reproduction. Four *Plasmodium* species can cause malaria, ranging in severity from relatively mild to fatal. *Falciparum* malaria is the most severe because it affects all ages of red blood cells. Destruction of the RBCs results in a condition called haemolytic anaemia (loss of RBCs through lysis). The infected blood cells also become sticky and block blood vessels to vital organs such as the kidneys and the brain.

Transmission and effects of malaria

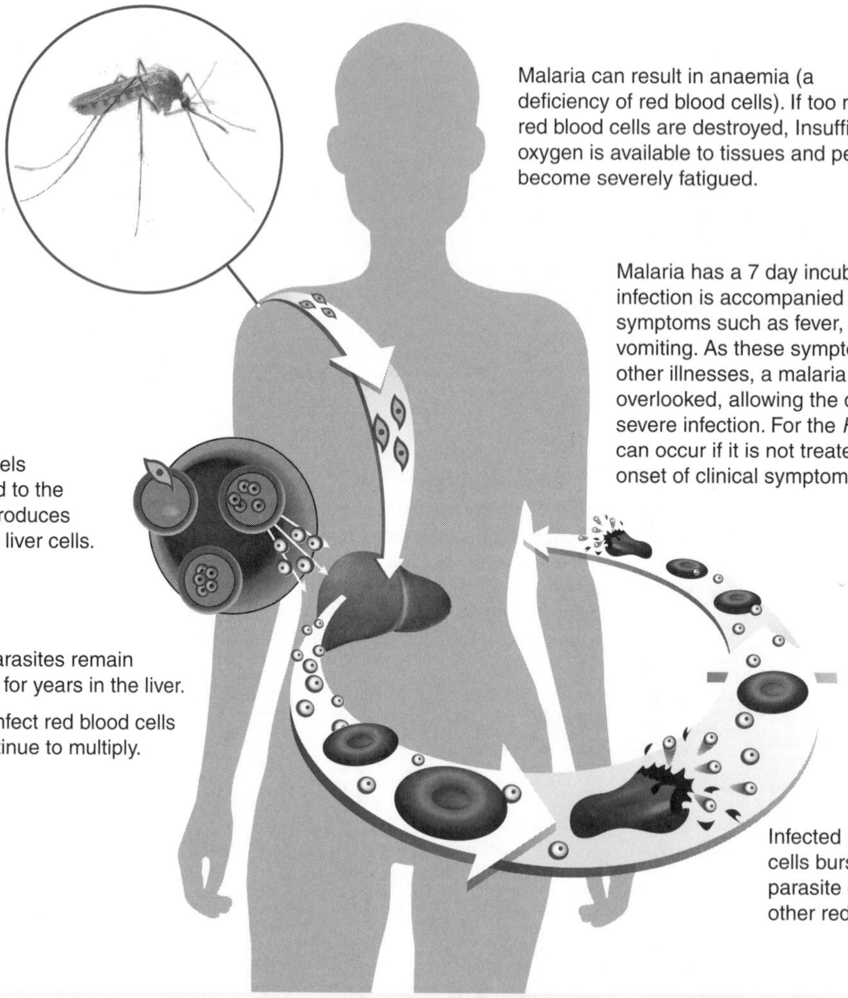

A mosquito infected with *Plasmodium* bites a human. The parasite completes the sexual part of its life cycle in the mosquito before being transferred to the human host.

Malaria can result in anaemia (a deficiency of red blood cells). If too many red blood cells are destroyed, Insufficient oxygen is available to tissues and people become severely fatigued.

Malaria has a 7 day incubation period and infection is accompanied by many general symptoms such as fever, headache, chills and vomiting. As these symptoms are common to other illnesses, a malaria diagnosis is sometimes overlooked, allowing the disease to progress to a severe infection. For the *Falciparum* form, death can occur if it is not treated within 24 hours of the onset of clinical symptoms.

The parasite travels through the blood to the liver where it reproduces rapidly within the liver cells.

Some parasites remain dormant for years in the liver.

Others infect red blood cells and continue to multiply.

Infected red blood cells burst, and the parasite can infect other red blood cells.

Control and prevention of malaria

All photos CDC

An integrated approach is used to control and prevent the spread of malaria. These include physical methods such using insecticide treated nets to stop mosquitoes biting a person while they are sleeping, drug treatments, especially for pregnant women and infants, and residual pesticide spraying (indoors and outdoors) to kill mosquitoes.

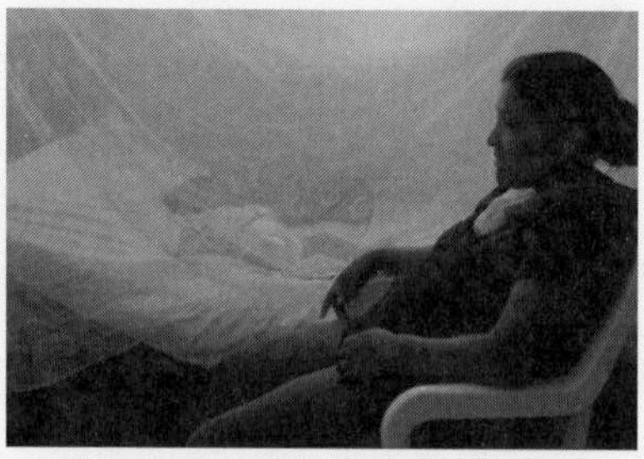

Social and economic factors have a significant role in the spread of malaria. People living in poor rural populations often cannot afford the bed nets that would protect them from mosquitoes. The governments of malaria-endemic countries often lack financial resources and do not have adequate equipment, medicine, or trained staff to treat malaria.

Larvae of the *Anopheles* mosquito can breed in diverse habitats, many of which are created as a result of human activity. For example, small pools of water in ditches, water troughs, containers, or rice fields are all potential breeding sites for mosquitoes. Mosquito numbers can be reduced by eliminating as many potential breeding sites as possible.

© 2015 **BIOZONE** International
ISBN:978-1-927309-31-5
Photocopying Prohibited

Global distribution and control of malaria

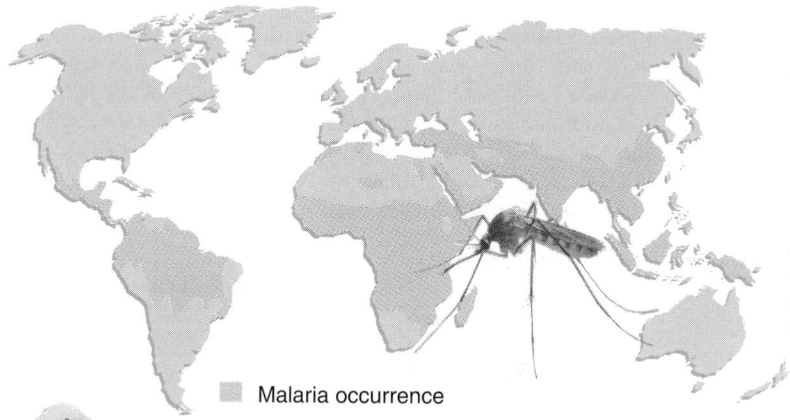
Malaria occurrence

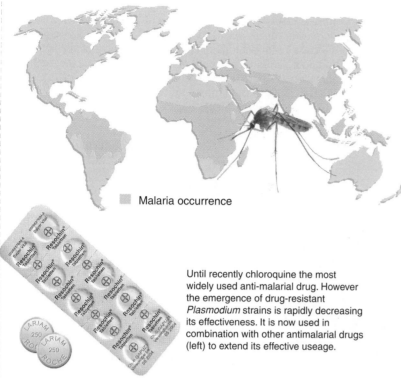

Malaria occurs in tropical and subtropical areas (left), where temperature, humidity, and rainfall levels are suitable for the *Anopheles* mosquitoes to survive and multiply, and where the malaria parasites can complete their life cycle. The highest transmission is found in Africa (south of the Sahara) and in parts of Oceania such as Papua New Guinea.

Malaria is a leading cause of death and disease in many developing countries, where young children and pregnant women are most affected. In 2015, 214 million people contracted malaria and around 438 000 people died. The economic cost of malaria is US$12 billion per year.

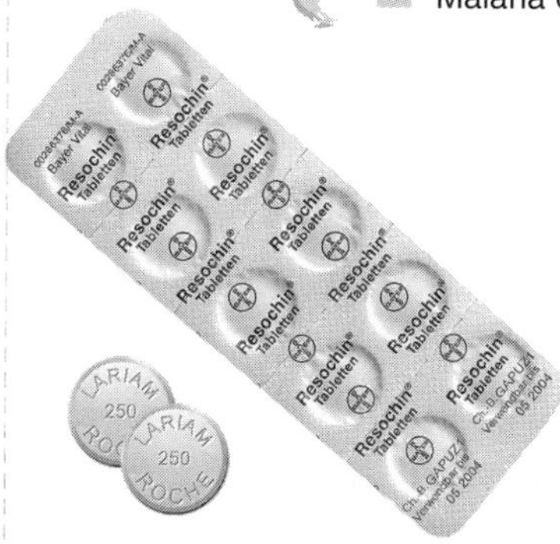
Resochin® Tabletten
LARIAM 250 ROCHE

Until recently chloroquine the most widely used anti-malarial drug. However the emergence of drug-resistant *Plasmodium* strains is rapidly decreasing its effectiveness. It is now used in combination with other antimalarial drugs (left) to extend its effective useage.

Why is malaria difficult to eradicate?

Several factors make malaria a very difficult disease to control. The *Plasmodium* parasite has two different hosts and a complex life cycle, making it very difficult to target with drugs. The parasite has also developed resistance to anti-malarial drugs, allowing it to continue to spread and, in some cases, re-emerge in areas where it had previously been eradicated. Likewise, mosquitoes are developing insecticide resistance and their numbers are remaining high, allowing a greater transmission of the *Plasmodium* parasite.

1. (a) Name the malaria pathogen: ____________________

   (b) State what type of pathogen it is: ____________________

2. How do humans become infected with malaria? ____________________

3. What aspects of the biology of this pathogen make it difficult to control? ____________________

4. (a) What biological factors are important in the global occurrence of malaria? ____________________

   (b) What measures could be most cost effective in controlling the number of new malaria infections? ____________________

5. Why has malaria been so difficult to treat and eradicate with drugs? ____________________

6. What effect do you think global warming will have on the geographical range of malaria? ____________________

© 2015 **BIOZONE** International
ISBN: 978-1-927309-31-5
Photocopying Prohibited

172 Tuberculosis

Key Idea: Tuberculosis is a contagious bacterial disease affecting the lungs, causing scarring of the lung tissue.

Tuberculosis (TB) is a contagious disease caused by the bacterium *Mycobacterium tuberculosis* (MTB). TB most commonly affects the lungs as **pulmonary TB**. Presence of the disease is indicated on a chest X-ray by opaque areas and large thick walled cavities in the lungs resulting from bacterial damage. TB affects millions globally and increasing drug resistance is contributing to its impact. Effective treatment requires a prolonged regime of antibiotics, and poor patient compliance with treatment contributes to its persistence. There were an estimated 9.6 million new cases of TB in 2014 and, of these, an estimated 480 000 involved multi-drug resistant (MDR) TB.

Infection and transmission

TB is a contagious disease, and is spread through the air when infectious people cough, sneeze, talk, or spit (below). Only a small number of *Mycobacterium tuberculosis* (MTB) need to be inhaled for a person to be infected.

Left untreated, each person with active TB will infect 10-15 people every year. Those infected do not necessarily become ill because the immune system can 'wall off' the MTB which then lie dormant for years, protected by a thick waxy coat. When the immune system is weakened, the chance of becoming ill is greater.

TB is treated with a 4-6 month course of antibiotics. However, many people fail to complete the prescribed course and are not clear of the disease. MTB has developed resistance to many antibiotics used to treat TB. This has made treatment more difficult.

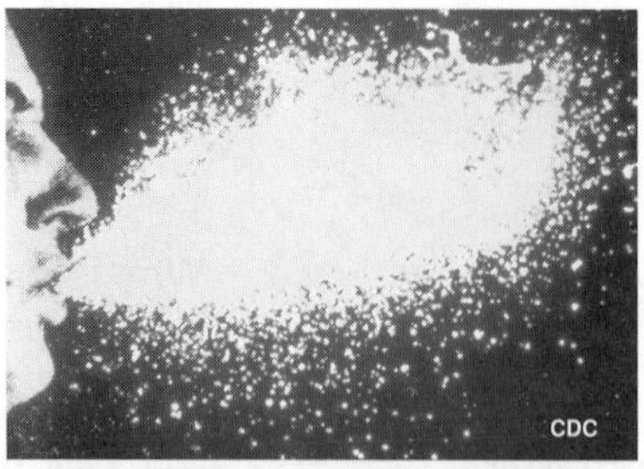
CDC

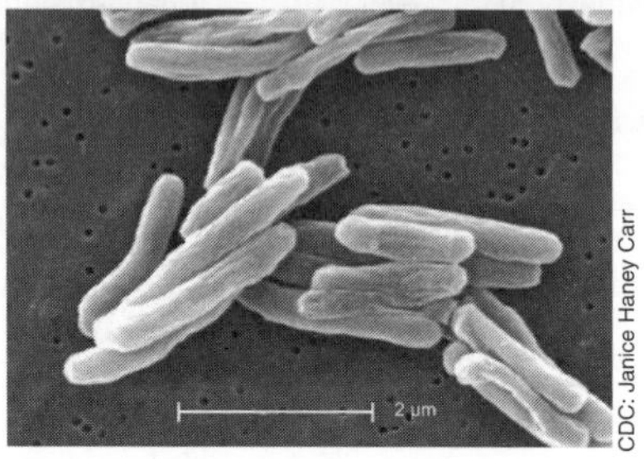
2 µm
CDC: Janice Haney Carr

Mycobacterium tuberculosis (MTB)

Effect on lung function

When MTB is inhaled, bacilli reach the lungs, where they are ingested by an alveolar macrophages. Usually the macrophages destroy the bacteria, but if they do not, the bacilli are hidden from the immune system and survive and multiply within the macrophages. More macrophages are attracted to the area and a tubercle forms. The disease may become dormant or the tubercle may rupture, releasing bacilli into the bronchioles (diagram panel, far right).

Affected tissue is replaced by scarring (fibrosis) and cavities filled with cheese-like white necrotic material. During active disease, some of these cavities are joined to the air passages. This material can be coughed up. It contains living bacteria which can pass on infection.

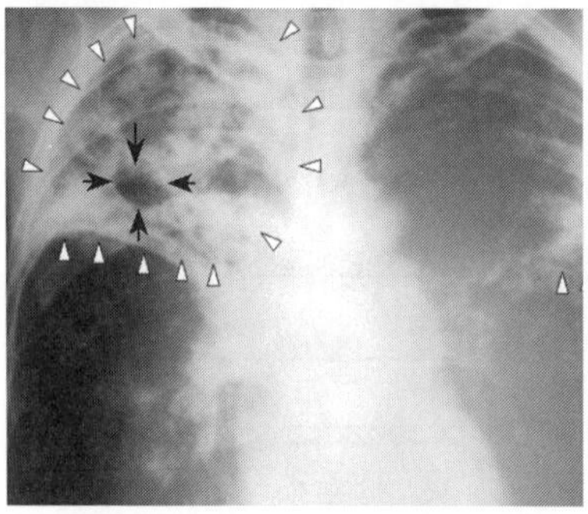

Above: X-ray of lungs affected by pulmonary TB. The white triangles indicate areas where the airspaces of the lung are congested with fluid, and the dark arrows indicate a cavity, from which infective material is coughed up. Surface area for gas exchange is reduced and lung function is adversely affected.

Stages in TB infection

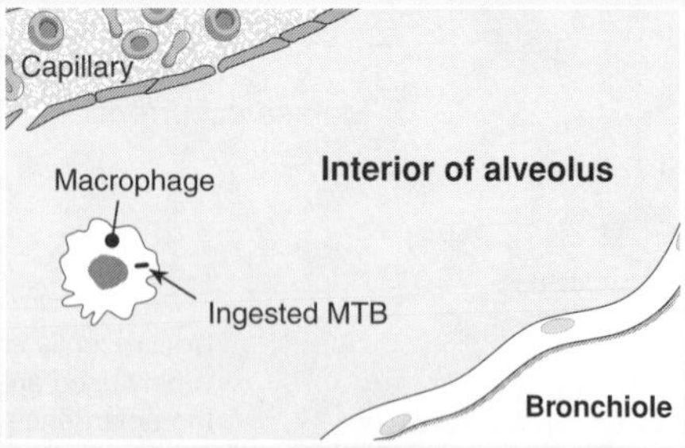
Capillary
Macrophage
Interior of alveolus
Ingested MTB
Bronchiole

MTB enter the lung and are ingested by macrophages (phagocytic white blood cells).

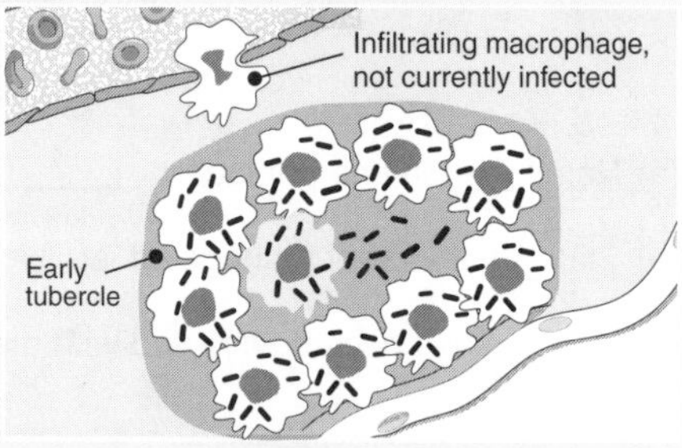
Infiltrating macrophage, not currently infected
Early tubercle

The multiplying bacteria cause the macrophages to swell and rupture. The newly released bacilli infect other macrophages. At this stage a tubercle may form and the disease may lie dormant.

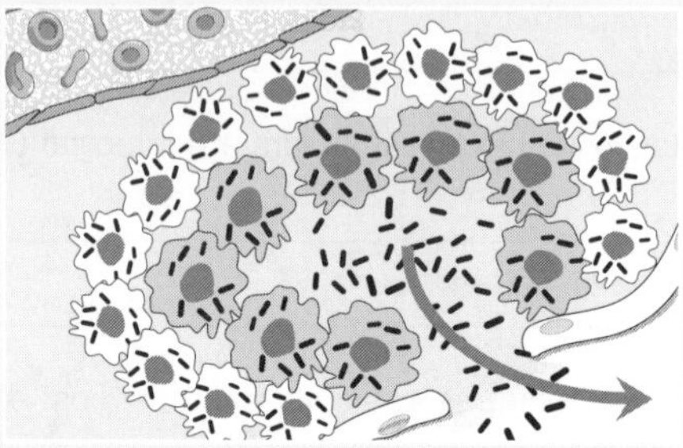

Eventually the tubercle ruptures, allowing bacilli to spill into the bronchiole. The bacilli can now be transmitted when the infected person coughs.

1. (a) Name the TB pathogen: ______________________________

   (b) State what type of pathogen it is: ______________________________

2. Describe how the TB pathogen causes infection and spreads between hosts: ______________________________

   ____

   ____

   ____

3. Why is lung function in a TB patient likely to be reduced? ______________________________

   ____

   ____

© 2015 BIOZONE International
ISBN:978-1-927309-31-5
Photocopying Prohibited

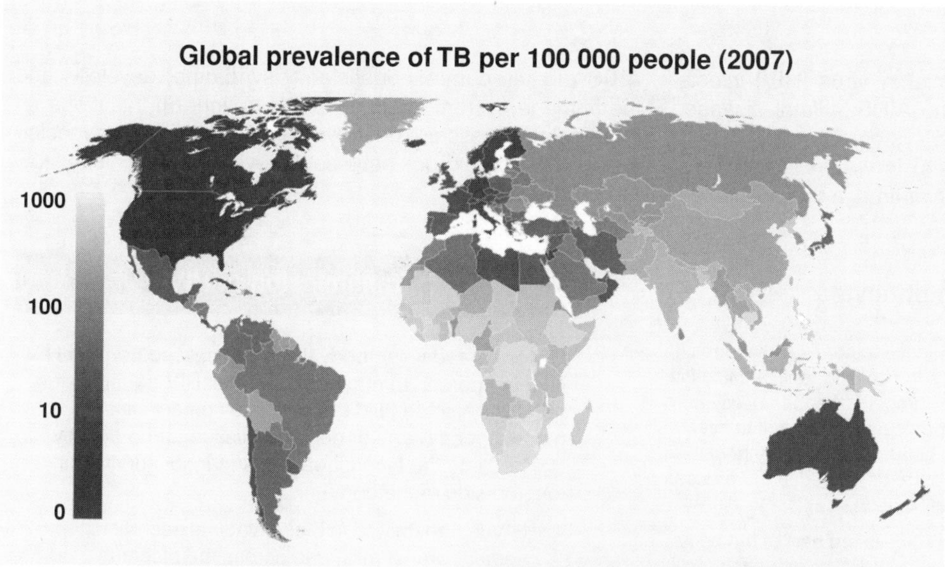
Global prevalence of TB per 100 000 people (2007)
1000
100
10
0

Global importance

The rate of TB infections is high with around 33% of the world's population infected. TB is disproportionately common in poor countries which have limited infrastructure and resources to combat the disease.

Most cases of TB (95%) and 98% of all TB deaths occur in developing countries, with most deaths occurring in sub-Saharan Africa and Asia. Diagnosis and treatment in developing countries is made difficult by a lack of funds to provide medicine, education, and trained health providers. Individuals in these countries are unlikely to be able to afford to buy the drugs required to treat TB.

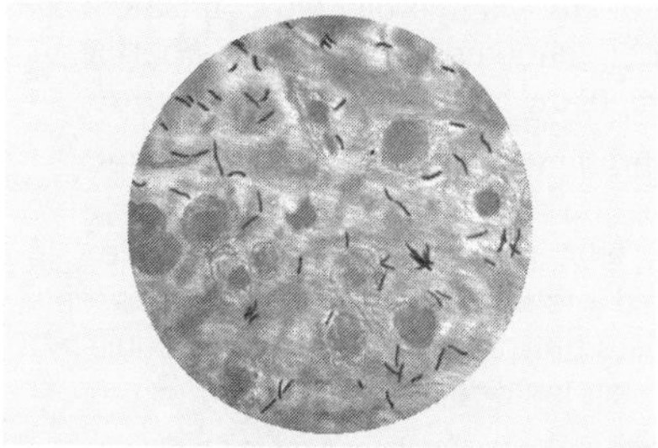

CDC

Early detection, isolation, and appropriate drug treatment are essential to controlling TB. However, people with latent TB may have no symptoms so can be carriers for years until active TB develops. Identifying and treating latent TB is crucial to preventing the disease spreading.

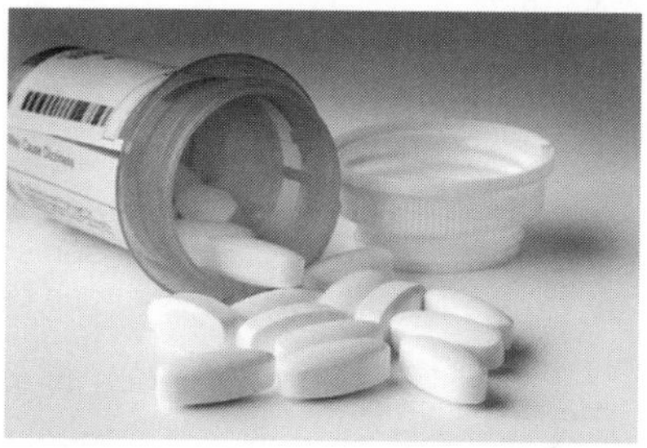

TB bacteria grow very slowly, so a prolonged course of different antibiotics is needed to ensure all the bacteria are killed. Patients can relapse (get TB again) if not all the bacteria are killed. Drug resistant strains can require longer treatments, so the likelihood of not taking the drugs correctly are higher.

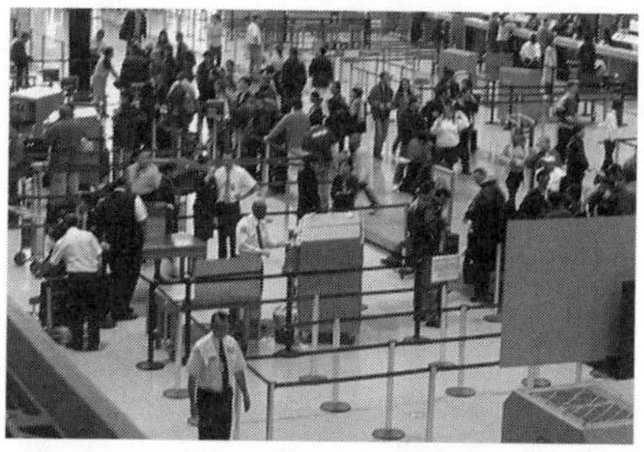

CDCTim Bray CC3.0

The majority (80%) of all TB infections occur in only 22 countries, but TB cases in developed countries have increased in recent decades. This has been attributed to increased international travel and a breakdown of TB control programmes. Overcrowding also allows the disease to spread more easily.

4. Explain how MTB may exist in a dormant state in a person for many years without causing disease symptoms:

5. Why is TB a very difficult disease to treat?

6. About 80% of the population in many Asian and African countries test positive for TB, while only 5–10% of the U.S. population test positive. Discuss possible reasons for the large difference in TB infections between the regions:

© 2015 **BIOZONE** International
ISBN: 978-1-927309-31-5
Photocopying Prohibited

173 HIV/AIDS

Key Idea: The human immunodeficiency virus (HIV) infects lymphocyte cells, eventually causing AIDS, a fatal disease, which acts by impairing the immune system.

HIV (human immunodeficiency virus) is virus which infects lymphocytes called helper T-cells. Over time, a disease called **AIDS** (acquired immunodeficiency syndrome) develops and the immune system loses its ability to fight off infections as more helper T-cells are destroyed. There is no cure or vaccine for HIV, but some drugs have been developed which can slow the progress of the disease.

HIV Infects lymphocytes

CDC

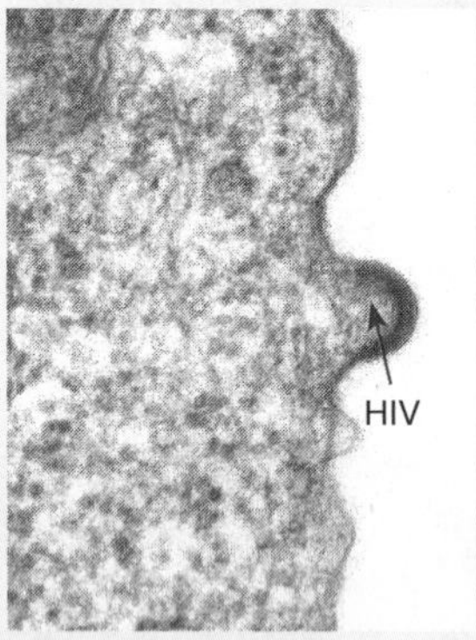
HIV

HIV budding from a lymphocyte

HIV infects helper T-cell lymphocytes. It uses the cells to replicate itself in great numbers, then the newly formed viral particles exit the cell to infect more helper T-cells. Many helper T-cells are destroyed in the process of HIV replication.

Helper T-cells are part of the body's immune system, so when their levels become too low, the immune system can no longer fight off infections. TB is the biggest killer of HIV patients in Africa.

The graph below shows the relationship between the level of HIV infection and the number of helper T-cells in an individual.

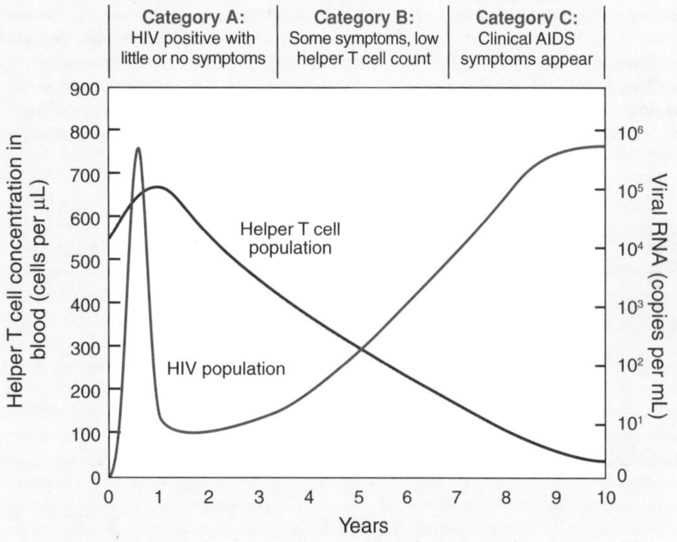
Category A:
HIV positive with little or no symptoms
Category B:
Some symptoms, low helper T cell count
Category C:
Clinical AIDS symptoms appear
Helper T cell concentration in blood (cells per µL)
900
800
700
600
500
400
300
200
100
0
Viral RNA (copies per mL)
10^6
10^5
10^4
10^3
10^2
10^1
0
Helper T cell population
HIV population
0 1 2 3 4 5 6 7 8 9 10
Years

Transmission of HIV

HIV is spread when body fluids are passed from an HIV infected person to another individual. HIV transmission requires infected fluid to come into contact with a mucous membrane or damaged tissue, or be directly injected into the bloodstream. HIV cannot survive for long outside of the body.

1. HIV is transmitted in blood, vaginal secretions, semen, breast milk, and across the placenta.
2. Transmission of HIV via unprotected or unsafe sex (e.g.sex without condoms or with multiple partners) has been particularly important to its spread.
3. HIV can be spread when intravenous drug users share needles. If a needle has been used by someone with HIV, infected blood in the needle can be injected into the next person who uses that needle. Infection between drug users is a significant HIV transmission factor.
4. Blood transfusions with infected blood can spread HIV. However, in developed countries, blood transfusions are no longer a likely source of infection because blood is tested for HIV.
5. HIV transmission from mother to child during pregnancy or breast feeding is higher in developing countries than other parts of the world.

HIV is easily transmitted between intravenous drug users who share needles.

1. (a) Name the HIV pathogen: ______________________________

   (b) State what type of pathogen it is: ______________________________

2. Consult the graph above showing the stages of HIV infection (remember, HIV infects and destroys helper T cells).

   (a) How do viral numbers change with the progression of the disease? ______________________________

   ____

   ____

   (b) How do the helper T cells respond to the infection? ______________________________

   ____

   ____

   ____

© 2015 BIOZONE International
ISBN:978-1-927309-31-5
Photocopying Prohibited

HIV prevention: biological, social and economic factors

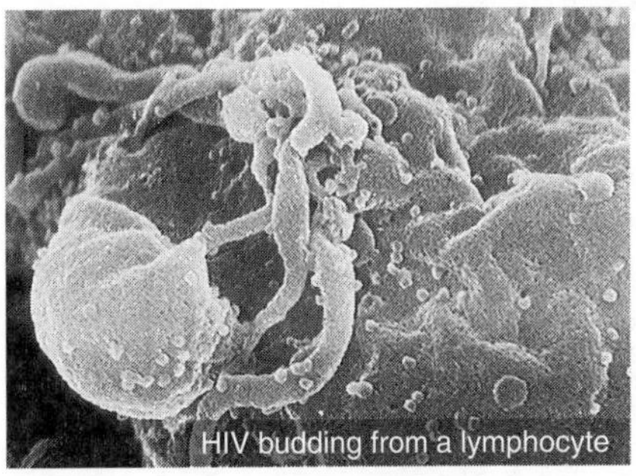
HIV budding from a lymphocyte

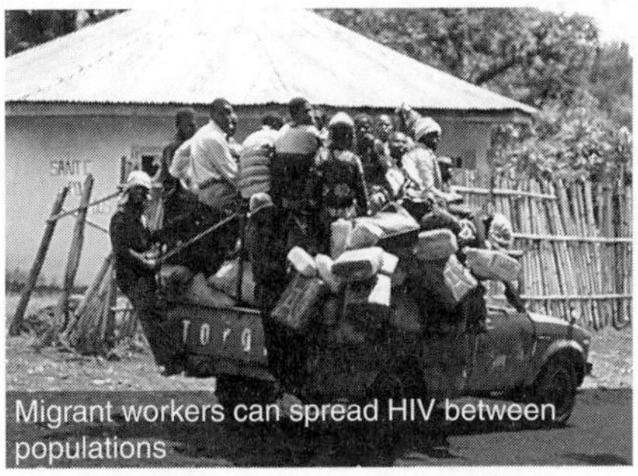
Migrant workers can spread HIV between populations

Biological factors: HIV is difficult to treat because it hides within the lymphocytes making it hard for anti-HIV drugs to target the virus. The HIV inside the cells eventually becomes active and quickly replicates and spreads. HIV mutates very quickly, making it difficult to produce an effective vaccine. Transmission is highest when a person is first infected and again in the later stages.

Social factors: Unsafe sex increases the likelihood of HIV transmission. Migration is also a factor, especially where men travel for work. They may develop sexual networks while they are away and return to their families with HIV. Male circumcision (MC) can reduce HIV transmission by up to 60% but for complex cultural and religious reasons is not a uniformly adopted practice.

Economic factors: HIV rates are higher in impoverished regions where access to HIV education and treatment is limited. Women are particularly vulnerable because they are often in very low paid jobs, or are dependent upon male family members for money. Sex may be used in exchange for food or other goods, and this increases their risk of contracting HIV.

HIV: Global prevalence in 2014

Since it was first discovered, HIV has infected nearly 78 million people and killed 39 million people. It was estimated that about 0.8% of the world's population (35 million) were living with HIV at the end of 2014.

Although HIV is a global disease, sub-Saharan Africa remains most severely affected, accounting for nearly 71% of the people living with HIV worldwide.

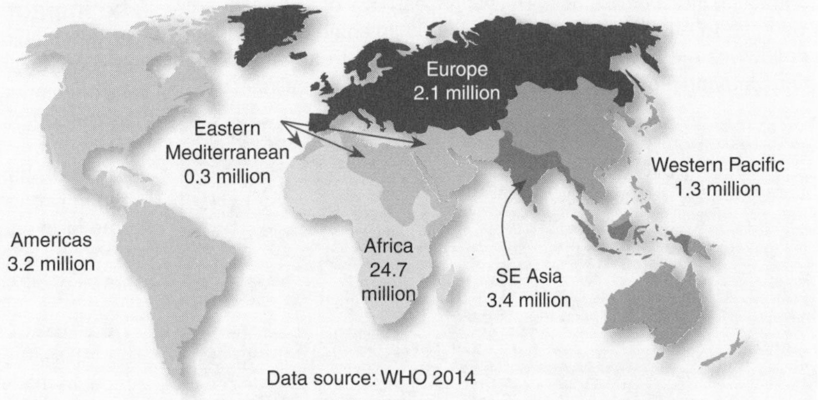
Europe
2.1 million
Eastern Mediterranean
0.3 million
Western Pacific
1.3 million
Americas
3.2 million
Africa
24.7 million
SE Asia
3.4 million
Data source: WHO 2014

3. (a) Describe how HIV can be transmitted between people: ______

(b) Suggest why HIV transmission rates during pregnancy and breast feeding are higher in developing countries: ______

4. (a) Why is HIV difficult to treat? ______

(b) Describe some of the difficulties associated with developing an effective HIV vaccine: ______

5. Discuss some of the social and economic factors that contribute to the spread of HIV: ______

© 2015 **BIOZONE** International
ISBN: 978-1-927309-31-5
Photocopying Prohibited

174 The Impact of HIV/AIDS in Africa

Key Idea: HIV infection is disproportionately high in sub-Saharan Africa. The social and economic effects are extensive. Around 10% of the world's population lives in sub-Saharan Africa, yet this region is home to two thirds of HIV-infected people. The impact of HIV-AIDS on Africa's populations, workplaces, and economies is enormous, and is setting back Africa's economic and social progress. The effects of the disease are disproportionate as the vast majority of people living with HIV in Africa are in their working prime. Life expectancies too have fallen and in many African countries they are half what they were 15 years ago (graph, right). This has been detrimental to all aspects of African social and economic structure.

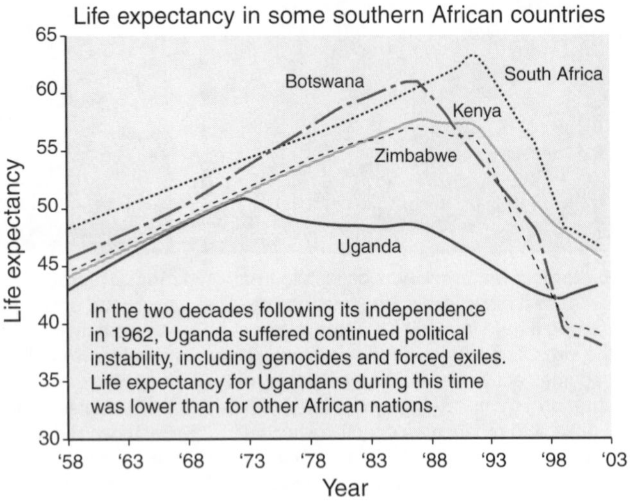
Life expectancy in some southern African countries
Life expectancy
65
60
55
50
45
40
35
30
'58
'63
'68
'73
'78
'83
'88
'93
'98
'03
Year
Botswana
South Africa
Kenya
Zimbabwe
Uganda
In the two decades following its independence in 1962, Uganda suffered continued political instability, including genocides and forced exiles. Life expectancy for Ugandans during this time was lower than for other African nations.

The impact on the health sector

Increasingly, the demand of the AIDS epidemic on health care facilities is not being adequately met. In sub-Saharan Africa, people with HIV-related diseases occupy more than half of all hospital beds. Health care workers are also at high risk of contracting HIV. For example, Botswana lost 17% of its healthcare workforce to AIDS between 1999 and 2005. In some regions, 40% of midwives are HIV positive. Although access to treatment is improving, most of those needing treatment do not receive it.

Photo courtesy of Karl Mueller; Flickr

This Malawi grandmother is now responsible for the care and support of her four grandchildren, whose parents both died of AIDS. The intergenerational effects of HIV/AIDS are the longest lasting and are related to how the epidemic intensifies poverty and leads to its persistence. The challenge to African countries is in achieving the sustainable development needed to respond effectively to the epidemic.

Information from various sources including UNAIDS, UNDP, and AVERT.org

The impact on households

The AIDS epidemic has the greatest impact on poor households. Loss of one or both parents to AIDS results in a loss of income, and leads to a dissolution of family structure. The burden on older people is immense. Parents of adults with AIDS often find themselves supporting a household and caring for their orphaned grandchildren (left). Children (especially girls) may be forced to abandon their educations to work at home or to care for sick relatives. Damage to the education sector has a feedback effect too, as poor education fuels the spread of HIV.

The impact on food security

The AIDS epidemic adds to food insecurity in sub-Saharan Africa. In many African countries, where food is already in short supply, HIV/AIDS is responsible for a severe depletion of the agricultural workforce and a consequent decline in agricultural output. Much of burden of coping rests with women, who are forced to take up roles outside their homes as well as continue as housekeepers, carers, and providers of food.

The future?

AIDS in Africa is linked to other problems, including poverty, food insecurity, and poor public infrastructure. Efforts to fight the epidemic must work within these constraints. Without control, the AIDS epidemic will continue to present the single greatest barrier to Africa's social and economic development.

1. With reference to the graph of life expectancies in southern African countries:

   (a) Describe and explain the trends in since the late 1980s: ______________________

   ____

   (b) Describe and give a likely explanation of the trends between 1958 and 1988: ______________________

   ____

   ____

2. Discuss the barriers sub-Saharan African nations will face in countering the effects of the HIV/AIDS:

____

____

____

____

____

© 2015 **BIOZONE** International
ISBN:978-1-927309-31-5
Photocopying Prohibited

175 Antibiotics

Key idea: Antibiotics are chemicals that kill bacteria or inhibit their growth. They are ineffective against viruses.

Antibiotics are chemical substances that act against bacterial infections by either killing the bacteria (**bactericidal**) or preventing them from growing (**bacteriostatic**). Antibiotics are ineffective against viruses because they target specific aspects of bacterial structure and metabolism, such as cell wall synthesis. Viruses have no metabolic machinery of their own and their structure is very different, so antibiotics have no effect on them. Antibiotics are produced naturally by bacteria and fungi, but most modern antibiotics are semi-synthetic modifications of these natural compounds.

How antibiotics work

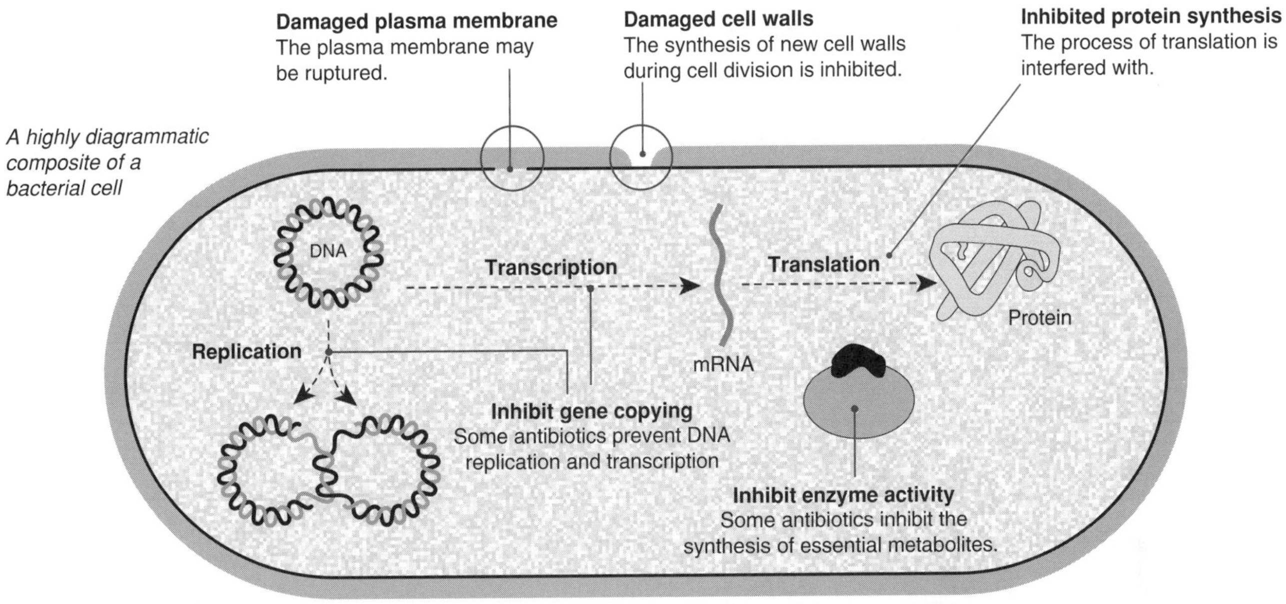
Damaged plasma membrane
The plasma membrane may be ruptured.
Damaged cell walls
The synthesis of new cell walls during cell division is inhibited.
Inhibited protein synthesis
The process of translation is interfered with.
A highly diagrammatic composite of a bacterial cell
DNA
Transcription
Translation
Protein
Replication
mRNA
Inhibit gene copying
Some antibiotics prevent DNA replication and transcription
Inhibit enzyme activity
Some antibiotics inhibit the synthesis of essential metabolites.

What is penicillin and how does it work?

Penicillins are a group of antibiotics produced by species of *Penicillium* fungi. Penicillin's antimicrobial properties were discovered by Alexander Fleming in 1928 and antibiotics in the penicillin family are still used today to treat a number of common bacterial infections.

When bacteria grow and divide they must synthesise a new cell wall. Penicillin inhibits bacterial growth by interfering with the normal cell wall synthesis. Penicillin stops the formation of the peptidoglycan cross-links in the cell wall. It does this by binding to the active site of the enzyme that forms the cross links and prevents it from carrying out its role. Without the cross links, the cell wall lacks the strength to enclose the cell contents. Pressure inside the cell becomes too much and the cell surface membrane bursts, killing the cell.

Penicillin is most effective against gram positive bacteria, in which the cell wall is composed almost entirely of a thick layer of peptidoglycan. In gram negative bacteria, the thin peptidoglycan layer lies below a thicker lipoprotein layer, so it is not as accessible.

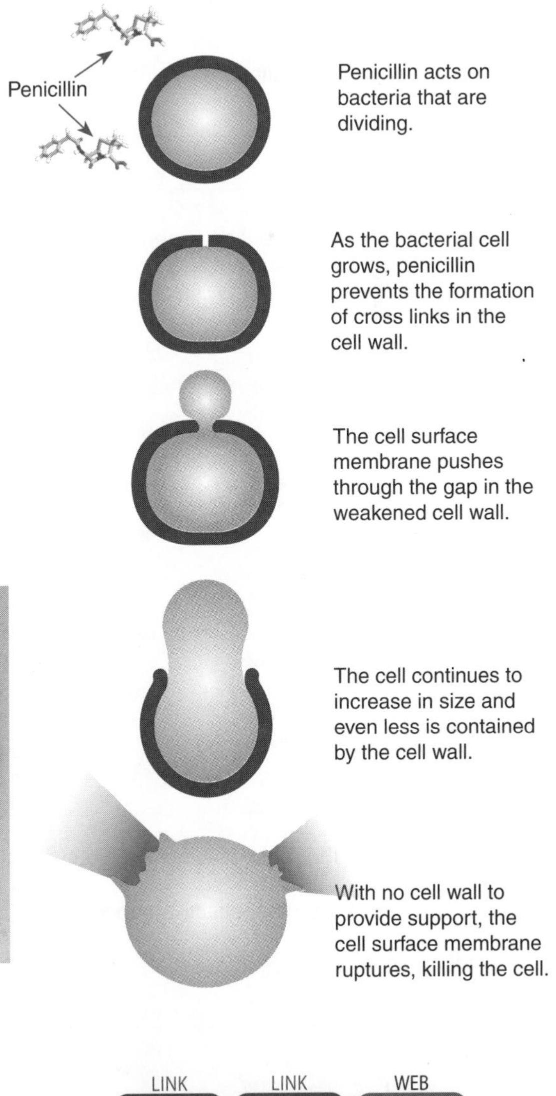
Penicillin
Penicillin acts on bacteria that are dividing.
As the bacterial cell grows, penicillin prevents the formation of cross links in the cell wall.
The cell surface membrane pushes through the gap in the weakened cell wall.
The cell continues to increase in size and even less is contained by the cell wall.
With no cell wall to provide support, the cell surface membrane ruptures, killing the cell.

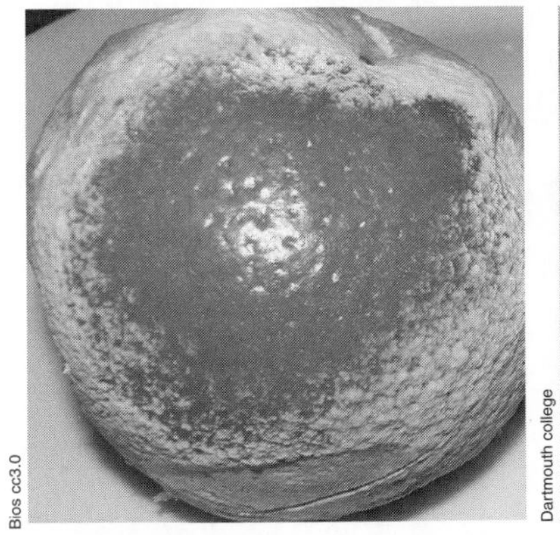
Bios cc3.0

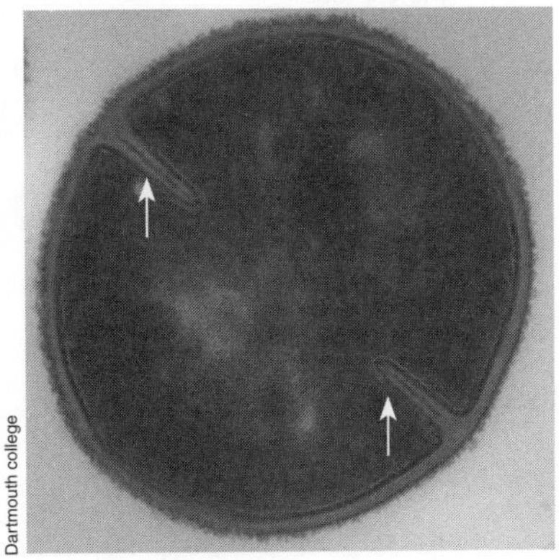
Dartmouth college

Photos: *Pencillium* mould growing on an orange (left) and a *Staphylococcus* bacterial cell dividing (right). The formation of the new cell wall is indicated by arrows.

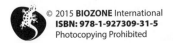

© 2015 **BIOZONE** International
ISBN: 978-1-927309-31-5
Photocopying Prohibited

1. Why are viruses not affected by antibiotics? ______

______

______

2. The graph right shows the effects of two antibiotics. Identify the antibiotic with a bacteriostatic action and the antibiotic with a bactericidal action. Explain your choice:

Bacteriostatic: ______

______

______

Bactericidal: ______

______

______

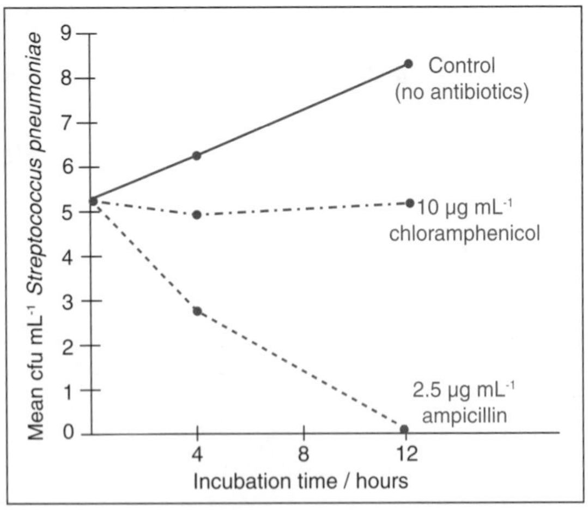

Mean cfu mL^{-1} *Streptococcus pneumoniae*
Incubation time / hours
Control (no antibiotics)
10 µg mL^{-1} chloramphenicol
2.5 µg mL^{-1} ampicillin

3. (a) How does penicillin act on bacteria? ______

______

______

______

(b) Why is penicillin only effective against bacteria undergoing division? ______

______

______

(c) Why is penicillin effective against gram positive bacteria but not against gram negative bacteria? ______

______

______

4. Two students carried out an experiment to determine the effect of antibiotics on bacteria. They placed discs saturated with antibiotic on petri dishes evenly coated with bacterial colonies. Dish 1 contained four different antibiotics labelled A to D and a control labelled CL. Dish 2 contained four different concentrations of a single antibiotic and a control labelled CL.

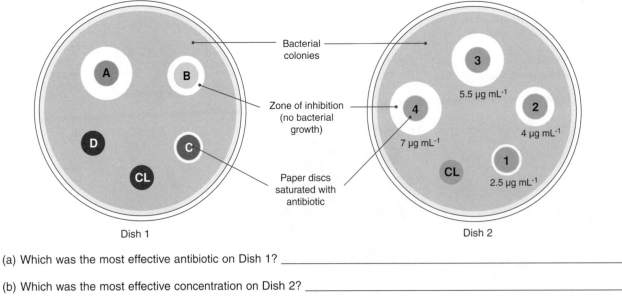

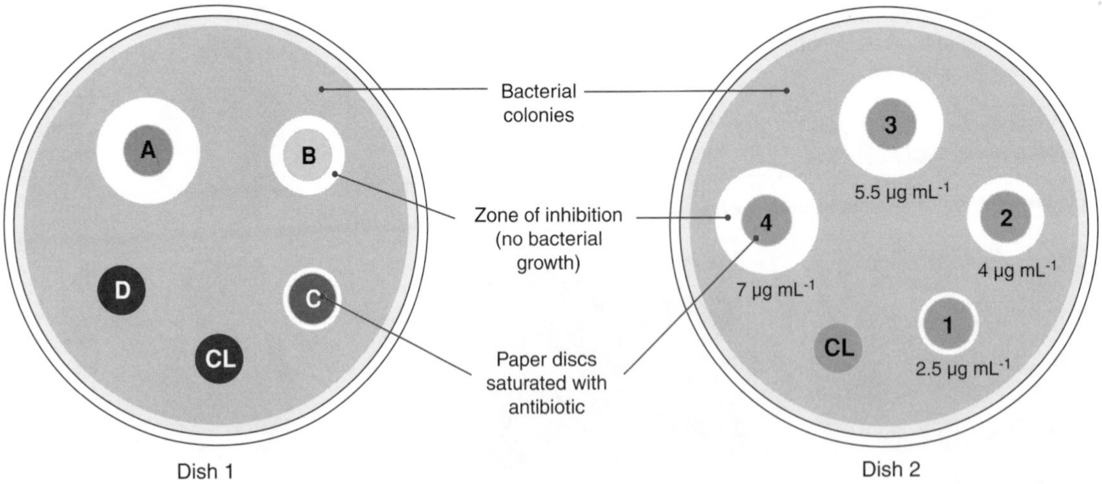

A
B
C
D
CL
Bacterial colonies
Zone of inhibition (no bacterial growth)
Paper discs saturated with antibiotic
3
5.5 µg mL^{-1}
4
7 µg mL^{-1}
2
4 µg mL^{-1}
1
2.5 µg mL^{-1}
CL
Dish 1
Dish 2

(a) Which was the most effective antibiotic on Dish 1? ______

(b) Which was the most effective concentration on Dish 2? ______

(c) Explain your choice in question 5(b): ______

______

© 2015 **BIOZONE** International
ISBN:978-1-927309-31-5
Photocopying Prohibited

176 The Evolution of Antibiotic Resistance

Key Idea: Bacteria can develop resistance to antibiotics and can pass this on to the next generation and to other populations. **Antibiotic resistance** arises when a genetic change allows bacteria to tolerate levels of antibiotic that would normally inhibit growth. This resistance may arise spontaneously by mutation or copying error, or by transfer of genetic material between microbes. Genomic analyses from 30 000 year old permafrost sediments show that the genes for antibiotic resistance have long been present in the bacterial genome. Modern use of antibiotics has simply provided the selective environment for their proliferation. Many bacterial strains have even acquired resistance to multiple antibiotics.

The evolution of antibiotic resistance in bacteria

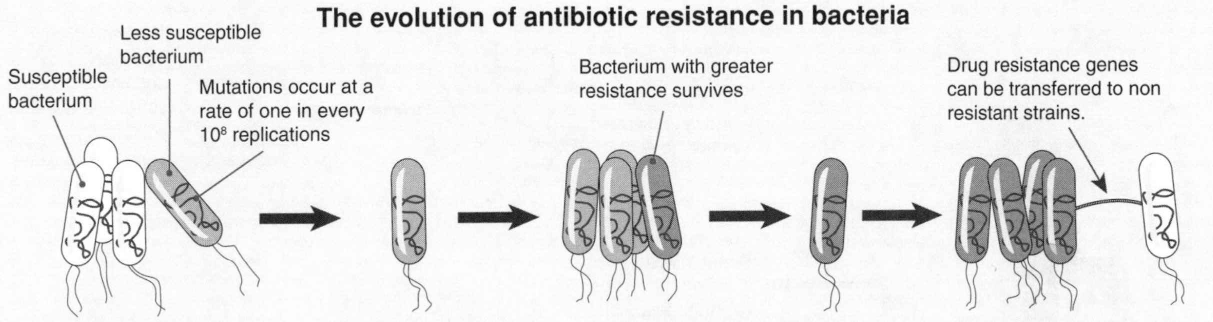
Susceptible bacterium
Less susceptible bacterium
Mutations occur at a rate of one in every 10^8 replications
Bacterium with greater resistance survives
Drug resistance genes can be transferred to non resistant strains.

Any population, including bacterial populations, includes variants with unusual traits, in this case reduced sensitivity to an antibiotic. These variants arise as a result of mutations in the bacterial chromosome. Such mutations are well documented and some are ancient.

When a person takes an antibiotic, only the most susceptible bacteria will die. The more resistant cells remain and continue dividing. Note that the antibiotic does not create the resistance; it provides the environment in which selection for resistance can take place.

If the amount of antibiotic delivered is too low, or the course of antibiotics is not completed, a population of resistant bacteria develops. Within this population too, there will be variation in susceptibility. Some will survive higher antibiotic levels.

A highly resistant population has evolved. The resistant cells can exchange genetic material with other bacteria (via horizontal gene transmission), passing on the genes for resistance. The antibiotic initially used against this bacterial strain will now be ineffective.

The bacterium responsible for TB, *Mycobacterium tuberculosis*, has developed resistance to several drugs.

Today, one in seven new TB cases is resistant to the two drugs most commonly used as treatments and 5% of these patients die. Some strains have evolved resistance to more than one drug. Multi-drug resistant TB (MDR TB) is the most common, but extensively drug resistant (XDR) strains are unaffected by most of the TB drugs.

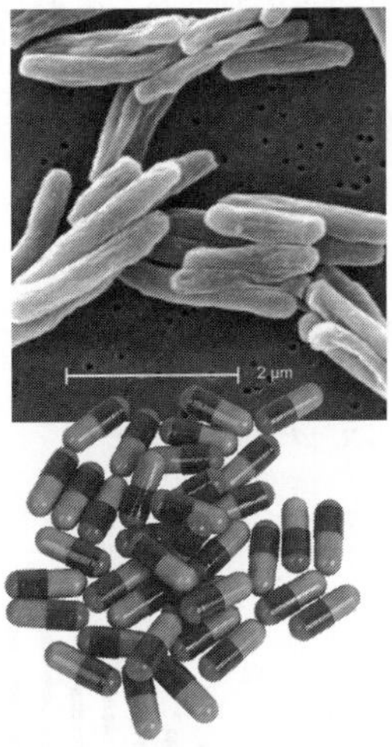
2 µm

Notification of multi-drug resistant TB cases in Africa and Asia

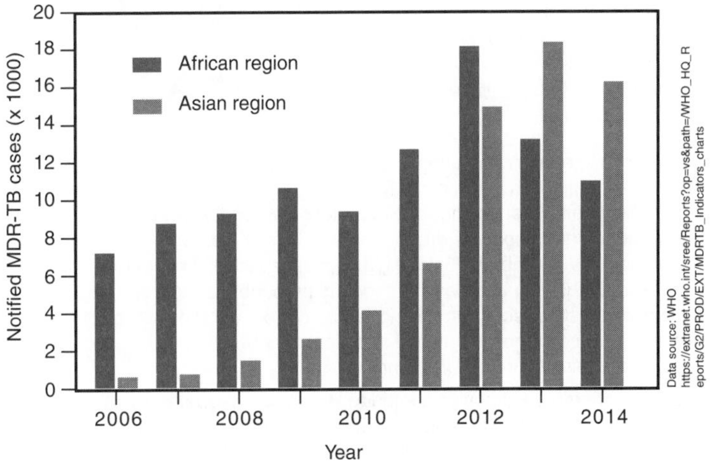
Notified MDR-TB cases (x 1000)
20
18
16
14
12
10
8
6
4
2
0
African region
Asian region
2006
2008
2010
2012
2014
Year
Data source: WHO
https://extranet.who.int/sree/Reports?op=vs&path=/WHO_HQ_Reports/G2/PROD/EXT/MDRTB_Indicators_charts

1. Describe two ways in which antibiotic resistance can become widespread:

   (a) ______________________

   (b) ______________________

2. Genomic evidence indicates that the genes for antibiotic resistance are ancient:

   (a) How could these genes have arisen in the first place? ______________________

   (b) Explain why these genes are proliferating now: ______________________

3. (a) Describe the trend in MDR TB over the last decade: ______________________

   (b) Why are the MDR and XDR strains of MTB so worrying? ______________________

© 2015 **BIOZONE** International
ISBN: 978-1-927309-31-5
Photocopying Prohibited

177 The Implications of Antibiotic Resistance

Key Idea: Antibiotic resistance makes it harder to treat and eliminate the causes of bacterial disease.

Antibiotic resistance makes it difficult to treat and control some bacterial diseases. Patients with infections caused by drug-resistant bacteria are more likely to suffer medical complications and death. Some bacteria have evolved resistance to multiple antibiotics. The infections they cause are very difficult to treat and are more easily spread through the population. It is very likely that, in the near future, there will be no effective antibiotics against some pathogens. New discoveries of effective antibiotics are rare, only four new antibiotics have been approved for use since 2000.

How antibiotic resistance can spread

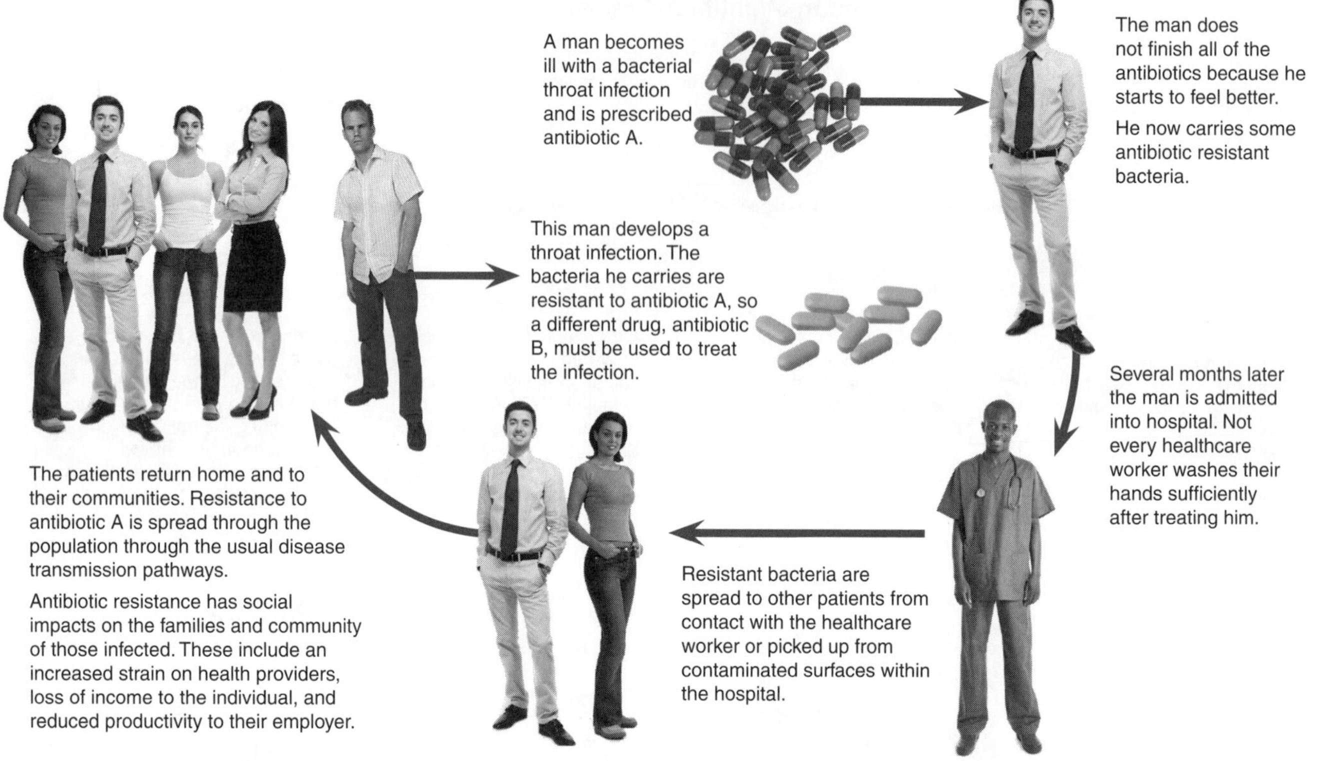
A man becomes ill with a bacterial throat infection and is prescribed antibiotic A.
The man does not finish all of the antibiotics because he starts to feel better.
He now carries some antibiotic resistant bacteria.
Several months later the man is admitted into hospital. Not every healthcare worker washes their hands sufficiently after treating him.
Resistant bacteria are spread to other patients from contact with the healthcare worker or picked up from contaminated surfaces within the hospital.
The patients return home and to their communities. Resistance to antibiotic A is spread through the population through the usual disease transmission pathways.
Antibiotic resistance has social impacts on the families and community of those infected. These include an increased strain on health providers, loss of income to the individual, and reduced productivity to their employer.
This man develops a throat infection. The bacteria he carries are resistant to antibiotic A, so a different drug, antibiotic B, must be used to treat the infection.

Resistant bacterial strains often occur because patients have been prescribed antibiotics unnecessarily, the dose is too low, or the patient did not finish all the antibiotics. Several steps can be taken to reduce the incidence and impact of drug resistance. These include reducing the spread in vulnerable people (e.g. hospital patients), limiting the access to antibiotics, and ensuring doctors prescribe an appropriate antibiotic at the correct strength and for the correct duration. Strict hygiene protocols and reporting of infections has helped reduce MRSA transmission in the UK (right).

In some countries, antibiotics are fed to livestock to promote growth and prevent disease. The resistant bacteria are passed on to people through consumption of meat that has not been handled or cooked properly, or from eating produce where animal faecal material containing the resistant bacteria has been used as fertiliser.

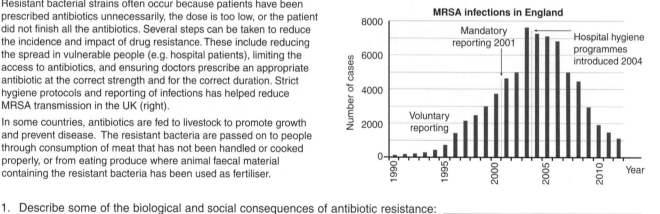

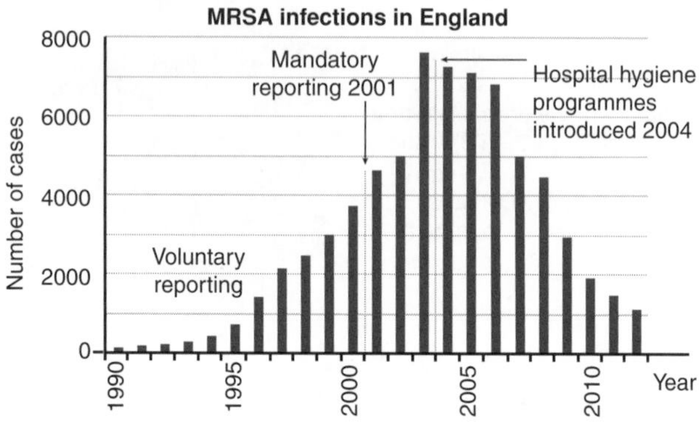
MRSA infections in England
Number of cases
8000
6000
4000
2000
0
Mandatory reporting 2001
Hospital hygiene programmes introduced 2004
Voluntary reporting
1990
1995
2000
2005
2010
Year

1. Describe some of the biological and social consequences of antibiotic resistance: ______

2. Using the example of MRSA in the UK, explain how the incidence and spread of resistant strains can be reduced: ______

© 2015 BIOZONE International
ISBN:978-1-927309-31-5
Photocopying Prohibited

178 Chapter Review

Summarise what you know about this topic under the headings provided. You can draw diagrams or mind maps, or write short notes to organise your thoughts. Use the images and hints to help you and refer back to the introduction to check the points covered:

Types of disease:

HINT: What is disease? How do infectious and non-infectious diseases differ?

Antibiotics:

HINT: How does penicillin act on bacteria? How does antibiotic resistance arise and spread?

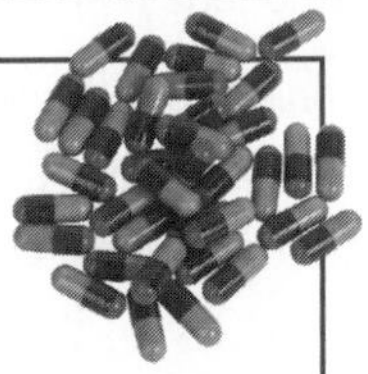

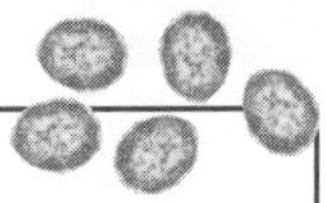

Pathogens and disease:

HINT: Describe causes, transmission, and control of cholera, malaria, TB, HIV/AIDS, smallpox, and measles.

© 2015 **BIOZONE** International
ISBN: 978-1-927309-31-5
Photocopying Prohibited

179 KEY TERMS AND IDEAS: Did You Get It?

1. Test your vocabulary by matching each term to its definition, as identified by its preceding letter code.

antibiotic	A	Any disease caused by the invasion of a host by a pathogen which grows and multiplies in the body and is transmissible to others.
antibiotic resistance	B	A non-infectious disease where there is uncontrolled cell growth in the lungs resulting in a tumour.
bacteria	C	A substance that can kill bacteria or inhibit their growth.
disease	D	The passing of an infectious disease from an infected individual to another individual.
horizontal gene transfer	E	A disease-causing organism.
infectious disease	F	The exchange of genetic material from one individual to another by mechanisms other than the vertical transmission. An important mechanism in the evolution of antibiotic resistance.
lung cancer	G	The ability of bacteria to grow in the presence of a chemical (drug) that would normally kill them or limit their growth.
mutation	H	A non-infectious disease caused by a mutation to the gene coding for the protein haemoglobin. It causes deformed red blood cells, which have limited ability to carry oxygen and clump together causing circulatory problems.
non-infectious disease	I	A non-cellular obligate intracellular parasite, requiring a living host to reproduce. Does not respond to antibiotics.
pathogen	J	A change in the DNA sequence of an organism. An important process in the development of antibiotic resistance in bacteria.
penicillin	K	An abnormal condition of the body when bodily functions are impaired.
sickle cell disease	L	A single celled microorganism surrounded by a cell wall containing the substance peptidoglycan. Some are pathogens responsible for serious diseases in humans.
transmission	M	An antibiotic that works by inhibiting cross bridge formation in the cell walls of gram positive bacteria.
virus	N	A type of disease that cannot be transmitted between individuals.

2. The table below lists some infectious diseases. Complete the table by naming the type of pathogen which causes the disease (bacteria, virus, protoctist), and the specific name of the pathogen.

Name of disease	Type of pathogen	Name of pathogen
Cholera		
Malaria		
TB		
HIV/AIDS		
Small pox		
Measles		

3. An agar plate with a bacterial lawn was used to test the effectiveness of different antibiotics at inhibiting growth. Six paper discs impregnated with six different antibiotics were placed on the law. The result after 48 hours incubation is shown:

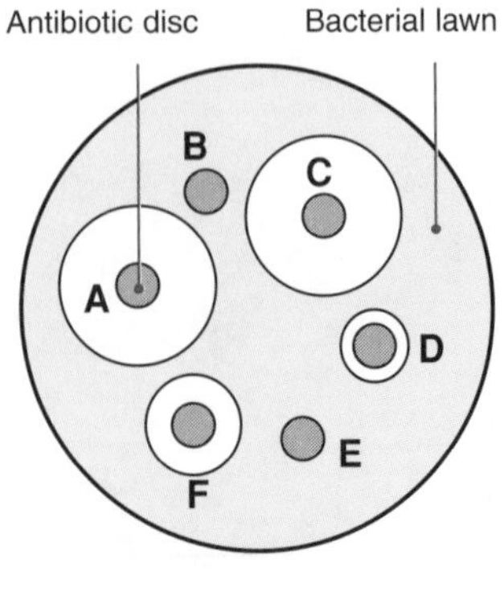
Antibiotic disc
Bacterial lawn
A
B
C
D
E
F

(a) Which antibiotic(s) were the most effective? ______

(b) Which antibiotics were the least effective? ______

(c) Antibiotics, A, C, D, and F are from the penicillin family of antibiotics. What does this tell you about the bacteria involved in this test?

______

______

© 2015 BIOZONE International
ISBN:978-1-927309-31-5
Photocopying Prohibited

Topic 11

Immunity

Key terms

active immunity
antibody (=immunoglobulin)
antigen
autoimmune disease
B cell (=B lymphocyte)
cell-mediated immunity
clonal selection
cytokines
humoral immunity
immunity
immunological memory
infection
inflammation
leucocyte
lymphocyte
macrophage
monoclonal antibody
non-specific defences (=innate immunity)
passive immunity
pathogen
phagocyte
primary response
secondary response
specific (=adaptive) immune response
T cell (=T lymphocyte)
vaccination

The immune system

Learning outcomes

		Learning outcome	Activity number
☐	1	Understand that the body has several levels of defence against infection. Distinguish between specific and non-specific responses to pathogens.	180
☐	2	Describe the origin and mode of action of phagocytes (phagocytic white blood cells) to include monocytes and neutrophils.	181
☐	3	Distinguish between the mode of action of T-lymphocytes (T-cells), which are responsible for cell-mediated immunity, and B-lymphocytes (B-cells), which are responsible for humoral (antibody-mediated) immunity.	182 183
☐	4	Describe and explain the use of differential blood cell counts in the diagnosis of infectious diseases and leukaemias.	180
☐	5	Explain what is meant by the immune response, including reference to the recognition of specific antigens and the development of self tolerance (distinguishing self from non-self).	183
☐	6	Explain the role of memory cells in long term immunity and explain how immunological memory develops.	183
☐	7	With reference to myasthenia gravis, explain how the self-recognition of the immune system can sometimes fail, leading to disease.	184

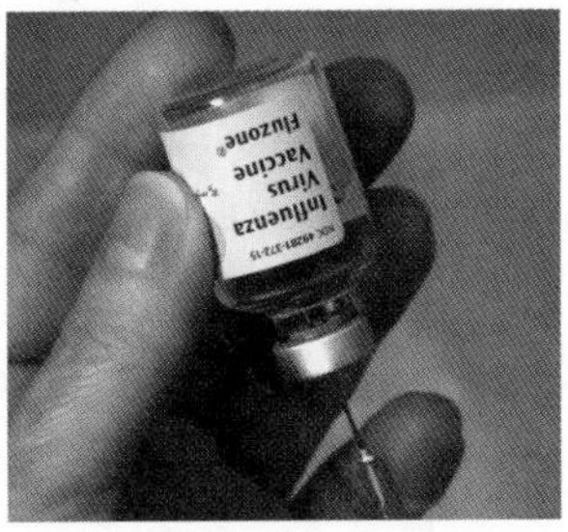
Influenza
Virus
Vaccine
Fluzone
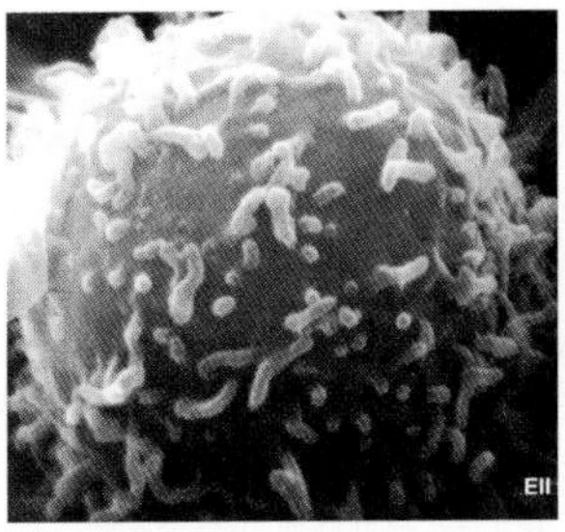
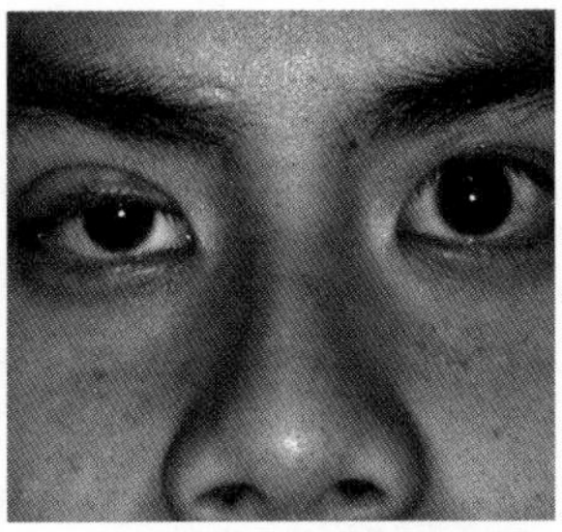

Antibodies and vaccination

Learning outcomes

		Learning outcome	Activity number
☐	8	Describe the structure of antibodies, and relate this to their mode of action and function in the immune response.	180 182 183 185
☐	9	Describe the hybridoma method for the production of monoclonal antibodies.	186
☐	10	Describe the use of monoclonal antibodies for diagnosing and treating disease.	186 187
☐	11	Using examples, distinguish between naturally acquired and artificially acquired immunity and between active and passive immunity. Distinguish the primary and secondary immune responses.	188
☐	12	Explain the basis of vaccination and explain the role of vaccination in the control of infectious disease.	189
☐	13	Discuss why vaccination was able to successfully eradicate smallpox. Explain why vaccination has not resulted in the similar eradication of other diseases, with reference to measles, TB, malaria, and cholera.	189

180 The Body's Defences

Key Idea: The human body has a tiered system of defences against disease-causing organisms.

The body has several lines of defence against disease causing organisms (**pathogens**). The first line of defence consists of an external barrier to stop pathogens entering the body. If this fails, a second line of defence targets any foreign bodies (including pathogens) that enter. Lastly, the immune system provides specific or targeted defence against the pathogen. The ability to ward off disease through the various defence mechanisms is called **resistance**. **Non-specific** (or innate) **resistance** protects against a broad range of pathogens and is provided by the first and second lines of defence. **Specific resistance** (the immune response) is the third tier of defence and is specific to a particular pathogen. Part of the immune response involves the production of **antibodies** (proteins that identify and neutralise foreign material). Antibodies recognise and respond to **antigens**, foreign or harmful substances that cause an immune response.

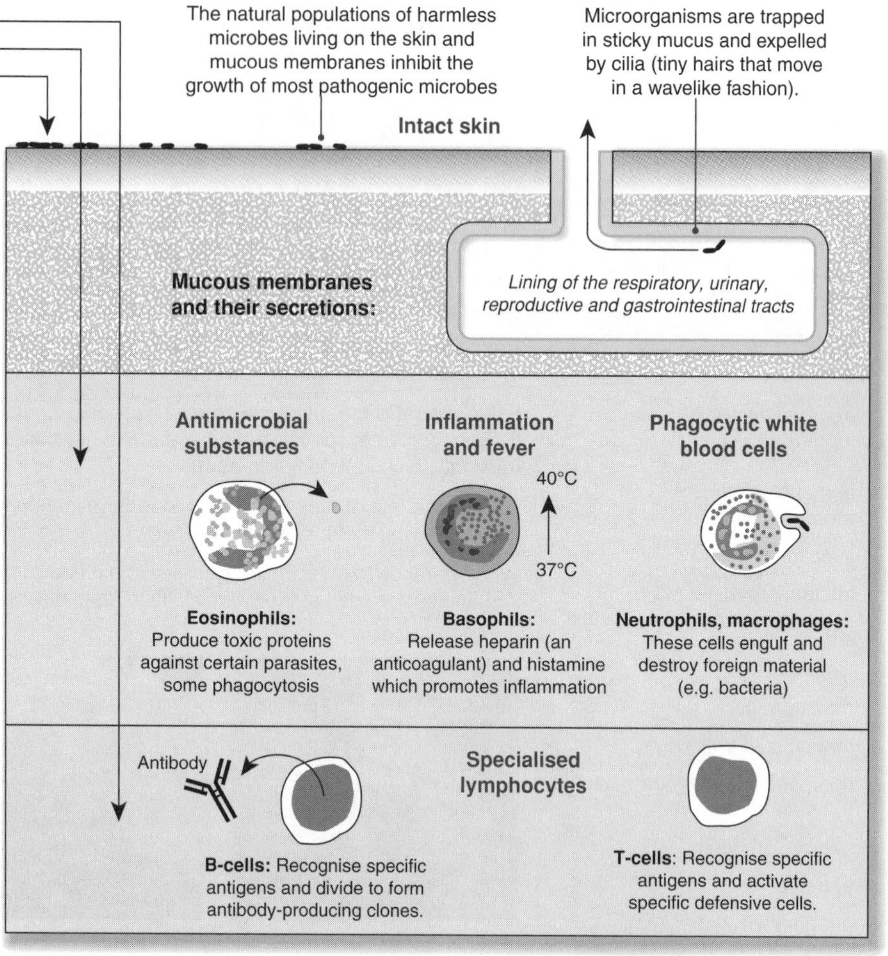

Most microorganisms find it difficult to get inside the body. If they succeed, they face a range of other defences.
The natural populations of harmless microbes living on the skin and mucous membranes inhibit the growth of most pathogenic microbes
Microorganisms are trapped in sticky mucus and expelled by cilia (tiny hairs that move in a wavelike fashion).
Intact skin
Mucous membranes and their secretions:
Lining of the respiratory, urinary, reproductive and gastrointestinal tracts
Antimicrobial substances
Inflammation and fever
Phagocytic white blood cells
40°C
37°C
Eosinophils: Produce toxic proteins against certain parasites, some phagocytosis
Basophils: Release heparin (an anticoagulant) and histamine which promotes inflammation
Neutrophils, macrophages: These cells engulf and destroy foreign material (e.g. bacteria)
Antibody
Specialised lymphocytes
B-cells: Recognise specific antigens and divide to form antibody-producing clones.
T-cells: Recognise specific antigens and activate specific defensive cells.

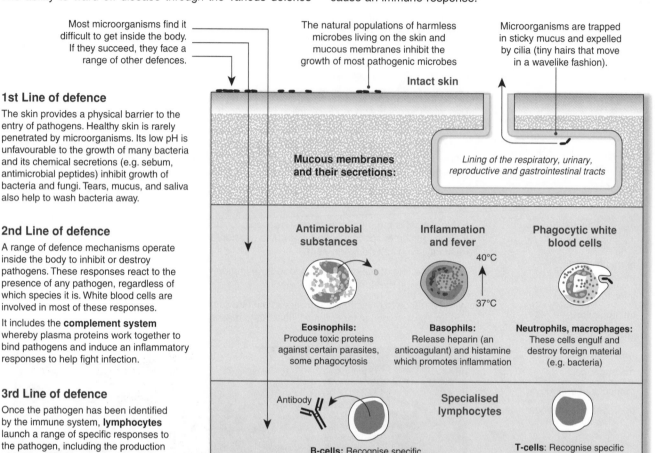

1st Line of defence

The skin provides a physical barrier to the entry of pathogens. Healthy skin is rarely penetrated by microorganisms. Its low pH is unfavourable to the growth of many bacteria and its chemical secretions (e.g. sebum, antimicrobial peptides) inhibit growth of bacteria and fungi. Tears, mucus, and saliva also help to wash bacteria away.

2nd Line of defence

A range of defence mechanisms operate inside the body to inhibit or destroy pathogens. These responses react to the presence of any pathogen, regardless of which species it is. White blood cells are involved in most of these responses.

It includes the **complement system** whereby plasma proteins work together to bind pathogens and induce an inflammatory responses to help fight infection.

3rd Line of defence

Once the pathogen has been identified by the immune system, **lymphocytes** launch a range of specific responses to the pathogen, including the production of **antibodies**. Each type of antibody is produced by a B cell clone and is specific against a particular antigen.

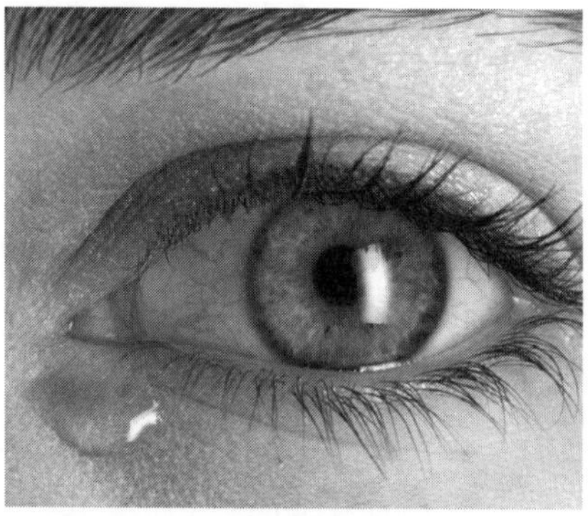

Tears contain antimicrobial substances as well as washing contaminants from the eyes.

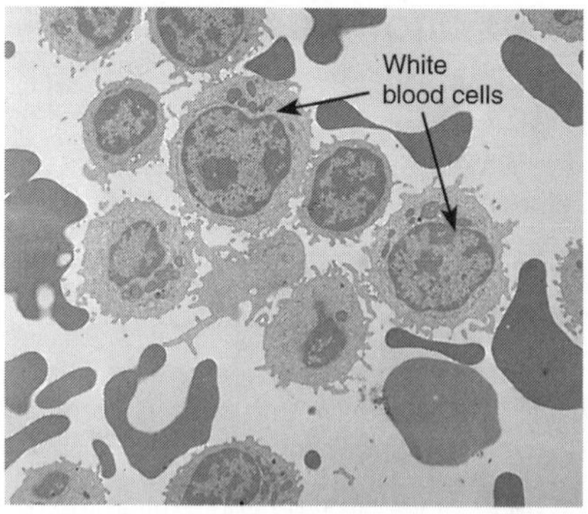

White blood cells

EII

A range of white blood cells (arrowed above) form the second line of defence.

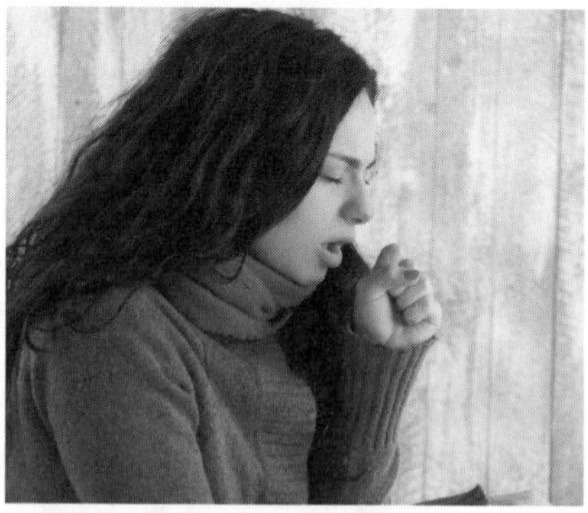

Wikimedia Commons

Expulsive reflexes such as coughing and vomiting help remove pathogens from the body.

1. Distinguish between specific and non-specific resistance: ______________________________

____

____

____

____

© 2015 BIOZONE International
ISBN:978-1-927309-31-5
Photocopying Prohibited

WBC counts can be diagnostic

White blood cells or leucocytes (box, right) play an important role in protecting the body against pathogens and other foreign bodies. In a healthy person, white blood cells (WBCs) occur in predictable ratios. Infection results in elevated numbers of WBCs, particularly neutrophils,whereas a change in the relative proportions of different WBCs can be diagnostic of specific diseases. An analysis of the relative proportions of the different types of white blood cells is called a **differential white cell count**.

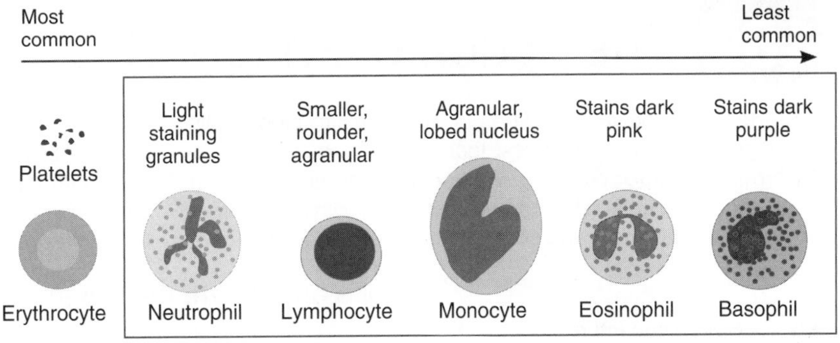

Most common
Least common
Platelets
Erythrocyte
Light staining granules
Smaller, rounder, agranular
Agranular, lobed nucleus
Stains dark pink
Stains dark purple
Neutrophil
Lymphocyte
Monocyte
Eosinophil
Basophil

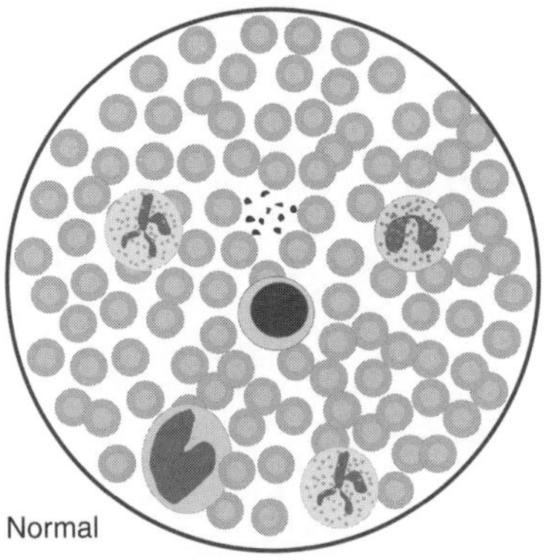

Normal

A normal blood smear. White blood cells normally make up only 1% of total blood volume (4-11 × 10^9 L^{-1}) and most of these are neutrophils. A high WBC count, or a change in the ratio of different WBCs, can indicate infection, inflammation, trauma or allergy.

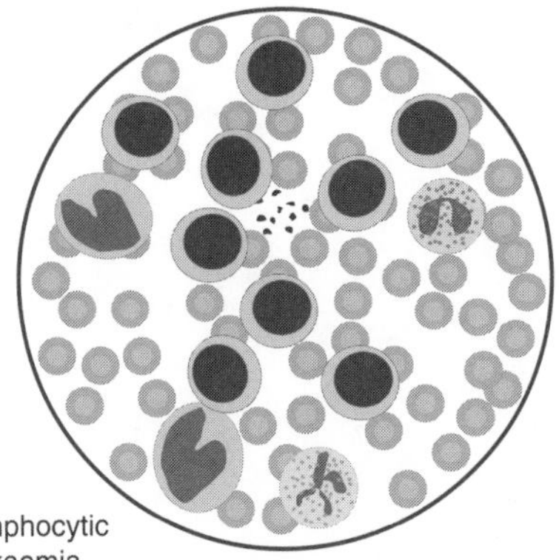

Lymphocytic leukaemia

A blood smear from a patient with leukaemia, a type of cancer in which the number of white blood cells increases greatly. Different types of leukaemia are characterised by proliferation of different types of WBC, commonly lymphocytes or monocytes. The WBCs are often non-functional.

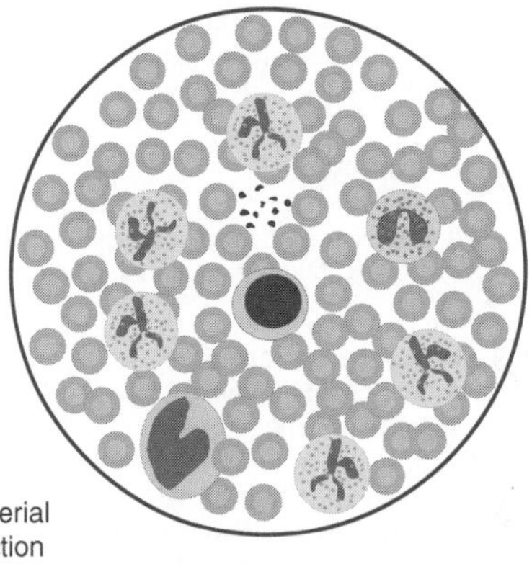

Bacterial infection

A blood smear from someone with a bacterial infection. The body produces more WBCs to fight off the invading pathogen. Specifically a person with an infection will have higher levels of mature neutrophils and band neutrophils (an immature form of a neutrophil).

2. How does the skin act as a barrier to prevent pathogens entering the body? ____________________

____

____

____

3. Explain the value of a three tiered system of defence against microbial invasion: ____________________

____

____

4. The appearance of white blood cells varies depending on the maturity of the white blood cell. For example, in band neutrophils, which are a common indicator of infection, the nucleus is curved, rather than lobular. Study the blood smears and answer the following questions.

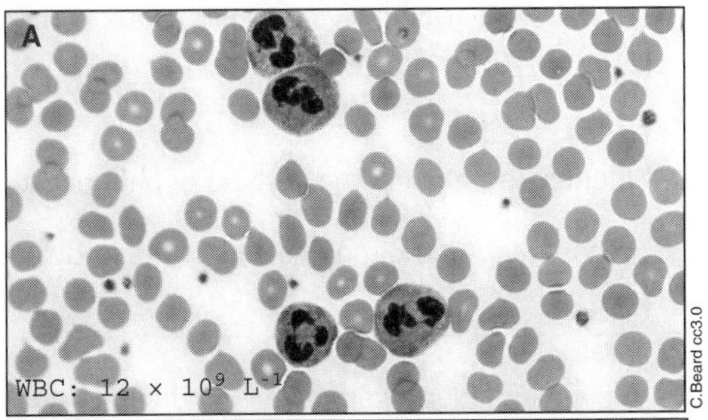

A
WBC: 12 × 10⁹ L⁻¹
C.Beard cc3.0

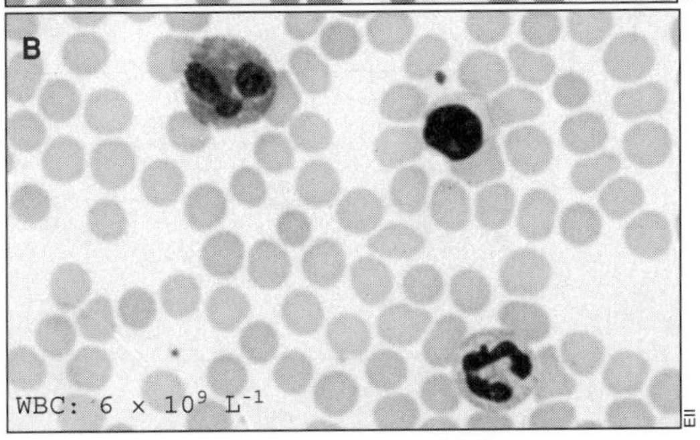

B
WBC: 6 × 10⁹ L⁻¹
Ell

(a) Identify the main type of white blood cell present in photo A:

____

(b) What does this blood smear tell you about the health of the person it was taken from?

____

____

(c) Study the blood smear labelled B. State whether you think the slide is normal or abnormal:

____

(d) Give a reason for the answer you gave in (c):

____

____

© 2015 **BIOZONE** International
ISBN: 978-1-927309-31-5
Photocopying Prohibited

181 The Action of Phagocytes

Key Idea: Phagocytes are types of mobile white blood cells that ingest microbes and digest them by phagocytosis.

All types of **phagocytes** (e.g. neutrophils and macrophages) are white blood cells. These specialised cells have receptors on their surfaces that can detect foreign or antigenic material, such as microbes. They then ingest the microbes and digest them by **phagocytosis.** During many kinds of infections, the total number of white blood cells increases by two to four times the normal number. The ratio of various white blood cell types changes during the course of an infection.

How a phagocyte destroys microbes

1 Detection and interaction
Microbe coated in opsonins is detected by the phagocyte and attaches to it. Opsonins are molecules in the blood and coat foreign material (e.g. a bacterial cell), marking it as a target for phagocytosis.

2 Engulfment
The opsonin markers trigger engulfment of the microbe by the phagocyte. The microbe is taken in by endocytosis.

3 Phagosome forms
A phagosome forms, enclosing the microbe in a membrane.

4 Fusion with lysosome
Phagosome fuses with a lysosome containing powerful antimicrobial proteins. The fusion forms a phagolysosome.

5 Digestion
The microbe is broken down into its chemical constituents.

6 Discharge
Indigestible material is discharged from the phagocyte.

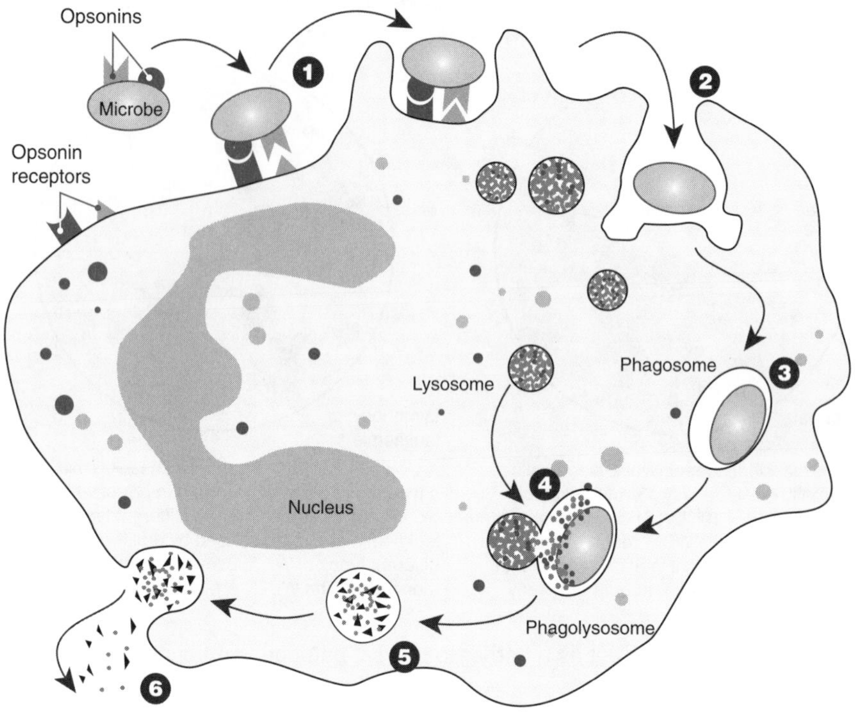

Opsonins
Microbe
Opsonin receptors
1
2
3
4
5
6
Phagosome
Lysosome
Nucleus
Phagolysosome

Neutrophils

Neutrophils, named for their neutral staining cytoplasm, are the most abundant type of white blood cell, constituting up to three-quarters of all white blood cells. Neutrophils are one of four types of granulocytes, distinguished by the granular appearance of the cytoplasm and their lobed nucleus.

When activated, neutrophils become highly mobile and amoeboid-like. They are some of the first immune cells to arrive at an infection site, attracted by microbial chemicals and by **cytokines** (proteins involved in cell signalling) expressed by macrophages and damaged endothelial cells. This movement to a site based on a gradient in chemical signals is called **chemotaxis**.

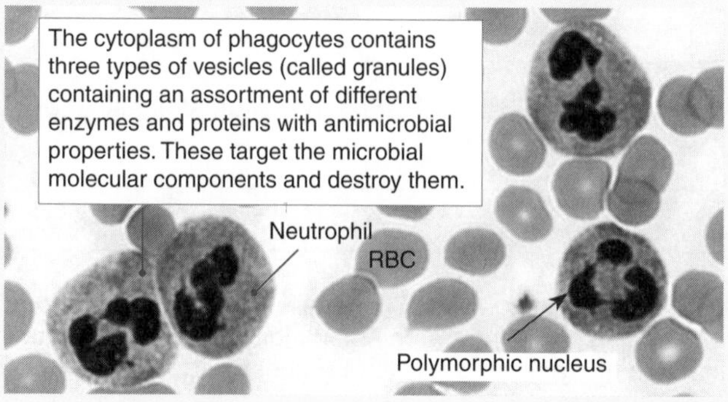

The cytoplasm of phagocytes contains three types of vesicles (called granules) containing an assortment of different enzymes and proteins with antimicrobial properties. These target the microbial molecular components and destroy them.
Neutrophil
RBC
Polymorphic nucleus

1. Identify the most common type of phagocytic white blood cell: ______________________

2. What is the role of chemotaxis in the body's response to infection? ______________________

____

3. How can a blood sample be used to diagnose a microbial infection (without looking for the microbes themselves)?

____

____

4. Explain the role of opsonins and phagocyte receptors in enhancing phagocytosis: ______________________

____

____

____

© 2015 BIOZONE International
ISBN:978-1-927309-31-5
Photocopying Prohibited

182 The Immune System

Key Idea: The defence provided by the immune system is based on its ability to respond specifically against foreign substances and hold a memory of this response.

There are two main components of the immune system: the humoral and the cell-mediated responses. They work separately and together to provide protection against disease. The **humoral immune response** is associated with the serum (the non-cellular part of the blood) and involves the action of antibodies secreted by B-cell lymphocytes. Antibodies are found in extracellular fluids including lymph, plasma, and mucus secretions. They protect the body against viruses, and bacteria and their toxins. The **cell-mediated immune response** is associated with the production of specialised lymphocytes called **T-cells**.

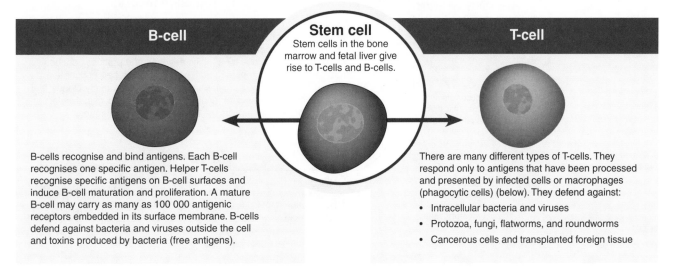

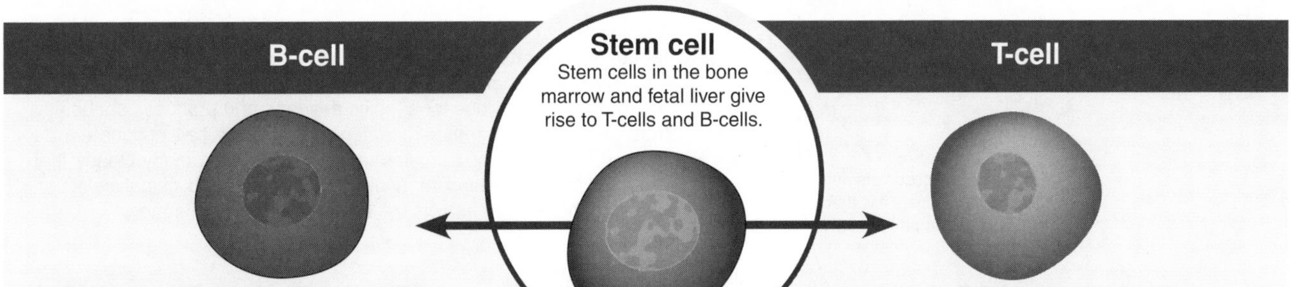
B-cell
Stem cell
Stem cells in the bone marrow and fetal liver give rise to T-cells and B-cells.
T-cell

B-cells recognise and bind antigens. Each B-cell recognises one specific antigen. Helper T-cells recognise specific antigens on B-cell surfaces and induce B-cell maturation and proliferation. A mature B-cell may carry as many as 100 000 antigenic receptors embedded in its surface membrane. B-cells defend against bacteria and viruses outside the cell and toxins produced by bacteria (free antigens).

There are many different types of T-cells. They respond only to antigens that have been processed and presented by infected cells or macrophages (phagocytic cells) (below). They defend against:

- Intracellular bacteria and viruses
- Protozoa, fungi, flatworms, and roundworms
- Cancerous cells and transplanted foreign tissue

B-cell and T-cell activation

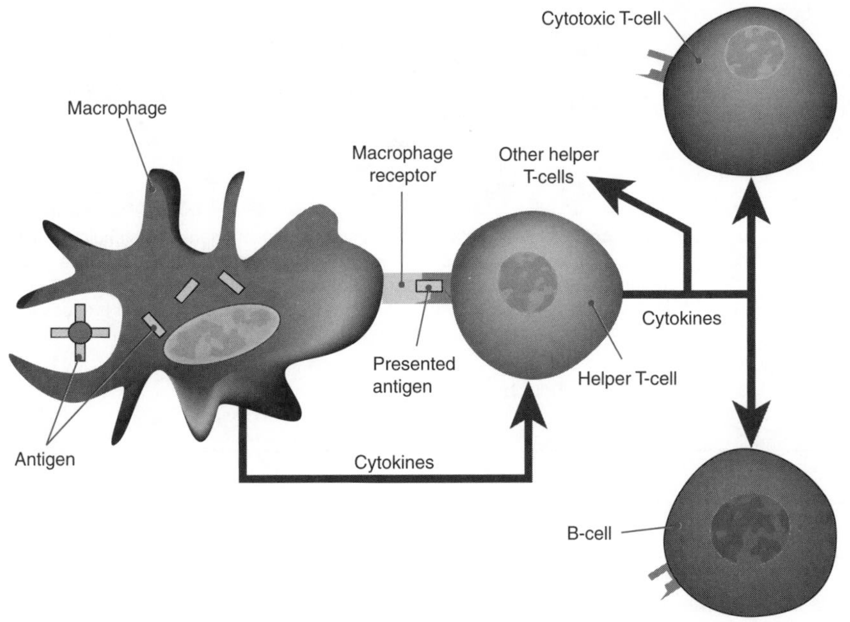
Cytotoxic T-cell
Macrophage
Macrophage receptor
Other helper T-cells
Cytokines
Presented antigen
Helper T-cell
Antigen
Cytokines
B-cell

Helper T-cells are activated by direct cell-to-cell signalling and by signalling to nearby cells using **cytokines** from macrophages.

Macrophages ingest antigens, process them, and present them on the cell surface where they are recognised by helper T-cells. The helper T-cell binds to the antigen and to the macrophage receptor, which leads to activation of the helper T-cell.

The macrophage also produces and releases cytokines, which enhance T-cell activation. The activated T-cell then releases more cytokines which causes the proliferation of other helper T-cells (positive feedback) and helps to activate cytotoxic T-cells and antibody-producing B-cells.

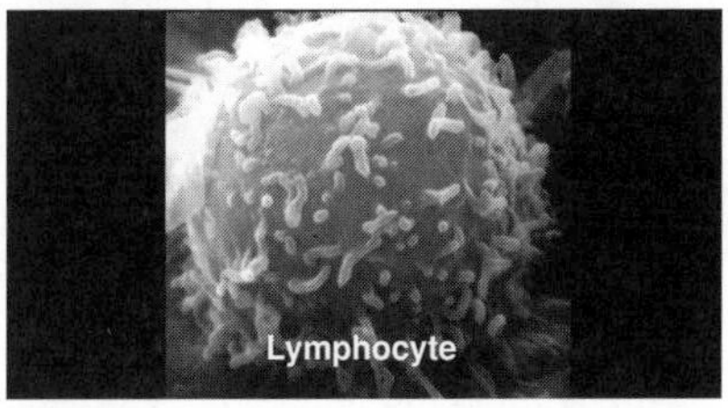
Lymphocyte

1. Describe the general action of the two major divisions in the immune system:

   (a) Humoral immune system: ___

   (b) Cell-mediated immune system: ___

2. Explain how an antigen causes the activation and proliferation of T-cells and B-cells: ___

© 2015 **BIOZONE** International
ISBN: 978-1-927309-31-5
Photocopying Prohibited

183 Clonal Selection

Key Idea: Clonal selection theory explains how lymphocytes can respond to a large and unpredictable range of antigens.

The **clonal selection theory** explains how the immune system can respond to the large and unpredictable range of potential antigens in the environment. The diagram below describes clonal selection after antigen exposure for B cells. In the same way, a T cell stimulated by a specific antigen will multiply and develop into different types of T cells. Clonal selection and differentiation of lymphocytes provide the basis for **immunological memory.**

Clonal selection theory

Millions of B cells form during development. Antigen recognition is randomly generated, so collectively they can recognise many antigens, including those that have never been encountered. Each B cell has receptors on its surface for specific antigens and produces antibodies that correspond to these receptors. When a B cell encounters its antigen, it responds by proliferating and producing many clones that produce the same kind of antibody. This is called clonal selection because the antigen selects the B cells that will proliferate.

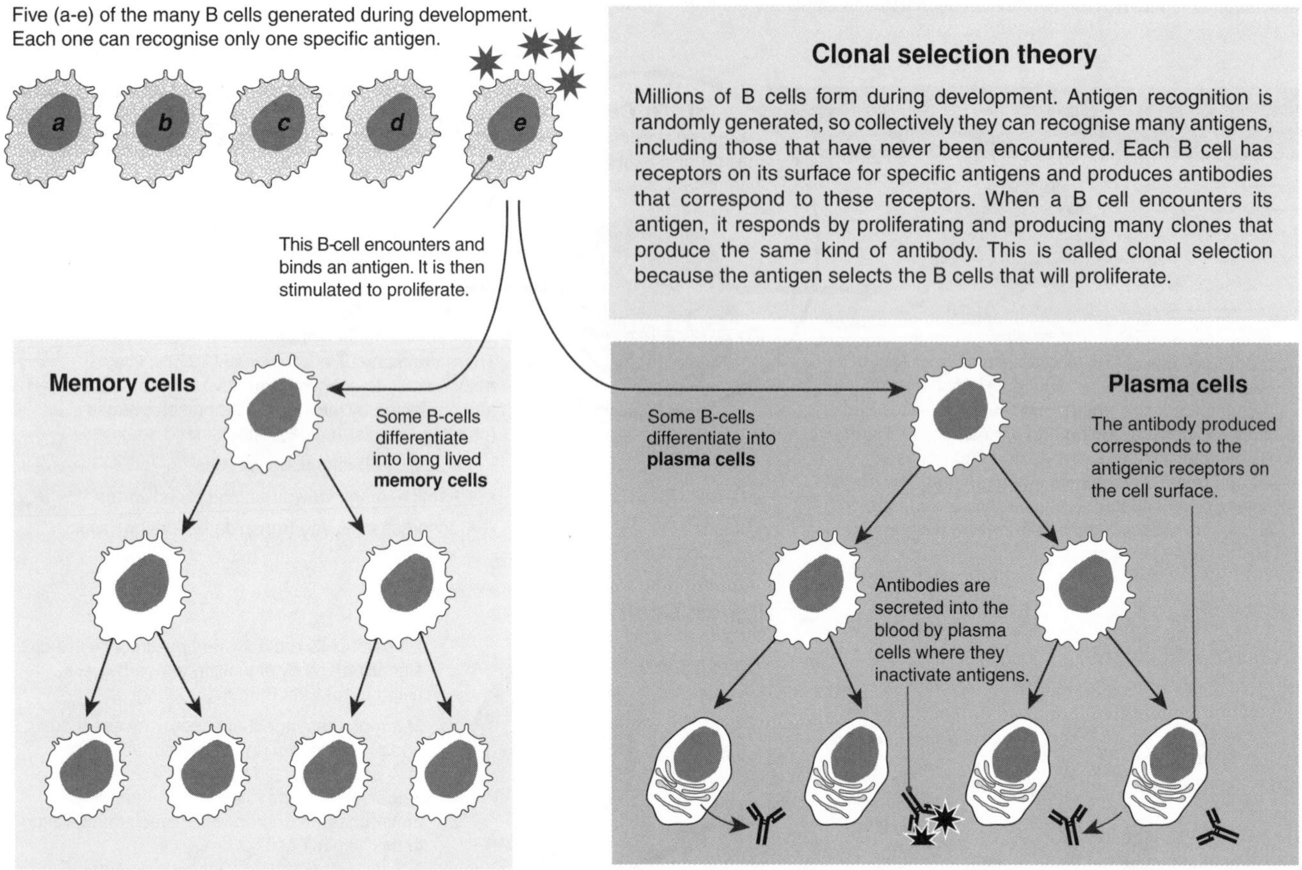
Five (a-e) of the many B cells generated during development. Each one can recognise only one specific antigen.
a
b
c
d
e
This B-cell encounters and binds an antigen. It is then stimulated to proliferate.
Memory cells
Some B-cells differentiate into long lived memory cells
Some B-cells differentiate into plasma cells
Plasma cells
The antibody produced corresponds to the antigenic receptors on the cell surface.
Antibodies are secreted into the blood by plasma cells where they inactivate antigens.

Some B cells differentiate into long lived **memory cells**. These are retained in the lymph nodes to provide future immunity (**immunological memory**). In the event of a second infection, memory B cells react more quickly and vigorously than the initial B cell reaction to the first infection.

Plasma cells secrete antibodies specific to the antigen that stimulated their development. Each plasma cell lives for only a few days, but can produce about 2000 antibody molecules per second. Note that during development, any B cells that react to the body's own antigens are selectively destroyed in a process that leads to **self tolerance** (acceptance of the body's own tissues).

1. Describe how clonal selection results in the proliferation of one particular B cell:

____

____

____

2. (a) What is the function of the plasma cells in the immune system response? _______________________

____

(b) What is the significance of B cells producing antibodies that correspond to (match) their antigenic receptors?

____

____

3. (a) Explain the basis of **immunological memory**: _______________________

____

____

(b) Why are memory B cells able to respond so rapidly to an encounter with an antigen long after an initial infection?

____

© 2015 BIOZONE International
ISBN:978-1-927309-31-5
Photocopying Prohibited

184 Autoimmune Diseases

Key Idea: Autoimmune diseases are caused when the body's immune system begins to attack the body's own tissues.

The immune system normally distinguishes self from non-self (foreign antigens). However, when the normal self recognition system fails the immune system may attack its own cells or tissues. This is called an **autoimmune disease**. Numerous diseases, including myasthenia gravis, multiple sclerosis, rheumatoid arthritis, and type 1 diabete are the result of immune system malfunctions. The exact mechanisms behind autoimmune diseases are not fully understood, but pathogens or drugs may play a role in triggering an autoimmune response in someone who already has a genetic predisposition. The reactions are similar to those that occur in allergies, except that in autoimmune disorders, the hypersensitivity response is to the body itself, rather than to an outside substance.

Myasthenia gravis

Myasthenia gravis (MG) is caused by a breakdown in the communication between nerves and muscles. Nerves release chemicals (neurotransmitters) that bind to specific receptor sites on muscles stimulating them to contract. In MG, a person's own antibodies bind to the receptor sites on the muscles and block them, and some of the fibres in the muscle do not receive the stimulus strength required to contract. This results in muscle weakness and fatigue. Drooping eyelids (ptosis) is a common first symptom in MG sufferers (below), but it also affects muscles in the face, throat, neck, and limbs. MG has no cure, but can be treated by surgery, neurotransmitter inhibitors, and immunosuppressant drugs to reduce the autoimmune response.

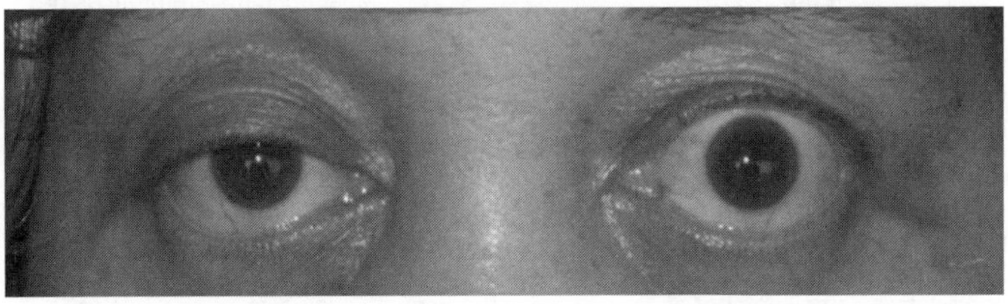

Mohankumar Kurukumbi *et al* cc2.0

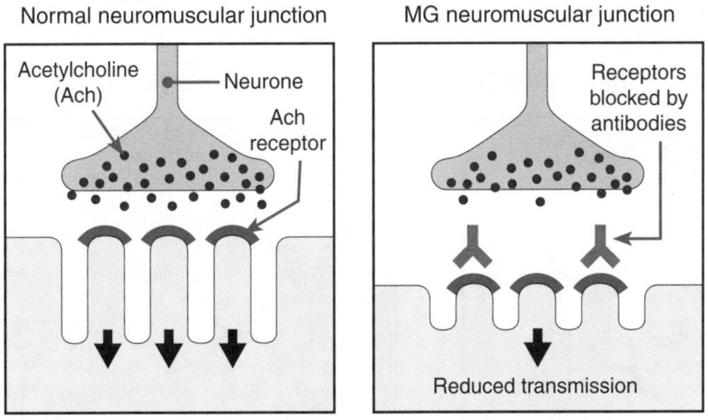
Normal neuromuscular junction
MG neuromuscular junction
Acetylcholine (Ach)
Neurone
Ach receptor
Receptors blocked by antibodies
Reduced transmission

In MG, antibodies bind to the receptors on the post synaptic junction preventing the neurotransmitter (acetylcholine) from binding. The excitatory effects of acetylcholine are reduced, and muscle contraction is impaired. Treatment often uses drugs that prevent acetylcholine from being broken down so it remains at the neuromuscular junction longer than usual. This allows more receptor sites to be activated.

Other immune system disorders

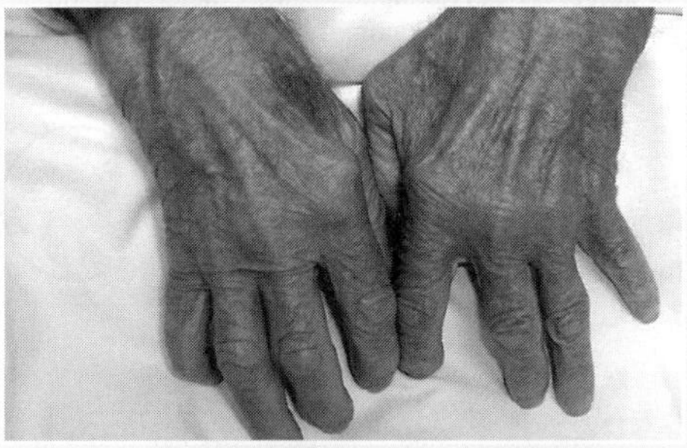

UCSD School of Medicine: Charles Goldberg

Rheumatoid arthritis is an autoimmune disease that causes joint inflammation, usually in the hands and feet, and results in destruction of cartilage and painful, swollen joints. The disease often begins in adulthood, but can also occur in children or the elderly. Rheumatoid arthritis affects more women than men and is treated with anti-inflammatory and immunosuppressant drugs, and physiotherapy.

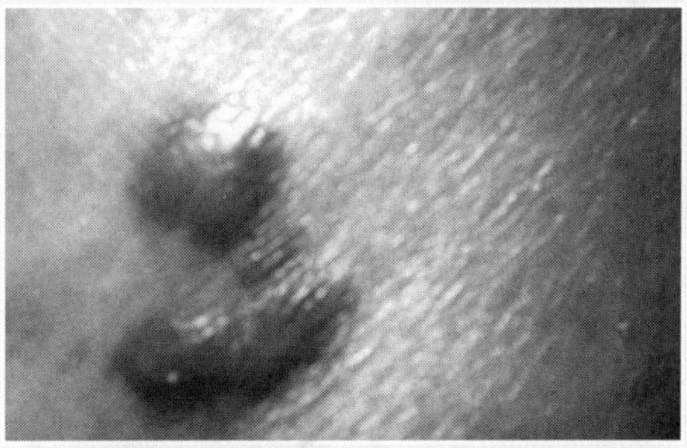

CDC

Lacking a sufficient immune response is called immune deficiency, and may be either congenital (present at birth) or acquired as a result of drugs, cancer, or infectious agents (e.g. HIV infection). HIV causes AIDS, which results in a steady destruction of the immune system. Sufferers then succumb to opportunistic infections and rare cancers such as Kaposi's sarcoma (above).

1. Explain why autoimmune diseases can be regarded as an intolerance to self? ______________________

2. Explain the basis of myasthenia gravis: ______________________

3. How does preventing acetylcholine breakdown help to reduce the symptoms of myasthenia gravis? ______________________

© 2015 **BIOZONE** International
ISBN: 978-1-927309-31-5
Photocopying Prohibited

185 Antibodies

Key Idea: Antibodies are large, Y-shaped proteins, made by plasma cells, which destroy specific antigens.

Antibodies and antigens play key roles in the response of the immune system. **Antigens** are foreign molecules which promote a specific immune response. Antigens include pathogenic microbes and their toxins, as well as substances such as pollen grains, blood cell surface molecules, and the surface proteins on transplanted tissues. **Antibodies** (or immunoglobulins) are proteins made in response to antigens. They are secreted from B cells into the plasma where they can recognise, bind to, and help destroy antigens. There are five classes of antibodies, each plays a different role in the immune response. Each type of antibody is specific to only one particular antigen.

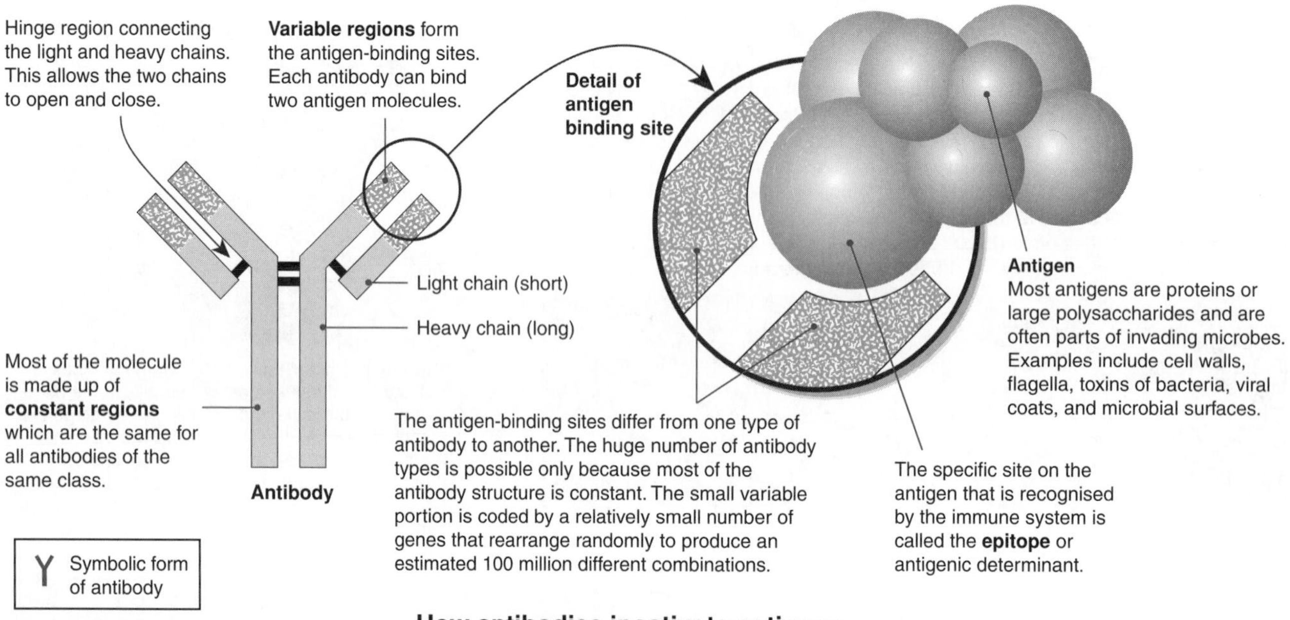
Hinge region connecting the light and heavy chains. This allows the two chains to open and close.
Variable regions form the antigen-binding sites. Each antibody can bind two antigen molecules.
Detail of antigen binding site
Light chain (short)
Heavy chain (long)
Most of the molecule is made up of constant regions which are the same for all antibodies of the same class.
Antibody
Antigen
Most antigens are proteins or large polysaccharides and are often parts of invading microbes. Examples include cell walls, flagella, toxins of bacteria, viral coats, and microbial surfaces.
The antigen-binding sites differ from one type of antibody to another. The huge number of antibody types is possible only because most of the antibody structure is constant. The small variable portion is coded by a relatively small number of genes that rearrange randomly to produce an estimated 100 million different combinations.
The specific site on the antigen that is recognised by the immune system is called the epitope or antigenic determinant.
Y Symbolic form of antibody

How antibodies inactivate antigens

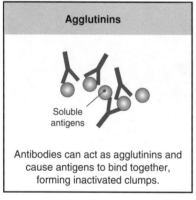

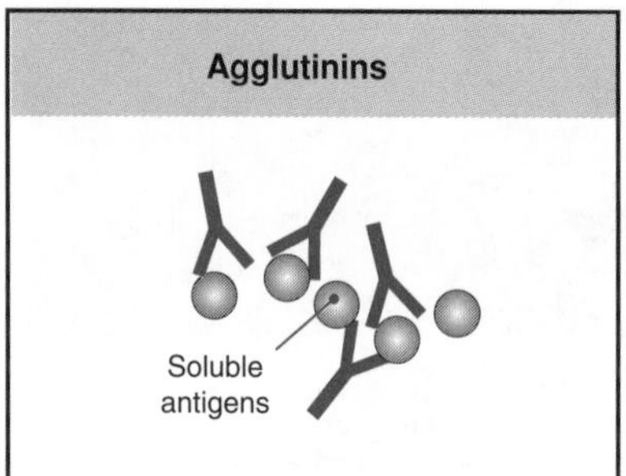
Agglutinins
Soluble antigens

Antibodies can act as agglutinins and cause antigens to bind together, forming inactivated clumps.

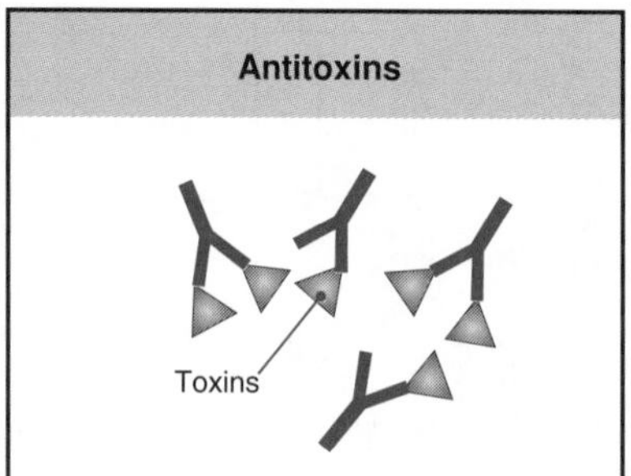
Antitoxins
Toxins

Antibodies can act as antitoxins by binding to toxins and neutralising them.

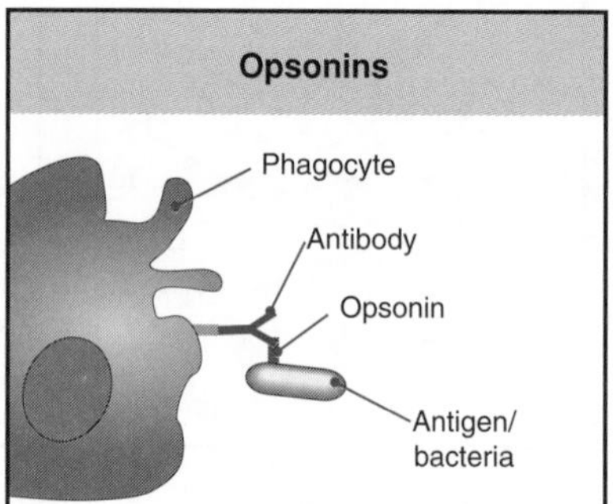
Opsonins
Phagocyte
Antibody
Opsonin
Antigen/ bacteria

Tags foreign cells for destruction by phagocytes.

1. Describe the structure of an antibody, identifying the specific features of its structure that contribute to its function:

___

___

___

2. Explain how the following actions by antibodies enhance the immune systems ability to stop infections:

(a) Acting as agglutinins: ___

___

(b) Acting as antitoxins: ___

___

(c) Working with opsonins: ___

___

© 2015 BIOZONE International
ISBN:978-1-927309-31-5
Photocopying Prohibited

186 Monoclonal Antibodies

Key idea: Monoclonal antibodies are artificially produced antibodies that neutralise specific antigens. They have wide applications in diagnosing and treating disease, in detecting pregnancy, and in food safety tests.

A **monoclonal antibody** is an artificially produced antibody that binds to and neutralises one specific type of antigen. A monoclonal antibody binds an antigen in the same way that a normally produced antibody does. Monoclonal antibodies are produced by stimulating the production of antibody-producing B-cells in mice injected with the antigen. The isolated B-cells are made to fuse with immortal tumour cells, and can be cultured indefinitely in a suitable growing medium. Monoclonal antibodies are useful because they are identical (i.e. clones), they can be produced in large quantities, and they are highly specific. Antibodies produced in this way are used in medical diagnosis and treatment.

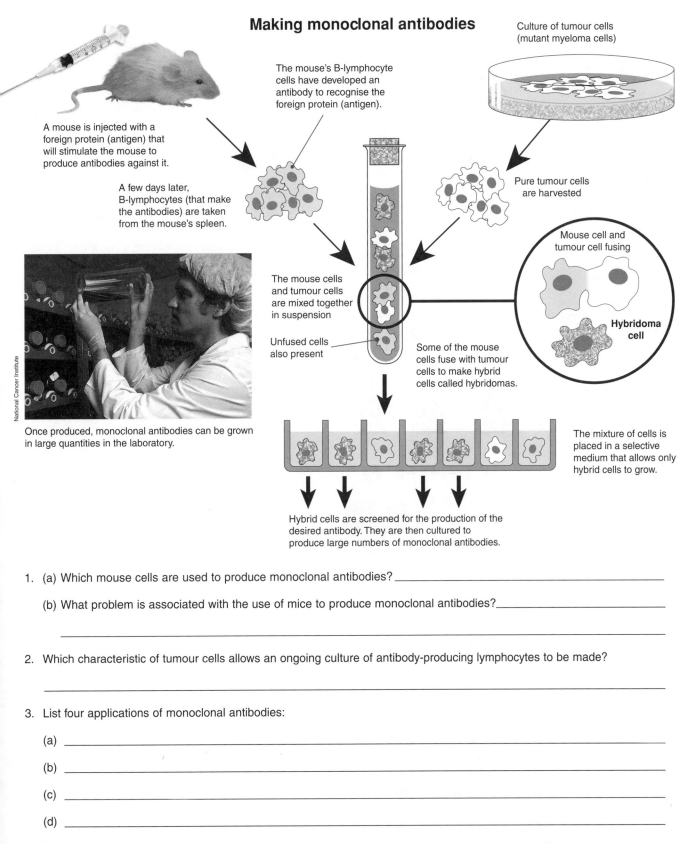

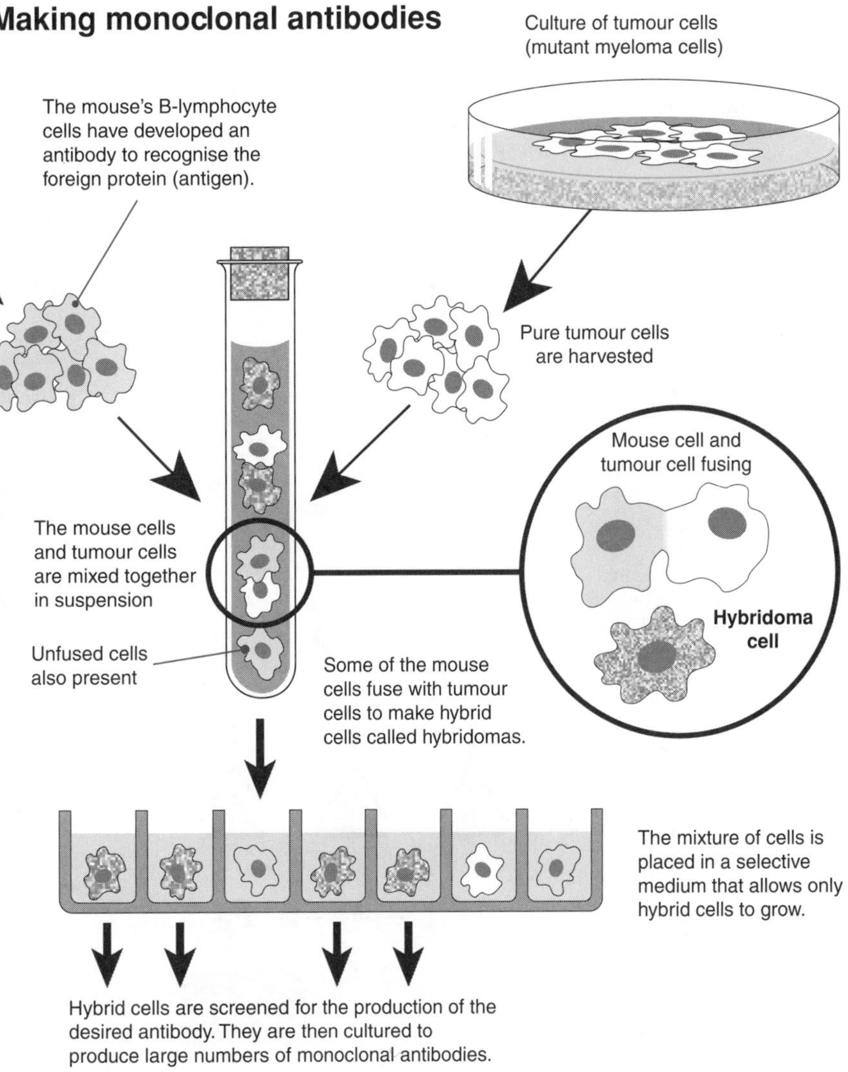
Making monoclonal antibodies
A mouse is injected with a foreign protein (antigen) that will stimulate the mouse to produce antibodies against it.
The mouse's B-lymphocyte cells have developed an antibody to recognise the foreign protein (antigen).
Culture of tumour cells (mutant myeloma cells)
A few days later, B-lymphocytes (that make the antibodies) are taken from the mouse's spleen.
Pure tumour cells are harvested
Mouse cell and tumour cell fusing
Hybridoma cell
The mouse cells and tumour cells are mixed together in suspension
Unfused cells also present
Some of the mouse cells fuse with tumour cells to make hybrid cells called hybridomas.
The mixture of cells is placed in a selective medium that allows only hybrid cells to grow.
Hybrid cells are screened for the production of the desired antibody. They are then cultured to produce large numbers of monoclonal antibodies.

National Cancer Institute

Once produced, monoclonal antibodies can be grown in large quantities in the laboratory.

1. (a) Which mouse cells are used to produce monoclonal antibodies? ____________________

   (b) What problem is associated with the use of mice to produce monoclonal antibodies? ____________________

   ____

2. Which characteristic of tumour cells allows an ongoing culture of antibody-producing lymphocytes to be made?

   ____

3. List four applications of monoclonal antibodies:

   (a) ____________________

   (b) ____________________

   (c) ____________________

   (d) ____________________

© 2015 **BIOZONE** International
ISBN: 978-1-927309-31-5
Photocopying Prohibited

Using monoclonal antibodies to detect HIV

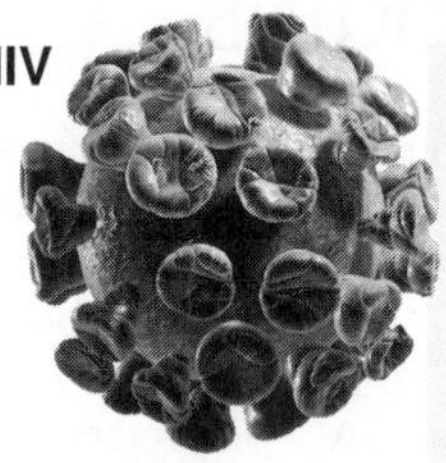

A monoclonal antibody test can be used to detect the presence of HIV (right) in blood serum. An outline of one testing method, using an enzyme-linked colour change reaction, is given below.

The HIV antigen is attached to a testing plate.

Blood serum from the patient being tested is passed over the plate. Any HIV antibodies naturally present in the blood will bind to the antigen. The plate is washed to remove unbound components.

A monoclonal antibody (MA) is passed over the plate. Its antigen is the HIV antibody and it will bind to it if it is present. The MA has an enzyme (E) attached.

The amount of the monoclonal antibody that is bound is proportional to the amount of bound HIV antibody.

A chromogen dye (C) is passed over the plate. A chromogen is able to become coloured and act as a dye after a reaction, e.g. oxidation.

The enzyme catalyses a change in the colour of the chromogen dye substrate. The more intense the colour on the plate, the more HIV antibody present in the patient's serum.

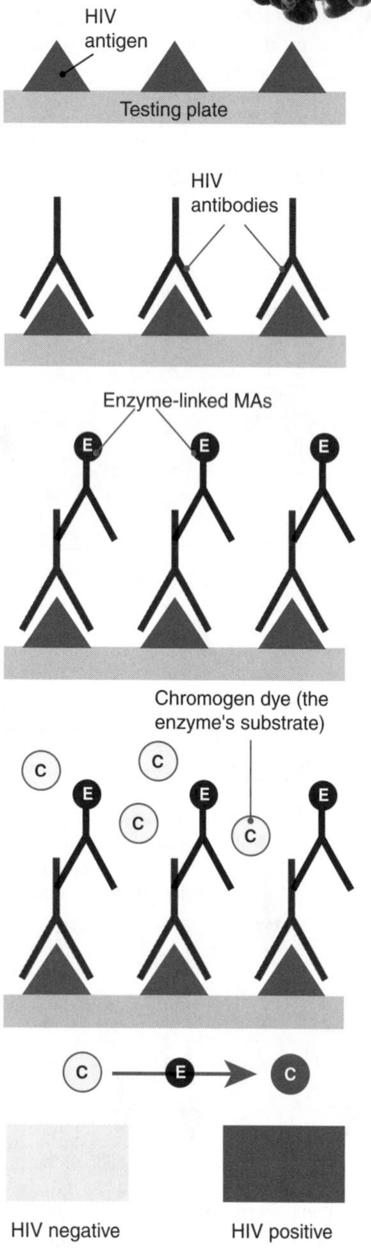
HIV antigen
Testing plate
HIV antibodies
Enzyme-linked MAs
E
Chromogen dye (the enzyme's substrate)
C
HIV negative
HIV positive

Other applications of monoclonal antibodies

Diagnostic uses

- Detecting the presence of pathogens such as *Chlamydia* and streptococcal bacteria, distinguishing between *Herpesvirus* I and II, and diagnosing AIDS.
- Measuring protein, toxin, or drug levels in serum.
- Blood and tissue typing.
- Detection of antibiotic residues in milk.
- Pregnancy testing.

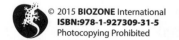

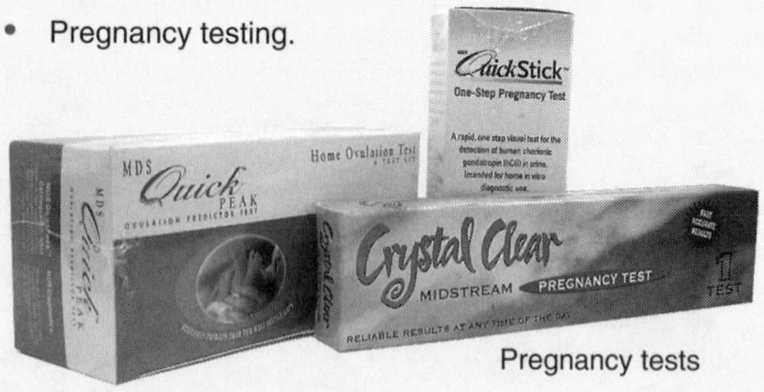
QuickStick
One-Step Pregnancy Test
MDS Quick PEAK
Home Ovulation Test
Crystal Clear
MIDSTREAM
PREGNANCY TEST

Pregnancy tests

Therapeutic uses

- Neutralising endotoxins produced by bacteria in blood infections.
- Used to prevent organ rejection, e.g. in kidney transplants, by interfering with the T-cells involved with the rejection of transplanted tissue.
- Used in the treatment of some auto-immune disorders such as rheumatoid arthritis and allergic asthma. The monoclonal antibodies bind to and inactivate factors involved in the cascade leading to the inflammatory response.
- Immunodetection and immunotherapy of cancer. Herceptin is a monoclonal antibody for the targeted treatment of breast cancer. Herceptin recognises receptor proteins on the outside of cancer cells and binds to them. The immune system can then identify the antibodies as foreign and destroy the cell.
- Inhibition of platelet clumping, which is used to prevent reclogging of coronary arteries in patients who have undergone angioplasty. The monoclonal antibodies bind to the receptors on the platelet surface that are normally linked by fibrinogen during the clotting process.

4. (a) The test described above does not directly measure the HIV virus. What does it measure? ______________________

____

(b) Explain how the presence of the substance in (a) indicates the presence of HIV: ______________________

____

(c) What is the antigen for the monoclonal antibodies? ______________________

(d) Why are the monoclonal antibodies linked to an enzyme? ______________________

____

(e) How could the HIV detection assay be quantified? ______________________

____

© 2015 **BIOZONE** International
ISBN:978-1-927309-31-5
Photocopying Prohibited

187 Herceptin: A Modern Monoclonal

Key Idea: Herceptin is a monoclonal antibody that attaches to the HER2 receptor protein on cells to help T-cells target them for destruction.

Herceptin is the patented name of a monoclonal antibody for the treatment of breast cancer. It targets the HER2 receptor proteins on cancerous cells that signal to the cell when it should divide. The proteins are produced by the proto-oncogene HER2. Cancerous cells contain 20-30% more of the HER2 gene than normal cells and this causes over-expression of HER2, and large amounts of HER2 protein. The over-expression causes the cell to divide more often than normal, producing a tumour. HER2 protein is not a foreign protein, so cancerous (**HER2$^+$**) cells are not recognised by the immune system as abnormal. Herceptin binds to the HER2 protein on the surface of the cancerous cell so that the immune system can recognise it as foreign and destroy it.

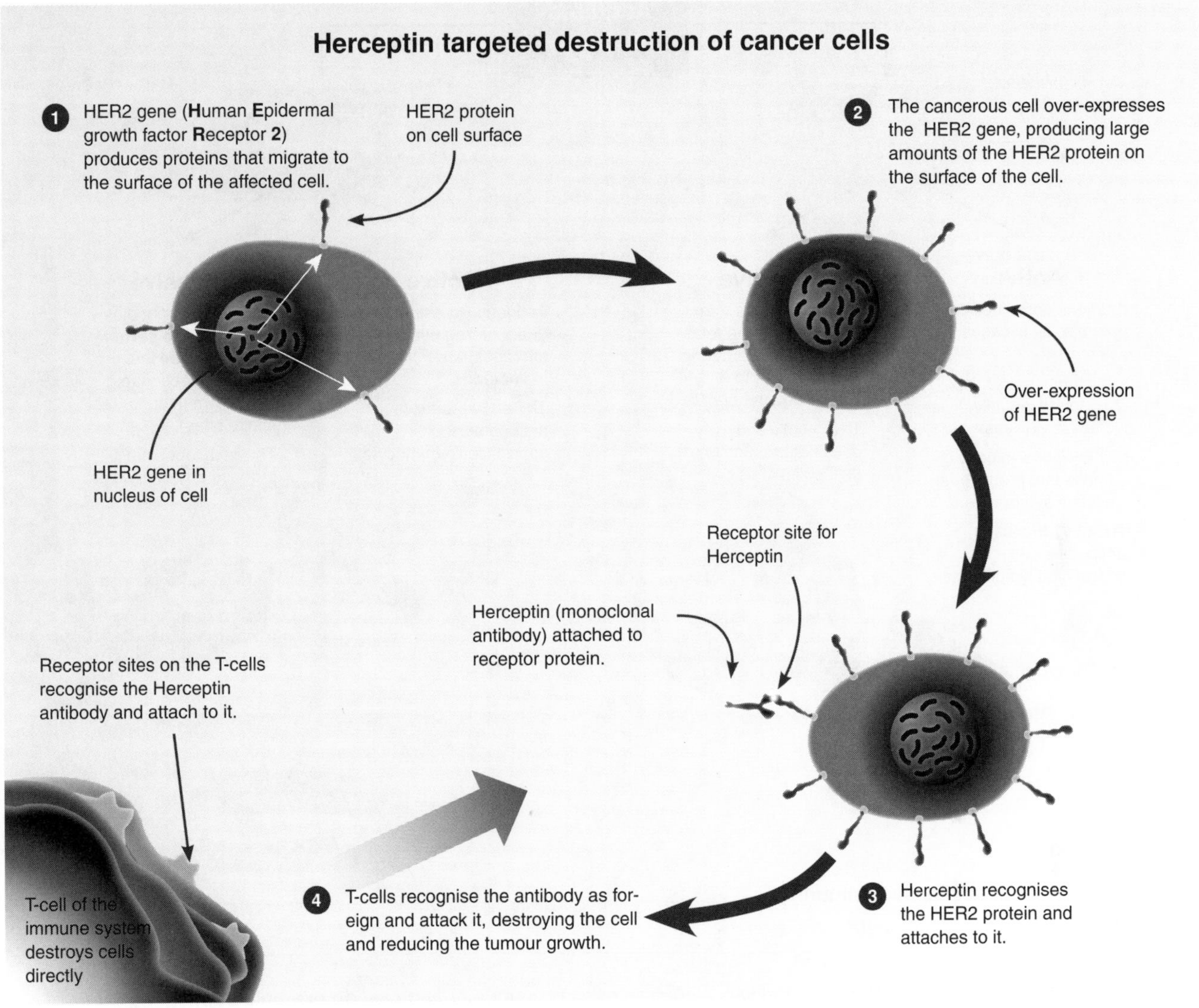

Herceptin targeted destruction of cancer cells
1 HER2 gene (Human Epidermal growth factor Receptor 2) produces proteins that migrate to the surface of the affected cell.
HER2 protein on cell surface
HER2 gene in nucleus of cell
2 The cancerous cell over-expresses the HER2 gene, producing large amounts of the HER2 protein on the surface of the cell.
Over-expression of HER2 gene
Receptor site for Herceptin
Herceptin (monoclonal antibody) attached to receptor protein.
Receptor sites on the T-cells recognise the Herceptin antibody and attach to it.
T-cell of the immune system destroys cells directly
4 T-cells recognise the antibody as foreign and attack it, destroying the cell and reducing the tumour growth.
3 Herceptin recognises the HER2 protein and attaches to it.

1. (a) Why does the immune system not detect HER2$^+$ cells as abnormal and destroy them? ______

(b) How does Herceptin detect and destroy HER2$^+$ cells?

(c) Study the graph (right). What effect does Herceptin have on survival rates of women treated for HER2$^+$?

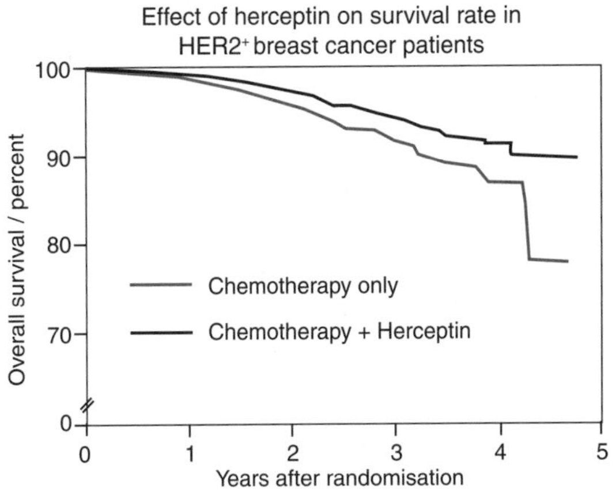

Effect of herceptin on survival rate in HER2+ breast cancer patients
Overall survival / percent
100
90
80
70
0
Chemotherapy only
Chemotherapy + Herceptin
0
1
2
3
4
5
Years after randomisation

© 2015 BIOZONE International
ISBN: 978-1-927309-31-5
Photocopying Prohibited

188 Acquired Immunity

Key Idea: Acquired immunity is a resistance to specific pathogens acquired over the life-time of an organism.

We are born with natural or **innate resistance** which provides non-specific immunity to certain illnesses. In contrast, **acquired immunity** is protection developed over time to specific antigens. **Active immunity** develops after the immune system responds to being exposed to microbes or foreign substances. **Passive immunity** is acquired when antibodies are transferred from one person to another. Immunity may also be naturally acquired, through natural exposure to microbes, or artificially acquired as a result of medical treatment (below).

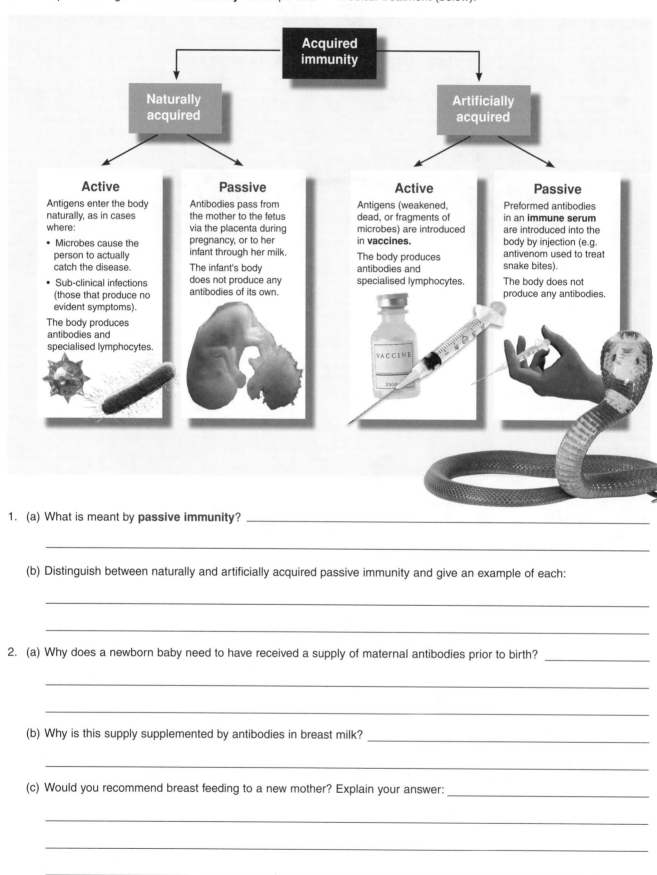

Acquired immunity

Naturally acquired

Active

Antigens enter the body naturally, as in cases where:

- Microbes cause the person to actually catch the disease.
- Sub-clinical infections (those that produce no evident symptoms).

The body produces antibodies and specialised lymphocytes.

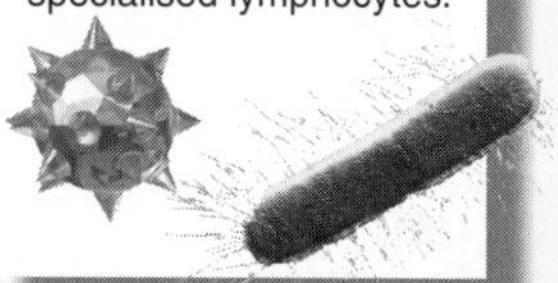

Passive

Antibodies pass from the mother to the fetus via the placenta during pregnancy, or to her infant through her milk.

The infant's body does not produce any antibodies of its own.

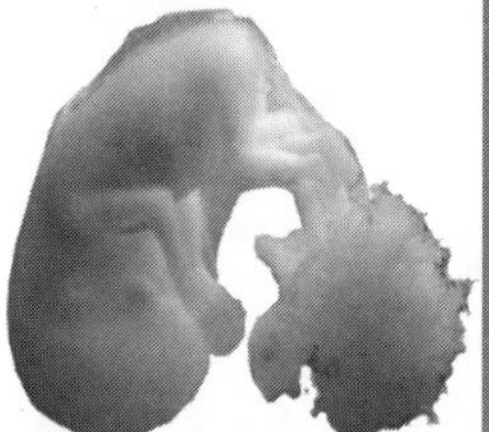

Artificially acquired

Active

Antigens (weakened, dead, or fragments of microbes) are introduced in **vaccines.**

The body produces antibodies and specialised lymphocytes.

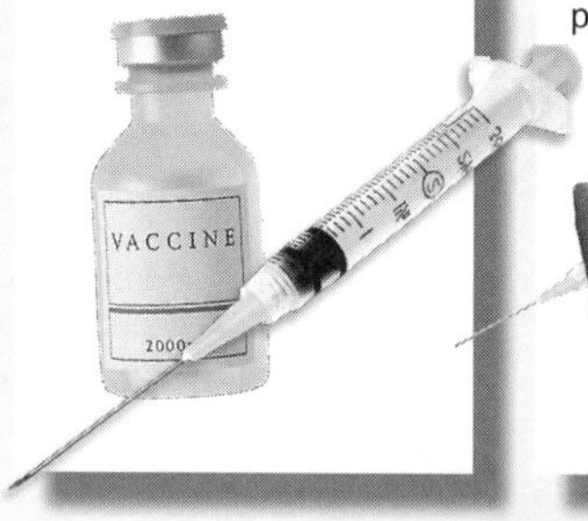
VACCINE
2000

Passive

Preformed antibodies in an **immune serum** are introduced into the body by injection (e.g. antivenom used to treat snake bites).

The body does not produce any antibodies.

1. (a) What is meant by **passive immunity**? ______________________________

   (b) Distinguish between naturally and artificially acquired passive immunity and give an example of each:

   ____

2. (a) Why does a newborn baby need to have received a supply of maternal antibodies prior to birth? ______________________________

   (b) Why is this supply supplemented by antibodies in breast milk? ______________________________

   (c) Would you recommend breast feeding to a new mother? Explain your answer: ______________________________

© 2015 BIOZONE International
ISBN:978-1-927309-31-5
Photocopying Prohibited

When the B cells encounter antigens and produce antibodies, the body develops **active immunity** against that antigen.

The initial response to antigenic stimulation, caused by the sudden increase in B cell clones, is called the **primary response**. Antibody levels as a result of the primary response peak a few weeks after the response begins and then decline. However, because the immune system develops an immunological memory of that antigen, it responds much more quickly and strongly when presented with the same antigen subsequently (the **secondary response**).

This forms the basis of immunisation programmes where one or more booster shots are provided following the initial vaccination.

Primary and secondary responses to antigens

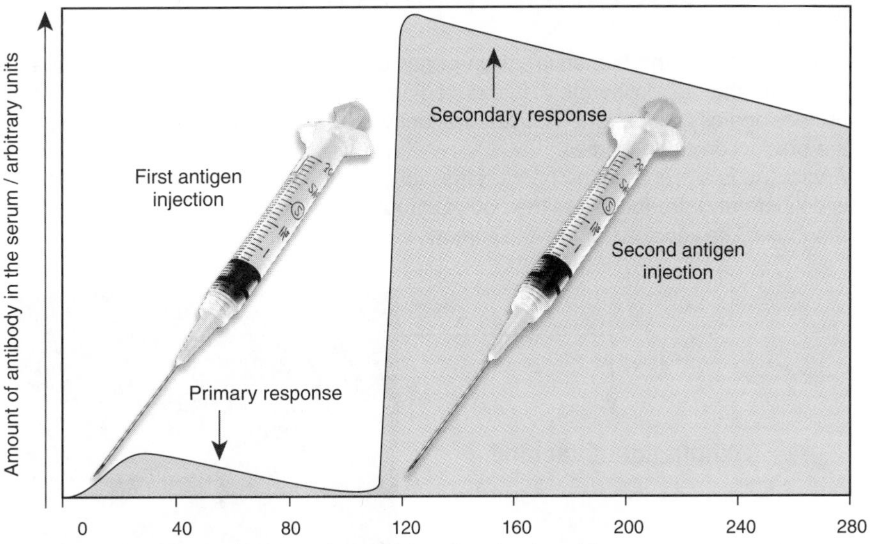
Amount of antibody in the serum / arbitrary units
Time after administration of antigen / days
0
40
80
120
160
200
240
280
First antigen injection
Primary response
Secondary response
Second antigen injection

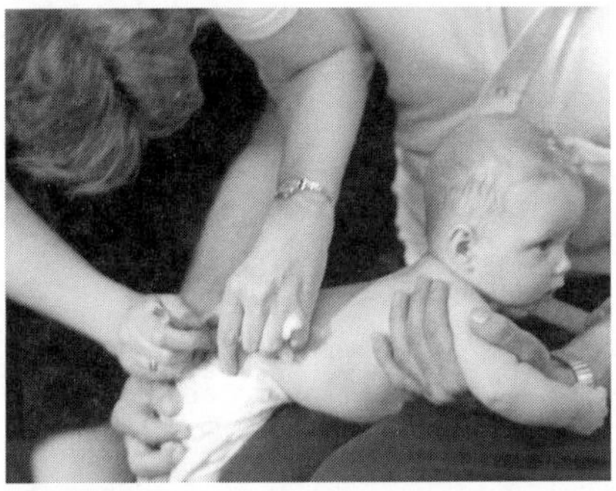

Vaccines against common diseases are given at various stages during childhood according to an immunisation schedule. Vaccination has been behind the decline of some once-common childhood diseases, such as mumps.

Many childhood diseases for which vaccination programmes exist are kept at a low level because of **herd immunity**. If most of the population is immune, those that are not immunised may be protected because the disease is uncommon.

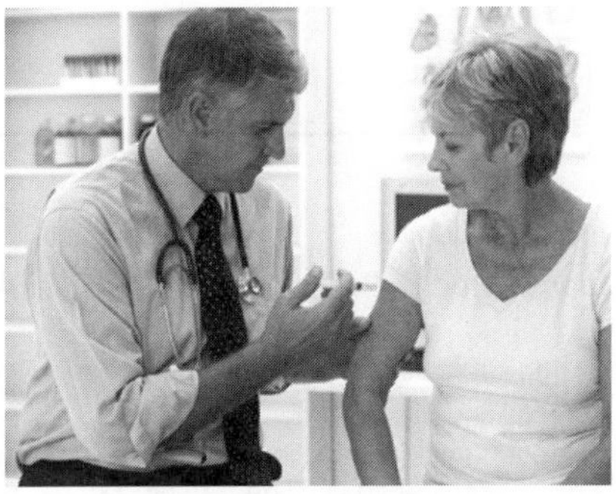

CDC

Most vaccinations are given in childhood, but adults may be vaccinated against a disease (e.g. TB, influenza) if they are in a high risk group (e.g. the elderly) or if they are travelling to a region in the world where a disease is prevalent.

3. (a) What is **active immunity**? ______________________________

____

(b) Distinguish between naturally and artificially acquired active immunity and give an example of each: ______________________________

____

____

4. (a) Describe two differences between the primary and secondary responses to presentation of an antigen: ______________________________

____

____

(b) Why is the secondary response so different from the primary response? ______________________________

____

____

5. (a) Explain the principle of **herd immunity**: ______________________________

____

____

(b) Why are health authorities concerned when the vaccination rates for an infectious disease fall? ______________________________

____

____

© 2015 **BIOZONE** International
ISBN: 978-1-927309-31-5
Photocopying Prohibited

189 Vaccines and Vaccination

Key Idea: A vaccine is a suspension of microbes (or pieces of them) that is deliberately introduced into the body to protect against disease. It induces immunity by stimulating the production of antibodies.

A **vaccine** is a preparation of a harmless foreign antigen that is deliberately introduced into the body to produce an immune response. The vaccine triggers the immune system to produce antibodies against the antigen, but it does not cause the disease. The immune system remembers its response and will produce the same antibodies if it encounters the antigen again. The basic principles of vaccination were discovered by Edward Jenner in the 1700s, when he developed the first vaccine against smallpox. To date, smallpox remains the only disease to have been successfully eradicated by vaccination.

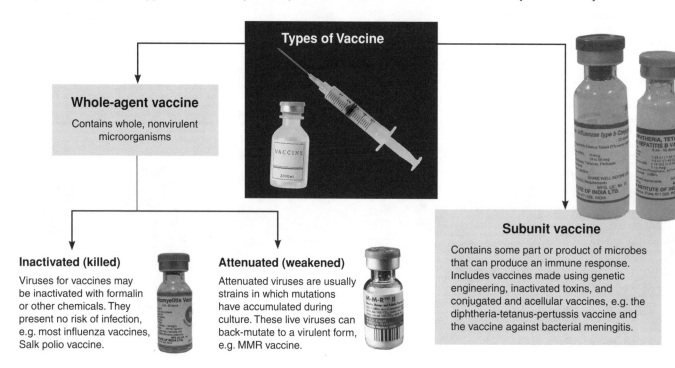

Types of Vaccine

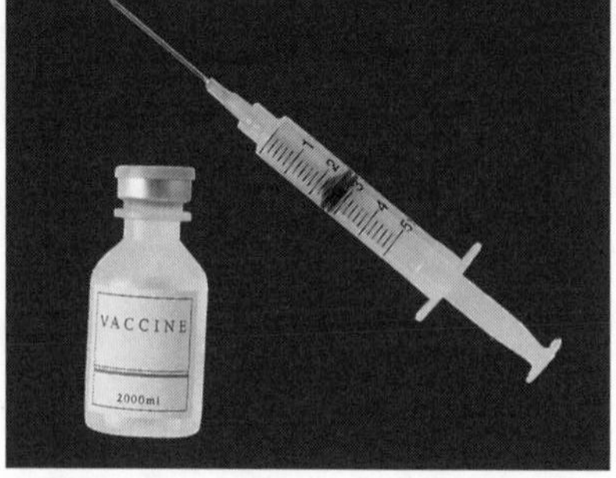

VACCINE
2000ml

Whole-agent vaccine

Contains whole, nonvirulent microorganisms

Inactivated (killed)

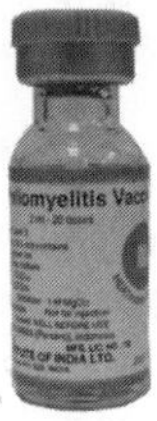

Viruses for vaccines may be inactivated with formalin or other chemicals. They present no risk of infection, e.g. most influenza vaccines, Salk polio vaccine.

Attenuated (weakened)

Attenuated viruses are usually strains in which mutations have accumulated during culture. These live viruses can back-mutate to a virulent form, e.g. MMR vaccine.

Subunit vaccine

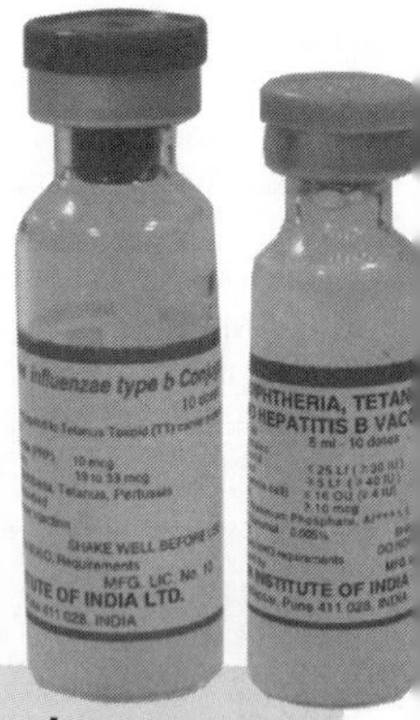

Contains some part or product of microbes that can produce an immune response. Includes vaccines made using genetic engineering, inactivated toxins, and conjugated and acellular vaccines, e.g. the diphtheria-tetanus-pertussis vaccine and the vaccine against bacterial meningitis.

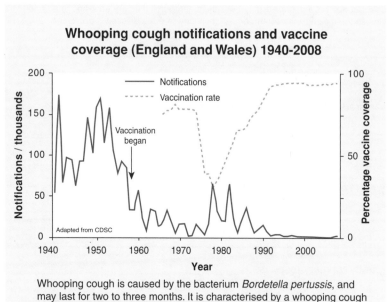

Whooping cough notifications and vaccine coverage (England and Wales) 1940-2008

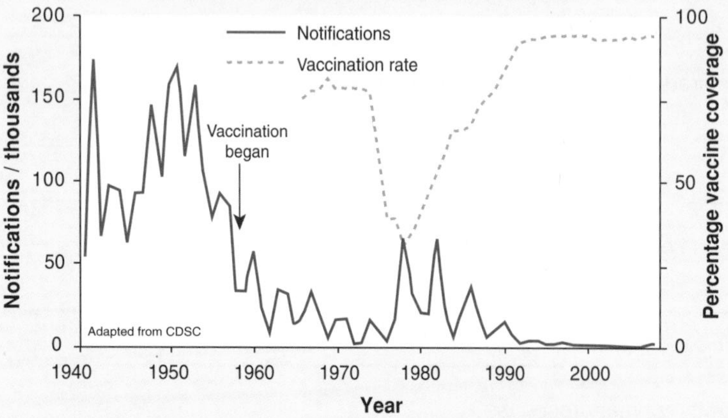

Notifications
Vaccination rate
Vaccination began
Notifications / thousands
Percentage vaccine coverage
Year
200
150
100
50
0
1940
1950
1960
1970
1980
1990
2000
Adapted from CDSC

Whooping cough is caused by the bacterium *Bordetella pertussis*, and may last for two to three months. It is characterised by a whooping cough and can be fatal. Including the whooping cough vaccine into the UK immunisation schedule has greatly reduced the incidence of the disease.

Smallpox eradication

Smallpox is a highly contagious disease caused by the *Variola* virus. It has two forms, *V. minor* and *V. major*, the latter being the more severe (30% mortality). Over several centuries, many smallpox epidemics swept the globe, killing and maiming millions.

In 1967, the WHO began a global vaccination programme that resulted in the complete eradication of smallpox 10 years later. The key to the strategy was intensive surveillance of outbreaks, containment, and vaccination. Eradication was helped by the fact that the eradication programme was a global initiative, humans were the only reservoir for infection, and there were no carriers.

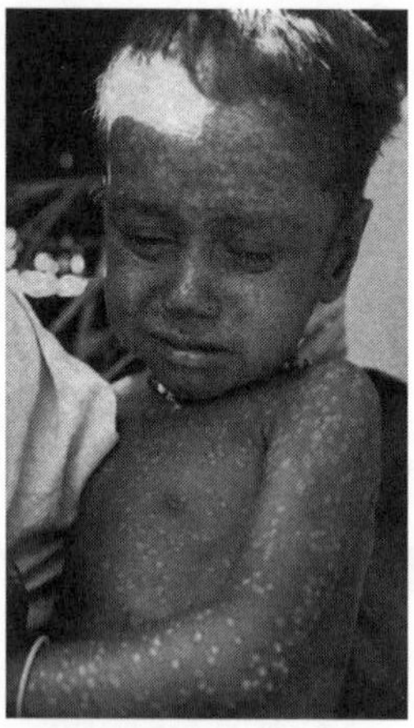

CDC

The last natural outbreak of *Variola major* occurred in a young Bangladeshi girl in 1975 (above) and the last case of *V. minor* was recorded in Somalia in 1977.

1. **Attenuated viruses** provide long term immunity to their recipients and generally do not require booster shots. Why do you think attenuated viruses provide such effective long-term immunity when inactivated viruses do not?

___

___

___

© 2015 BIOZONE International
ISBN:978-1-927309-31-5
Photocopying Prohibited

Could vaccines eradicate all infectious diseases?

Some diseases are difficult to eradicate because of biological characteristics of the pathogen itself and the disease process. Other diseases could be eradicated but low vaccination rates allow the disease to persist in the population.

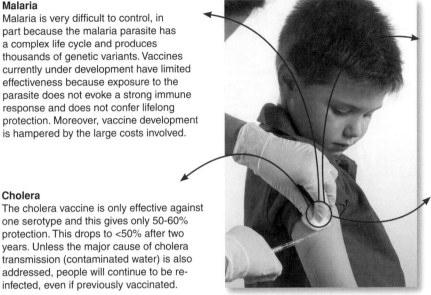

Malaria
Malaria is very difficult to control, in part because the malaria parasite has a complex life cycle and produces thousands of genetic variants. Vaccines currently under development have limited effectiveness because exposure to the parasite does not evoke a strong immune response and does not confer lifelong protection. Moreover, vaccine development is hampered by the large costs involved.

Cholera
The cholera vaccine is only effective against one serotype and this gives only 50-60% protection. This drops to <50% after two years. Unless the major cause of cholera transmission (contaminated water) is also addressed, people will continue to be re-infected, even if previously vaccinated.

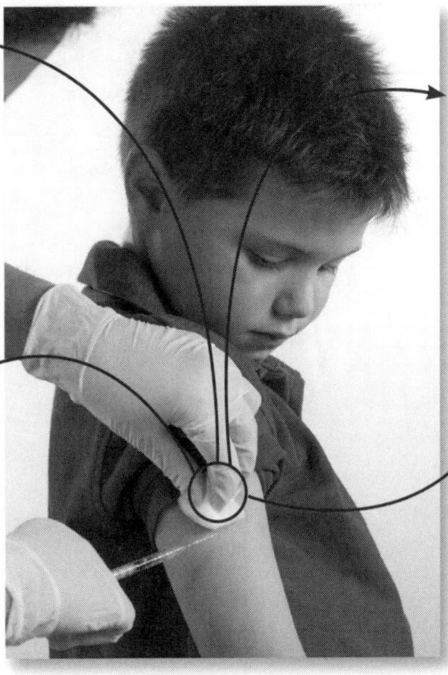

Measles
Measles fits the profile of a disease that could quite easily be eradicated: people are the only carriers of the virus, there is an effective vaccine, and accurate diagnostic tests are available. However, low vaccination rates, particularly in geographic clusters, allow the disease to persist and spread. In addition, travellers reintroduce the disease into areas where it has previously been eliminated.

Tuberculosis
The effectiveness of the TB vaccine is quite low and variable amongst different sectors of the population. It also does not stop latent TB from developing into the contagious active form. People with latent TB cannot infect others, but latent TB is difficult to treat and the disease can become active at any point.

2. (a) How can vaccination help lead to the eradication of an infectious disease? ____________________

(b) What features of a pathogen and the disease it causes make it a candidate for successful eradication?

____

(c) Discuss factors in the success of the smallpox eradication programme: ____________________

3. Using named examples, discuss factors that make eradication of a disease by vaccination difficult to achieve: ____________________

4. In 1975, the UK vaccination rate for whooping cough decreased to 30% because of concerns about the vaccine's safety. Use the data in the graph opposite to describe what effect this had on rates of whooping cough reported:

____

© 2015 **BIOZONE** International
ISBN: 978-1-927309-31-5
Photocopying Prohibited

190 Chapter Review

Summarise what you know about this topic under the headings provided. You can draw diagrams or mind maps, or write short notes to organise your thoughts. Use the images and hints to help you and refer back to the introduction to check the points covered:

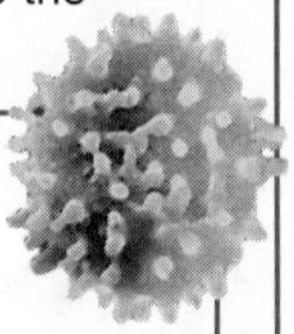

The body's defences:
HINT: Distinguish between non-specific and specific responses.

The immune response:
HINT: Describe the immune response and how autoimmune diseases arise.

Antibodies:
HINT: Relate the structure of antibodies to their function. How are monoclonal antibodies made, and what are their uses?

Vaccinations:
HINT: Describe the principles and applications of vaccination.

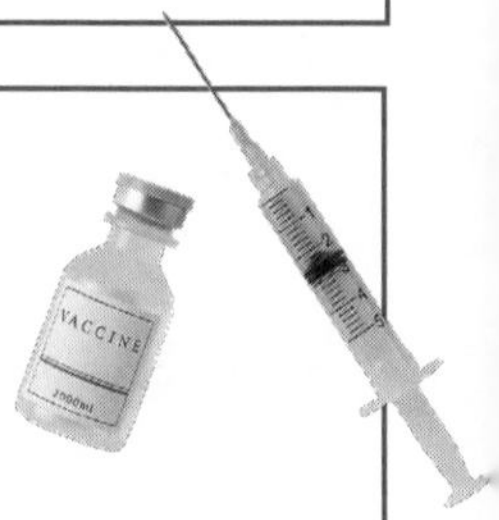
VACCINE

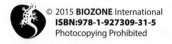

© 2015 BIOZONE International
ISBN:978-1-927309-31-5
Photocopying Prohibited

191 KEY TERMS AND IDEAS: Did You Get It?

1. Test your vocabulary by matching each term to its correct definition, as identified by its preceding letter code.

- active immunity ....
- antibodies ....
- antigen ....
- autoimmune disease ....
- B cells ....
- cell mediated immunity ....
- humoral immunity ....
- immunity ....
- leucocytes ....
- lymphocytes ....
- non-specific defences ....
- passive immunity ....
- phagocytes ....
- primary response ....
- secondary response ....
- specific immune response ....
- T cells ....
- vaccination ....

A Immune response that is mediated by secreted antibodies.

B The more rapid and stronger response of the immune system to an antigen that it has encountered before.

C Immunoglobulin proteins in the blood or other bodily fluids, which identify and neutralise foreign material, such as bacteria and viruses.

D The deliberate introduction of antigenic material to produce immunity to a disease.

E Generalised defence mechanisms against pathogens, e.g. physical barriers, secretions, inflammation, and phagocytosis.

F Long-lasting immunity that is induced in the host itself by the antigen.

G Lymphocytes that are responsible for the cell mediated immune response.

H A disease resulting from an overactive immune response against substances and tissues normally present in the body.

I White blood cells that destroy foreign material, e.g. bacteria, by ingesting them.

J Resistance of an organism to infection or disease.

K White blood cells, including lymphocytes, and macrophages and other phagocytes.

L Specific white blood cells involved in the adaptive immune response.

M Lymphocytes that make antibodies against specific antigens.

N A pathogen and antigen-specific immune response with both cell-mediated and humoral components. Characterised by immunological memory.

O Immune response involving the activation of macrophages, specific T cells, and cytokines against antigens.

P The initial response of the immune system to exposure to an antigen.

Q Immunity gained by the receipt of ready-made antibodies

R A molecule that is recognised by the immune system as foreign.

2. The graph below shows the number of measles cases in the UK, together with percentage vaccination, 1994-2008. In 1998, Wakefield and 12 others published a 'study' linking the MMR (measles) vaccine to autism and he began a campaign to discredit its use. Wakefield's study was based on flawed and manipulated data, and was quickly discredited.

(a) What happened to MMR vaccination rates after the publication of Wakefield's study?

____

____

(b) What is the trend in measles cases in the UK since 2006?

____

____

(c) Give a likely explanation for this trend: ______________________________

____

____

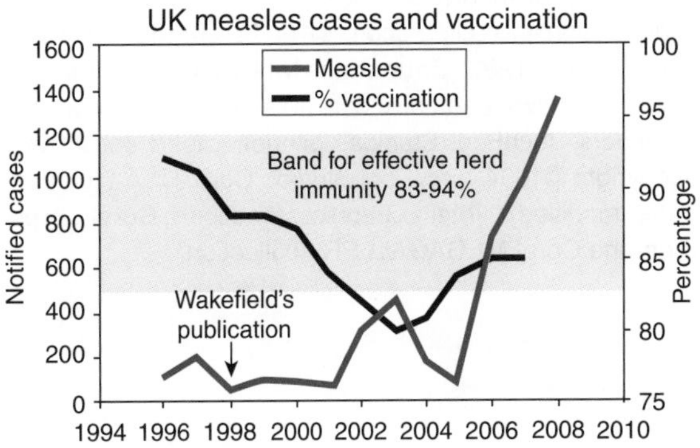
UK measles cases and vaccination
Measles
% vaccination
Band for effective herd immunity 83-94%
Wakefield's publication
Notified cases
Percentage
0
200
400
600
800
1000
1200
1400
1600
75
80
85
90
95
100
1994 1996 1998 2000 2002 2004 2006 2008 2010

© 2015 BIOZONE International
ISBN: 978-1-927309-31-5
Photocopying Prohibited

TEST

Image credits

The writing team would like to thank the following people and organisations who have kindly provided photographs or illustrations for this edition:

• PASCO for their photographs of probeware • Kjetil Lenes for the image of the duckweed • Karl Nueller for the photo of the Malawi grandmother • Dartmouth College for the image of the dividing *Staphylcoccus* cell • UCSD School of Medicine: Charles Goldberg for the image of the rheumatoid arthritis • CDC Jane Haney Carr • National Cancer Institute • Dartmouth College and Dr Louisa Howard for TEMs of cell structures • USDE Genomic Science Program • Wadsworth Centre (NYSDH) for the photo of the cell undergoing cytokinesis • John Main PLU for the cross section through a dicot stem • Western New Mexico University Department of Natural Sciences / Dale A Zimmerman Herbarium for the image of the mesophyll leaf • Dan Butler for the image of the cut finger

We also acknowledge the photographers who have made images available through **Wikimedia Commons** under Creative Commons Licences 2.0, 2.5, 3.0, or 4.0: • Enwinoseen • Synamorphy • Goran Ekstrom (PLoS) • CDC Dr Lucille K. Georg • Olaboy • Alison Roberts • Y tambe • Allonweiner • Mnolf • Miquel, Vilavella, Shimalov & Torres • CDC James Gathany • Ute Frevert • Doreen Mbalo • Bios • C Beard • Mohankumar Kurukumbi • Vossman • A2-33 • Zephyris • Madprime • Brocken Inaglory • Jpbarrass • Emmanuelm • McKDandy • Capkuckokos • Nicolas Grandjean • Tommo Leonardi • Mnoff

Contributors identified by coded credits

BF: Brian Finerran (University of Canterbury), Centers for Disease Control and Prevention, Atlanta, USA, **EII**: Education Interactive Imaging, **GW**: Graham Walker, **JDG**: John Green (University of Waikato), **KP**: Kent Pryor, **NIH**: National Institute of Health, **RA**: Richard Allan, **RCN**: Ralph Cocklin, **TG**: Tracey Greenwood, **USDA**: United States Department of Agriculture **WBS**: Warwick Silvester (University of Waikato), **WMU**: Waikato Microscope Unit.

Image libraries

We also acknowledge our use of royalty-free images, purchased by BIOZONE International Ltd from the following sources: **Corel** Corporation from various titles in their Professional Photos CD-ROM collection; Dollar Photo Club, dollarphotoclub.com; istock photos, istockphoto.com; **IMSI** (International Microcomputer Software Inc.) images from IMSI's MasterClips® and MasterPhotosTM Collection, 1895 Francisco Blvd. East, San Rafael, CA 94901-5506, USA; ©1996 **Digital Stock**, Medicine and Health Care collection; ©**Hemera** Technologies Inc, 1997-2001; © 2005 JupiterImages Corporation www.clipart.com; ©1994., ©**Digital Vision**; Gazelle Technologies Inc.; ©1994-1996 **Education Interactive Imaging** (UK), **PhotoDisc®**, Inc. USA, www.photodisc.com. We also acknowledge the following clipart providers: TechPool Studios, for their clipart collection of human anatomy: Copyright ©1994, TechPool Studios Corp. USA (some of these images have been modified); Totem Graphics, for clipart; Corel Corporation, for vector art from the Corel MEGAGALLERY collection.

© 2015 BIOZONE International Photocopying Prohibited

Index

© 2015 BIOZONE International **Photocopying Prohibited**